THE COVENANT
HYMNAL

COVENANT PRESS - CHICAGO

COVENANT PRESS
3200 W. Foster Ave., Chicago, Illinois 60625
Printed in the United States of America

FOREWORD

The reality of man's relationship with the living God has always resulted in a deep desire within him to respond with majesty, beauty, and dignity. The poetry in his soul and the song in his heart had to find release through expressions approximating his sense of gratitude. He found very early that music and song could express his feelings and give place to his moods while they conveyed the message of his mind. He learned that music and worship belonged together and were capable of building fellowship, of expressing praise, and of lifting the soul. So the history of the Christian church is wealthy in its tradition of beautiful hymnody.

The church is greatly in debt to the Hymnal Commission of the Evangelical Covenant Church of America for researching, compiling, editing, and preparing the fine selection of hymns and aids to worship for the enrichment and inspiration of the members of the church of Jesus Christ for our day and for years to come.

"Christ for the world we sing! The world to Christ we bring!", wrote Samuel Wolcott a century ago. As we give ourselves to contemporize his dream, let us put this hymnbook to work by responding to the invitation of the psalmist, "Come into his presence with singing."

Milton B. Engebretson, President
The Evangelical Covenant Church of America

PREFACE

Each new generation responds to God in its own way and looks for new or different modes of expression in its worship. While **The Hymnal** (1950) has served us well for over twenty years, it is appropriate that a new hymnal be published—one that reflects the changing times. This is not to say that **The Covenant Hymnal** (1973) is entirely new; a little less than two-thirds of the songs in the present hymnal are retained, and many other traditional hymns from various sources have been included. In short, the Hymnal Commission has aspired to a volume containing the best from the past along with something new and fresh. The work was facilitated by the recent appearance of several excellent new hymnals and by the publications of the Hymn Society of America.

All texts were carefully examined by the editorial committee of the Commission. In some cases alterations were made to improve the lyrical quality and clarify the meaning. Several of the new texts were written or translated by Commission members. Most of the translations from the Swedish have been retained—with slight revisions—and several more have been added. It seems that the Covenant has become the custodian of this rich heritage.

Some of the familiar texts have been given new or different melodies. Many of the contemporary texts have familiar tunes though some have new settings. Several of the new tunes have been composed by members of the Commission's music committee. Other musical settings have been reworked or reharmonized, and in some cases transposed to lower, more singable keys. When a tune appears more than once, two different keys have been given in most cases. In order to increase the book's usefulness, notations have been provided on many pages referring to alternate tunes and different keys or harmonizations. Several unison settings have been included, as well as descant arrangements.

Attention is directed to the enlarged section of service music which provides a wide variety of old and new material suitable for choral and congregational introits and responses. At the beginning of this section there is a supplemental list of hymns also suitable for use as service music.

It is believed that the expanded section of Worship Aids will enhance the usefulness of the hymnal as a worship book, and will therefore commend itself to pastor and laymen alike. Although the emphasis is on biblical selections, both historic and contemporary materials are included. The main divisions of this section are as follows: Scripture Readings, Other Worship Resources, and the Lectionary.

Historically, Covenanters have valued freedom and variety in worship while also recognizing the need for an order which is "reverent, festive, and beautiful." In keeping with this tradition, the Worship Aids Committee has reaffirmed the principle of freedom by refusing to move in the direction of liturgical uniformity. It has furthermore reaffirmed the need for good order by providing a variety of materials which will allow both pastor and congregation to develop ways of worshipping that will be edifying to the whole body.

Members of the Worship Aids Committee were Glenn P. Anderson, Earl C. Dahlstrom, J. Irving Erickson, James R. Hawkinson, Donald J. Pearson, Delmar E. Peterson, and Glen V. Wiberg. The Lectionary revision was undertaken by C. John Weborg and Glen V. Wiberg.

Several changes have been made in the indexing of this hymnal. Authors, translators, composers, arrangers, and sources of texts and music all appear in the same index. A listing of Scripture references in hymns and a topical index to the Scripture readings have been added. To the index of first lines we have appended the tune names. Several indexes included in **The Hymnal** (1950) have been omitted.

We express our appreciation to those individuals and publishers who granted permission for use of their copyrighted materials, many with nominal and some with no charge. We have made every effort to trace the ownership of all copyrights. If any omissions have been made, subsequent editions will be corrected on notification by the copyright holders. Gratitude is expressed to the many individuals who submitted suggestions, texts, tunes, and translations. Every item was given due consideration by the Commission. We also thank Bonnie Borgeson and Rosalie Bengtson, who assisted us at various stages in our work, and Morton Blatt, Linda Bergquist, and Mary Helfrich, who helped in the production process.

We wish to record here our special gratitude to three members of the Commission: Marjorie M. Nelson, for her dedicated service as secretary, and A. Royce Eckhardt and Norman E. Johnson for sharing the greater part of the task of proofreading. We are deeply grateful also to A. Milton Freedholm for help in the preparation of the Index of Scripture References in Hymns.

Finally, we express warm thanks to every member of the Commission: Carl Philip Anderson, James P. Davies, A. Royce Eckhardt, Eric G. Hawkinson, Norman E. Johnson, Bryan J. Leech, Marjorie M. Nelson, Harry Opel, and Glen V. Wiberg. It has been a privilege to work with this group of devoted and talented people who have given of themselves so generously in the preparation of this hymnal. We offer it now with the prayer that it may help us all to worship and praise God in church and home.

J. Irving Erickson
Chairman, The Hymnal Commission

James R. Hawkinson
Executive Secretary of Publications

contents

the hymns

WORSHIP

GOD THE FATHER

JESUS CHRIST THE LORD

indexes

THE COVENANT HYMNAL

Sing Praise to God Who Reigns Above

Johann J. Schütz, 1640-1690
Tr. Frances E. Cox, 1812-1897

MIT FREUDEN ZART 8.7.8.7.8.8.7.
Bohemian Brethren's "Kirchengesänge," 1566

1 Sing praise to God who reigns a-bove, The God of all cre -
2 What God's al-might - y pow'r hath made His gra-cious mer - cy
3 The Lord is nev - er far a - way, But, thru all grief dis -
4 Thus all my toil-some way a - long I sing a - loud his
a - tion, The God of pow'r, the God of love, The God of our
keep-eth, By morn-ing glow or eve-ning shade His watch-ful eye
tress-ing, An ev - er-pres - ent help and stay, Our peace and joy
prais-es, That men may hear the grate-ful song My voice un-wea -
sal - va - tion; With heal-ing balm my soul he fills, And
ne'er sleep - eth; With - in the king-dom of his might, Lo!
and bless - ing; As with a moth - er's ten - der hand He
ried rais - es; Be joy - ful in the Lord, my heart! Both
ev - 'ry faith-less mur-mur stills: To God all praise and glo - ry!
all is just and all is right: To God all praise and glo - ry!
leads his own, his cho - sen band: To God all praise and glo - ry!
soul and bod - y bear your part: To God all praise and glo - ry!

2 All Creatures of Our God and King

St. Francis of Assisi, 1182-1226
Tr. William H. Draper, 1855-1933

LASST UNS ERFREUEN 8.8.4.4.8.8. *with Alleluias*
"Geistliche Kirchengesäng," Cologne, 1623
Harm. by Norman E. Johnson, 1928-

1 All crea-tures of our God and King, Lift up your voice and with us sing
2 Thou rush-ing wind that art so strong, Ye clouds that sail in heav'n a - long,
3 Thou flow-ing wa - ter, pure and clear, Make mu-sic for thy Lord to hear,
4 And all ye men of ten-der heart, For- giv - ing oth-ers, take your part,
5 Let all things their Cre - a - tor bless, And wor-ship him in hum-ble - ness,
Al - le - lu - ia, Al - le - lu - ia! Thou burn-ing sun with gold-en beam,
O praise him, Al - le - lu - ia! Thou ris - ing morn, in praise re - joice,
Al - le - lu - ia, Al - le - lu - ia! Thou fire so mas - ter - ful and bright,
O sing ye, Al - le - lu - ia! Ye who long pain and sor - row bear,
O praise him, Al - le - lu - ia! Praise, praise the Fa-ther, praise the Son,
Thou sil - ver moon with soft - er gleam, O praise him, O praise him,
Ye lights of eve-ning, find a voice, O praise him, O praise him,
That giv-est man both warmth and light, O praise him, O praise him,
Praise God and on him cast your care: O praise him, O praise him,
And praise the Spir - it, Three in One: O praise him, O praise him,
Al - le - lu - ia, Al - le - lu - ia! Al - le - lu - ia! A-men.

A lower setting may be found at No. 351

From All That Dwell Below the Skies **3**

Based on Psalm 117
Isaac Watts, 1674-1748
Doxology by Thomas Ken, 1637-1711

LASST UNS ERFREUEN 8.8.4.4.8.8. *with Alleluias*
"Geistliche Kirchengesäng," Cologne, 1623
Harm. by Norman E. Johnson, 1928-

1 From all that dwell below the skies
Let the Creator's praise arise:
Alleluia, Alleluia!
Let the Redeemer's name be sung
Through ev'ry land, in ev'ry tongue:
Alleluia, Alleluia, Alleluia,
Alleluia, Alleluia!

2 In ev'ry land begin the song,
To ev'ry land the strains belong:
Alleluia, Alleluia!
In cheerful sound all voices raise
And fill the world with joyful praise:
Alleluia, Alleluia, Alleluia,
Alleluia, Alleluia!

3 Eternal are thy mercies, Lord;
Eternal truth attends thy word:
Alleluia, Alleluia!
Thy praise shall sound from shore to shore,
Till suns shall rise and set no more:
Alleluia, Alleluia, Alleluia,
Alleluia, Alleluia! Amen.

Praise God from whom all blessings flow;
Praise him, all creatures here below:
Alleluia, Alleluia!
Praise him above, ye heav'nly host;
Praise Father, Son, and Holy Ghost:
Alleluia, Alleluia, Alleluia,
Alleluia, Alleluia!

All People That on Earth Do Dwell **4**

Based on Psalm 100
Attr. to William Kethe, ?-1608, alt.

OLD 100th L.M.
"Genevan Psalter," 1551
Attr. to Louis Bourgeois, c.1510-c.1561

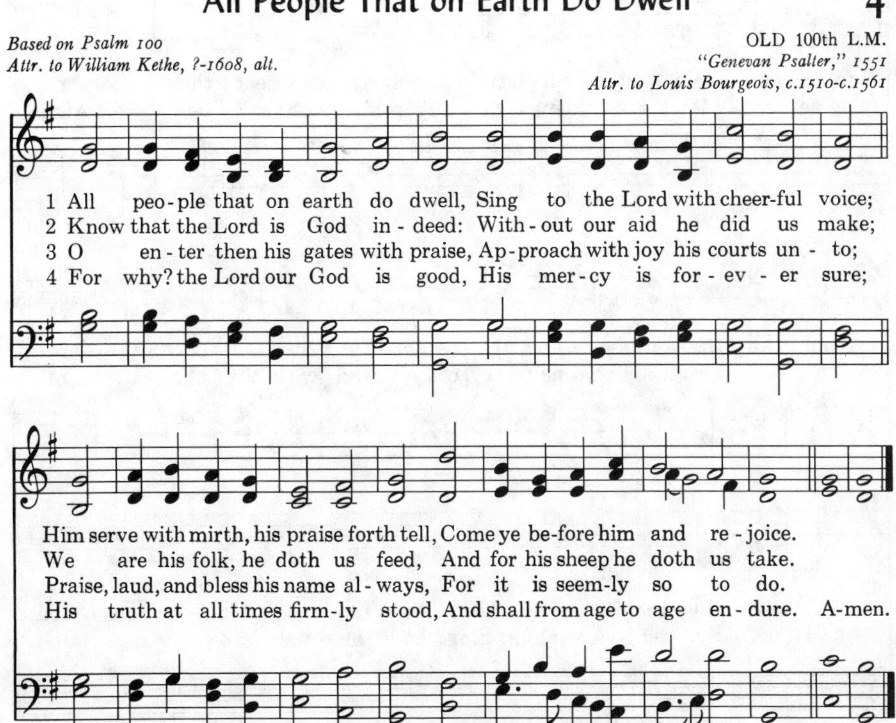

1 All peo-ple that on earth do dwell, Sing to the Lord with cheer-ful voice;
2 Know that the Lord is God in-deed: With-out our aid he did us make;
3 O en-ter then his gates with praise, Ap-proach with joy his courts un-to;
4 For why? the Lord our God is good, His mer-cy is for-ev-er sure;
Him serve with mirth, his praise forth tell, Come ye be-fore him and re-joice.
We are his folk, he doth us feed, And for his sheep he doth us take.
Praise, laud, and bless his name al-ways, For it is seem-ly so to do.
His truth at all times firm-ly stood, And shall from age to age en-dure. A-men.

5 Holy Majesty! Before Thee

Samuel J. Hedborn, 1783-1849
Tr. Composite

WACHET AUF *Irregular*
Philipp Nicolai, 1556-1608
Harm. by Norman E. Johnson, 1928-

1 Ho - ly Maj - es - ty! be - fore thee We bow to wor - ship and a -
2 Bless us, Lord, and keep us ev - er, Re - veal thy face and show thy
dore thee; Our hearts thy sov-'reign - ty ac - claim. Bound-less are thy
fa - vor; Up - on thy peo - ple smile with peace. Here we sing thy
might and glo - ry, All heav'n and earth re - peat thy sto - ry;
name re - joic - ing, Un - til thy praise we shall be voic - ing
Lo! all thy works ex - alt thy name. To thee all cher - u - bim
In loft - ier strains that nev - er cease, And with thy cher - u - bim
And all thy ser - a - phim Sing ho - san - na! Ho - ly is God,
And all thy ser - a - phim Sing ho - san - na! Ho - ly is God,

ADORATION

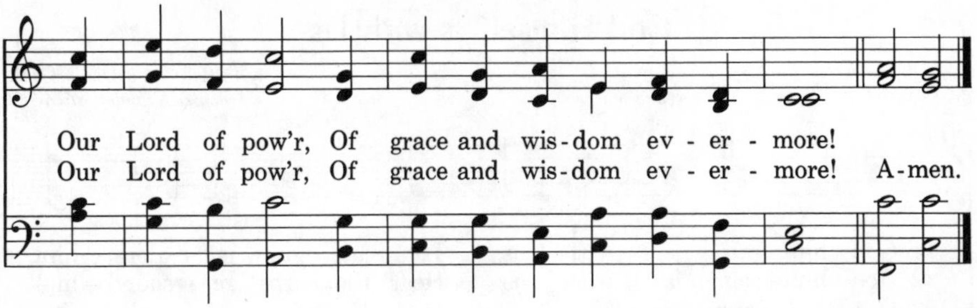

Our Lord of pow'r, Of grace and wis-dom ev-er-more!
Our Lord of pow'r, Of grace and wis-dom ev-er-more! A-men.

Awake, My Tongue, Thy Tribute Bring

6

John Needham, ?-1787

DUKE STREET L.M.
John Hatton, c.1710-1793
Harm. by A. Royce Eckhardt, 1937-

1 Awake, my tongue, thy tribute bring
To him who gave thee pow'r to sing;
Praise him who is all praise above,
The source of wisdom and of love.

2 How vast his knowledge, how profound!
A deep where all our tho'ts are drowned;
The stars he numbers, and their names
He gives to all those heav'n-ly flames.

3 Thru each bright world above, behold
Ten thousand thousand charms unfold;
Earth, air, and mighty seas combine
To speak his wisdom all divine.

4 But in redemption, O what grace!
Its wonders, O what tho't can trace!
Here wisdom shines forever bright:
Praise him, my soul, with sweet delight. A-men.

Another harmonization in a higher setting may be found at No. 362

7 God Himself Is with Us

Gerhardt Tersteegen, 1697-1769
Tr. Frederick W. Foster, 1760-1835, and others

ARNSBERG 6.6.8.6.6.8.3.3.6.6.
Joachim Neander, 1650-1680

1 God him - self is with us: Let us now a - dore him,
2 God him - self is with us: Hear the harps re - sound - ing!
3 O thou Fount of bless - ing, Pur - i - fy my spir - it;
And with awe ap - pear be - fore him. God is in his
See the crowds the throne sur - round - ing! "Ho - ly, ho - ly,
Trust - ing on - ly in thy mer - it, Like the ho - ly
tem - ple, All with - in keep si - lence, And be - fore him
ho - ly," Hear the hymn as - cend - ing, An - gels, saints, their
an - gels Who be - hold thy glo - ry, May I cease - less -
bow with rev - 'rence. Him a - lone God we own,
voic - es blend - ing! Bow thine ear To us here:
ly a - dore thee! And in all, Great and small,

Him, our God and Sav - ior: Praise his name for - ev - er.
Hear, O Christ, the prais - es That thy church now rais - es.
Seek to do most near - ly What thou lov - est dear - ly. A-men.
Before the Lord Jehovah's Throne
8
Based on Psalm 100
Isaac Watts, 1674-1748
Alt. by John Wesley, 1703-1791
WINCHESTER NEW L.M.
Adapted from "Musikalisches Handbuch," Hamburg, 1690
1 Be - fore the Lord Je - ho - vah's throne, Ye na - tions, bow with sa - cred joy; Know that the Lord is God a - lone— He can cre - ate, and he de - stroy.
2 His sov - 'reign pow'r with - out our aid Made us of clay and formed us men; And when like wan - d'ring sheep we strayed, He brought us to his fold a - gain.
3 We are his peo - ple, we his care, Our souls and all our mor - tal frame; What last - ing hon - ors shall we rear, Al - might - y Mak - er, to thy name?
4 We'll crowd thy gates with thank - ful songs, High as the heav'ns our voic - es raise; And earth, with her ten thou - sand tongues, Shall fill thy courts with sound - ing praise.
5 Wide as the world is thy com - mand, Vast as e - ter - ni - ty thy love; Firm as a rock thy truth must stand, When roll - ing years shall cease to move. A-men.

9 Earth and All Stars

Herbert F. Brokering, 1926-

DEXTER 4.5.7.D. *with Refrain*
David N. Johnson, 1922-
Harm. by Jan Bender, 1909-

In unison
1 Earth and all stars, Loud rush - ing plan - ets,
2 Hail, wind and rain, Loud blow - ing snow - storm,
3 Trum - pet and pipes, Loud clash - ing cym - bals,
4 En - gines and steel, Loud pound - ing ham - mers,
5 Knowl - edge and truth, Loud sound - ing wis - dom,
Sing to the Lord a new song! O vic - to - ry,
Sing to the Lord a new song! Flow - ers and trees,
Sing to the Lord a new song! Harp, lute and lyre,
Sing to the Lord a new song! Lime-stone and beams,
Sing to the Lord a new song! Daugh-ter and son,
Loud shout-ing ar - my, Sing to the Lord a new song!
Loud rus-tling dry leaves, Sing to the Lord a new song!
Loud hum-ming cel - los, Sing to the Lord a new song!
Loud build-ing work - men, Sing to the Lord a new song!
Loud prais-ing mem - bers, Sing to the Lord a new song!

ADORATION

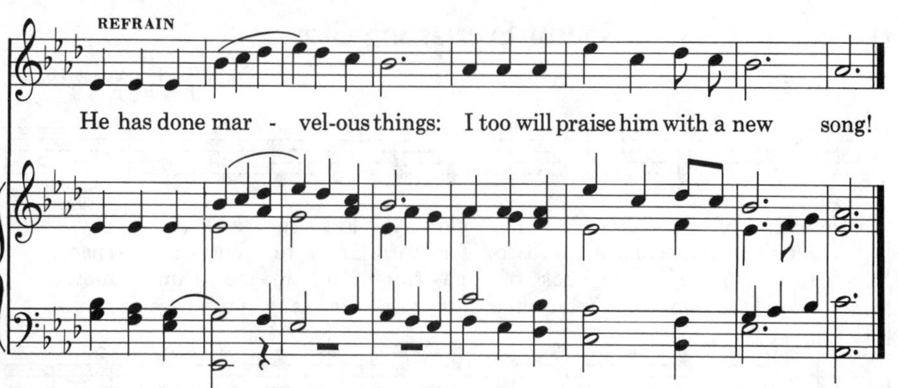
REFRAIN
He has done mar - vel-ous things: I too will praise him with a new song!

My God, How Wonderful Thou Art 10

Frederick W. Faber, 1814-1863

DUNDEE C.M.
"Scottish Psalter," 1615

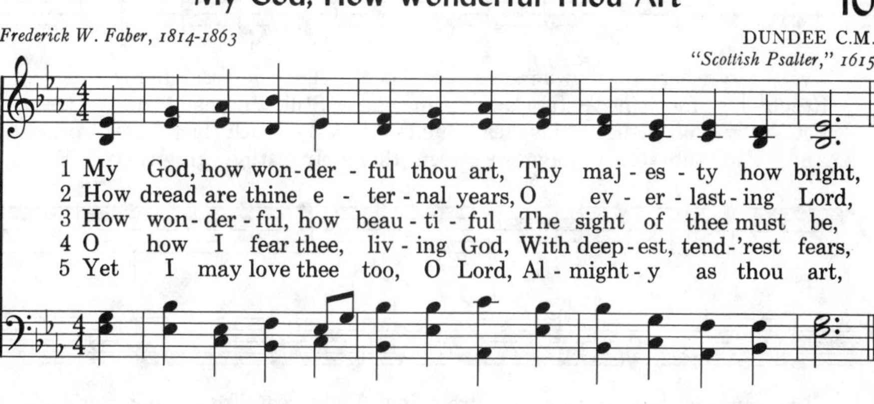
1 My God, how won-der - ful thou art, Thy maj - es - ty how bright,
2 How dread are thine e - ter - nal years, O ev - er - last - ing Lord,
3 How won - der - ful, how beau - ti - ful The sight of thee must be,
4 O how I fear thee, liv - ing God, With deep - est, tend-'rest fears,
5 Yet I may love thee too, O Lord, Al - might - y as thou art,

How beau - ti - ful thy mer - cy seat, In depths of burn-ing light!
By pros-trate spir-its day and night In - ces-sant - ly a - dored!
Thine end-less wis-dom, bound-less pow'r And aw - ful pur - i - ty!
And wor-ship thee with trem-bling hope And pen - i - ten - tial tears!
For thou hast stooped to ask of me The love of my poor heart. A-men.

6 No earthly father loves like thee,
No mother, half so mild,
Bears and forbears as thou hast done
With me, thy sinful child.

7 Father of Jesus, love's reward,
What rapture will it be
Prostrate before thy throne to lie
And gaze and gaze on thee. Amen.

11

God of Everlasting Glory

John W. Peterson, 1921-

BRETON ROAD 8.5.8.5.D.
John W. Peterson, 1921-

1 God of ev - er - last - ing glo - ry, Fill - ing earth and sky,
2 As we push man's fron-tiers for-ward In - to out - er space,
3 In the o - pen book of na - ture Faith re - mains un - moved—
4 Thru the course of hu - man his - t'ry Has thy pur - pose run,
Ev - 'ry-where thy won-ders o - pen To our search-ing eye:
Reach - ing for the stars and plan - ets, Still thy hand we trace;
Pat - terns of the Mas - ter Build - er By each fact are proved;
And in sub-stance have we seen thee In thy glo - rious Son:
In our tel - e - scop - ic prob - ing—Light years from our world,
In the lab - 'ra - to - ry's si - lence, Where thy se - crets hide,
So with rev - 'rent hearts we pon - der All the grand de - sign
He it was who came to save us And our hopes to raise—
In the at - om's theo-ried struc-ture Sci - ence has un - furled.
There the mar-vels of cre - a - tion Are for us sup - plied.
Of the u - ni - verse a - round us, Wrought by hands di - vine.
God of ev - er - last-ing glo - ry, Thy great name we praise! A-men.

ADORATION

Great God of Wonders

Samuel Davies, 1723-1761

SURREY L.M. *with Refrain*
Henry Carey, 1692-1743

1 Great God of won - ders, all thy ways Are match-less, God-like,
2 In won - der lost, with trem-bling joy, We take the par - don
3 O may this strange, this won - drous grace, This match-less mir - a -
and di - vine; But the fair glo - ries of thy grace More God-like
of our God, Par - don for sins of deep - est dye, A par-don
cle of love, Fill the wide earth with grate-ful praise, And all an-
REFRAIN
and un - ri - valled shine:
sealed with Je - sus' blood: Who is a par - d'ning God like
gel - ic choirs a - bove:
thee? Or who has grace so rich and free? A - men.

13 Holy God, We Praise Thy Name

Attr. to Ignaz Franz, 1719-1790
Tr. Clarence A. Walworth, 1820-1900

GROSSER GOTT 7.8.7.8.7.7.
"Allgemeines Katholisches Gesangbuch," Vienna, c.1774

1 Ho - ly God, we praise thy name; Lord of all, we bow be - fore thee; All on earth thy scep - ter claim, All in heav'n a - bove a - dore thee: In - fi - nite thy vast do - main, Ev - er - last - ing is thy reign.
2 Hark, the glad ce - les - tial hymn An - gel choirs a - bove are rais - ing; Cher - u - bim and ser - a - phim, In un - ceas - ing cho - rus prais - ing; Fill the heav'ns with sweet ac - cord: Ho - ly, ho - ly, ho - ly Lord.
3 Lo! the ap - os - tol - ic train Joins thy sa - cred name to hal - low; Proph - ets swell the glad re - frain, And the bless - ed mar - tyrs fol - low; And from morn to set of sun, Thru the church the song goes on.
4 Ho - ly Fa - ther, ho - ly Son, Ho - ly Spir - it: three we name thee, Though in es - sence on - ly one; Un - di - vid - ed God we claim thee, And a - dor - ing bend the knee While we own the mys - ter - y. A-men.

ADORATION

I'll Praise My Maker While I've Breath

Based on Psalm 146
Isaac Watts, 1674-1748
Alt. by John Wesley, 1703-1791

OLD 113th 8.8.8.8.8.8.
"Strassburger Kirchenamt," 1525
Attr. to Mattaeus Greiter, c.1500-1550
Harm. by V. Earle Copes, 1921-

1 I'll praise my Mak - er while I've breath; And when my voice is lost in death, Praise shall em - ploy my no - bler pow'rs. My days of praise shall ne'er be past, While life and thought and be - ing last, Or im - mor - tal - i - ty en - dures.
2 Hap - py the man whose hopes re - ly On Is - rael's God; he made the sky And earth and seas, with all their train. His truth for - ev - er stands se - cure, He saves th'op-pressed, he feeds the poor, And none shall find his prom - ise vain.
3 The Lord pours eye - sight on the blind; The Lord sup - ports the faint - ing mind; He sends the la - b'ring con-science peace. He helps the stran - ger in dis - tress, The wid - ow and the fa - ther - less, And grants the pris-'ner sweet re - lease.
4 I'll praise him while he lends me breath; And when my voice is lost in death, Praise shall em - ploy my no - bler pow'rs. My days of praise shall ne'er be past, While life and thought and be - ing last, Or im - mor - tal - i - ty en - dures. A - men.

ADORATION

15 Immortal, Invisible, God Only Wise

Walter Chalmers Smith, 1824-1908, alt.
ST. DENIO 11.11.11.11.
Welsh Melody
John Roberts' "Caniadau y Cyssegr," 1839
1 Im - mor - tal, in - vis - i - ble, God on - ly wise,
2 Un - rest - ing, un - hast - ing, and si - lent as light,
3 To all, life thou giv - est, to both great and small;
4 Great Fa - ther of glo - ry, pure Fa - ther of light,
In light in - ac - ces - si - ble hid from our eyes,
Nor want - ing, nor wast - ing, thou rul - est in might;
In all life thou liv - est, the true life of all;
Thine an - gels a - dore thee, all veil - ing their sight;
Most bless - ed, most glo - rious, the An - cient of Days,
Thy jus - tice like moun - tains high soar - ing a - bove
We blos - som and flour - ish as leaves on the tree,
All praise we would ren - der: O help us to see
Al - might - y, vic - to - rious, thy great name we praise.
Thy clouds, which are foun - tains of good - ness and love.
And with - er and per - ish—but naught chang - eth thee.
'Tis on - ly the splen - dor of light hid - eth thee. A - men.

Another harmonization in a lower setting may be found at No. 346

ADORATION

Alternate tune: FOUNDATION, *No. 385*

Let All the World in Every Corner Sing 16

George Herbert, 1593-1632

ALL THE WORLD 10.4.6.6.6.6.10.4.
Robert G. McCutchan, 1877-1958

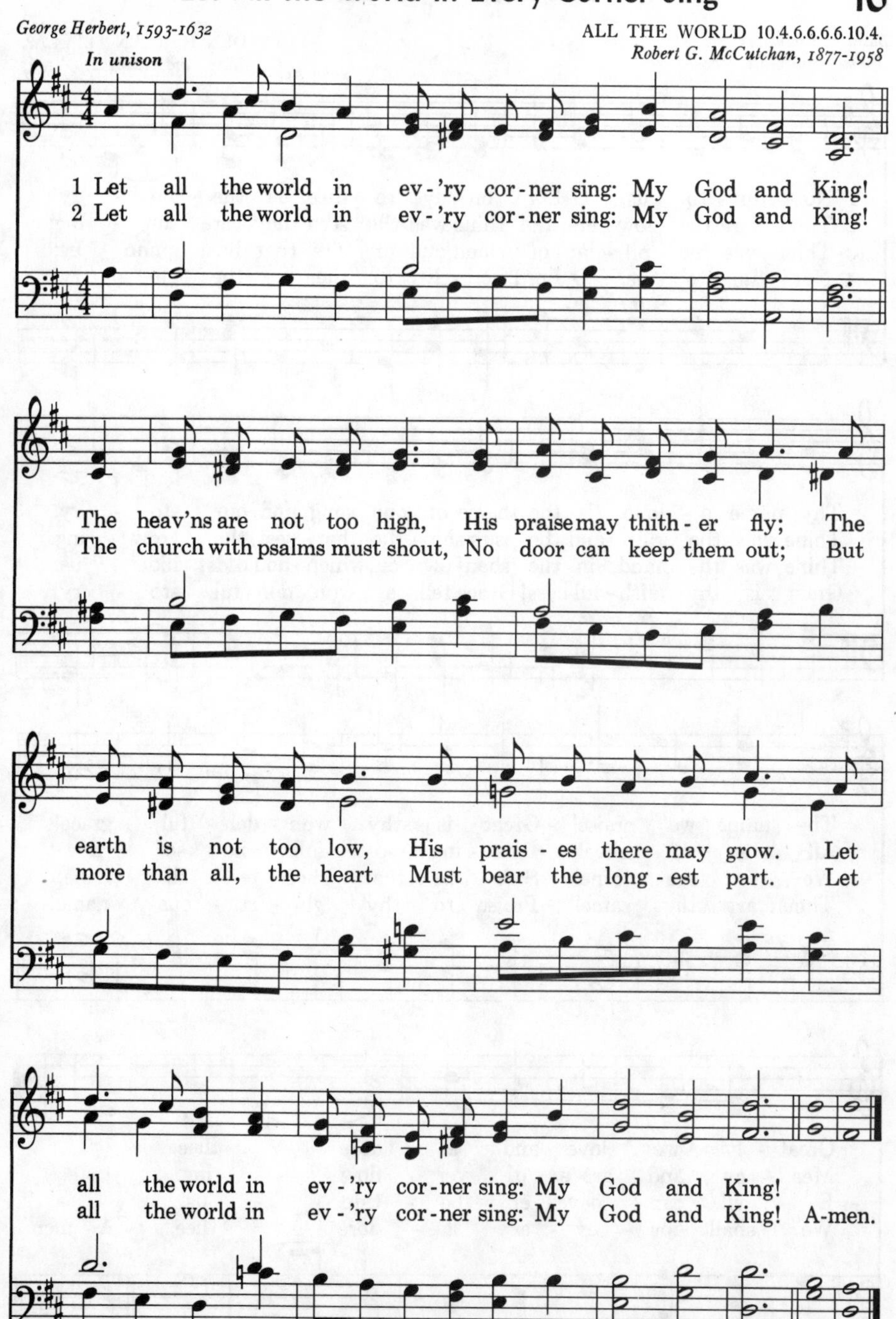
In unison
1 Let all the world in ev - 'ry cor - ner sing: My God and King!
2 Let all the world in ev - 'ry cor - ner sing: My God and King!
The heav'ns are not too high, His praise may thith - er fly; The
The church with psalms must shout, No door can keep them out; But
earth is not too low, His prais - es there may grow. Let
more than all, the heart Must bear the long - est part. Let
all the world in ev - 'ry cor - ner sing: My God and King!
all the world in ev - 'ry cor - ner sing: My God and King! A-men.

ADORATION

17

Not unto Us, O Lord

Based on Psalm 115:1
Hjalmar Sundquist, 1869-1949

LOBE DEN HERREN 14.14.4.7.8.
"Stralsund Gesangbuch," 1665

1 Not un - to us, O Lord, on - ly to thee be the glo - ry!
2 Thine were the sow - ers and thine was the seed they were sow - ing;
3 Thine was the pil - lar of cloud and of fire that didst guide us;
4 Not un - to us, O Lord, on - ly to thee be the glo - ry!
Thy name a - lone is the theme of our song and our sto - ry.
Thine was the rain and the sun-shine, the har - vest, the grow - ing.
Thine was the hand, in the shad - ow of which thou didst hide us.
Great is thy faith - ful-ness! Grace tells a won - der - ful sto - ry.
Thy name we praise! Great is thy won - der - ful grace!
All is of thee! Bless - ing so full and so free—
We too are thine! Safe in that shel - ter di - vine,
Thou art the same! Praise to thy glo - ri - ous name!
Great - ly we love and a - dore thee.
Mer - cy and grace o - ver - flow - ing.
E - vil can nev - er be - tide us.
We shall for - ev - er a - dore thee. A - men.

ADORATION

Now Thank We All Our God 18

Martin Rinkart, 1586-1649
Tr. Catherine Winkworth, 1827-1878

NUN DANKET 6.7.6.7.6.6.6.6.
Johann Crüger, 1598-1662
Harm. by Felix Mendelssohn, 1809-1847

1 Now thank we all our God With hearts and hands and voic - es,
2 O may this boun-teous God Thru all our life be near us,
3 All praise and thanks to God The Fa - ther now be giv - en,
Who won-drous things hath done, In whom his world re - joic - es;
With ev - er joy - ful hearts And bless - ed peace to cheer us;
The Son, and him who reigns With them in high - est heav - en,
Who, from our moth - ers' arms, Hath blessed us on our way
And keep us in his grace, And guide us when per - plexed,
The one e - ter - nal God, Whom earth and heav'n a - dore;
With count-less gifts of love, And still is ours to - day.
And free us from all ills In this world and the next.
For thus it was, is now, And shall be ev - er - more. A-men.

19 O Mighty God, When I Behold the Wonder

Carl Boberg, 1859-1940
Tr. E. Gustav Johnson, 1893-
O STORE GUD 11.10.11.10. with Refrain
Swedish Folk Melody
Harm. by Norman E. Johnson, 1928-
1 O might - y God, when I be - hold the won - der
2 When I be - hold the heav - ens in their vast - ness,
3 And when I hear the roar of storms and thun - der,
4 When sum - mer winds o'er ver - dant fields are play - ing,
5 And when I see, in ho - ly Scrip - ture read - ing,
Of na - ture's beau - ty, wrought by words of thine,
Where gold - en ships in az - ure is - sue forth,
When light - ning cleaves the heav - y sky in twain,
When flow - ers bloom by cool - ing wa - ters' edge,
Thy deeds, O God, on earth since birth of man,
And how thou lead - est all from realms up yon - der,
Where sun and moon keep watch up - on the fast - ness
And rain - bow fair, the sign of prom - ise ten - der,
When sing - ing birds on ev - 'ry tree are sway - ing
Thy grace and wis - dom that is shown in lead - ing
Sus - tain - ing earth - ly life with love be - nign,
Of chang - ing sea - sons and of time on earth,
Re - veals it - self when ends re - fresh - ing rain,
And fill with mel - o - dy each grove and hedge,
Thy peo - ple ev - er safe a - cross life's span,

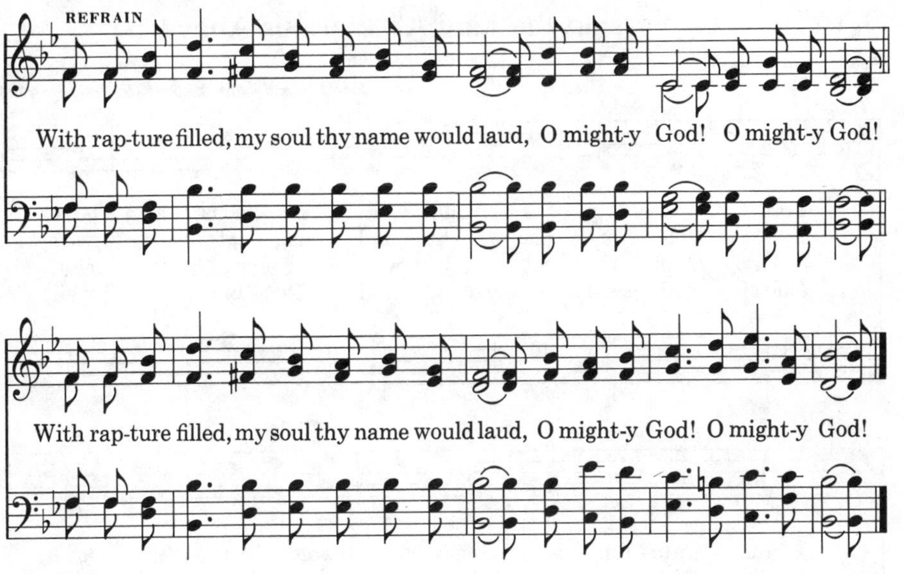
REFRAIN
With rap-ture filled, my soul thy name would laud, O might-y God! O might-y God!
With rap-ture filled, my soul thy name would laud, O might-y God! O might-y God!

6 When I hear fools in ignorance and folly
Deny thee, God, and taunt thy holy word,
And yet perceive that thou supplieth wholly
Their ev'ry need, thy love in grace conferred,

7 When I behold thy Son to earth descending,
To heal and save and teach distressed mankind,
When evil flees and death is seen recoiling
Before the glory of the Lord divine,

8 When crushed by guilt of sin, before thee kneeling
I plead for mercy and for grace and peace,
I feel thy balm and, all my bruises healing,
My soul is filled, my heart is set at ease.

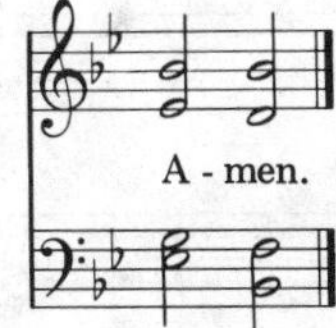
A - men.

9 And when at last the mists of time have vanished
And I in truth my faith confirmed shall see,
Upon the shores where earthly ills are banished
I'll enter, Lord, to dwell in peace with thee. Amen.

O Store Gud, originally written in the summer of 1885 by the Rev. Carl Boberg of the Mission Covenant Church of Sweden, was first published in *Mönsterås-Tidningen*, March 3, 1886.

All nine stanzas included here are from E. Gustav Johnson's translation of the Swedish original poem, first published in *The Children's Friend*, 1925. A shorter version of the words and music first appeared in *The Covenant Hymnal*, published and copyrighted in 1931.

The text widely known as *How Great Thou Art* is an English translation of a Russian version based on an earlier German translation of the original.

20 O Worship the King All Glorious Above

Robert Grant, 1779-1838

LYONS 10.10.11.11.

Adapted from Johann Michael Haydn, 1737-1806

1 O worship the King all glorious above,
2 O tell of his might and sing of his grace,
3 Thy bountiful care what tongue can recite?
4 Frail children of dust, and feeble as frail,
And gratefully sing his wonderful love;
Whose robe is the light, whose canopy space;
It breathes in the air, it shines in the light,
In thee do we trust, nor find thee to fail;
Our Shield and Defender, the Ancient of Days,
His chariots of wrath the deep thunder-clouds form,
It streams from the hills, it descends to the plain,
Thy mercies how tender, how firm to the end,
Pavilioned in splendor and girded with praise.
And dark is his path on the wings of the storm.
And sweetly distills in the dew and the rain.
Our Maker, Defender, Redeemer and Friend. Amen.

Praise the Lord, His Glories Show

Based on Psalm 150
Henry Francis Lyte, 1793-1847
LLANFAIR 7.7.7.7. with Alleluias
Robert Williams, c.1781-1821
Harm. by John Roberts, 1822-1877
1 Praise the Lord, his glo - ries show, Al - le - lu - ia!
2 Earth to heav'n and heav'n to earth, Al - le - lu - ia!
3 Praise the Lord, his mer - cies trace, Al - le - lu - ia!
Saints with - in his courts be - low, Al - le - lu - ia!
Tell his won - ders, sing his worth, Al - le - lu - ia!
Praise his prov - i - dence and grace, Al - le - lu - ia!
An - gels round his throne a - bove, Al - le - lu - ia!
Age to age and shore to shore, Al - le - lu - ia!
All that he for man hath done, Al - le - lu - ia!
All that see and share his love. Al - le - lu - ia!
Praise him, praise him ev - er - more! Al - le - lu - ia!
All he sends us thru his Son. Al - le - lu - ia!

22 Praise, My Soul, the King of Heaven

Based on Psalm 103
Henry Francis Lyte, 1793-1847, alt.
PRAISE MY SOUL 8.7.8.7.8.7.
John Goss, 1800-1880
1 Praise, my soul, the King of heav - en, To his feet thy
2 Praise him for his grace and fa - vor To our fa - thers
3 Fa - ther-like he tends and spares us; Well our fee - ble
4 An - gels, help us to a - dore him, Ye be - hold him
trib - ute bring; Ran - somed, healed, re - stored, for - giv - en,
in dis - tress; Praise him, still the same as ev - er,
frame he knows; In his hands he gen - tly bears us,
face to face; Sun and moon, bow down be - fore him,
Ev - er - more his prais - es sing: Al - le - lu - ia!
Slow to chide, and swift to bless: Al - le - lu - ia!
Res - cues us from all our foes. Al - le - lu - ia!
Dwell - ers all in time and space. Al - le - lu - ia!
Al - le - lu - ia! Praise the ev - er - last - ing King.
Al - le - lu - ia! Glo - rious in his faith - ful - ness.
Al - le - lu - ia! Wide - ly yet his mer - cy flows.
Al - le - lu - ia! Praise with us the God of grace. A - men.

Alternate tunes: REGENT SQUARE, *No. 71;* DULCE CARMEN, *No. 460*

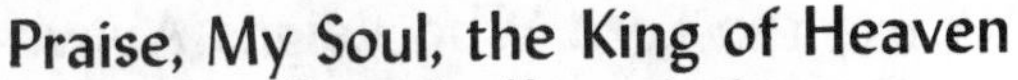

Praise, My Soul, the King of Heaven

Alternative Harmonization

This harmonization may be used for one or more stanzas, the congregation and the choir singing the melody.

23 Stand Up and Bless the Lord

James Montgomery, 1771-1854

ST. THOMAS S.M.

Williams' "New Universal Psalmodist," 1770

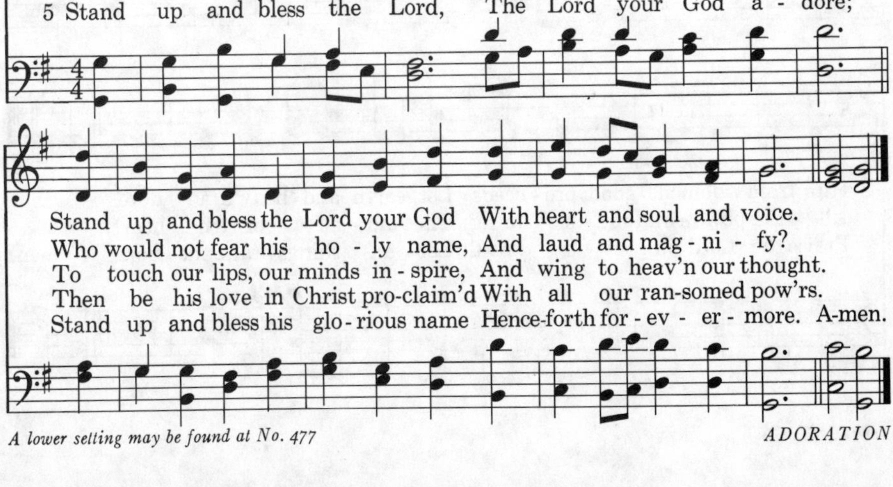

1 Stand up and bless the Lord, Ye people of his choice;
Stand up and bless the Lord your God With heart and soul and voice.

2 Though high above all praise, Above all blessing high,
Who would not fear his holy name, And laud and magnify?

3 O for the living flame, From his own altar brought,
To touch our lips, our minds inspire, And wing to heav'n our thought.

4 God is our strength and song, And his salvation ours;
Then be his love in Christ proclaim'd With all our ransomed pow'rs.

5 Stand up and bless the Lord, The Lord your God adore;
Stand up and bless his glorious name Henceforth for evermore. Amen.

A lower setting may be found at No. 477

ADORATION

24 Praise the Lord Who Reigns Above

Based on Psalm 150
Charles Wesley, 1707-1788

AMSTERDAM 7.6.7.6.7.7.7.6.
James Nares, 1715-1783
"The Foundery Collection," 1742

1 Praise the Lord who reigns a - bove And keeps his courts be - low;
2 Cel - e - brate th'e - ter - nal God With harp and psal - ter - y,
3 Him in whom they move and live Let ev - 'ry crea - ture sing,
Praise the ho - ly God of love And all his great - ness show;
Tim - brels soft and cym - bals loud In his high praise a - gree;
Glo - ry to their Mak - er give And hom - age to their King;
Praise him for his no - ble deeds, Praise him for his match - less pow'r:
Praise him ev - 'ry tune - ful string, All the reach of heav'n - ly art:
Hal - lowed be his name be - neath, As in heav'n on earth a - dored:
Him from whom all good pro - ceeds Let earth and heav'n a - dore.
All the pow'rs of mu - sic bring, The mu - sic of the heart.
Praise the Lord in ev - 'ry breath, Let all things praise the Lord. A - men.

Praise the Lord! Ye Heavens, Adore Him 25

Based on Psalm 148
"Foundling Hospital Collection," 1796, Sts. 1, 2
Edward Osler, 1798-1863, St. 3

AUSTRIAN HYMN 8.7.8.7.D.
Franz Joseph Haydn, 1732-1809

1 Praise the Lord! ye heav'ns, a - dore him, Praise him, an-gels in the height;
2 Praise the Lord! for he is glo - rious, Nev - er shall his prom - ise fail;
3 Wor - ship, hon - or, glo - ry, bless - ing, Lord, we of - fer un - to thee;

Sun and moon, re - joice be - fore him, Praise him, all ye stars of light.
God hath made his saints vic - to - rious, Sin and death shall not pre - vail.
Young and old, thy praise ex - press-ing, In glad hom - age bend the knee.

Praise the Lord! for he hath spo - ken, Worlds his might-y voice o - beyed;
Praise the God of our sal - va - tion, Hosts on high, his pow'r pro - claim;
All the saints in heav'n a - dore thee, We would bow be - fore thy throne;

Laws which nev-er shall be bro-ken For their guid-ance he hath made.
Heav'n and earth and all cre-a - tion, Laud and mag - ni - fy his name.
As thine an-gels serve be-fore thee, So on earth thy will be done. A-men.

Alternate tune: HYFRYDOL, *No. 335*

26 To God Be the Glory

Fanny J. Crosby, 1820-1915

TO GOD BE THE GLORY 11.11.11.11. *with Refrain*
William H. Doane, 1832-1915

1 To God be the glo - ry—great things he hath done! So loved he the
2 O per - fect re-demp-tion, the pur-chase of blood, To ev - 'ry be-
3 Great things he hath taught us, great things he hath done, And great our re-
world that he gave us his Son, Who yield - ed his life an a-
liev - er the prom - ise of God; The vil - est of - fen - der who
joic - ing thru Je - sus the Son; But pu - rer, and high - er, and
tone-ment for sin, And o - pened the life - gate that all may go in.
tru - ly be - lieves, That mo-ment from Je - sus a par - don re - ceives.
great - er will be Our won - der, our trans-port, when Je - sus we see.
REFRAIN
Praise the Lord, praise the Lord, Let the earth hear his voice! Praise the
Lord, praise the Lord, Let the peo - ple re - joice! O come to the Fa - ther thru

Je - sus the Son, And give him the glo - ry—great things he hath done!

Sing to the Lord a Joyful Song 27

John S. B. Monsell, 1811-1875

GONFALON ROYAL L.M.
Percy C. Buck, 1871-1947

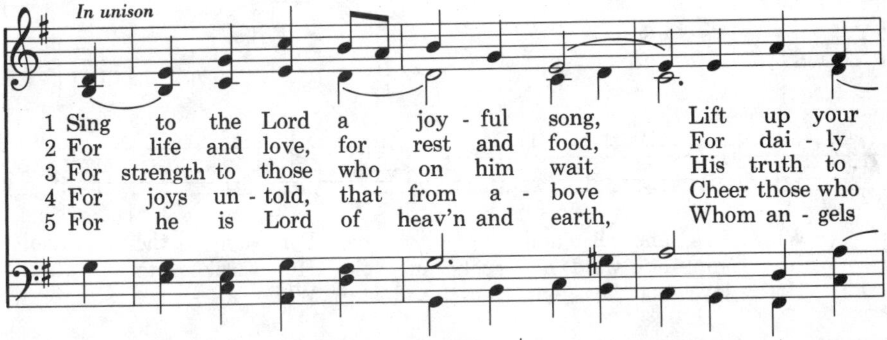

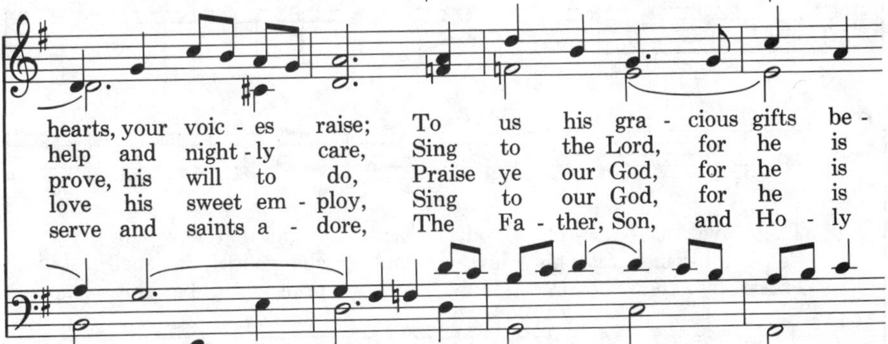

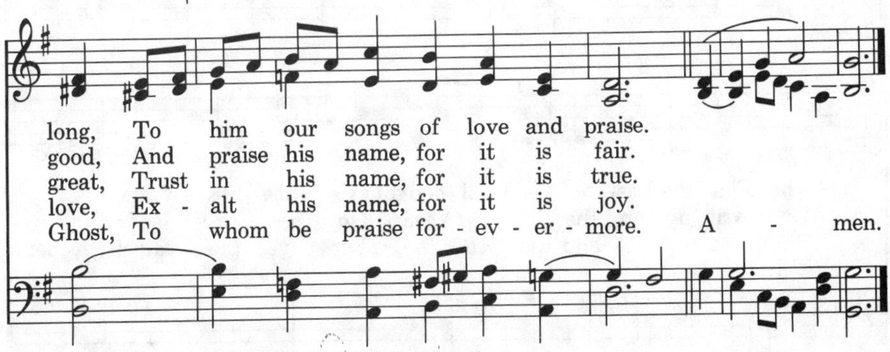

In unison

1 Sing to the Lord a joy - ful song, Lift up your hearts, your voic - es raise; To us his gra - cious gifts be - long, To him our songs of love and praise.

2 For life and love, for rest and food, For dai - ly help and night - ly care, Sing to the Lord, for he is good, And praise his name, for it is fair.

3 For strength to those who on him wait His truth to prove, his will to do, Praise ye our God, for he is great, Trust in his name, for it is true.

4 For joys un - told, that from a - bove Cheer those who love his sweet em - ploy, Sing to our God, for he is love, Ex - alt his name, for it is joy.

5 For he is Lord of heav'n and earth, Whom an - gels serve and saints a - dore, The Fa - ther, Son, and Ho - ly Ghost, To whom be praise for - ev - er - more. A - men.

The singing of Amen after stanza five is necessary for the harmonic completion of the tune.

ADORATION

28 The God of Abraham Praise

Revised Version of the "Yigdal"
Daniel ben Judah, c.1400
Tr. Newton Mann, 1836-1926,
and Max Landsberg, 1845-1928

LEONI 6.6.8.4.D.
Hebrew Melody
Adapted by Meyer Lyon, 1751-1797

1 The God of A-braham praise, All prais - ed be his name,
2 His spir - it flow-eth free, High surg - ing where it will;
3 He hath e - ter - nal life Im - plant - ed in the soul;
Who was, and is, and is to be, For aye the same!
In proph-et's word he spoke of old, He speak - eth still.
His love shall be our strength and stay While a - ges roll.
The one e - ter - nal God, Ere aught that now ap - pears;
Es - tab-lished is his law, And change-less it shall stand,
Praise to the liv - ing God! All prais - ed be his name,
The First, the Last: be - yond all thought His time - less years!
Deep writ up - on the hu - man heart, On sea or land.
Who was, and is, and is to be, For aye the same! A-men.

Praise to the Lord, the Almighty

Joachim Neander, 1650-1680
Tr. Catherine Winkworth, 1827-1878, alt.

LOBE DEN HERREN 14.14.4.7.8.
"Stralsund Gesangbuch," 1665

1 Praise to the Lord, the Al-might-y, the King of cre-a-tion!
2 Praise to the Lord, who o'er all things so won-drous-ly reign-eth,
3 Praise to the Lord, who doth pros-per thy work and de-fend thee;
4 Praise to the Lord! O let all that is in me a-dore him!
O my soul, praise him, for he is thy health and sal-va-tion!
Shel-ters thee un-der his wings, yea, so gen-tly sus-tain-eth!
Sure-ly his good-ness and mer-cy here dai-ly at-tend thee.
All that hath life and breath, come now with prais-es be-fore him.
All ye who hear, Now to his tem-ple draw near;
Hast thou not seen How thy de-sires e'er have been
Pon-der a-new What the Al-might-y can do,
Let the A-men Sound from his peo-ple a-gain:
Join me in glad ad-o-ra-tion!
Grant-ed in what he or-dain-eth?
If with his love he be-friend thee.
Glad-ly for aye we a-dore him. A-men.

30 We Gather Together

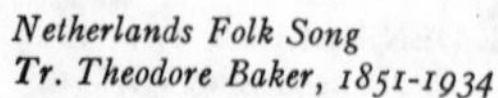

Netherlands Folk Song
Tr. Theodore Baker, 1851-1934

KREMSER *Irregular*
Netherlands Folk Song, 1626
Harm. by Edward Kremser, 1838-1914

1 We gath - er to - geth - er to ask the Lord's bless-ing–He chas - tens and
2 Be - side us to guide us, our God with us join - ing, Or - dain - ing, main-
3 We all do ex - tol thee, thou lead - er tri - um-phant, And pray that thou

has - tens his will to make known; The wick - ed op-press-ing now cease from dis-
tain-ing his king-dom di - vine; So from the be - gin-ning the fight we were
still our de - fend - er wilt be; Let thy con-gre - ga - tion es - cape trib - u -

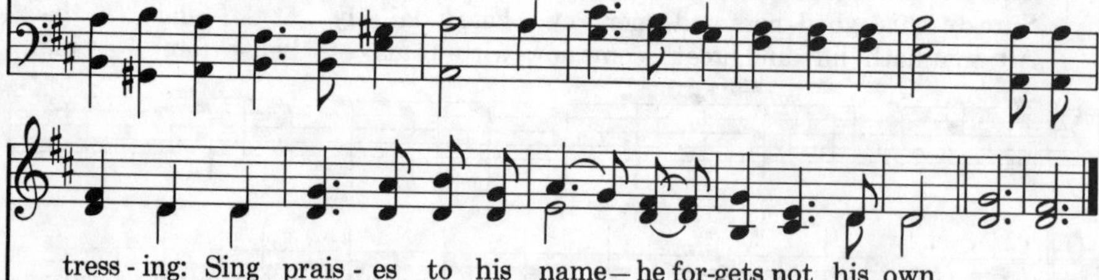

tress - ing: Sing prais - es to his name— he for-gets not his own.
win - ning: Thou, Lord, wast at our side— all glo - ry be thine.
la - tion: Thy name be ev - er praised! O Lord, make us free! A - men.

Words used by permission of G. Schirmer, Inc.

31 We Praise Thee, O God

Julia C. Cory, 1882-1963

KREMSER *Irregular*
Netherlands Folk Song, 1626
Harm. by Edward Kremser, 1838-1914

1 We praise thee, O God, our Redeemer, Creator,
In grateful devotion our tribute we bring;
We lay it before thee, we kneel and adore thee,
We bless thy holy name, glad praises we sing.

2 We worship thee, God of our fathers, we bless thee,
Through life's storm and tempest our guide hast thou been;
When perils o'ertake us, thou wilt not forsake us,
And with thy help, O Lord, life's battles we win.

3 With voices united our praises we offer,
And gladly our songs of true worship we raise;
Our sins now confessing, we pray for thy blessing:
To thee, our great Redeemer, forever be praise. Amen.

Safely Through Another Week

John Newton, 1725-1807

EASTER GLORY 7.7.7.7.7.7.
Ludvig M. Lindeman, 1812-1887

1 Safe - ly through an - oth - er week God has brought us
2 While we pray for pard - 'ning grace Thru the dear Re -
3 Here we come thy name to praise, Let us feel thy
4 May thy gos - pel's joy - ful sound Con - quer sin - ners,
on our way; Let us now a bless - ing seek,
deem - er's name, Show thy rec - on - cil - ing face,
pres - ence near; May thy glo - ry meet our eyes,
com - fort saints; May the fruits of grace a - bound,
Wait - ing in his courts to - day: Day of all the
Take a - way our sin and shame: From our world - ly
While we in thy house ap - pear: Here af - ford us,
Bring re - lief for all com - plaints: Thus may all our
week the best, Em - blem of e - ter - nal rest.
cares set free, May we rest this day in thee.
Lord, a taste Of our ev - er - last - ing feast.
sab - baths prove, Till we join the church a - bove. A - men.

33 Sabbath Day of Rest and Cheer!

Joel Blomqvist, 1840-1930
Tr. A. L. Skoog, 1856-1934, alt.

SABBATSDAG 7.7.7.7.
Joel Blomqvist, 1840-1930

1 Sab - bath day of rest and cheer! Day di - vine, to us so dear!
2 Now the week of toil is o'er, And in peace we sit once more
3 Lord, our God, we seek thy face, Bless us with thy sav - ing grace;
4 Let thy might - y word hold sway O - ver men on earth to - day;
5 May, O Lord, the day be near, When we pass from tri - als here

Come, O come to old and young, Gath-'ring all for prayer and song.
In thy pres-ence, gra-cious Lord, List-'ning to thy ho - ly word.
May thy her-alds ev - 'ry-where Fer-vent - ly thy truth de-clare.
Our poor souls, good Shep-herd, feed, In - to pas - tures green us lead.
In - to thine e - ter - nal rest, In the man-sions of the blest. A-men.

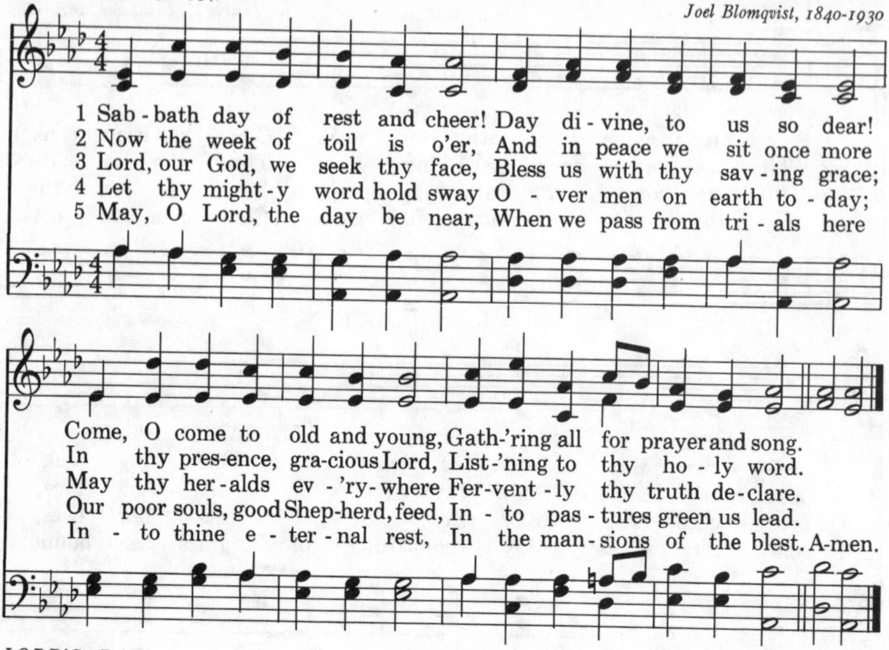

LORD'S DAY

Another harmonization in a lower setting may be found at No. 621

34 Christ, Whose Glory Fills the Skies

Charles Wesley, 1707-1788

EASTER GLORY 7.7.7.7.7.7.
Ludvig M. Lindeman, 1812-1887

1 Christ, whose glo - ry fills the skies, Christ, the true, the on - ly light,
2 Dark and cheer-less is the morn Un - ac-com-pa - nied by thee;
3 Vis - it, then, this soul of mine; Pierce the gloom of sin and grief;
Sun of right-eous-ness, a - rise, Tri-umph o'er the shades of night;
Joy - less is the day's re - turn Till thy mer - cy's beams I see,
Fill me, Ra - dian - cy di - vine; Scat - ter all my un - be - lief;

MORNING

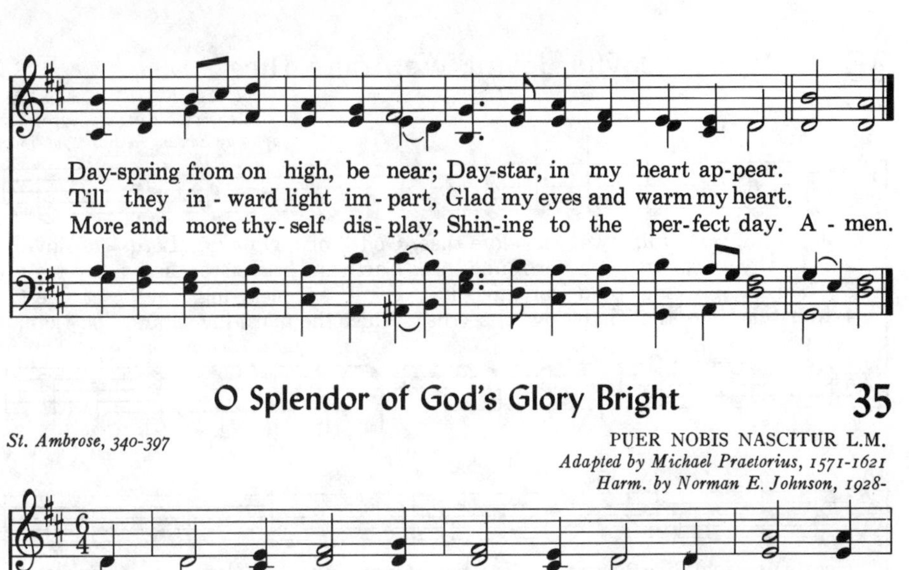
Day-spring from on high, be near; Day-star, in my heart ap-pear.
Till they in-ward light im-part, Glad my eyes and warm my heart.
More and more thy-self dis-play, Shin-ing to the per-fect day. A-men.

O Splendor of God's Glory Bright 35

St. Ambrose, 340-397

PUER NOBIS NASCITUR L.M.
Adapted by Michael Praetorius, 1571-1621
Harm. by Norman E. Johnson, 1928-

1 O splen - dor of God's glo - ry bright, Who bring - est
2 Come, ver - y Sun of truth and love, Come in thy
3 Teach us to work with all our might; Put Sa - tan's
4 All praise to God the Fa - ther be, All praise, e -

forth the light from Light; O Light of light, the
ra - diance from a - bove, And shed the Ho - ly
fierce as - saults to flight; Turn all to good that
ter - nal Son, to thee, Whom with the Spir - it

foun - tain spring; O Day, our days il - lu - min - ing;
Spir - it's ray On all we think or do to - day.
seems most ill; Help us our call - ing to ful - fill.
we a - dore, For - ev - er and for - ev - er - more. A-men.

Another harmonization may be found at No. 161

36 Joyful, Joyful, We Adore Thee

Henry van Dyke, 1852-1933

HYMN TO JOY 8.7.8.7.D.
Ludwig van Beethoven, 1770-1827
Adapted by Edward Hodges, 1796-1867

1 Joy - ful, joy - ful, we a - dore thee, God of glo - ry, Lord of love;
2 All thy works with joy sur-round thee, Earth and heaven re - flect thy rays,
3 Thou art giv - ing and for - giv - ing, Ev - er bless-ing, ev - er blest,
4 Mor-tals, join the hap - py cho - rus Which the morn-ing stars be - gan;
Hearts un - fold like flowers be - fore thee, Open - ing to the sun a - bove.
Stars and an - gels sing a-round thee, Cen - ter of un - bro - ken praise.
Well-spring of the joy of liv - ing, O - cean depth of hap - py rest!
Fa - ther love is reign - ing o'er us, Broth - er love binds man to man.
Melt the clouds of sin and sad-ness, Drive the dark of doubt a - way;
Field and for - est, vale and moun-tain, Flow - ery mead-ow, flash - ing sea,
Thou our Fa - ther, Christ our Broth-er— All who live in love are thine;
Ev - er sing - ing, march we on-ward, Vic - tors in the midst of strife,
Giv - er of im - mor-tal glad-ness, Fill us with the light of day.
Chant-ing bird and flow-ing foun-tain, Call us to re - joice in thee.
Teach us how to love each oth - er, Lift us to the joy di-vine.
Joy - ful mu - sic leads us sun-ward In the tri-umph song of life. A-men.

MORNING

When Morning Gilds the Skies 37

From the German, c.1800
Tr. Edward Caswall, 1814-1878

LAUDES DOMINI 6.6.6.6.6.6.
Joseph Barnby, 1838-1896

1 When morn - ing gilds the skies, My heart a - wak - ing
2 Does sad - ness fill my mind? A sol - ace here I
3 The night be - comes as day, When from the heart we
4 Ye na - tions of man - kind, In this your con - cord
5 Sing, suns and stars of space, Sing, ye that see his
6 Be this, while life is mine, My can - ti - cle di -
cries, May Je - sus Christ be praised! A -
find, May Je - sus Christ be praised! Or
say, May Je - sus Christ be praised! The
find, May Je - sus Christ be praised! Let
face, May Je - sus Christ be praised! God's
vine, May Je - sus Christ be praised! Be
like at work and prayer To Je - sus I re -
fades my earth - ly bliss? My com - fort still is
pow'rs of dark - ness fear When this sweet chant they
all the earth a - round Ring joy - ous with the
whole cre - a - tion o'er, For aye and ev - er -
this th'e - ter - nal song Through all the a - ges
pair, May Je - sus Christ be praised!
this, May Je - sus Christ be praised!
hear, May Je - sus Christ be praised!
sound, May Je - sus Christ be praised!
more May Je - sus Christ be praised!
long, May Je - sus Christ be praised! A - men.

MORNING

38 New Every Morning Is the Love

John Keble, 1792-1866, alt.

MELCOMBE L.M.
Samuel Webbe, 1740-1816

1 New ev - 'ry morn - ing is the love
2 New mer - cies, each re - turn - ing day,
3 If on our dai - ly course our mind
4 The triv - ial round, the com - mon task,
5 On - ly, O Lord, in thy dear love,
Our wak - 'ning and up - ris - ing prove:
Hov - er a - round us while we pray;
Be set to hal - low all we find,
Will fur - nish all we ought to ask:
Fit us for per - fect rest a - bove;
Thru sleep and dark - ness safe - ly brought,
New per - ils past, new sins for - giv'n,
New treas - ures still, of count - less price,
Room to de - ny our - selves— a road
And help us, this and ev - 'ry day,
Re - stored to life and pow'r and thought.
New thoughts of God, new hopes of heav'n.
God will pro - vide for sac - ri - fice.
To bring us dai - ly near - er God.
To live more near - ly as we pray. A - men.

Again Thy Glorious Sun Doth Rise

39

Johann Olof Wallin, 1779-1839
Tr. Composite

STÖRL C.M.
Johann Georg Christian Störl, 1675-1719

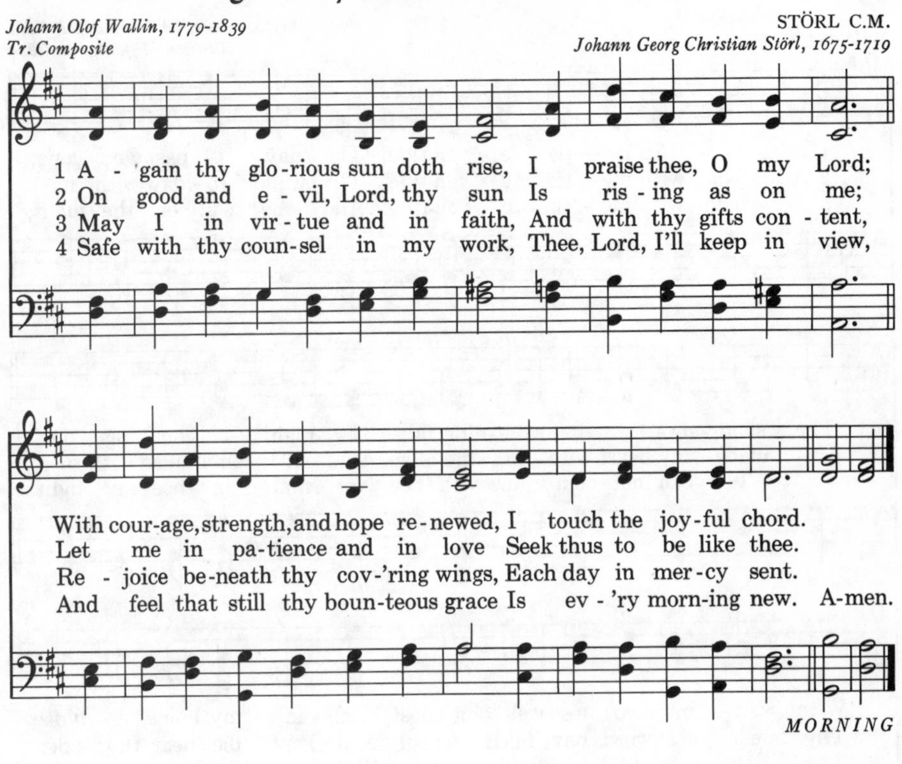

1 A - 'gain thy glo-rious sun doth rise, I praise thee, O my Lord;
2 On good and e - vil, Lord, thy sun Is ris - ing as on me;
3 May I in vir - tue and in faith, And with thy gifts con - tent,
4 Safe with thy coun-sel in my work, Thee, Lord, I'll keep in view,
With cour-age, strength, and hope re - newed, I touch the joy-ful chord.
Let me in pa-tience and in love Seek thus to be like thee.
Re - joice be-neath thy cov-'ring wings, Each day in mer-cy sent.
And feel that still thy boun-teous grace Is ev - 'ry morn-ing new. A-men.

MORNING

Again a Day Has from Us Gone

40

Johann Friedrich Herzog, 1647-1699
Tr. Gerhard W. Palmgren, 1880-1959

STÖRL C.M.
Johann Georg Christian Störl, 1675-1719

1 Again a day has from us gone,
Gone ever from our sight;
Once more, its daily labors done,
Come peace and rest of night.

2 But thou remainest, God of grace,
Forevermore the same;
Thou all our nights and all our days
Didst number ere they came.

3 Safe in thy keeping let me rest,
When daylight fades away;
With joyful praise thy name be blest
When dawns another day.

4 And if death's solemn call I hear,
While in my sleep I lie,
What comfort, Lord, that thou art near:
In thee I live and die. Amen.

EVENING

41 Abide with Me—'Tis Eventide!

Based on Luke 24:29-32
M. Lowrie Hofford

MILLARD 8.6.8.6.8.6. *with Refrain*
Harrison Millard, 1829-1895

1 A - bide with me—'tis e - ven-tide! The day is past and gone;
2 A - bide with me—'tis e - ven-tide! Thy walk to - day with me
3 A - bide with me—'tis e - ven-tide! And lone will be the night,
The shad - ows of the eve-ning fall, The night is com - ing on.
Has made my heart with - in me burn, As I com-muned with thee.
If I can-not com-mune with thee Nor find in thee my light.
With - in my heart, a wel-come guest, With - in my home a - bide:
Thy ear - nest words have filled my soul And kept me near thy side:
The dark - ness of the world, I fear, Would in my home a - bide:
REFRAIN
O Sav - ior, stay this night with me— Be - hold, 'tis e - ven - tide!
O Sav - ior, stay this night with me— Be - hold, 'tis e - ven - tide! A-men.

All Praise to Thee, My God
42
Thomas Ken, 1637-1711, alt.
TALLIS' CANON L.M.
Thomas Tallis, c.1505-1585
1 All praise to thee, my God, this night, For all the bless-ings of the light!
2 For-give me, Lord, for thy dear Son, The ill that I this day have done,
3 O may my soul on thee re-pose, And with sweet sleep mine eye-lids close,
4 Praise God, from whom all bless-ings flow; Praise him, all crea-tures here be-low;
Keep me, O keep me, King of kings, Be-neath thine own al-might-y wings!
That with the world, my-self, and thee, I, ere I sleep, at peace may be.
Sleep that may me more vig-'rous make To serve my God when I a-wake.
Praise him a-bove, ye heav'n-ly host; Praise Fa-ther, Son, and Ho-ly Ghost. A-men.
Now the Day Is Over
43
Sabine Baring-Gould, 1834-1924
MERRIAL 6.5.6.5.
Joseph Barnby, 1838-1896
1 Now the day is o-ver, Night is draw-ing nigh;
2 Je-sus, give the wea-ry Calm and sweet re-pose;
3 Thru the long night watch-es, May thine an-gels spread
4 When the morn-ing wak-ens, Then may I a-rise
Shad-ows of the eve-ning Steal a-cross the sky.
With thy ten-d'rest bless-ing May mine eye-lids close.
Their white wings a-bove me, Watch-ing round my bed.
Pure and fresh and sin-less In thy ho-ly eyes. A-men.

44 At Even, Ere the Sun Was Set

Henry Twells, 1823-1900

ANGELUS L.M.
Georg Joseph, c. 1650
"Heilige Seelenlust," 1657
Altered in "Cantica Spiritualia," 1847

1 At e - ven, ere the sun was set, The sick, O Lord, a - round thee lay; O in what di - vers pains they met! O with what joy they went a - way!
2 Once more 'tis e - ven - tide, and we, Op - pressed with va - rious ills, draw near; What if thy form we can - not see? We know and feel that thou art here.
3 O Sav - ior Christ, our woes dis - pel, For some are sick, and some are sad, And some have nev - er loved thee well, And some have lost the love they had;
4 And none, O Lord, have per - fect rest, For none are whol - ly free from sin; And they who fain would serve thee best Are con - scious most of wrong with - in. A - men.

5 O Savior Christ, thou too art man;
Thou hast been troubled, tempted, tried;
Thy kind but searching glance can scan
The very wounds that shame would hide.

6 Thy touch has still its ancient power;
No word from thee can fruitless fall;
Hear, in this solemn evening hour,
And in thy mercy heal us all. Amen.

Thy Holy Wings, Dear Savior

Lina Sandell, 1832-1903
Tr. Ernest Edwin Ryden, 1886-

HOLY WINGS 7.6.7.6.D.
Swedish Folk Melody
Harm. by Mark S. Dickey, 1885-1961

1 Thy ho - ly wings, dear Sav - ior, Spread gen - tly o - ver me;
2 Thy par - don, Sav - ior, grant me, And cleanse me in thy blood;

And thru the long night watch - es, I'll rest se - cure in thee.
Give me a will - ing spir - it, A heart both clean and good.

What - ev - er may be - tide me, Be thou my hid - ing place,
O take in - to thy keep - ing Thy chil - dren, great and small,

And let me live and la - bor Each day, Lord, by thy grace.
And, while we sweet - ly slum - ber, En - fold us, one and all. A - men.

EVENING

46 Now, on Land and Sea Descending

Samuel Longfellow, 1819-1892

VESPER HYMN 8.7.8.7.8.6.8.7.
Attr. to Dmitri S. Bortniansky, 1751-1825
Adapted by John A. Stevenson, 1761-1833

1 Now, on land and sea de-scend-ing, Brings the night its peace pro-found;
2 Soon as dies the sun-set glo-ry, Stars of heav'n shine out a-bove,
3 Now, our wants and bur-dens leav-ing To his care who cares for all,
4 As the dark-ness deep-ens o'er us, Lo! e-ter-nal stars a-rise;

Let our ves-per hymn be blend-ing With the ho-ly calm a-round.
Tell-ing still the an-cient sto-ry—Their Cre-a-tor's change-less love.
Cease we fear-ing, cease we griev-ing: At his touch our bur-dens fall.
Hope and faith and love rise glo-rious, Shin-ing in the spir-it's skies.

Ju-bi-la-te! Ju-bi-la-te! Ju-bi-la-te! A-men!

Let our ves-per hymn be blend-ing With the ho-ly calm a-round.
Tell-ing still the an-cient sto-ry—Their Cre-a-tor's change-less love.
Cease we fear-ing, cease we griev-ing: At his touch our bur-dens fall.
Hope and faith and love rise glo-rious, Shin-ing in the spir-it's skies. A-men.

Savior, Breathe an Evening Blessing
47
James Edmeston, 1791-1867
Godfrey Thring, 1823-1903, St. 4
EVENING PRAYER 8.7.8.7.
George C. Stebbins, 1846-1945
1 Sav - ior, breathe an eve - ning bless-ing Ere re - pose our spir - its seal:
2 Tho de - struc - tion walk a - round us, Tho the ar - rows past us fly,
3 Tho the night be dark and drear - y, Dark-ness can - not hide from thee;
4 Be thou nigh should death o'er-take us– Je - sus, then our re - fuge be;
Sin and want we come con-fess-ing, Thou canst save, and thou canst heal.
An - gel-guards from thee sur-round us, We are safe if thou art nigh.
Thou art he who, nev - er wea - ry, Watch-est where thy peo - ple be.
And in par - a - dise a - wake us, There to rest in peace with thee. A-men.
When All the World Is Sleeping
48
Lina Sandell, 1832-1903
Tr. Karl A. Olsson, 1913-
NOCTURN 7.6.7.6.
J. A. Hultman, 1861-1942
Harm. by A. Royce Eckhardt, 1937-
1 When all the world is sleep - ing, God watch - es through the night;
2 When all the world is sleep - ing And dark is ev - 'ry - where,
3 When all the world is sleep - ing, We some-times see his face;
4 When all the world is sleep - ing In deep tran-quil - li - ty,
His eyes are in the heav - ens, We sense their ten - der light.
How bless - ed to re - mem - ber Our Fa-ther's con-stant care.
In qui - et dreams he gives us As - sur - ance of his grace.
Give bod - y, mind, and spir - it, O Fa - ther, rest in thee. A-men.

49 Father, Give a Tranquil Spirit

Eric G. Hawkinson, 1896-

EARNEST 8s. 10L.
Frank Earnest, 1885-1952

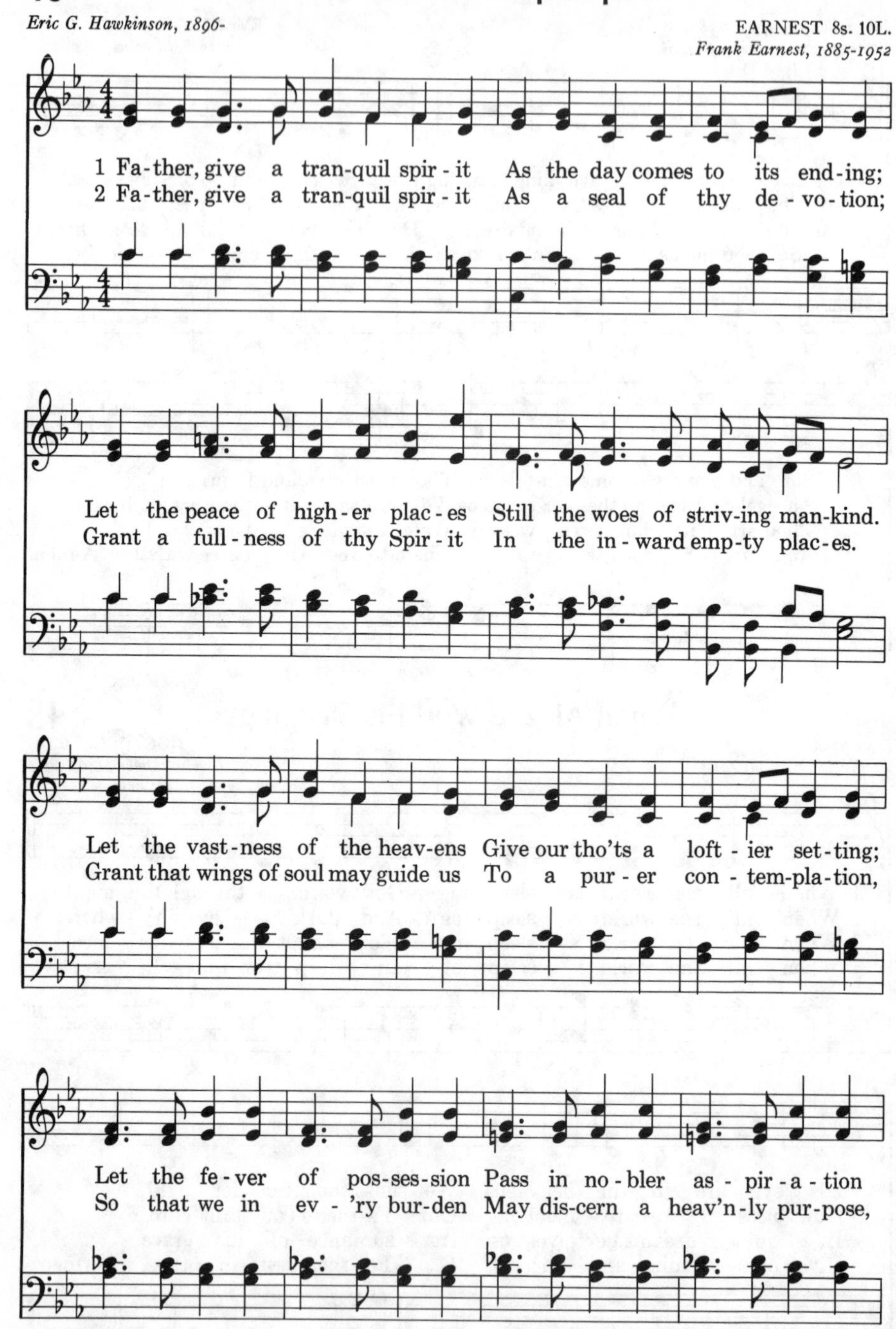

1 Fa-ther, give a tran-quil spir-it As the day comes to its end-ing;
2 Fa-ther, give a tran-quil spir-it As a seal of thy de-vo-tion;
Let the peace of high-er plac-es Still the woes of striv-ing man-kind.
Grant a full-ness of thy Spir-it In the in-ward emp-ty plac-es.
Let the vast-ness of the heav-ens Give our tho'ts a loft-ier set-ting;
Grant that wings of soul may guide us To a pur-er con-tem-pla-tion,
Let the fe-ver of pos-ses-sion Pass in no-bler as-pir-a-tion
So that we in ev-'ry bur-den May dis-cern a heav'n-ly pur-pose,

EVENING

Like the pass-ing whims of chil-dren End at night in sweet con-tent-ment.
Add-ing worth to hu - man sto-ry, End-ing with thy ben-e - dic-tion. A-men.
The Day Thou Gavest, Lord, Is Ended
50
John Ellerton, 1826-1893
ST. CLEMENT 9.8.9.8.
Clement C. Scholefield, 1839-1904
1 The day thou gav - est, Lord, is end-ed, The dark - ness
2 We thank thee that thy Church, un - sleep-ing While earth rolls
3 As o'er each con - ti - nent and is-land The dawn leads
4 The sun, that bids us rest, is wak-ing Our breth - ren
5 So be it, Lord! thy throne shall nev-er, Like earth's proud
falls at thy be-hest; To thee our morn-ing hymns as-
on - ward in - to light, Thru all the world her watch is
on an - oth - er day, The voice of prayer is nev - er
'neath the west - ern sky, And hour by hour fresh lips are
em - pires, pass a - way; Thy king-dom stands and grows for-
cend-ed, Thy praise shall sanc - ti - fy our rest.
keep-ing, And rests not now by day or night.
si - lent, Nor dies the strain of praise a - way.
mak-ing Thy won - drous do - ings heard on high.
ev - er, Till all thy crea-tures own thy sway. A-men.

51 Day Is Dying in the West

Mary A. Lathbury, 1841-1913

CHAUTAUQUA 7.7.7.7.4. *with Refrain*
William F. Sherwin, 1826-1888

1 Day is dy - ing in the west, Heav'n is touch - ing earth with rest; Wait and wor - ship while the night Sets her eve - ning lamps a - light Through all the sky.
2 Lord of life, be - neath the dome Of the u - ni - verse, thy home, Gath - er us who seek thy face To the fold of thy em - brace, For thou art nigh.
3 When for - ev - er from our sight Pass the stars, the day, the night, Lord of an - gels, on our eyes Let e - ter - nal morn - ing rise, And shad - ows end.
REFRAIN
Ho - ly, ho - ly, ho - ly, Lord God of hosts! Heav'n and earth are full of thee! Heav'n and earth are prais - ing thee, O Lord most high! A - men.

EVENING

Open Now Thy Gates of Beauty

52

Benjamin Schmolck, 1672-1737
Tr. Catherine Winkworth, 1827-1878
UNSER HERRSCHER 8.7.8.7.7.7.
Joachim Neander, 1650-1680
1 O - pen now thy gates of beau - ty, Zi - on, let me
2 Yes, my God, I come be - fore thee, Come thou al - so
3 Here thy praise is glad - ly chant - ed, Here thy seed is
4 Speak, O God, and I will hear thee, Let thy will be
en - ter there, Where my soul in joy - ful du - ty
down to me; Where we find thee and a - dore thee,
du - ly sown; Let my soul, where it is plant - ed,
done in - deed; May I un - dis - turbed draw near thee
Waits for him who an - swers prayer: O how bless - ed
There a heav'n on earth must be: To my heart, O
Bring forth pre - cious sheaves a - lone, So that all I
While thou dost thy peo - ple feed: Here of life the
is this place, Filled with sol - ace, light, and grace.
en - ter thou, Let it be thy tem - ple now.
hear may be Fruit - ful un - to life in me.
foun - tain flows, Here is balm for all our woes. A - men.

Alternate tune: DANA, No. 66

OPENING

53 Come, Thou Fount of Every Blessing

Robert Robinson, 1735-1790

NETTLETON 8.7.8.7.D.
John Wyeth, 1770-1858

1 Come, thou Fount of ev - 'ry bless - ing, Tune my heart to sing thy grace;
2 Here I raise mine Eb - en - e - zer, Hith - er by thy help I'm come;
3 O to grace how great a debt - or Dai - ly I'm con-strained to be!

Streams of mer - cy, nev - er ceas - ing, Call for songs of loud - est praise.
And I hope, by thy good pleas - ure, Safe - ly to ar - rive at home.
Let thy good - ness, like a fet - ter, Bind my wan-d'ring heart to thee:

Teach me some me - lo - dious son - net, Sung by flam-ing tongues a - bove;
Je - sus sought me when a stran-ger, Wan - d'ring from the fold of God;
Prone to wan - der, Lord, I feel it, Prone to leave the God I love:

Praise the mount! I'm fixed up-on it, Mount of thy re-deem-ing love.
He, to res - cue me from dan-ger, In - ter-posed his pre-cious blood.
Here's my heart, O take and seal it, Seal it for thy courts a - bove. A-men.

In Thy Temple Courts, O Father

David Nyvall, 1863-1946
Tr. E. Gustav Johnson, 1893-

LAMMETS FOLK 8.7.8.7.D.
Attr. to Anders Carl Rutström, 1721-1772
"Sions Nya Sånger," 1854

1 In thy tem-ple courts, O Fa-ther, Once a-gain as-sem-bled now,
2 For the hour of mer-cy grant-ed We pre-sent our heart-felt praise;
3 Help us now thy word to cher-ish, Sanc-ti-fy our serv-ice, Lord!

Sing we prais-es as we gath-er, In con-tri-tion hum-bly bow.
Thanks, O Lord, for truths im-plant-ed, Thanks for to-kens of thy grace.
That thy truth our souls may nour-ish, Be thy will in us re-stored!

Here a fore-taste we are giv-en Of the ho-ly sab-bath peace
Thanks for warn-ings, for in-struc-tion, Thanks for new-born hope re-ceived;
Help us in our dai-ly liv-ing, As we face the days a-head,

Which for us is stored in heav-en, When life's woes and strife shall cease.
Thanks for light—blind fear's de-struc-tion, For anx-i-e-ty re-lieved.
That we may be al-ways giv-ing Room to thee, by thee be led. A-men.

OPENING

55 What Joy There Is in Coming

Johan Ludvig Runeberg, 1804-1877
Tr. A. Samuel Wallgren, 1885-1940

SANCTUARY 7.6.7.6.D.
Johan Isidor Dannström, 1812-1897

1 What joy there is in com - ing To God's own courts so fair,
2 How beau - ti - ful the un - ion Of souls re-deemed and free,
3 Come, see the Lord's sal - va - tion And taste his love sin - cere;
4 May ne'er my foot-steps fal - ter Tow'rd night a - way from day;
Where faith - ful souls are bloom - ing Like lil - ies in his care!
Who hold with God com - mun - ion In faith and pu - ri - ty!
Come, pray with-out ces - sa - tion, Watch with his peo - ple here.
My light shines from God's al - tar—My sun I'll seek al - way.
They raise their cha-lic - es ten - der For heav'n's re-fresh - ing dew,
While songs of praise are fill - ing Their sa - cred place of rest,
Out - side, the world makes mer - ry, Un - hap - py 'mid its toys,
Here in his pres - ence glo - rious It is so good to be—
'Mid bless - ings God doth ren - der They life and strength re - new.
Who then can be un - will - ing To join their cir - cle blest?
But in God's sanc - tu - a - ry The soul finds heav'n - ly joys.
Let here my soul vic - to - rious Its tab - er - na - cle see.

OPENING

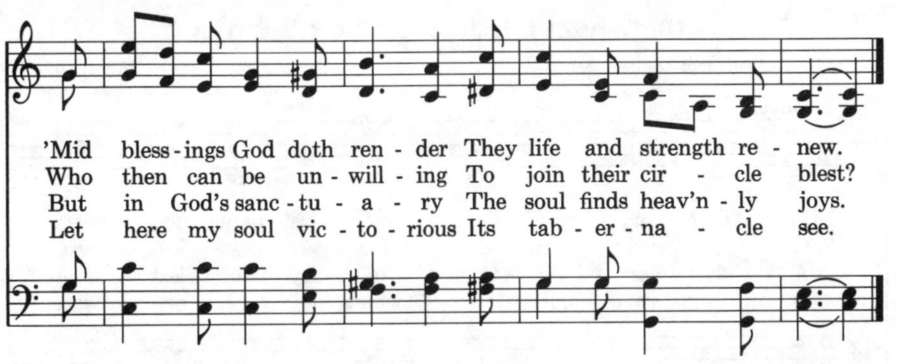
'Mid bless-ings God doth ren - der They life and strength re - new.
Who then can be un - will - ing To join their cir - cle blest?
But in God's sanc - tu - a - ry The soul finds heav'n - ly joys.
Let here my soul vic - to - rious Its tab - er - na - cle see.

Praise the Lord, Each Tribe and Nation 56

Johann Franck, 1618-1677
Tr. Ernst W. Olson, 1870-1958

KALMAR 8.7.8.7.7.7.
Swedish Melody, 1676

1 Praise the Lord, each tribe and na - tion, Praise him with a joy - ous heart;
2 He's our God and our Cre - a - tor, We his flock and cho - sen seed;
3 Give him thanks with - in his por - tals, In the courts his deeds pro - claim;

Ye who know his full sal - va - tion, Gath - er now from ev - 'ry part:
He, our Lord and lib - er - a - tor, Us from sin and per - il freed:
Hith - er come, ye ran-somed mor - tals, Glo - ri - fy our Sav - ior's name:

Let your voic - es glo - ri - fy, In his tem - ple, God on high.
And at last his flock shall rest In the man-sions of the blest.
Ev - er lov - ing Lord is he, Keep-ing faith e - ter - nal - ly. A-men.

Another harmonization in a lower setting may be found at No. 433

57 Father, Again in Jesus' Name We Meet

Lucy E. G. Whitmore, 1792-1840

ELLERS 10.10.10.10.
Edward J. Hopkins, 1818-1901

In unison
1 Fa - ther, a - gain in Je - sus' name we meet,
2 O we would bless thee for thy cease - less care,
3 A - las, un - wor - thy of thy bound - less love,
4 O by that name in whom all full - ness dwells,
And bow in pen - i - tence be - neath thy feet;
And all thy work from day to day de - clare;
Too oft with care - less feet from thee we rove;
O by that love which ev - 'ry love ex - cels,
A - gain to thee our fee - ble voic - es raise
Is not our life with hour - ly mer - cies crowned?
But now, en - cour - aged by thy voice, we come,
O by that blood so free - ly shed for sin,
To sue for mer - cy and to sing thy praise.
Does not thine arm en - cir - cle us a - round?
Re - turn - ing sin - ners to a Fa - ther's home.
O - pen blest mer - cy's gate and take us in. A - men.

OPENING

Savior, Again to Thy Dear Name We Raise 58

John Ellerton, 1826-1893

ELLERS 10.10.10.10.
Edward J. Hopkins, 1818-1901

1 Savior, again to thy dear name we raise
With one accord our parting hymn of praise;
Once more we bless thee ere our worship cease,
Then, lowly kneeling, wait thy word of peace.

2 Grant us thy peace upon our homeward way:
With thee began, with thee shall end the day;
Guard thou the lips from sin, the hearts from shame,
That in this house have called upon thy name.

3 Grant us thy peace, Lord, through the coming night,
Turn thou for us its darkness into light;
From harm and danger keep thy children free,
For dark and light are both alike to thee.

4 Grant us thy peace throughout our earthly life,
Our balm in sorrow, and our stay in strife;
Then, when thy voice shall bid our conflict cease,
Call us, O Lord, to thine eternal peace. Amen.

The Lord Be with Us 59

John Ellerton, 1826-1893

BELMONT C.M.
William Gardiner's "Sacred Melodies," 1812

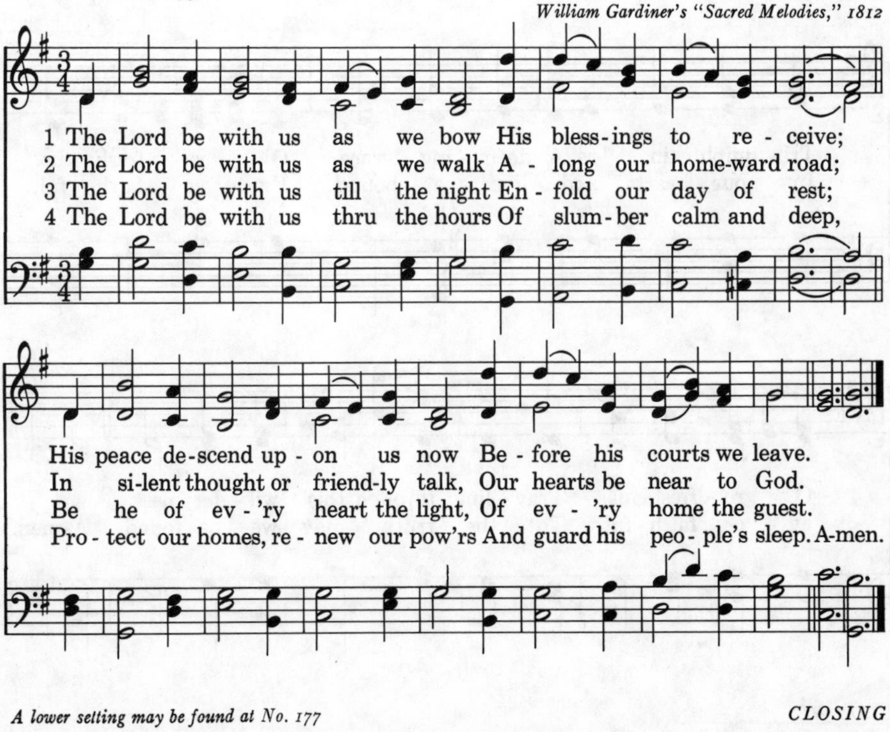

1 The Lord be with us as we bow His bless-ings to re - ceive;
2 The Lord be with us as we walk A - long our home-ward road;
3 The Lord be with us till the night En - fold our day of rest;
4 The Lord be with us thru the hours Of slum - ber calm and deep,

His peace de-scend up - on us now Be - fore his courts we leave.
In si-lent thought or friend-ly talk, Our hearts be near to God.
Be he of ev - 'ry heart the light, Of ev - 'ry home the guest.
Pro - tect our homes, re - new our pow'rs And guard his peo - ple's sleep. A-men.

A lower setting may be found at No. 177

60 Lord, Dismiss Us with Thy Blessing

John Fawcett, 1740-1817, alt.

SICILIAN MARINERS 8.7.8.7.8.7.
Tattersall's "Psalmody," 1794

1 Lord, dis - miss us with thy bless - ing, Fill our hearts with
2 Thanks we give and ad - o - ra - tion For thy gos - pel's
joy and peace; Let us each, thy love pos - sess - ing,
joy - ful sound; May the fruits of thy sal - va - tion
Tri - umph in re - deem - ing grace. O re - fresh us,
In our hearts and lives a - bound. Ev - er faith - ful,
O re - fresh us, Trav - 'ling through this wil - der - ness.
ev - er faith - ful To the truth may we be found. A - men.

CLOSING

God Be with You Till We Meet Again

61

First Tune

Jeremiah E. Rankin, 1828-1904

GOD BE WITH YOU 9.8.8.9.
William G. Tomer, 1832-1896
Harm. by A. Royce Eckhardt, 1937-

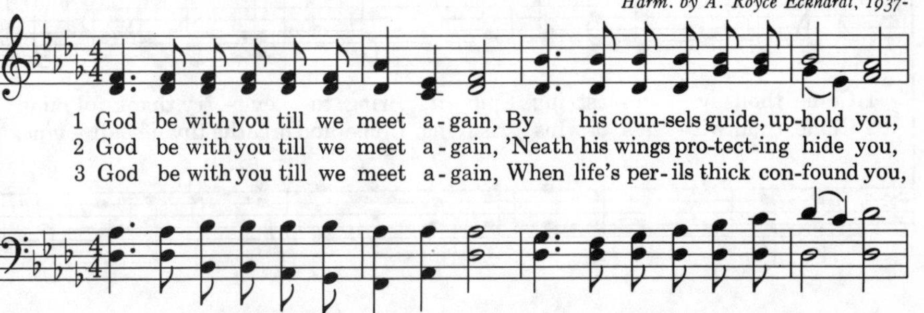

1 God be with you till we meet a-gain, By his coun-sels guide, up-hold you,
2 God be with you till we meet a-gain, 'Neath his wings pro-tect-ing hide you,
3 God be with you till we meet a-gain, When life's per-ils thick con-found you,

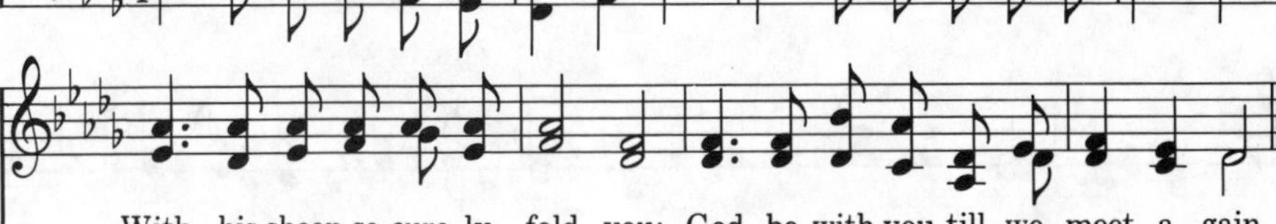

With his sheep se-cure-ly fold you: God be with you till we meet a-gain.
Dai-ly man-na still pro-vide you: God be with you till we meet a-gain.
Put his arms un-fail-ing round you: God be with you till we meet a-gain.

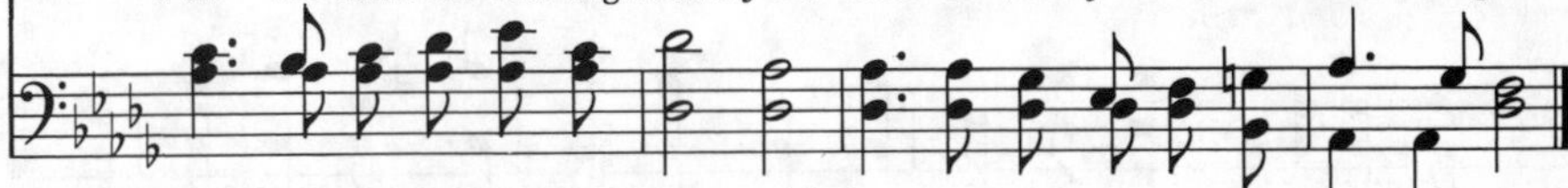

Harm. copyright 1973 by Covenant Press.

God Be with You Till We Meet Again

62

Second Tune

Jeremiah E. Rankin, 1828-1904

KEMPER 9.8.8.9.
Anna J. Morse, 1893-

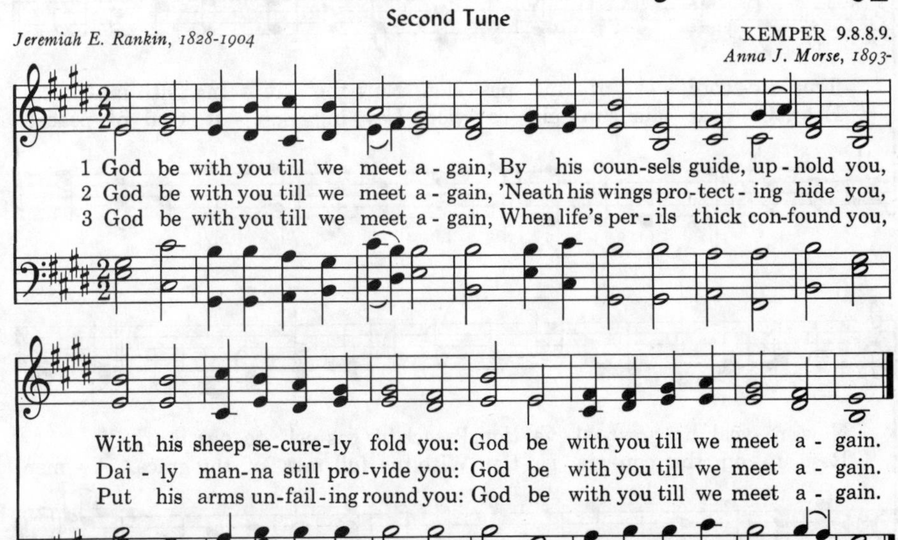

1 God be with you till we meet a-gain, By his coun-sels guide, up-hold you,
2 God be with you till we meet a-gain, 'Neath his wings pro-tect-ing hide you,
3 God be with you till we meet a-gain, When life's per-ils thick con-found you,

With his sheep se-cure-ly fold you: God be with you till we meet a-gain.
Dai-ly man-na still pro-vide you: God be with you till we meet a-gain.
Put his arms un-fail-ing round you: God be with you till we meet a-gain.

Music used by permission of Anna J. Morse.

63 Come, Thou Everlasting Spirit

Charles Wesley, 1707-1788

ARENDAL 8.7.8.7.D.
Elevine Heede, 1820-1883

1 Come, thou ev - er - last - ing Spir - it, Bring to ev - 'ry thank-ful mind
2 Come, thou wit - ness of his ris - ing, Come and breathe thy life di - vine;
All the Sav - ior's dy - ing mer - it, All his suf - f'rings for man-kind.
Let us feel thy pow'r ap - ply - ing Christ to ev - 'ry soul, and mine.
True re - cord - er of his pas - sion, Now the liv - ing faith im - part;
Hear, O hear our sup - pli - ca - tion, Lov - ing Spir - it, God of peace!
Now re - veal his great sal - va - tion, Preach his gos - pel to our heart.
Rest up - on this con - gre - ga - tion With the full - ness of thy grace. A - men.

Dearest Jesus, Draw Thou Near Me 64

Thomas Kingo, 1634-1703
Tr. C. K. Solberg, 1872-1954, alt.
WERDE MUNTER 8.7.8.7.7.7.8.8.
Johann Schop, c.1590-c.1664
1 Dear - est Je - sus, draw thou near me, Let thy Spir - it dwell with mine;
2 Un - der - neath thy wings a - bid - ing, In thy Church, O Sav - ior dear,
3 Thou earth's great-est joy and glad-ness And sal - va - tion, full and free;
O - pen now my ear to hear thee, Take my heart and seal it thine;
Let me dwell, in thee con - fid - ing, Hold me in thy faith and fear;
Let thy pres-ence cheer my sad-ness And pre-pare my soul for thee!
Keep me, lead me on my way, Thee to fol - low and o - bey,
Take a - way from me each thought That with wick - ed - ness is fraught,
In the hour when I de - part, Touch my spir - it, lips and heart,
E'er to do thy will and fear thee, And re-joice to know and hear thee.
Tempt-ing me to dis - o - bey thee, Root it out, O Lord, I pray thee.
With thy word as - sure, up-hold me Till the heav'n-ly gates en-fold me. A-men.

PULPIT

65 Look Upon Us, Blessed Lord

Tobias Clausnitzer, 1619-1684
Tr. Robert A. S. Macalister, 1870-1950

LIEBSTER JESU 7.8.7.8.8.8.
Johann R. Ahle, 1625-1673
Harm. by J. S. Bach, 1685-1750, alt.

1 Look up - on us, bless - ed Lord, Take our wan-d'ring thoughts and
2 For thy Spir - it's ra - diance bright We, as - sem - bled here, are
3 Bright-ness of the Fa - ther's face, Light of light, from God pro -
guide us; We have come to hear thy word, With thy
hop - ing; If thou shouldst with-hold the light, In the
ceed - ing, Make us read - y in this place; Ear and
teach - ing now pro - vide us, That, from earth's dis -
dark our souls were grop - ing. In each word and
heart a - wait thy lead - ing. Fill with life and
trac - tions turn - ing, We thy mes-sage may be learn - ing.
thought di - rect us: Thou, thou on - ly, canst cor - rect us.
in - spi - ra - tion Ev - 'ry prayer and med - i - ta - tion. A-men.

PULPIT

Words from *The Lutheran Service Book and Hymnal*, by permission of the Commission on the Liturgy and Hymnal.

Master, Speak! Thy Servant Heareth

Frances Ridley Havergal, 1836-1879

DANA 8.7.8.7.7.7.
Andreas Peter Berggren, 1801-1880

1 Mas - ter, speak! thy serv - ant hear - eth, Wait - ing
2 Speak to me by name, O Mas - ter, Let me
3 Mas - ter, speak! tho least and low - est, Let me
4 Mas - ter, speak! and make me read - y, When thy

for thy gra - cious word, Long - ing for thy voice that
know it is to me; Speak, that I may fol - low
not un - heard de - part; Mas - ter, speak! For O thou
voice is tru - ly heard, With o - be - dience glad and

cheer - eth; Mas - ter! let it now be heard. I am
fast - er, With a step more firm and free, Where the
know - est All the yearn - ing of my heart, Know - est
stead - y Still to fol - low ev - 'ry word. I am

lis-t'ning, Lord, for thee: What hast thou to say to me?
Shep-herd leads the flock, In the shad-ow of the rock.
all its tru - est need: Speak! and make me blest in - deed.
lis-t'ning, Lord, for thee: Mas - ter, speak! O speak to me! A-men.

67 Now Before Thee, Lord, We Gather

Lina Sandell, 1832-1903
Tr. A. L. Skoog, 1856-1934

MONTCLAIR 8.7.8.7.8.8.8.7.
William B. Bradbury, 1816-1868

1 Now be - fore thee, Lord, we gath - er To re - ceive thy pre-cious word;
2 May thy word, to us now giv - en, Be re - tained in hearts con - trite;
3 Of the time may we a - vail us, When to seek us thou art near;
Let thy grace in show'rs, O Fa - ther, On our parch - ed hearts be poured.
On the nar - row way to heav - en Lead us in thy per - fect light.
Soon the day of grace may fail us, And no mes - sage more we hear.
Send thy Ho - ly Spir - it o'er us, With thy quick-'ning fire re - store us,
Hush with - in us all com - mo - tion, Si - lence each dis - turb - ing no - tion;
Turn our minds to med - i - ta - tion On our need of thy sal - va - tion;
At thy ta - ble spread be - fore us Fill our hun-g'ring souls, dear Lord.
May we, Lord, with true de - vo - tion Use this hour of grace a - right.
Urge on all thine in - vi - ta - tion—To our prayer in - cline thine ear. A-men.

O Lord, Give Heed unto Our Plea

Jesper Swedberg, 1653-1735

HEAVENLY HOST 8.7.8.7.8.8.7.
Swedish Melody. 1697

1 O Lord, give heed un - to our plea, O Spir - it, grant thy grac - es, That we who put our trust in thee May right - ly sing thy prais - es. Thy word, O Christ, un - to us give, That grace and pow'r we may re - ceive To fol - low thee, our Mas - ter.
2 Touch thou the shep-herd's lips, O Lord, That in this bless-ed hour He may pro-claim thy sa - cred word With unc - tion and with po - wer. What thou wouldst have thy serv - ant say, Put thou in - to his heart, we pray, With grace and strength to say it.
3 Let heart and ear be o-pened wide Un - to thy word and plead - ing; Our minds, O Ho - ly Spir - it, guide By thine own light and lead - ing. The law of Christ we would ful - fill, And walk ac - cord - ing to his will, His word our rule of liv - ing. A - men.

69
Send Down Thy Truth, O God
Edward R. Sill, 1841-1887
SWABIA S.M.
Johann Martin Spiess, 1715-c.1766
1 Send down thy truth, O God, Too long the shad-ows frown,
2 Send down thy Spir-it free, Till wil-der-ness and town
3 Send down thy love, thy life, Our less-er lives to crown,
4 Send down thy peace, O Lord, Earth's bit-ter voic-es drown
Too long the dark-ened way we've trod–Thy truth, O Lord, send down.
One tem-ple for thy wor-ship be– Thy Spir-it, O send down.
And cleanse them of their hate and strife–Thy liv-ing love send down.
In one deep o-cean of ac-cord–Thy peace, O God, send down. A-men.
PULPIT
70
Let Us with a Gladsome Mind
Based on Psalm 136
John Milton, 1608-1674, alt.
INNOCENTS 7.7.7.7.
"The Parish Choir," 1850
1 Let us with a glad-some mind Praise the Lord, for he is kind:
2 He, with all-com-mand-ing might, Filled the new-made world with light:
3 Let us then with glad-some mind Praise the Lord, for he is kind:
Let us sound his name a-broad, For of gods he is the God.
All things liv-ing he doth feed, His full hand sup-plies their need.
For his mer-cies shall en-dure, Ev-er faith-ful, ev-er sure. A-men.

God, the Lord, a King Remaineth

REGENT SQUARE 8.7.8.7.8.7.

Based on Psalm 93
John Keble, 1792-1866

Henry T. Smart, 1813-1879

1 God, the Lord, a King re-main-eth, Robed in his own
2 In her ev - er - last - ing sta - tion Earth is poised, to
3 With all tones of wa - ters blend - ing, Glo - rious is the
4 Lord, the words thy lips are tell - ing Are the per - fect
glo - rious light; God hath robed him, and he reign - eth,
swerve no more; Thou hast laid thy throne's foun - da - tion
break - ing deep; Glo - rious, beau - teous, with - out end - ing,
ver - i - ty; Of thine high e - ter - nal dwell - ing,
He hath gird - ed him with might. Al - le - lu - ia!
From all time where thought can soar. Al - le - lu - ia!
God, who reigns on heav'n's high steep. Al - le - lu - ia!
Ho - li - ness shall in - mate be. Al - le - lu - ia!
Al - le - lu - ia! God is King in depth and height!
Al - le - lu - ia! Lord, thou art for - ev - er - more!
Al - le - lu - ia! Songs of o - cean nev - er sleep.
Al - le - lu - ia! Pure is all that lives with thee. A - men.

72 Our Mighty God Works Mighty Wonders

Nils Frykman, 1842-1911
Tr. A. L. Skoog, 1856-1934
Tr. Andrew T. Frykman, 1875-1943

CELEBRATION 9.8.9.8.8.8.
Swedish Folk Melody

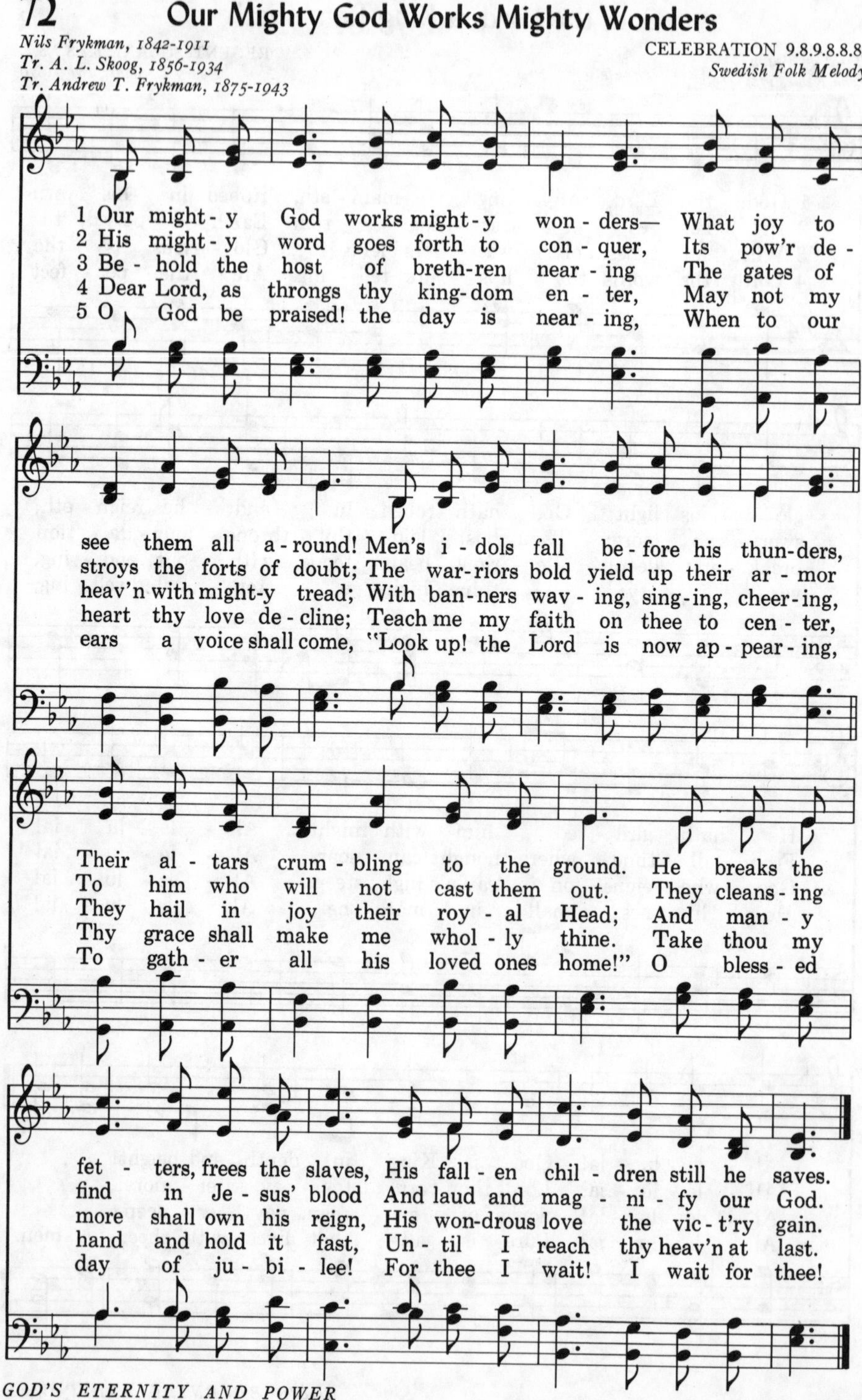
1 Our might - y God works might - y won - ders— What joy to
2 His might - y word goes forth to con - quer, Its pow'r de -
3 Be - hold the host of breth - ren near - ing The gates of
4 Dear Lord, as throngs thy king - dom en - ter, May not my
5 O God be praised! the day is near - ing, When to our
see them all a - round! Men's i - dols fall be - fore his thun - ders,
stroys the forts of doubt; The war - riors bold yield up their ar - mor
heav'n with might - y tread; With ban - ners wav - ing, sing - ing, cheer - ing,
heart thy love de - cline; Teach me my faith on thee to cen - ter,
ears a voice shall come, "Look up! the Lord is now ap - pear - ing,
Their al - tars crum - bling to the ground. He breaks the
To him who will not cast them out. They cleans - ing
They hail in joy their roy - al Head; And man - y
Thy grace shall make me whol - ly thine. Take thou my
To gath - er all his loved ones home!" O bless - ed
fet - ters, frees the slaves, His fall - en chil - dren still he saves.
find in Je - sus' blood And laud and mag - ni - fy our God.
more shall own his reign, His won - drous love the vic - t'ry gain.
hand and hold it fast, Un - til I reach thy heav'n at last.
day of ju - bi - lee! For thee I wait! I wait for thee!

Praise the Lord with Joyful Song

A. L. Skoog, 1856-1934
Tr. E. Gustav Johnson, 1893-

LOVEN GUD 7.6.7.6. *with Refrain*
A. L. Skoog, 1856-1934

1 Praise the Lord with joy - ful song, U - nite with full ac - cord!
2 Praise him for his maj - es - ty, His great and glo - rious pow'r!
3 Praise him with the sound of harps, With mu - sic loud and clear!
4 Praise him with har - mo-nious chimes, With chords of joy pro - claim!
For his glo - ry and his might Sing prais - es to the Lord!
Hail him with a wor - thy hymn, Ex - alt his name this hour!
With glad strains of mel - o - dy Our gra - cious God re - vere!
Great and ho - ly is the Lord: Sing prais - es to his name!
REFRAIN
Sing his prais-es, ev - 'ry liv - ing thing, Un - to him de - vo - ted hom-age bring,
Of his love and good-ness ev - er sing! Hal - le - lu - jah! Praise the Lord!

74 O God, Our Help in Ages Past

Based on Psalm 90
Isaac Watts, 1674-1748

ST. ANNE C.M.
Attr. to William Croft, 1678-1727

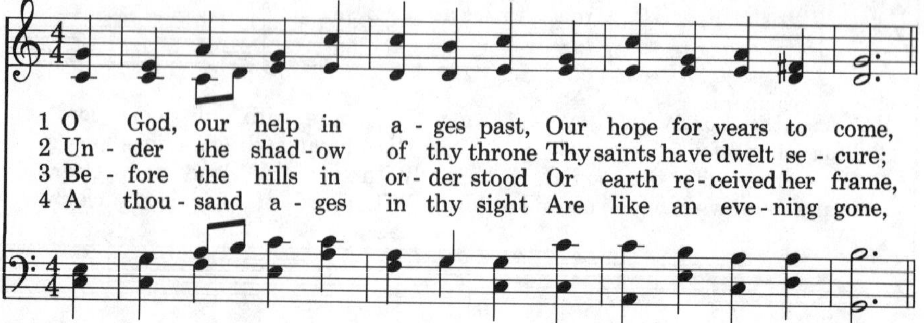

1 O God, our help in a - ges past, Our hope for years to come,
2 Un - der the shad - ow of thy throne Thy saints have dwelt se - cure;
3 Be - fore the hills in or - der stood Or earth re - ceived her frame,
4 A thou - sand a - ges in thy sight Are like an eve - ning gone,

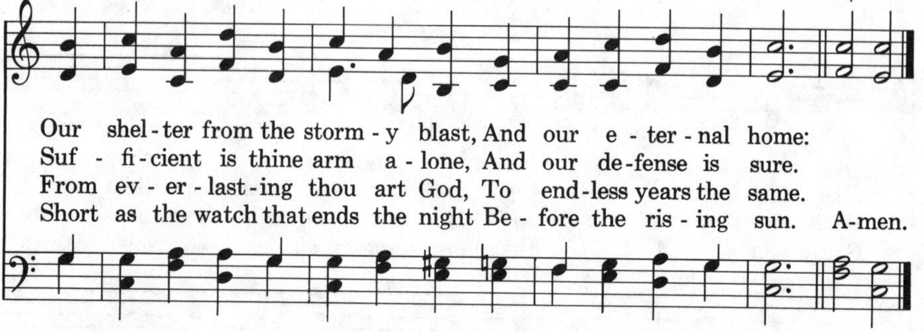

Our shel - ter from the storm - y blast, And our e - ter - nal home:
Suf - fi - cient is thine arm a - lone, And our de - fense is sure.
From ev - er - last - ing thou art God, To end - less years the same.
Short as the watch that ends the night Be - fore the ris - ing sun. A-men.

5 Time, like an ever-rolling stream,
Bears all its sons away;
They fly, forgotten, as a dream
Dies at the opening day.

6 O God, our help in ages past,
Our hope for years to come,
Be thou our guard while troubles last,
And our eternal home. Amen.

GOD'S ETERNITY AND POWER

75 God, Who Touchest Earth with Beauty

Mary S. Edgar, 1889-

BULLINGER 8.5.8.5.
Ethelbert W. Bullinger, 1837-1913, alt.

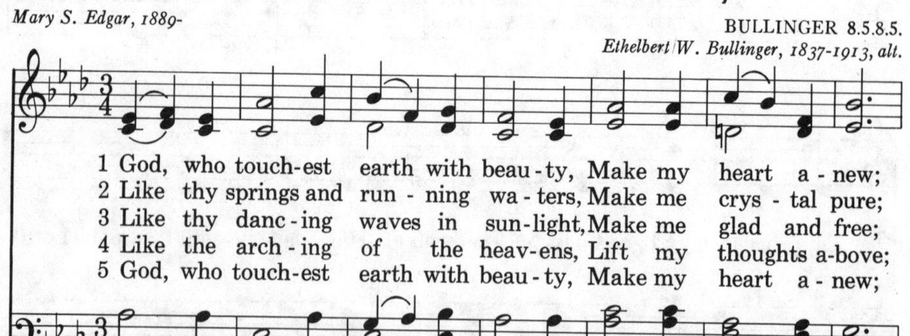
1 God, who touch - est earth with beau - ty, Make my heart a - new;
2 Like thy springs and run - ning wa - ters, Make me crys - tal pure;
3 Like thy danc - ing waves in sun - light, Make me glad and free;
4 Like the arch - ing of the heav - ens, Lift my thoughts a - bove;
5 God, who touch - est earth with beau - ty, Make my heart a - new;

GOD IN NATURE

With thy Spir - it re - cre - ate me, Pure and strong and true.
Like thy rocks of tow-'ring gran-deur, Make me strong and sure.
Like the straight-ness of the pine trees, Let me up - right be.
Turn my dreams to no - ble ac - tion—Min - is - tries of love.
Keep me ev - er, by thy Spir - it, Pure and strong and true. A-men.
For the Beauty of the Earth
76
Folliott S. Pierpoint, 1835-1917, alt.
DIX 7.7.7.7.7.7.
Adapted from a chorale by Conrad Kocher, 1786-1872
1 For the beau - ty of the earth, For the glo - ry of the skies,
2 For the won - der of each hour Of the day and of the night,
3 For the joy of hu - man love, Broth-er, sis - ter, par - ent, child,
4 For thy Church that ev - er - more Lift - eth ho - ly hands a - bove,
5 For thy - self, best gift di - vine, To our race so free - ly giv'n;
For the love which from our birth O - ver and a - round us lies:
Hill and vale and tree and flow'r, Sun and moon and stars of light:
Friends on earth and friends a - bove; For all gen - tle thoughts and mild:
Off - 'ring up on ev - 'ry shore Her pure sac - ri - fice of love:
For that great, great love of thine, Peace on earth and joy in heav'n:
Lord of all, to thee we raise This our hymn of grate - ful praise. A-men.

A higher setting may be found at No. 158

77 All Beautiful the March of Days

Frances W. Wile, 1878-1939

FOREST GREEN C M.D.
English Melody
Harm. by Ralph Vaughan Williams, 1872-1958

1 All beau - ti - ful the march of days, As sea - sons come and go;
2 O'er white ex - pan - ses spark-ling pure The ra - diant morns un - fold;
3 O thou from whose un - fath - omed law The year in beau - ty flows,

The hand that shaped the rose hath wrought The crys - tal of the snow,
The sol - emn splen - dors of the night Burn bright-er through the cold.
Thy - self the vi - sion pass-ing by In crys - tal and in rose,

Hath sent the hoar - y frost of heaven, The flow - ing wa - ters sealed,
Life mounts in ev - ery throbbing vein, Love deep - ens round the hearth,
Day un - to day doth ut - ter speech, And night to night pro - claim,

And laid a si - lent love - li - ness On hill and wood and field.
And clear-er sounds the an - gel hymn, "Good will to men on earth."
In ev - er-chang-ing words of light, The won - der of thy name. A-men.

All Nature's Works His Praise Declare

Henry Ware, Jr., 1794-1843

BETHLEHEM C.M.D.
Gottfried W. Fink, 1783-1846

1 All na-ture's works his praise de-clare, To whom they all be-long;
2 To God the tribes of o-cean cry, And birds up-on the wing;
3 Great God, to thee we con-se-crate Our voic-es and our skill;
There is a voice in ev-'ry star, In ev-'ry breeze a song.
To God the pow'rs that dwell on high Their tune-ful trib-ute bring.
We bid the peal-ing or-gan wait To speak a-lone thy will.
Sweet mu-sic fills the world a-broad With strains of love and pow'r;
Like them, let man the throne sur-round, With them loud cho-rus raise,
Lord, while the mu-sic round us floats, May earth-born pas-sions die;
The storm-y sea sings praise to God, The thun-der and the show'r.
While in-stru-ments of loft-ier sound As-sist his earth-ly praise.
O grant its rich and swell-ing notes May lift our souls on high! A-men.

A higher setting may be found at No. 282

79 How Marvelous God's Greatness

Valdimar Briem, 1848-1930
Tr. Charles Venn Pilcher, 1879-1961

BLOMSTERTID 7.6.7.6.D.
Swedish "Koralbok," 1697

1 How mar - vel - ous God's great - ness, How glo - ri - ous his might!
2 Each ti - ny flow'r-et whis - pers The great life - giv - er's name;
3 The o - cean's vast a - byss - es In one grand psalm re - cord
4 The star - ry hosts are sing - ing Thru all the light-strewn sky
To this the world bears wit - ness In won - ders day and night.
The might - y moun - tain mass - es His maj - es - ty pro - claim;
The deep mys - te - rious coun - sels And mer - cies of the Lord;
Of God's ma - jes - tic tem - ple And pal - ace - courts on high;
In form of flow'r and snow - flake, In morn's re-splend-ent birth,
The hol - low vales are hymn - ing God's shel - ter for his own;
The i - cy waves of win - ter Are thun-d'ring on the strand;
When in these out - er cham - bers Such glo - ry gilds the night,
In af - ter - glow at e - ven, In sky and sea and earth.
The snow-capped peaks are point - ing To God's al - might - y throne.
E'en grief's chill stream is guid - ed By God's all - gra - cious hand.
What the tran - scend - ent bright - ness Of God's e - ter - nal light!

Words from *The Lutheran Service Book and Hymnal,* by permission of the Commission on the Liturgy and Hymnal.

I Sing the Mighty Power of God

Isaac Watts, 1674-1748, alt.

ELLACOMBE C.M.D.
"Gesangbuch der Herzogl," Wirtemberg, 1784

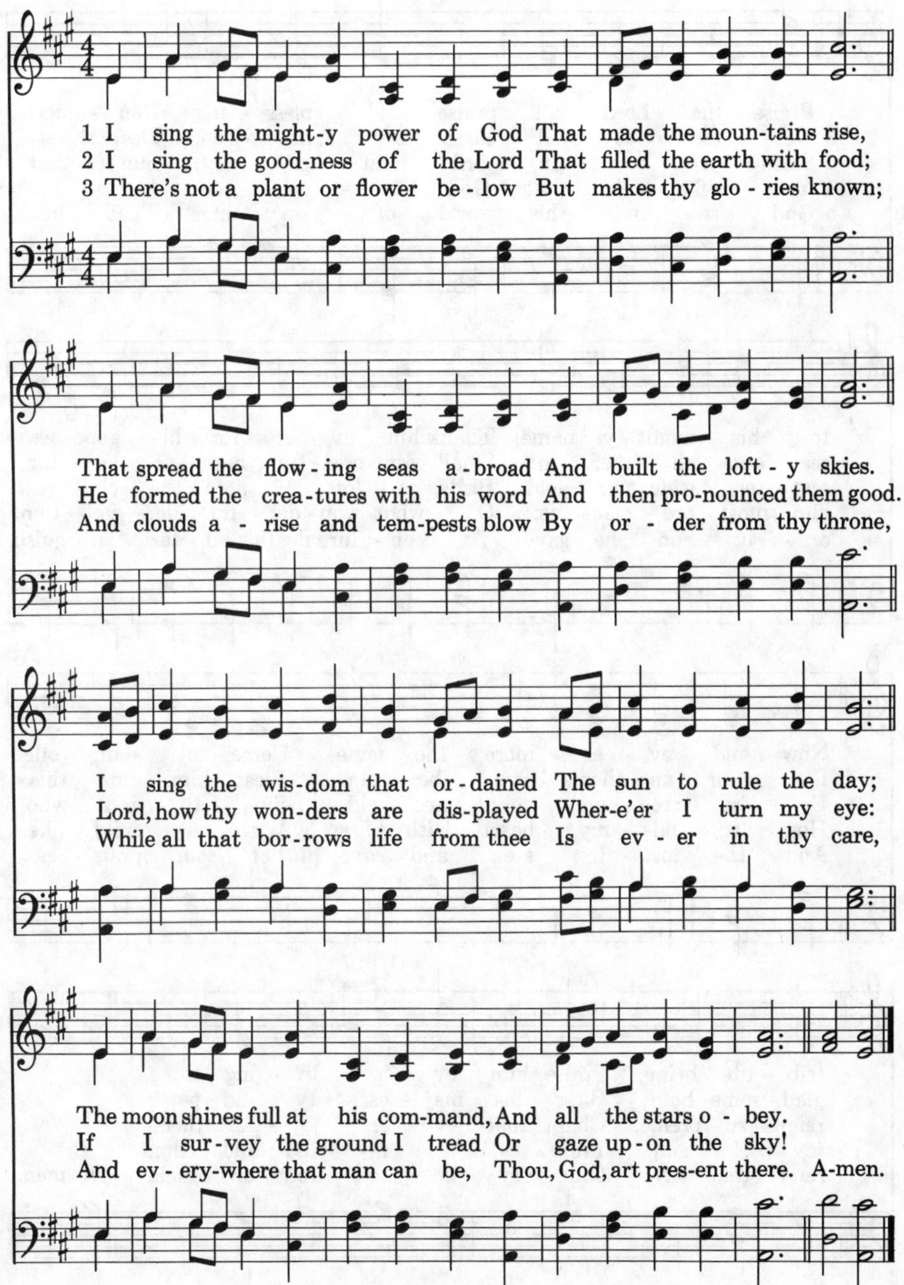

1 I sing the might-y power of God That made the moun-tains rise,
2 I sing the good-ness of the Lord That filled the earth with food;
3 There's not a plant or flower be-low But makes thy glo-ries known;
That spread the flow-ing seas a-broad And built the loft-y skies.
He formed the crea-tures with his word And then pro-nounced them good.
And clouds a-rise and tem-pests blow By or-der from thy throne,
I sing the wis-dom that or-dained The sun to rule the day;
Lord, how thy won-ders are dis-played Wher-e'er I turn my eye:
While all that bor-rows life from thee Is ev-er in thy care,
The moon shines full at his com-mand, And all the stars o-bey.
If I sur-vey the ground I tread Or gaze up-on the sky!
And ev-ery-where that man can be, Thou, God, art pres-ent there. A-men.

A lower setting may be found at No. 183

81 Praise the Lord, All Praise and Blessing

Joel Blomqvist, 1840-1930
Tr. Gerhard W. Palmgren, 1880-1959

LOVEN HERREN 8.7.8.7.7.7.
Joel Blomqvist, 1840-1930

1 Praise the Lord, all praise and bless - ing Ren - der to his might - y name; Thank him ev - er for his good-ness, Now and ev - er - more the same. Come, my soul, your trib - ute bring, Praise him ev - 'ry liv - ing thing.
2 He cre - at - ed earth and heav - en, Deep - est sea and all there - in; Small - est crea - ture, high - est be - ing, Let your an - thems now be - gin. Bless him in this glad - some hour, Bless his maj - es - ty and pow'r.
3 Stars a - bove in bril - liant glo - ry, Sun that scat - ters wide its gold, Birds a - loft, all join the cho - rus, Ev - 'ry crea - ture, young and old, Sing to him who reigns su - preme, Chant that ev - er - joy - ful theme.
4 Yet of all that God cre - at - ed Man to him most pre - cious is; O what won - der - ful de - vo - tion, How it fills my heart with bliss! With a child - like joy I sing Prais - es to my God and King!
5 God so loved this world of sin - ners That his on - ly Son he gave To en - dure death's bit - ter an - guish And the lost to seek and save. Let our prais - es rend the sky, Glo - ry be to God on high. A-men.

GOD IN NATURE

This Is My Father's World

Maltbie D. Babcock, 1858-1901

TERRA BEATA S.M.D.
English Melody
Adapted by Franklin L. Sheppard, 1852-1930

1 This is my Fa-ther's world, And to my lis-t'ning ears All na - ture sings, and round me rings The mu - sic of the spheres.
2 This is my Fa-ther's world, The birds their car - ols raise, The morn - ing light, the lil - y white, De - clare their mak - er's praise.
3 This is my Fa-ther's world, O let me ne'er for - get That though the wrong seems oft so strong, God is the rul - er yet.

This is my Fa-ther's world: I rest me in the thought Of rocks and trees, of skies and seas–His hand the won-ders wrought.
This is my Fa-ther's world: He shines in all that's fair; In the rus - tling grass I hear him pass, He speaks to me ev-'ry-where.
This is my Fa-ther's world: The bat - tle is not done; Je - sus who died shall be sat - is - fied, And earth and heav'n be one.

83 Are You Dismayed, Lonely, Afraid

Selma S. Lagerström, 1859-1927
Tr. E. Gustav Johnson, 1893-
GUDS TROFASTHET 4.4.7.D.
Swedish Folk Melody
1 Are you dis - mayed, Lone - ly, a - fraid, Think - ing your - self for - sak - en? God is your stay, Trust him and pray; New hope he will a - wak - en.
2 Mer - cy and love, Gifts from a - bove, Come in a - bun - dant mea - sure. Great things and small God gives to all, Gra - cious - ly in his pleas - ure.
3 Friends may de - ceive, Cause you to grieve, God is your con - so - la - tion! Faith - ful and true He is to you, Com - fort in trib - u - la - tion.
4 Al - ways his grace You may em - brace, He is your con - stant bless - ing. When you are tried, Flee to his side, Need for his help con - fess - ing.
5 Cour - age and might, Guid - ance and light, God will in mer - cy ren - der. In ev - 'ry pain, Con - flict and strain, He is your true de - fend - er.
6 Praise now his name! Hear him pro - claim, "I will for - sake you nev - er!" Un - to the end On him de - pend, He is the same for - ev - er!

God Is My Strong Salvation

Based on Psalm 27
James Montgomery, 1771-1854

WEDLOCK 7.6.7.6.D.
"The Sacred Harp," 1844
Harm. by Austin C. Lovelace, 1919-

In unison

1 God is my strong sal - va - tion: What foe have I to fear?
2 Place on the Lord re - li - ance; My soul, with cour-age wait;

In dark-ness and temp - ta - tion, My light, my help, is near.
His truth be thine af - fi - ance When faint and des - o - late.

Though hosts en-camp a - round me, Firm in the fight I stand;
His might thy heart shall strength-en, His love thy joy in - crease;

What ter-ror can con-found me, With God at my right hand?
Mer - cy thy days shall length-en, The Lord will give thee peace. A-men.

Alternate tune: GREENLAND, *No. 574*

85 Begin, My Tongue, Some Heavenly Theme
Isaac Watts, 1674-1748
MANOAH C.M.
Henry W. Greatorex's "Collection," 1851
1 Be - gin, my tongue, some heav'n-ly theme And speak some bound-less thing:
2 Tell of his won-drous faith-ful-ness And sound his pow'r a - broad;
3 His ver - y word of grace is strong As that which built the skies;
4 O might I hear thy heav'n-ly tongue But whis - per, "Thou art mine!"
The might-y works or might-ier name Of our e - ter - nal King.
Sing the sweet prom-ise of his grace, The love and truth of God.
The voice that rolls the stars a - long Speaks all the prom - is - es.
Those gen - tle words shall raise my song To notes al - most di - vine. A-men.
A lower setting may be found at No. 160
86 O Love of God Most Full
AYLESBURY S.M.
Oscar Clute, 1837-1901
John Chetham's "Psalmody," 1718
Adapted in James Green's "Psalm Tunes," 1724
Harm. by Louise McAllister, 1913-1960
1 O love of God most full, O love of God most free,
2 Warm as the glow - ing sun, So shines thy love on me;
3 The wild - est sea is calm, The tem - pest brings no fear;
4 I tri - umph o - ver sin, I put temp - ta - tion down;
Come warm my heart, come fill my soul, Come lead me un - to thee!
It wraps me round with kind-ly care, It draws me un - to thee.
The dark-est night is full of light, Be - cause thy love is near.
Thy love, O God, doth give me strength To win the vic - tor's crown. A-men.
Music copyright, 1953 by Louise McAllister.
Used by permission of Dr. Russell G. McAllister.

Alternate tune: TRENTHAM, No. 259

I Greet Thee, Who My Sure Redeemer Art

Attr. to John Calvin, 1509-1564
Tr. Elizabeth L. Smith, 1817-1898, alt.

TOULON 10.10.10.10.
Abridged from "Genevan Psalter," 1551

1 I greet thee, who my sure Re - deem - er art,
2 Thou art the King of mer - cy and of grace,
3 Thou art the Life, by which a - lone we live
4 Thou hast the true and per - fect gen - tle - ness,
5 Our hope is in no oth - er save in thee;
My on - ly Trust and Sav - ior of my heart,
Reign - ing om - ni - po - tent in ev - 'ry place:
And all our sub - stance and our strength re - ceive;
No harsh - ness hast thou and no bit - ter - ness:
Our faith is built up - on thy prom - ise free;
Who pain didst un - der - go for my poor sake;
So come, O King, and our whole be - ing sway;
Com - fort us by thy faith and by thy pow'r,
Make us to taste the sweet grace found in thee
Come, give us peace, make us so strong and sure,
I pray thee from our hearts all cares to take.
Shine on us with the light of thy pure day.
Nor daunt our hearts when comes the try - ing hour.
And ev - er stay in thy sweet u - ni - ty.
That we may con-qu'rors be and ills en - dure. A - men.

A lower setting may be found at No. 181

88 God of Our Life, Through All the Circling Years

Hugh T. Kerr, 1872-1950, alt.

SANDON 10.4.10.4.10.10.
Charles H. Purday, 1799-1885

1 God of our life, thru all the cir-cling years We trust in thee;
2 God of the past, our times are in thy hand: With us a - bide;
3 God of the com - ing years, thru paths un-known We fol - low thee;
In all the past, thru all our hopes and fears, Thy hand we see.
Lead us by faith to hope's true prom-ised land: Be thou our guide.
When we are strong, Lord, leave us not a - lone: Our ref - uge be.
With each new day, when morn - ing lifts the veil,
With thee to bless, the dark - ness shines as light,
Be thou for us in life our dai - ly bread,
We own thy mer - cies, Lord, which nev - er fail.
And faith's fair vi - sion chang - es in - to sight.
Our heart's true home when all our years have sped. A - men.

Unto the Hills Around

89

Based on Psalm 121
John Campbell, 1845-1914

SANDON 10.4.10.4.10.10.
Charles H. Purday, 1799-1885

1 Unto the hills around do I lift up
My longing eyes;
O whence for me shall my salvation come,
From whence arise?
From God the Lord doth come my certain aid,
From God the Lord who heav'n and earth hath made.

2 He will not suffer that thy foot be moved—
Safe shall thou be;
No careless slumber shall his eyelids close
Who keepeth thee.
Behold, he sleepeth not, he slumb'reth ne'er,
Who keepeth Israel in his holy care.

3 Jehovah is himself thy keeper true,
Thy changeless shade;
Jehovah thy defense on thy right hand
Himself hath made.
And thee no sun by day shall ever smite;
No moon shall harm thee in the silent night.

4 From ev'ry evil shall he keep thy soul,
From ev'ry sin;
Jehovah shall preserve thy going out,
Thy coming in.
Above thee watching, he whom we adore
Shall keep thee henceforth, yea, for evermore. Amen.

God, My God, in Heaven Above

90

Nils Frykman, 1842-1911
Tr. E. Gustav Johnson, 1893-

GUDS GODHET 7.7.7.3.
Oscar Ahnfelt, 1813-1882

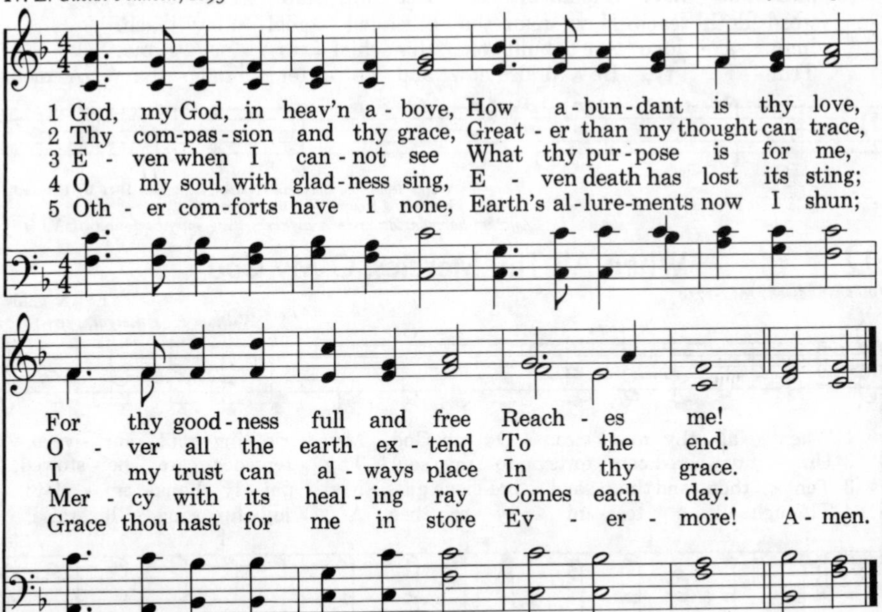

1 God, my God, in heav'n a - bove, How a - bun - dant is thy love,
2 Thy com - pas - sion and thy grace, Great - er than my thought can trace,
3 E - ven when I can - not see What thy pur - pose is for me,
4 O my soul, with glad - ness sing, E - ven death has lost its sting;
5 Oth - er com - forts have I none, Earth's al - lure - ments now I shun;

For thy good - ness full and free Reach - es me!
O - ver all the earth ex - tend To the end.
I my trust can al - ways place In thy grace.
Mer - cy with its heal - ing ray Comes each day.
Grace thou hast for me in store Ev - er - more! A - men.

91 God Loved the World So That He Gave

Based on John 3:16-18
Unknown, 1791
Tr. August Crull, 1836-1923

ST. CRISPIN L.M.
George J. Elvey, 1816-1893

1 God loved the world so that he gave His on - ly
2 God would not have the sin - ner die, His Son with
3 Christ Je - sus is the ground of faith, Who was made
4 Glo - ry to God— the Fa - ther, Son, And Ho - ly
Son the lost to save, That all who would in
sav - ing grace is nigh; His Spir - it in the
flesh and suf - fered death; All that con - fide in
Spir - it, Three in One! To thee, O bless - ed
him be - lieve Should ev - er - last - ing life re - ceive.
word doth teach How man the bless - ed goal may reach.
him a - lone Are built on this chief cor - ner - stone.
Trin - i - ty, Be praise now and e - ter - nal - ly! A-men.
Words from *The Lutheran Hymnal*, copyright 1941 by Concordia Publishing House. Used by permission.
Another harmonization in a higher setting may be found at No. 165
92 When All Thy Mercies, O My God
Joseph Addison, 1672-1719
EVAN C.M.
William H. Havergal, 1793-1870
1 When all thy mer - cies, O my God, My ris - ing soul sur - veys,
2 Un - num-bered com - forts to my soul Thy ten - der care be - stowed,
3 Ten thou-sand thou - sand pre-cious gifts My dai - ly thanks em - ploy;
4 Through all e - ter - ni - ty to thee A joy - ful song I'll raise;

A higher setting may be found at No. 358

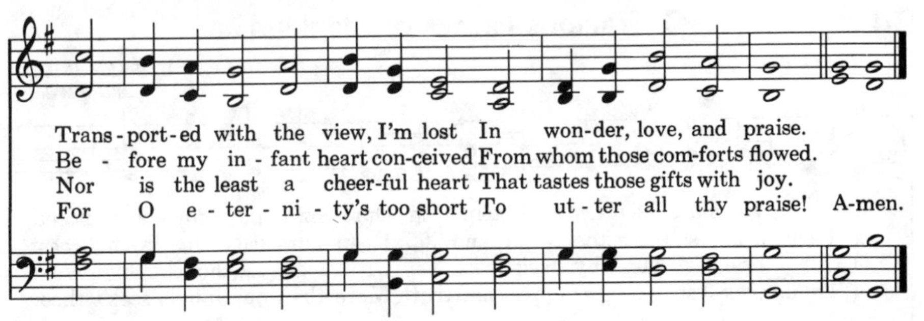
Trans-port-ed with the view, I'm lost In wonder, love, and praise.
Be - fore my in - fant heart con-ceived From whom those com-forts flowed.
Nor is the least a cheer-ful heart That tastes those gifts with joy.
For O e - ter - ni - ty's too short To ut - ter all thy praise! A-men.

O God, Thou Giver of All Good

93

Based on Matthew 6:11
Samuel Longfellow, 1819-1892

PUER NOBIS NASCITUR L.M.
Adapted by Michael Praetorius, 1571-1621
Harm. by Norman E. Johnson, 1928-

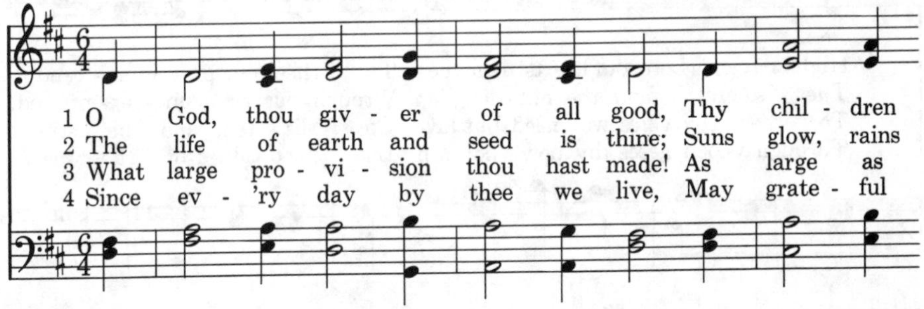

1 O God, thou giv - er of all good, Thy chil - dren
2 The life of earth and seed is thine; Suns glow, rains
3 What large pro - vi - sion thou hast made! As large as
4 Since ev - 'ry day by thee we live, May grate - ful

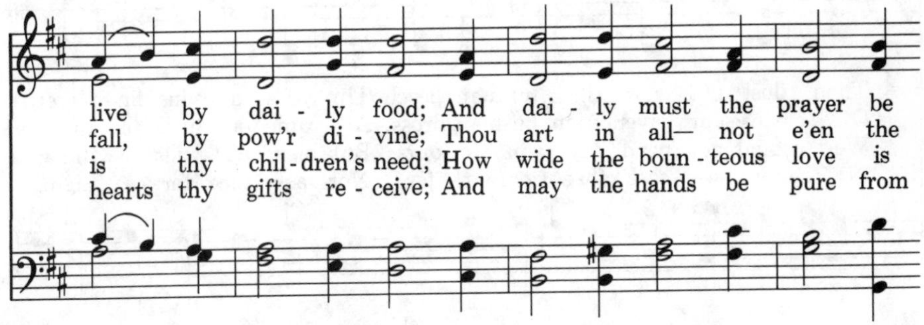

live by dai - ly food; And dai - ly must the prayer be
fall, by pow'r di - vine; Thou art in all— not e'en the
is thy chil - dren's need; How wide the boun - teous love is
hearts thy gifts re - ceive; And may the hands be pure from

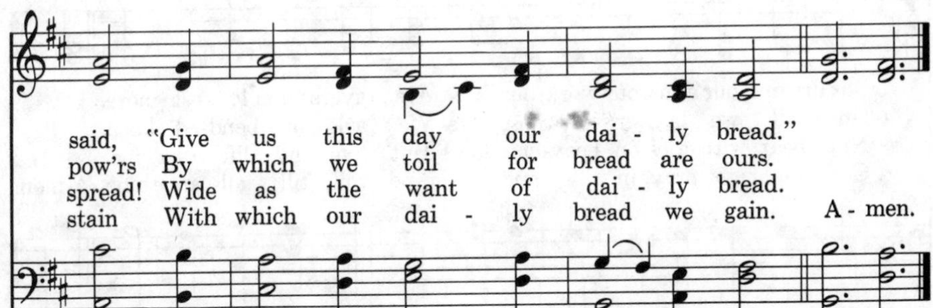

said, "Give us this day our dai - ly bread."
pow'rs By which we toil for bread are ours.
spread! Wide as the want of dai - ly bread.
stain With which our dai - ly bread we gain. A - men.

Another harmonization may be found at No. 161

94 O Gracious Father of Mankind

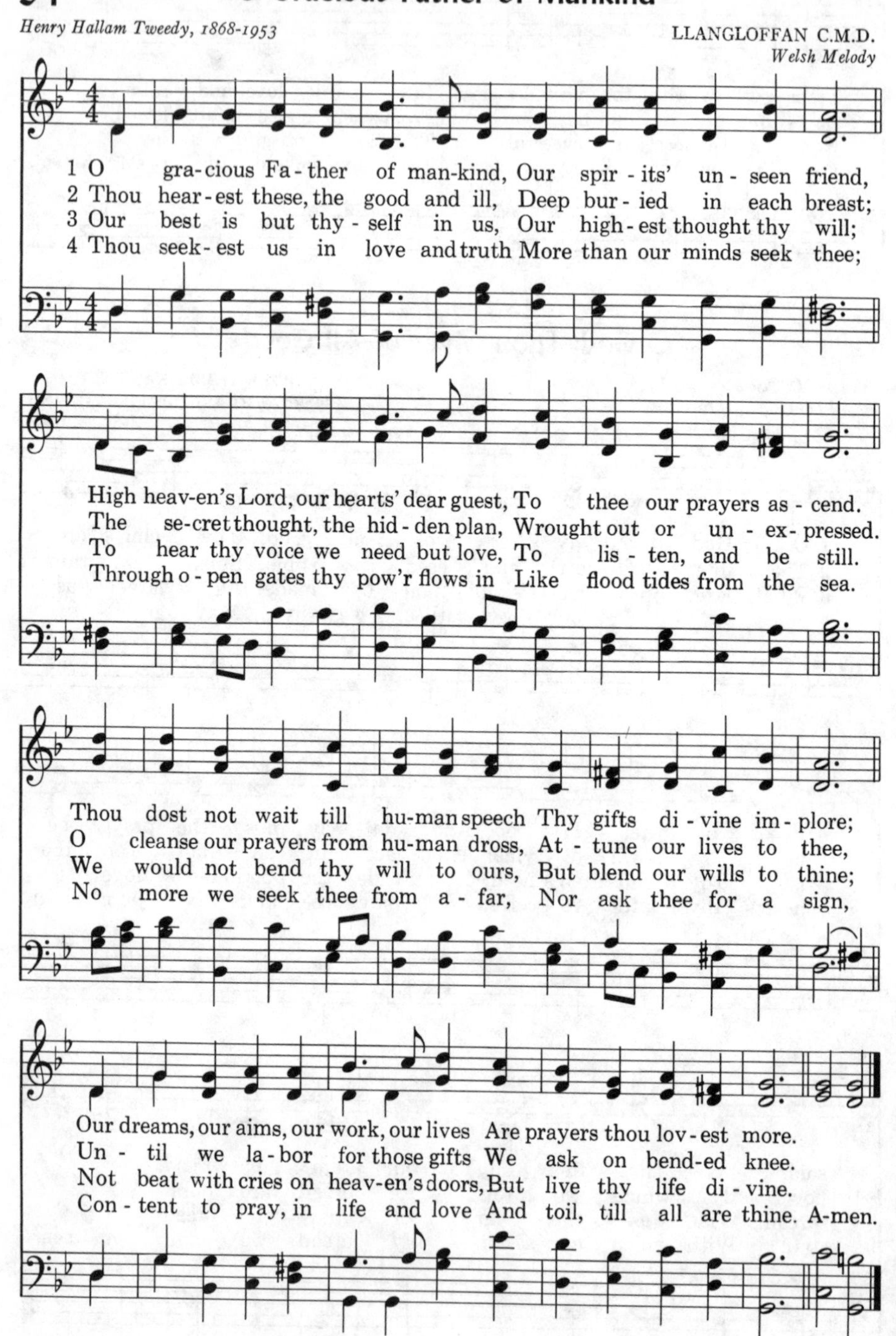

Henry Hallam Tweedy, 1868-1953
LLANGLOFFAN C.M.D.
Welsh Melody
1 O gra-cious Fa-ther of man-kind, Our spir-its' un-seen friend,
2 Thou hear-est these, the good and ill, Deep bur-ied in each breast;
3 Our best is but thy-self in us, Our high-est thought thy will;
4 Thou seek-est us in love and truth More than our minds seek thee;
High heav-en's Lord, our hearts' dear guest, To thee our prayers as-cend.
The se-cret thought, the hid-den plan, Wrought out or un-ex-pressed.
To hear thy voice we need but love, To lis-ten, and be still.
Through o-pen gates thy pow'r flows in Like flood tides from the sea.
Thou dost not wait till hu-man speech Thy gifts di-vine im-plore;
O cleanse our prayers from hu-man dross, At-tune our lives to thee,
We would not bend thy will to ours, But blend our wills to thine;
No more we seek thee from a-far, Nor ask thee for a sign,
Our dreams, our aims, our work, our lives Are prayers thou lov-est more.
Un-til we la-bor for those gifts We ask on bend-ed knee.
Not beat with cries on heav-en's doors, But live thy life di-vine.
Con-tent to pray, in life and love And toil, till all are thine. A-men.

O My Soul, Bless God the Father

Based on Psalm 103
"United Presbyterian Book of Psalms," 1871
CORINTH 8.7.8.7.D.
"An Essay on the Church Plain Chant," 1782
Harm. by Norman E. Johnson, 1928-
1 O my soul, bless God the Father, All with-in me bless his name;
Bless the Fa-ther, and for-get not All his mer-cies to pro-claim:
Who for-giv-eth thy trans-gres-sions, Thy dis-eas-es all who heals;
Who re-deems thee from de-struc-tion, Who with thee so kind-ly deals.
2 Far as east from west is dis-tant He hath put a-way our sin;
Like the pit-y of a fa-ther Hath the Lord's com-pas-sion been.
As it was with-out be-gin-ning, So it lasts with-out an end;
To their chil-dren's chil-dren ev-er Shall his right-eous-ness ex-tend:
3 Un-to such as keep his cov-'nant And are stead-fast in his way;
Un-to those who still re-mem-ber His com-mand-ments and o-bey.
Bless the Fa-ther, all his crea-tures, Ev-er un-der his con-trol,
All through-out his vast do-min-ion; Bless the Fa-ther, O my soul. A-men.

96 There's a Wideness in God's Mercy

Frederick W. Faber, 1814-1863

BLAENWERN 8.7.8.7.D.
William P. Rowlands, 1860-1937

1 There's a wide-ness in God's mer-cy Like the wide-ness of the sea;
2 For the love of God is broad-er Than the meas-ures of man's mind,
3 Souls of men, why will you scat-ter Like a crowd of fright-ened sheep?
There's a kind-ness in his jus-tice Which is more than lib-er-ty.
And the heart of the E-ter-nal Is most won-der-ful-ly kind.
Fool-ish hearts, why will you wan-der From a love so true and deep?
There is plen-ti-ful re-demp-tion In the blood that has been shed;
If our love were but more sim-ple We should take him at his word,
There is wel-come for the sin-ner And more grac-es for the good;
There is joy for all the mem-bers In the sor-rows of the Head.
And our lives would be all sun-shine In the sweet-ness of our Lord.
There is mer-cy with the Sav-ior, There is heal-ing in his blood.

Thou Tender, Gracious Father

Lina Sandell, 1832-1903
Tr. Carl O. Dahlen, 1867-1938

FAR-OFF LANDS 7.6.7.6.D.
From the Bohemian Brethren

1 Thou ten - der, gra - cious Fa - ther, Who watch-es o - ver me,
2 With rai - ment, food and shel - ter, What - e'er my needs im - ply,
3 In child - like, true o - be-dience Help me to do the right;
4 Thy heart is all com - pas - sion, With love it o - ver - flows;
How shall I ev - er praise thee, How love and hon - or thee?
For soul and bod - y ev - er, Do thou in grace sup - ply.
May pre - cious be thy stat - utes, Thy yoke be pleas - ant, light!
What - e'er of ill be - tide me, Thou know-est, and my woes.
Thou guid - est me with cau - tion From ev - 'ry se - cret snare,
O Lord, I soon would per - ish If aught thou should ex - clude;
And when some hard-ship threat-ens, A dan - ger fright - ens me,
Thou dost not sleep nor slum - ber By night nor thru the days;
And 'neath thy wings a ref - uge I find in my de - spair.
O could I love thee bet - ter And prove my grat - i - tude.
May thou in all my tri - als My pres - ent help-er be.
Thine arms, al - might-y Fa-ther, En - fold all time and space. A-men.

Words used by permission of Harvest Publications.

98 Guide Me, O Thou Great Jehovah

William Williams, 1717-1791
Tr. Peter Williams, 1722-1796, and others

CWM RHONDDA 8.7.8.7.8.7.
John Hughes, 1873-1932

1 Guide me, O thou great Je - ho - vah, Pil - grim through this
2 O - pen now the crys - tal foun - tain, Whence the heal - ing
3 When I tread the verge of Jor - dan, Bid my anx - ious
bar - ren land; I am weak, but thou art might-y— Hold me with thy
stream doth flow; Let the fire and cloud - y pil - lar Lead me all my
fears sub - side; Bear me through the swell - ing cur-rent, Land me safe on
pow'r - ful hand: Bread of heav - en, Bread of heav - en,
jour - ney through: Strong De - liv - 'rer, strong De - liv - 'rer,
Ca - naan's side: Songs of prais - es, songs of prais - es
Feed me till I want no more, Feed me till I want no more.
Be thou still my strength and shield, Be thou still my strength and shield.
I will ev - er give to thee, I will ev - er give to thee. A-men.

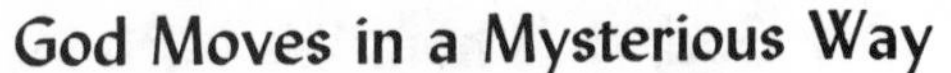
God Moves in a Mysterious Way

99

William Cowper, 1731-1800

DUNDEE C.M.
"Scottish Psalter," 1615

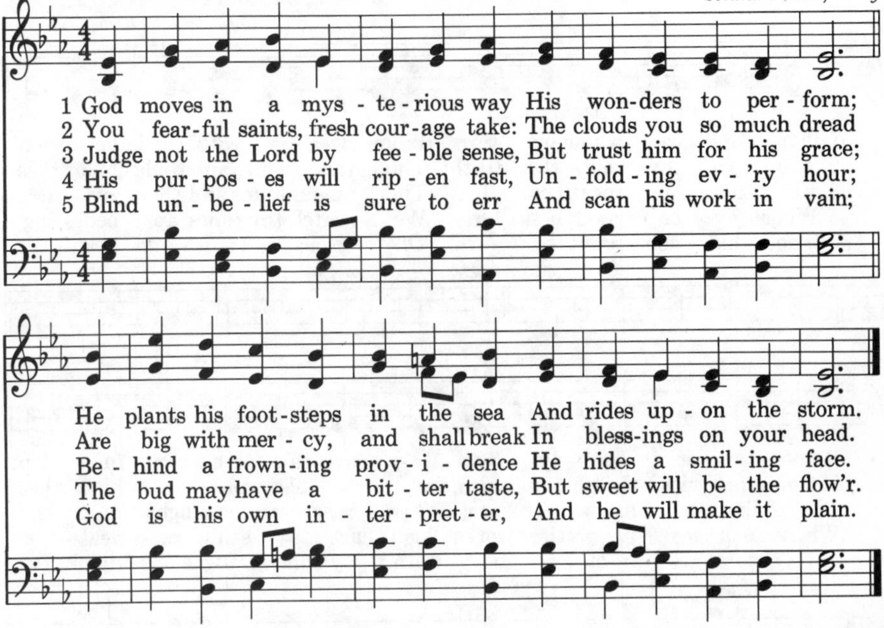

1 God moves in a mys - te - rious way His won-ders to per - form;
2 You fear-ful saints, fresh cour-age take: The clouds you so much dread
3 Judge not the Lord by fee - ble sense, But trust him for his grace;
4 His pur-pos - es will rip - en fast, Un - fold - ing ev - 'ry hour;
5 Blind un - be - lief is sure to err And scan his work in vain;

He plants his foot-steps in the sea And rides up - on the storm.
Are big with mer - cy, and shall break In bless-ings on your head.
Be - hind a frown-ing prov - i - dence He hides a smil - ing face.
The bud may have a bit - ter taste, But sweet will be the flow'r.
God is his own in - ter - pret - er, And he will make it plain.

O Love Divine, That Stooped to Share

100

Oliver Wendell Holmes, 1809-1894

QUEBEC L.M.
Henry Baker, 1835-1910

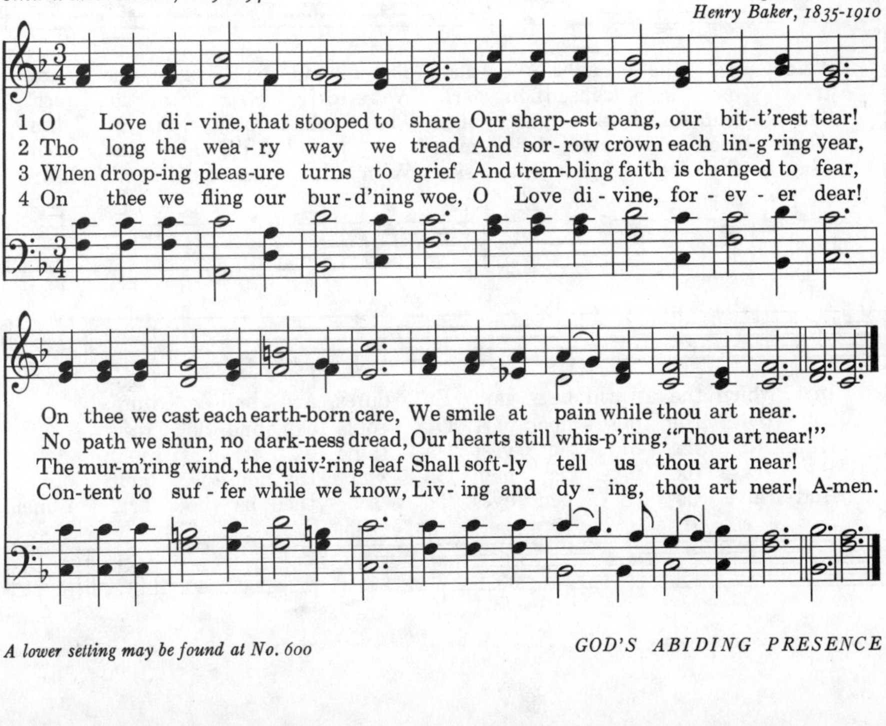

1 O Love di - vine, that stooped to share Our sharp-est pang, our bit-t'rest tear!
2 Tho long the wea - ry way we tread And sor-row crown each lin-g'ring year,
3 When droop-ing pleas-ure turns to grief And trem-bling faith is changed to fear,
4 On thee we fling our bur - d'ning woe, O Love di - vine, for - ev - er dear!

On thee we cast each earth-born care, We smile at pain while thou art near.
No path we shun, no dark-ness dread, Our hearts still whis-p'ring, "Thou art near!"
The mur-m'ring wind, the quiv-'ring leaf Shall soft-ly tell us thou art near!
Con-tent to suf - fer while we know, Liv - ing and dy - ing, thou art near! A-men.

A lower setting may be found at No. 600

101 Our God, to Whom We Turn

Edward Grubb, 1854-1939

DARMSTADT 6.7.6.7.6.6.6.6.
Ahasuerus Fritsch's "Himmels-Lust," 1679
Harm. by J. S. Bach, 1685-1750

1 Our God, to whom we turn When wea - ry with il - lu - sion,
2 Thou art thy - self the truth; Though we, who fain would find thee,
3 All beau - ty speaks of thee— The moun-tains and the riv - ers,
4 Wher - ev - er good - ness lurks We catch thy tones ap - peal - ing;
5 Thou hid - den fount of love, Of peace, and truth, and beau - ty,
Whose stars se - rene - ly burn A - bove this earth's con - fu - sion,
Have tried, with thoughts un-couth, In fee - ble words to bind thee.
The line of lift - ed sea, Where spread-ing moon-light quiv - ers;
Where man for jus - tice works Thou art thy - self re - veal - ing;
In - spire us from a - bove With joy and strength for du - ty;
Thine is the might - y plan, The stead - fast or - der sure,
It is be - cause thou art We're driv - en to the quest;
The deep-toned or - gan blast That rolls through arch - es dim
The blood of man, for man On friend-ship's al - tar spilt,
May thy fresh light a - rise With - in each cloud - ed heart,
In which the world be - gan, En - dures, and shall en - dure.
Till truth from false - hood part, Our souls can find no rest.
Hints of the mu - sic vast Of thine e - ter - nal hymn.
Be - trays the mys - tic plan On which thy house is built.
And give us o - pen eyes To see thee as thou art. A - men.

Great Hills May Tremble

Based on Isaiah 54:10
Lina Sandell, 1832-1903
Tr. E. Lincoln Pearson, 1917- , Sts. 1,4, alt.
Bryan Jeffery Leech, 1931- , Sts. 2,3
BERGEN MÅ VIKA 11.10.11.10.
Source unknown
1 Great hills may trem - ble and moun - tains may crum - ble,
2 Though peace be shat - tered by war's ag - i - ta - tion,
3 Strong to pre - serve us in mo - ments of dan - ger,
4 Teach us, O Lord, thy com - mand - ments to pon - der,
God's lov - ing - kind - ness re - main - eth se - cure;
Though change and ten - sion give birth to great fears,
Strong when frus - tra - tion and frail - ty in - crease;
Help us to heed them wher - ev - er we roam,
Peace he will give to the con - trite and hum - ble:
God still re - mains an un - shak - en foun - da - tion,
Strong to e - quip us for lov - ing the stran - ger,
Wait - ing the day thou shalt call us up yon - der,
Thus saith the Lord— his prom - ise is sure.
Strong to sup - port us through tur - bu - lent years;
Strong where our hu - man re - sourc - es may cease.
Trust - ing thy prom - ise to car - ry us home. A - men.

103 The King of Love My Shepherd Is

Based on Psalm 23
Henry W. Baker, 1821-1877

DOMINUS REGIT ME 8.7.8.7.
John B. Dykes, 1823-1876

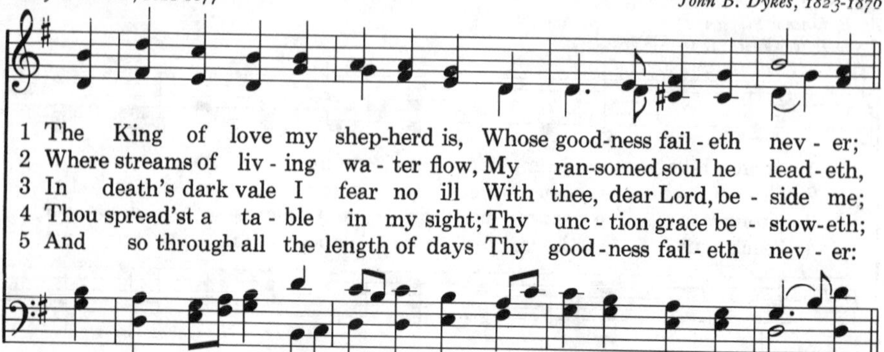

1 The King of love my shep-herd is, Whose good-ness fail-eth nev - er;
2 Where streams of liv - ing wa - ter flow, My ran-somed soul he lead-eth,
3 In death's dark vale I fear no ill With thee, dear Lord, be - side me;
4 Thou spread'st a ta - ble in my sight; Thy unc - tion grace be - stow-eth;
5 And so through all the length of days Thy good-ness fail-eth nev - er:

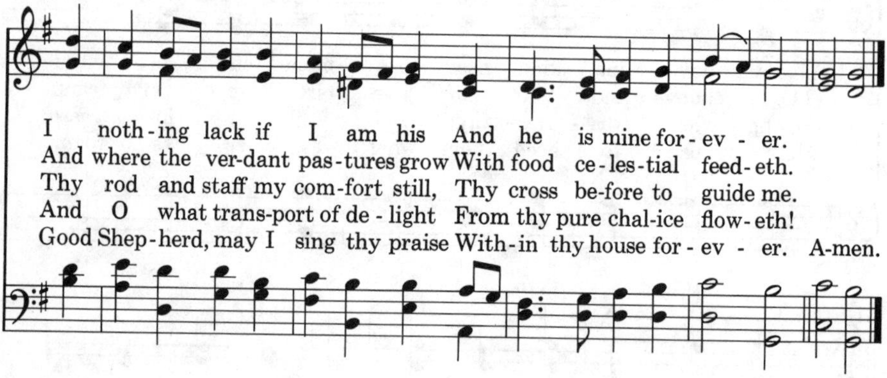

I noth-ing lack if I am his And he is mine for - ev - er.
And where the ver-dant pas-tures grow With food ce-les-tial feed-eth.
Thy rod and staff my com-fort still, Thy cross be-fore to guide me.
And O what trans-port of de - light From thy pure chal-ice flow-eth!
Good Shep-herd, may I sing thy praise With-in thy house for - ev - er. A-men.

104 The Lord's My Shepherd, I'll Not Want

Based on Psalm 23
"Scottish Psalter," 1650, alt.

CRIMOND C.M.
Jessie S. Irvine, 1836-1887

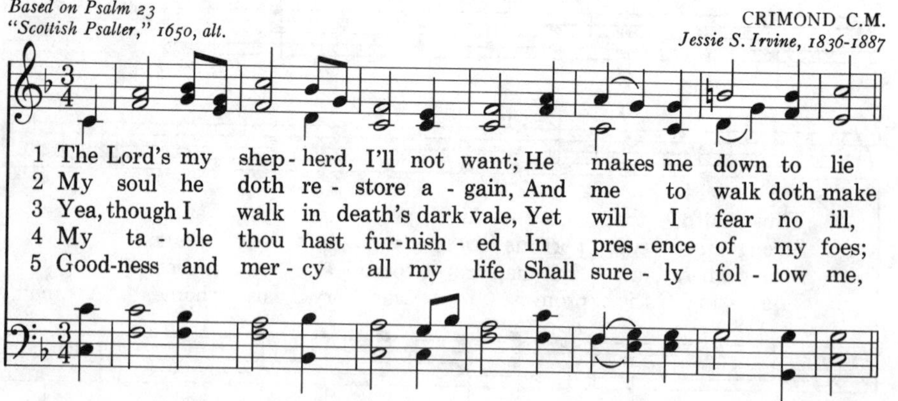
3
4
1 The Lord's my shep - herd, I'll not want; He makes me down to lie
2 My soul he doth re - store a - gain, And me to walk doth make
3 Yea, though I walk in death's dark vale, Yet will I fear no ill,
4 My ta - ble thou hast fur-nish - ed In pres - ence of my foes;
5 Good-ness and mer - cy all my life Shall sure - ly fol - low me,
3
4

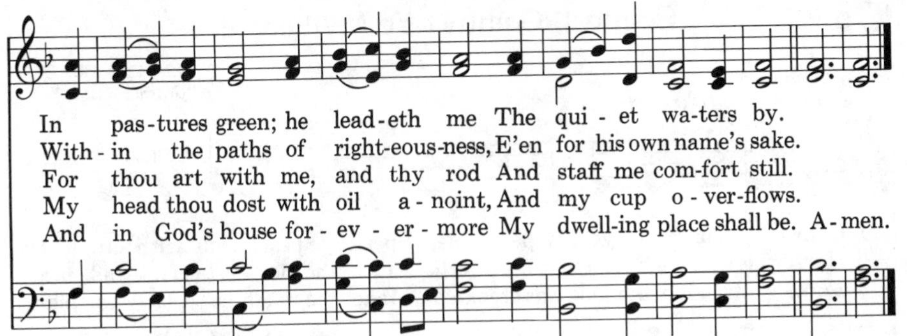
In pas-tures green; he lead-eth me The qui - et wa-ters by.
With - in the paths of right-eous-ness, E'en for his own name's sake.
For thou art with me, and thy rod And staff me com-fort still.
My head thou dost with oil a - noint, And my cup o - ver-flows.
And in God's house for - ev - er - more My dwell-ing place shall be. A - men.

Jerusalem, Lift Up Thy Voice! 105

VOM HIMMEL HOCH L.M.
"*Geistliche Lieder*," *Leipzig*, 1539

Johann Olof Wallin, 1779-1839
Tr. Ernst W. Olson, 1870-1958

1 Je - ru - sa - lem, lift up thy voice! Daugh - ter of Zi - on,
2 He comes to ev - 'ry tribe and race, A mes - sen - ger of
3 In God's e - ter - nal cov - e - nant, He comes for our sal -
4 Let all the world with one ac - cord Now hail the com - ing

now re - joice! Thy King is come, whose might - y hand
truth and grace; With peace he comes from heav'n a - bove,
va - tion sent; The star of hope moves on be - fore,
of the Lord: Praise to the prince of heav'n-ly birth,

Hence - forth shall reign o'er ev - 'ry land.
On earth to found his realm of love.
And hosts as - sem - ble to a - dore.
Who bring - eth peace to all the earth! A - men.

Words used by permission of Fortress Press.

106 Comfort, Comfort Ye My People

Based on Isaiah 40:1-8
Johann Olearius, 1611-1684
Tr. Catherine Winkworth, 1827-1878, alt.

PSALM 42 8.7.8.7.7.7.8.8.
"Genevan Psalter," 1551

1 Com-fort, com-fort ye my peo-ple, Speak ye peace, thus saith our God;
2 Hark, the voice of one that cri-eth In the des-ert far and near,
3 Make ye straight what long was crook-ed, Make the rough-er plac-es plain;
Com-fort those who sit in dark-ness, Mourn-ing 'neath their sor-rows' load.
Bid-ding all men to re-pent-ance Since the king-dom now is here.
Let your hearts be true and hum-ble, As be-fits his ho-ly reign.
Speak ye to Je-ru-sa-lem Of the peace that waits for them;
O that warn-ing cry o-bey! Now pre-pare for God a way;
For the glo-ry of the Lord Now o'er earth is shed a-broad;
Tell her that her sins I cov-er, And her war-fare now is o-ver.
Let the val-leys rise to meet him And the hills bow down to greet him.
And all flesh shall see the to-ken That his word is nev-er bro-ken. A-men.

Hail to the Lord's Anointed 107

Based on Psalm 72
James Montgomery, 1771-1854

ROCKPORT 7.6.7.6.D.
T. Tertius Noble, 1867-1953

1 Hail to the Lord's A - noint - ed, Great Da - vid's great - er Son!
2 He comes with suc - cor speed - y To those who suf - fer wrong,
3 He shall come down like show - ers Up - on the fruit - ful earth,
4 O'er ev - 'ry foe vic - to - rious, He on his throne shall rest,

Hail, in the time ap - point - ed, His reign on earth be - gun!
To help the poor and need - y And bid the weak be strong;
And love, joy, hope, like flow - ers, Spring in his path to birth;
From age to age more glo - rious, All - bless - ing and all - blest;

He comes to break op - pres - sion, To set the cap - tive free,
To give them songs for sigh - ing, Their dark - ness turn to light,
Be - fore him on the moun - tains Shall peace, the her - ald, go,
The tide of time shall nev - er His cov - e - nant re - move:

To take a - way trans - gres - sion, And rule in eq - ui - ty.
Whose souls, con - demned and dy - ing, Were pre - cious in his sight.
And right - eous - ness, in foun - tains, From hill to val - ley flow.
His name shall stand for - ev - er—That name to us is Love.

Alternate tune: ELLACOMBE, *No. 183*

108 There's a Voice in the Wilderness Crying

Based on Isaiah 40:1-5, 9-11
James L. Milligan, 1876-1961

HEREFORD *Irregular*
Francis D. Heins, 1878-1949

1 There's a voice in the wil-der-ness cry-ing, A call from the
2 O Zi-on, that bring-est good ti-dings, Get thee up to the
3 But the word of our God en-dur-eth, The arm of the
4 There's a voice in the wil-der-ness cry-ing, A call from the
ways un-trod: Pre-pare in the des-ert a high-way,
heights and sing! Pro-claim to a des-o-late peo-ple
Lord is strong; He stands in the midst of na-tions,
ways un-trod: Pre-pare in the des-ert a high-way,
A high-way for our God! The val-leys shall be ex-
The com-ing of their King. Like the flow'rs of the field they
And he will right the wrong. He shall feed his flock like a
A high-way for our God! The val-leys shall be ex-
alt-ed, The loft-y hills brought low; Make straight all the
per-ish, The works of men de-cay; The pow'r and
shep-herd And fold the lambs to his breast; In pas-tures of
alt-ed, The loft-y hills brought low; Make straight all the

crook - ed plac - es, Where the Lord our God may go!
pomp of na - tions Shall pass like a dream a - way.
peace he'll lead them And give to the wea - ry rest.
crook - ed plac - es, Where the Lord our God may go! A-men.

Hark! a Thrilling Voice Is Sounding

109

MERTON 8.7.8.7.

Latin Hymn, c.6th century
Tr. Edward Caswall, 1814-1878

William Henry Monk, 1823-1889

1 Hark! a thrill - ing voice is sound - ing: "Christ is
2 Wak - ened by the sol - emn warn - ing, Let the
3 Lo, the Lamb, so long ex - pect - ed, Comes with
4 So when next he comes in glo - ry And the
5 Hon - or, glo - ry, might and bless - ing Be to

nigh," it seems to say; "Cast a - way the
earth - bound soul a - rise; Christ, her sun, all
par - don down from heav'n; Let us haste, with
world is wrapped in fear, With his mer - cy
God: the Fa - ther, Son, And the ev - er -

works of dark - ness, O ye chil - dren of the day."
ill dis - pell - ing, Shines up - on the morn - ing skies.
tears of sor - row, One and all to be for - giv'n;
may he shield us And with words of love draw near.
last - ing Spir - it, While e - ter - nal a - ges run. A - men.

110 Jesus Came, the Heavens Adoring

Godfrey Thring, 1823-1903

CWM RHONDDA 8.7.8.7.8.7.
John Hughes, 1873-1932

1 Je - sus came, the heav'ns a - dor - ing, Came with peace from
2 Je - sus comes a - gain in mer - cy, When our hearts are
3 Je - sus comes in joy and sor - row, Shares a - like our
4 Je - sus comes on clouds tri - um - phant, When the heav'ns shall
realms on high, Je - sus came for man's re - demp - tion, Low - ly came on
bowed with care; Je - sus comes a - gain in an - swer To an ear - nest,
hopes and fears; Je - sus comes, what - e'er be - falls us, Glads our hearts and
pass a - way; Je - sus comes a - gain in glo - ry, Let us then our
earth to die; Al - le - lu - ia! Al - le - lu - ia!
heart - felt prayer; Al - le - lu - ia! Al - le - lu - ia!
dries our tears; Al - le - lu - ia! Al - le - lu - ia!
hom - age pay; Al - le - lu - ia! Al - le - lu - ia!
Came in deep hu - mil - i - ty, Came in deep hu - mil - i - ty.
Comes to save us from de - spair, Comes to save us from de - spair,
Cheer - ing e'en our fail - ing years, Cheer - ing e'en our fail - ing years.
Till the dawn of end - less day, Till the dawn of end - less day. A - men.

ADVENT

Joy to the World! the Lord Is Come

111

ANTIOCH C.M.

Based on Psalm 98
Isaac Watts, 1674-1748

Adapted from George Frederick Handel, 1685-1759
Arr. by Lowell Mason, 1792-1872

1 Joy to the world! the Lord is come: Let earth re -
2 Joy to the earth! the Sav - ior reigns: Let men their
3 He rules the world with truth and grace, And makes the
ceive her King; Let ev - 'ry heart pre - pare him room,
songs em - ploy; While fields and floods, rocks, hills, and plains
na - tions prove The glo - ries of his right - eous - ness,
And heav'n and na - ture sing, And heav'n and na - ture
Re - peat the sound - ing joy, Re - peat the sound - ing
And won - ders of his love, And won - ders of his
And heav'n and na - ture sing, And
Re - peat the sound - ing joy, Re -
And won - ders of his love, And
sing, And heav'n, and heav'n and na - ture sing.
joy, Re - peat, re - peat the sound - ing joy.
love, And won - ders, won - ders of his love.
heav'n and na - ture sing, And heav'n and na - ture sing.
peat the sound - ing joy, Re - peat the sound - ing joy.
won - ders of his love, And won - ders of his love.

112 Let All Mortal Flesh Keep Silence

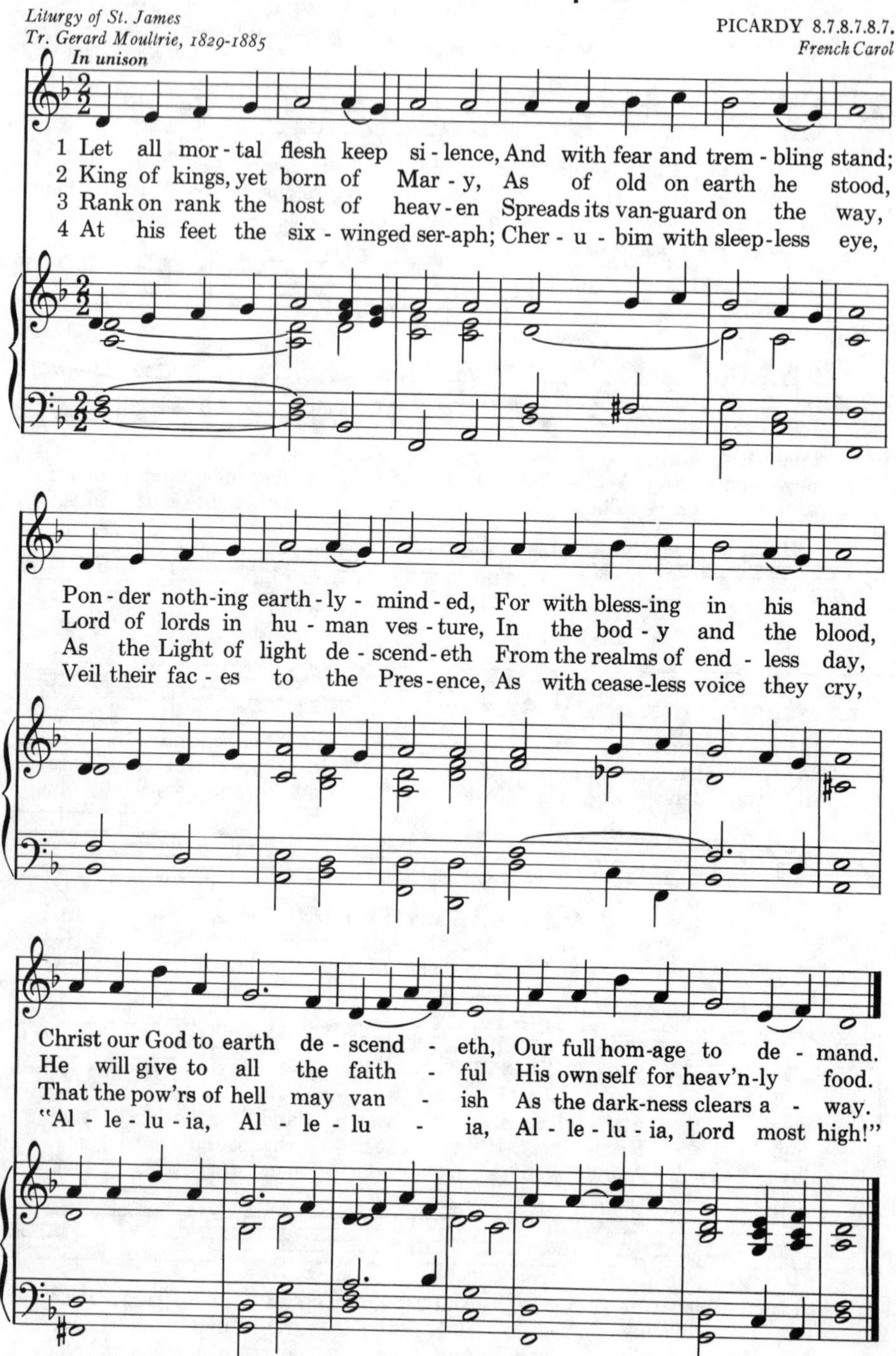
Liturgy of St. James
Tr. Gerard Moultrie, 1829-1885
PICARDY 8.7.8.7.8.7.
French Carol
In unison
1 Let all mor-tal flesh keep si-lence, And with fear and trem-bling stand;
2 King of kings, yet born of Mar-y, As of old on earth he stood,
3 Rank on rank the host of heav-en Spreads its van-guard on the way,
4 At his feet the six-winged ser-aph; Cher-u-bim with sleep-less eye,
Pon-der noth-ing earth-ly-mind-ed, For with bless-ing in his hand
Lord of lords in hu-man ves-ture, In the bod-y and the blood,
As the Light of light de-scend-eth From the realms of end-less day,
Veil their fac-es to the Pres-ence, As with cease-less voice they cry,
Christ our God to earth de-scend-eth, Our full hom-age to de-mand.
He will give to all the faith-ful His own self for heav'n-ly food.
That the pow'rs of hell may van-ish As the dark-ness clears a-way.
"Al-le-lu-ia, Al-le-lu-ia, Al-le-lu-ia, Lord most high!"

Lift Up Your Heads, Ye Mighty Gates 113

Based on Psalm 24:7
Georg Weissel, 1590-1635
Tr. Catherine Winkworth, 1827-1878

TRURO L.M.
"Psalmodia Evangelica," 1789

1 Lift up your heads, ye might - y gates: Be - hold, the King of
2 O blest the land, the cit - y blest, Where Christ the rul - er
3 Fling wide the por - tals of your heart: Make it a tem - ple,
4 Re - deem-er, come! I o - pen wide My heart to thee: here,
5 So come, my Sov-'reign, en - ter in! Let new and no - bler
glo - ry waits! The King of kings is draw - ing
is con - fessed! O hap - py hearts and hap - py
set a - part From earth - ly use for heav'n's em -
Lord, a - bide! Let me thy in - ner pres - ence
life be - gin! Thy Ho - ly Spir - it guide us
near, The Sa - vior of the world is here.
homes To whom this King of tri - umph comes!
ploy, A - dorned with prayer and love and joy.
feel: Thy grace and love in me re - veal.
on, Un - til the glor - ious crown be won. A - men.

114 Now Hail We Our Redeemer

St. Ambrose, 340-397
Olavus Petri, 1493-1552
Tr. Ernst W. Olson, 1870-1958

ENCHIRIDION 7.6.7.6.7.7.6.
"Enchiridion," Erfurt, 1524

1 Now hail we our Re - deem - er, E - ter - nal Son of
2 A man, of God be - got - ten, Bro't in the age of
3 O Je - sus, grant us mer - cy, And grace on us be -
4 In - to thy hand the Fa - ther Gave all, that we might
God, Born in the flesh to save us And cleanse us
grace; Lo, all the earth is ra - diant With light and
stow, To walk by thine own guid - ance, Thy sav - ing
be In bonds of faith u - nit - ed, And ded - i -
in his blood. The morn - ing star as - cend - eth, Light to the
hope and peace. Our pris - on he de - mol - ished, Death's pow - er
truth to know. For thee our hearts are yearn - ing, From world - ly
cate to thee: A peo - ple through thy mer - it En - ti - tled
world he lend - eth— Our guide in grief and gloom.
he a - bol - ished And o - pened heav - en's gate.
pleas - ures turn - ing Un - to thy right - eous - ness.
to in - her - it Thy realm e - ter - nal - ly. A - men.

ADVENT

O Bride of Christ, Rejoice!

Johann Olof Wallin, 1779-1839
Tr. Victor O. Peterson, 1864-1929

AUF MEINEN LIEBEN GOTT 6.6.7.7.7.7.
Jacob Regnart, 1540-c.1600
Harm. by A. Royce Eckhardt, 1937-

In unison
1 O Bride of Christ, re - joice! Ex - ul - tant raise thy
2 Let shouts of glad - ness rise Tri - um - phant to the
3 He wears no king - ly crown, Yet as a king he's
4 Thy heart now o - pen wide, Bid Christ with thee a -
5 E'en babes with one ac - cord With thee shall praise the
voice To hail the day of glo - ry, Fore -
skies; Here comes the King most glo - rious To
known; Though not ar - rayed in splen - dor, He
bide; He gra - cious - ly will hear thee And
Lord, And ev - 'ry gen - tile na - tion Re -
told in sa - cred sto - ry.
reign o'er all vic - to - rious.
still makes death sur - ren - der. Ho - san - na, praise and
be for - ev - er near thee.
spond with ex - ul - ta - tion.
glo - ry: Our King, we bow be - fore thee. A - men.

116 O Come, O Come, Emmanuel

Latin: c.9th century
Tr. John M. Neale, 1818-1866, Sts. 1,2, alt.
Tr. Henry S. Coffin, 1877-1954, Sts. 3,4, alt.
VENI EMMANUEL L.M. with Refrain
Adapted from Plainsong, Mode I
Thomas Helmore, 1811-1890
In unison
1 O come, O come, Em - man - u - el, And ran - som cap - tive Is - ra - el, That mourns in lone - ly ex - ile here, Un - til the Son of God ap - pear.
2 O come, thou Day-spring, come and cheer Our spir - its by thine ad - vent here; Dis - perse the gloom - y clouds of night, And death's dark shad-ows put to flight.
3 O come, thou Wis - dom from on high, And or - der all things, far and nigh; To us the path of knowl - edge show, And cause us in her ways to go.
4 O come, De - sire of na - tions, bind In one the hearts of all man - kind; Bid thou our sad di - vi - sions cease, And be thy - self our King of peace.
REFRAIN
Re - joice! Re - joice! Em - man - u - el Shall come to thee, O Is - ra - el! A-men.

O How Shall I Receive Thee 117

Paul Gerhardt, 1607-1676
Tr. Composite

PASSION CHORALE 7.6.7.6.D.
Hans Leo Hassler, 1564-1612
Harm. by J. S. Bach, 1685-1750

1 O how shall I re - ceive thee, How greet thee, Lord, a - right?
2 Thy Zi - on palms is strew - ing, And branch-es fresh and fair;
3 Love caused thine in - car - na - tion, Love brought thee down to me;
4 Re - joice then, ye sad - heart - ed, Who sit in deep - est gloom,

All na - tions long to see thee, My hope, my heart's de - light!
My heart, its pow'rs re - new - ing, An an - them shall pre - pare.
Thy thirst for my sal - va - tion Pro - cured my lib - er - ty.
Who mourn o'er joys de - part - ed And trem - ble at your doom.

O kin - dle, Lord most ho - ly, Thy lamp with - in my breast,
My soul puts off her sad - ness Thy glo - ries to pro - claim;
O love be - yond all tell - ing That led thee to em - brace,
He who a - lone can cheer you Is stand - ing at the door;

To do in spir - it low - ly All that may please thee best.
With all her strength and glad - ness She fain would serve thy name.
In love all love ex - cell - ing, Our lost and fall - en race!
He brings his pit - y near you And bids you weep no more. A-men.

Alternate tune: ST. THEODULPH, *No. 178*
Another harmonization may be found at No. 182

118 O Zion, Acclaim Your Redeemer!

Mary Elizabeth Servoss, 1849-?
Tr. Erik Nyström, 1842-1907
Tr. E. Gustav Johnson, 1893-

GÅ SION 9.8.9.8. *with Refrain*
James McGranahan, 1840-1907
Harm. by Norman E. Johnson, 1928-

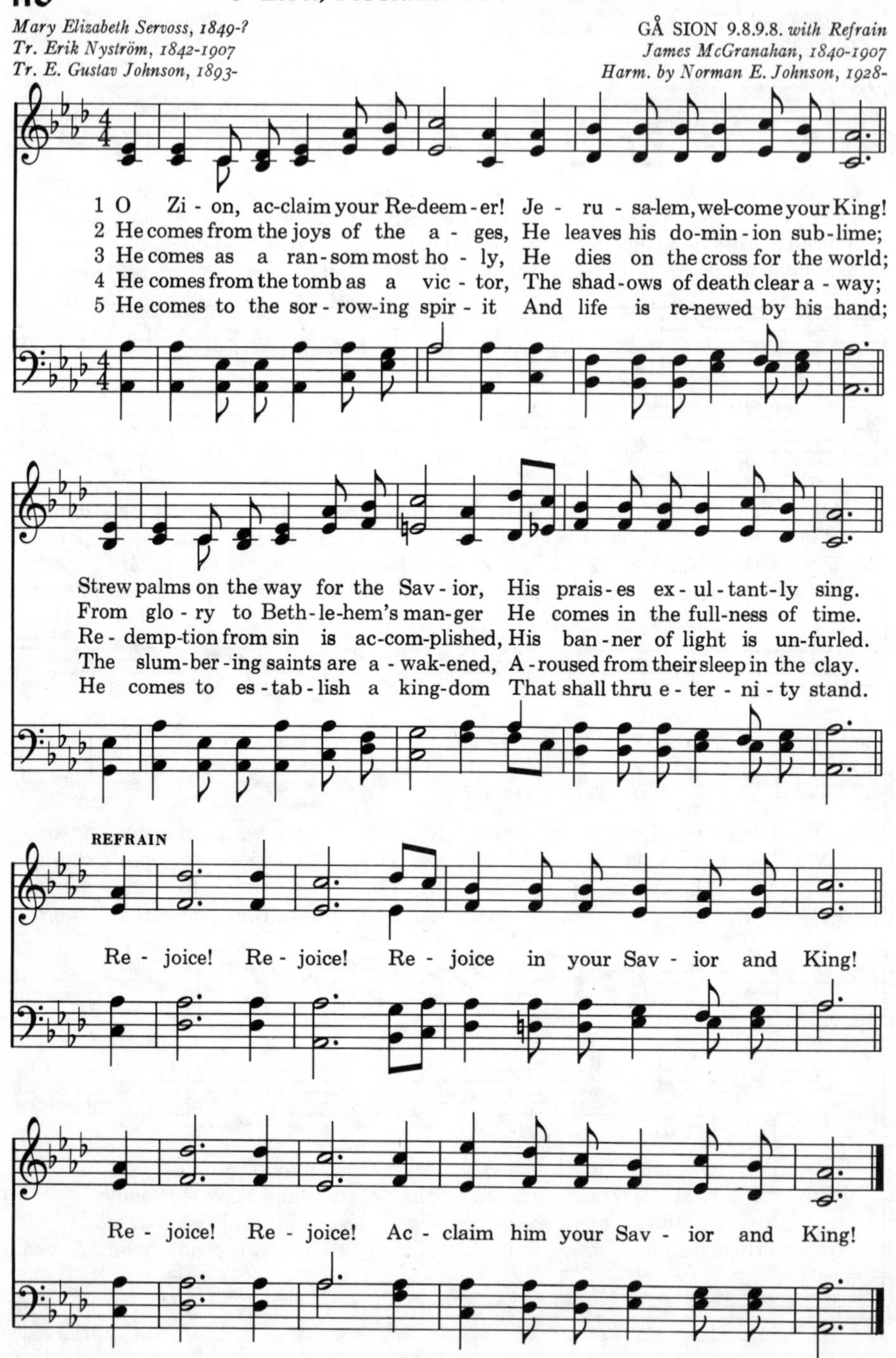
1 O Zi - on, ac-claim your Re-deem - er! Je - ru - sa-lem, wel-come your King!
2 He comes from the joys of the a - ges, He leaves his do-min - ion sub-lime;
3 He comes as a ran - som most ho - ly, He dies on the cross for the world;
4 He comes from the tomb as a vic - tor, The shad-ows of death clear a - way;
5 He comes to the sor - row-ing spir - it And life is re-newed by his hand;
Strew palms on the way for the Sav - ior, His prais - es ex - ul - tant - ly sing.
From glo - ry to Beth - le-hem's man-ger He comes in the full-ness of time.
Re - demp-tion from sin is ac-com-plished, His ban - ner of light is un-furled.
The slum-ber-ing saints are a - wak-ened, A - roused from their sleep in the clay.
He comes to es - tab - lish a king-dom That shall thru e - ter - ni - ty stand.
REFRAIN
Re - joice! Re - joice! Re - joice in your Sav - ior and King!
Re - joice! Re - joice! Ac - claim him your Sav - ior and King!

ADVENT

Prepare the Way, O Zion! 119

Frans Michael Franzén, 1772-1847
Tr. Augustus Nelson, 1863-1949

MESSIAH 7.6.7.6.7.7.6.6.
Swedish Melody, 1694

1 Pre - pare the way, O Zi - on! Ye aw - ful deeps, rise high;
2 O Zi - on, he ap - proach - es, Your Lord and King for aye;
3 Fling wide your por - tals, Zi - on, And hail your glo - rious King;
4 The throne which he as - cend - ed Is fixed in heav'n a - bove;

Sink low, ye loft - y moun-tains, The Lord is draw - ing nigh.
Strew palms where he ad - vanc - es, Spread gar-ments in his way.
His ti - dings of sal - va - tion To ev - 'ry peo - ple bring,
His ev - er - last - ing king - dom Is light and joy and love.

The right-eous King of glo - ry, Fore - told in sa - cred sto - ry:
God's prom - ise fail - eth nev - er, Ho - san - na sound for - ev - er:
Who, wait - ing still in sad - ness, Would sing his praise with glad - ness:
Let us his praise be sound - ing For grace and peace a - bound - ing:

O blest is he who came In God the Fa - ther's name. A - men.

Words from *The Lutheran Service Book and Hymnal*, by permission of the Commission on the Liturgy and Hymnal.

120 Rejoice, Rejoice, Believers!

Laurentius Laurenti, 1660-1722
Tr. Sarah B. Findlater, 1823-1907, alt.

VIGIL 7.6.7.6.D.
Swedish Folk Melody

1 Re - joice, re - joice, be - liev - ers! And let your lights ap - pear;
2 See that your lamps are burn - ing, Re - plen - ish them with oil;
3 All ye who wait his com - ing, Re - hearse the joy - ful song,
4 Our hope and ex - pec - ta - tion, O Je - sus, now ap - pear;

The eve - ning is ad - vanc - ing, And dark - er night is near.
Look now for your sal - va - tion, The end of sin and toil.
Which we shall sing in glo - ry With all the an - gel throng.
A - rise, thou Sun so longed for, O'er this be - night - ed sphere!

The Lord is now a - ris - ing, And soon he will draw nigh;
The watch-ers on the moun - tain Pro - claim the Lord is near;
The ho - ly feast is wait - ing, The gates wide o - pen stand;
With hearts and hands up - lift - ed, We plead, O Lord, to see

Up, watch in ex - pec - ta - tion! At mid-night comes the cry.
Go meet him as he com - eth, With al - le - lu - ias clear.
Rise up, ye heirs of glo - ry! The Mas - ter is at hand.
The day of earth's re - demp - tion, And ev - er be with thee. A-men.

Watchman, Tell Us of the Night

John Bowring, 1792-1872

ABERYSTWYTH 7.7.7.7.D.
Joseph Parry, 1841-1903

1 Watch-man, tell us of the night, What its signs of prom - ise are.
2 Watch-man, tell us of the night, High - er yet that star as - cends.
3 Watch-man, tell us of the night, For the morn - ing seems to dawn.

Trav - 'ler, o'er yon moun-tain's height, See that glo - ry - beam-ing star.
Trav - 'ler, bless-ed - ness and light, Peace and truth its course por-tends.
Trav - 'ler, dark-ness takes its flight, Doubt and ter - ror are with-drawn.

Watch-man, does its beau - teous ray Aught of joy or hope fore - tell?
Watch-man, will its beams a - lone Gild the spot that gave them birth?
Watch-man, let thy wan - d'rings cease: Has - ten to thy qui - et home.

Trav - 'ler, yes— it brings the day, Prom - ised day of Is - ra - el.
Trav - 'ler, a - ges are its own: See, it bursts o'er all the earth.
Trav - 'ler, lo, the Prince of peace, Lo, the Son of God is come.

122 Wake, Awake, for Night Is Flying

Philipp Nicolai, 1556-1608
Tr. Catherine Winkworth, 1827-1878, alt.
Tr. Paul English, ?-1932, Alt. St.

WACHET AUF *Irregular*
Philipp Nicolai, 1556-1608
Harm. by J. S. Bach, 1685-1750

1 Wake, a-wake, for night is fly - ing, The watch-men on the heights are cry - ing; A - wake, Je - ru - sa - lem, a - rise!
2 Zi - on hears the watch-men sing - ing, Her heart with deep de-light is spring - ing; She wakes, she ris - es from her gloom:
Mid-night's sol - emn hour is toll - ing, His char - iot wheels are near - er roll - ing; He comes! O Church, lift up thine eyes!
For her Lord comes down all - glo - rious, In grace ar - rayed, by truth vic - to - rious; Her star is ris'n, her light is come!

ADVENT

Rise up! with will-ing feet Go forth, the Bride-groom meet:
Ah, come, thou bless-ed One, God's own be-lov-ed Son,
Hal-le-lu-jah! Lo, great and small, we an-swer all;
Hal-le-lu-jah! We haste a-long, an ea-ger throng,
We fol-low where thy voice shall call.
And glad-some join the ad-vent song. A-men.

Alternate stanza

Now let ev'ry tongue adore thee!
Let men with angels sing before thee!
Let harps and cymbals now unite!
All thy gates with pearl are glorious,
Where we partake, through faith victorious,
With angels round thy throne of light.
No mortal eye hath seen,
No mortal ear hath heard
Such wondrous things;
Therefore with joy our song shall soar
In praise to God for evermore. Amen.

123 Come, Thou Long-Expected Jesus

Charles Wesley, 1707-1788, alt.

STUTTGART 8.7.8.7.
Attr. to Christian F. Witt, 1660-1716
"Psalmodia Sacra," Gotha, 1715

1 Come, thou long - ex - pect - ed Je - sus, Born to set thy peo - ple free;
2 Is - rael's strength and con - so - la - tion, Hope of all the earth thou art:
3 Born thy peo - ple to de - liv - er, Born a child, and yet a king,
4 By thine own e - ter - nal Spir - it Rule in all our hearts a - lone;

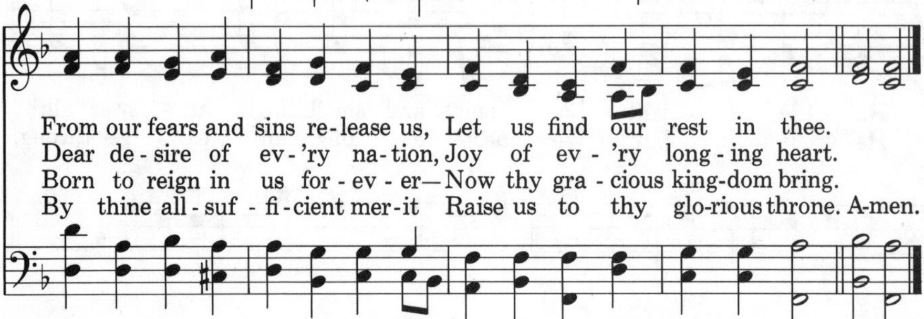

From our fears and sins re - lease us, Let us find our rest in thee.
Dear de - sire of ev - 'ry na - tion, Joy of ev - 'ry long - ing heart.
Born to reign in us for - ev - er—Now thy gra - cious king - dom bring.
By thine all - suf - fi - cient mer - it Raise us to thy glo - rious throne. A - men.

ADVENT

A higher setting may be found at No. 658

124 All Hail to Thee, O Blessed Morn!

Johann Olof Wallin, 1779-1839
Tr. Ernst W. Olson, 1870-1958

WIE SCHÖN LEUCHTET 8.8.7.8.8.7.4.8.4.8.
Philipp Nicolai, 1556-1608

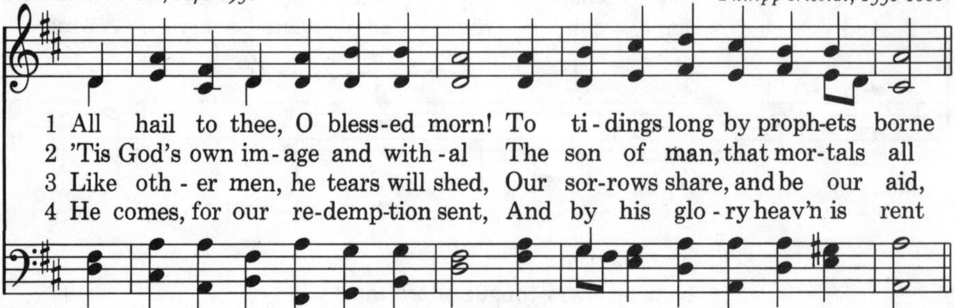

1 All hail to thee, O bless - ed morn! To ti - dings long by proph - ets borne
2 'Tis God's own im - age and with - al The son of man, that mor - tals all
3 Like oth - er men, he tears will shed, Our sor - rows share, and be our aid,
4 He comes, for our re - demp - tion sent, And by his glo - ry heav'n is rent

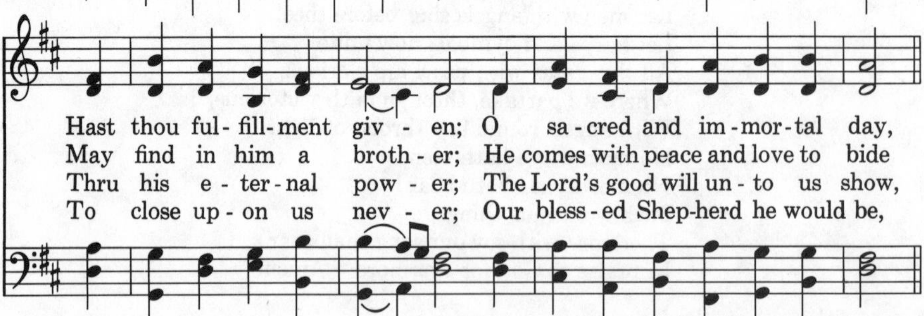

Hast thou ful - fill - ment giv - en; O sa - cred and im - mor - tal day,
May find in him a broth - er; He comes with peace and love to bide
Thru his e - ter - nal pow - er; The Lord's good will un - to us show,
To close up - on us nev - er; Our bless - ed Shep - herd he would be,

Words from *The Lutheran Service Book and Hymnal*, by permission of the Commission on the Liturgy and Hymnal.

BIRTH

Other harmonizations may be found at Nos. 157 and 263

When un - to earth, in glo - rious ray, De- scends the grace of heav - en!
On earth, the err - ing race to guide, And help, as could no oth - er:
And min - gle in our cup of woe The drops of mer-cy's show - er:
Whom we may fol - low faith-ful - ly And be with him for - ev - er:
Sing - ing, ring - ing, Sounds are blend - ing, Prais - es send - ing
Rath - er gath - er Clos - er, fond - er, Sheep that wan - der,
Dy - ing, buy - ing Thru his pas - sion Our sal - va - tion,
High - er, nigh - er, Glo - ry wing - ing, Prais - es sing - ing
Un - to heav - en For the Sav - ior to us giv - en.
Feed and fold them, Than let e - vil pow - ers hold them.
And to mor - tals O - pen - ing the heav'n-ly por - tals.
To the Fa - ther And his Son, our Lord and broth - er.

Var hälsad, sköna morgonstund,
Som av profeters helga mun
Är oss bebådad vorden!
Du stora dag, du sälla dag,
På vilken himlens välbehag
Ännu besöker jorden!
Unga sjunga Med de gamla,
Sig församla Jordens böner
Kring den störste av dess söner.

125 Angels We Have Heard on High

Traditional French Carol

GLORIA 7.7.7.7. *with Refrain*
French Carol Melody

1 An - gels we have heard on high Sweet - ly sing - ing o'er the plains,
2 Shep-herds, why this ju - bi - lee? Why your joy - ous strains pro - long?
3 Come to Beth - le - hem and see Him whose birth the an - gels sing;
And the moun-tains in re - ply Ech - o back their joy - ous strains
Say what may the ti - dings be, Which in - spire your heaven - ly song.
Come a - dore, on bend - ed knee, Christ, the Lord, the new - born King.
REFRAIN
Glo - - - - - - - - - - - ri - a
in ex - cel - sis De - o, Glo - - - - - - - - - -

BIRTH

- - - - - - - - - ri - a in ex - cel - sis De - o.

All My Heart This Night Rejoices 126

Paul Gerhardt, 1607-1676
Tr. Catherine Winkworth, 1827-1878

WARUM SOLLT ICH 8.3.3.6.D.
Johann G. Ebeling, 1637-1676

1 All my heart this night re - joic - es As I hear, Far and near,
2 Hark! a voice from yon - der man - ger, Soft and sweet, Doth en - treat:
3 Come, then, let us has - ten yon - der! Here let all, Great and small,

Sweet - est an - gel voic - es. "Christ is born," their choirs are sing - ing,
"Flee from woe and dan - ger! Breth - ren, come! from all doth grieve you,
Kneel in awe and won - der! Love him who with love is yearn - ing!

Till the air Ev - 'ry - where Now with joy is ring - ing.
You are freed— All you need I will sure - ly give you."
Hail the star That from far Bright with hope is burn - ing!

Break Forth, O Beauteous Heavenly Light

Johann Rist, 1607-1667
Tr. John Troulbeck, 1832-1899, St. 1
Norman E. Johnson, 1928- , St. 2

ERMUNTRE DICH 8.7.8.7.8.8.7.7.
Johann Schop, c.1590-1664
Harm. by J. S. Bach, 1685-1750

1 Break forth, O beau-teous heav'n-ly light, And ush - er in the morn - ing; Ye shep-herds, shrink not with af - fright, But hear the an-gel's warn - ing. This child, now weak in in - fan - cy, Our con - fi - dence and joy shall be, The pow'r of Sa - tan

2 Break forth, O beau-teous heav'n-ly light, To her - ald our sal - va - tion; He stoops to earth—the God of might, Our hope and ex - pec - ta - tion. He comes in hu - man flesh to dwell, Our God with us, Im - man - u - el, The night of dark - ness

For choir, transpose to a higher key.

BIRTH

break - ing, Our peace e - ter - nal mak - ing.
end - ing, Our fall - en race be - friend - ing.

Angels, from the Realms of Glory 128

James Montgomery, 1771-1854

REGENT SQUARE 8.7.8.7.8.7.
Henry T. Smart, 1813-1879

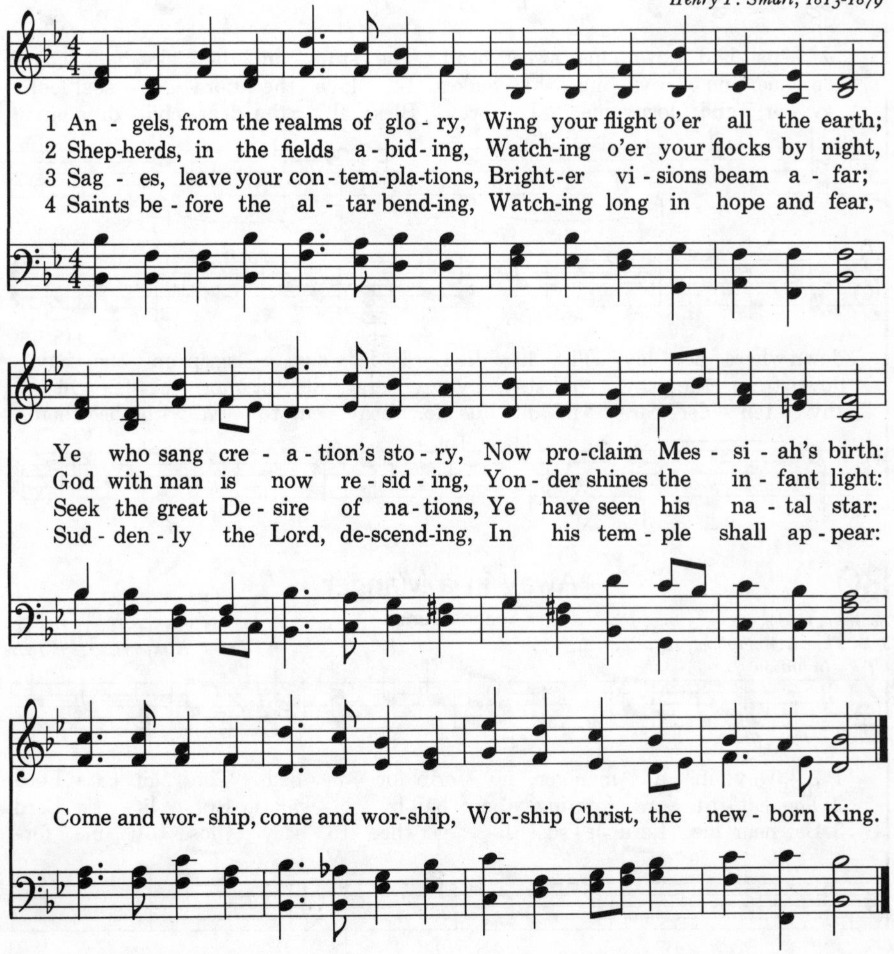

1 An - gels, from the realms of glo - ry, Wing your flight o'er all the earth;
2 Shep-herds, in the fields a - bid - ing, Watch-ing o'er your flocks by night,
3 Sag - es, leave your con - tem - pla - tions, Bright - er vi - sions beam a - far;
4 Saints be - fore the al - tar bend - ing, Watch-ing long in hope and fear,

Ye who sang cre - a - tion's sto - ry, Now pro - claim Mes - si - ah's birth:
God with man is now re - sid - ing, Yon - der shines the in - fant light:
Seek the great De - sire of na - tions, Ye have seen his na - tal star:
Sud - den - ly the Lord, de - scend - ing, In his tem - ple shall ap - pear:

Come and wor - ship, come and wor - ship, Wor - ship Christ, the new - born King.

129 Away in a Manger

First Tune

Source unknown, Sts. 1, 2
John Thomas McFarland, 1851-1913, St. 3

AWAY IN A MANGER 11.11.11.11.
James R. Murray, 1841-1905

In unison
1 A - way in a man - ger, no crib for a bed, The lit - tle Lord
2 The cat - tle are low - ing, the ba - by a - wakes, But lit - tle Lord
3 Be near me, Lord Je - sus! I ask thee to stay Close by me for -
Je - sus laid down his sweet head. The stars in the sky looked
Je - sus, no cry - ing he makes. I love thee, Lord Je - sus! look
ev - er, and love me, I pray. Bless all the dear chil - dren in
down where he lay, The lit - tle Lord Je - sus, a - sleep on the hay.
down from the sky, And stay by my cra - dle till morn - ing is nigh.
thy ten - der care, And fit us for heav - en, to live with thee there.

130 Away in a Manger

Second Tune

Source unknown, Sts. 1, 2
John Thomas McFarland, 1851-1913, St. 3

CRADLE SONG 11.11.11.11.
William J. Kirkpatrick, 1838-1921

In unison
1 A - way in a man - ger, no crib for a bed, The lit - tle Lord
2 The cat - tle are low - ing, the ba - by a - wakes, But lit - tle Lord
3 Be near me, Lord Je - sus! I ask thee to stay Close by me for -

Je - sus laid down his sweet head. The stars in the bright sky looked
Je - sus, no cry - ing he makes. I love thee, Lord Je - sus! look
ev - er, and love me, I pray. Bless all the dear chil - dren in

down where he lay, The lit - tle Lord Je - sus, a - sleep on the hay.
down from the sky, And stay by my cra - dle till morn-ing is nigh.
thy ten - der care, And fit us for heav-en, to live with thee there.

How Glad I Am Each Christmas Eve 131

Marie Wexelsen, 1832-1911
Tr. Peter A. Sveeggen, 1881-1959

CHRISTMAS EVE C.M.
Peder Knudsen, 1819-1863

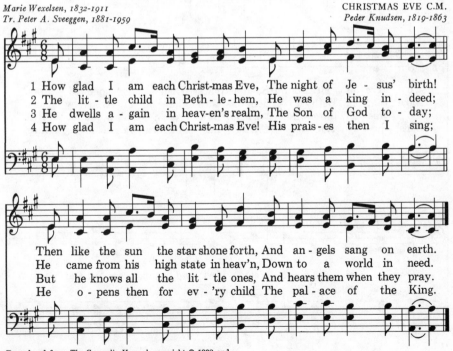

1 How glad I am each Christ-mas Eve, The night of Je - sus' birth!
2 The lit - tle child in Beth - le - hem, He was a king in - deed;
3 He dwells a - gain in heav-en's realm, The Son of God to - day;
4 How glad I am each Christ-mas Eve! His prais - es then I sing;

Then like the sun the star shone forth, And an - gels sang on earth.
He came from his high state in heav'n, Down to a world in need.
But he knows all the lit - tle ones, And hears them when they pray.
He o - pens then for ev - 'ry child The pal - ace of the King.

132 God Rest You Merry, Gentlemen

English Carol, 18th century

GOD REST YOU MERRY 8.6.8.6.8.6. *with Refrain*
English Melody, 18th century
Harm. by John Stainer, 1840-1901

1 God rest you mer - ry, gen - tle - men, Let noth - ing you dis - may;
2 From God, our heaven - ly Fa - ther, A bless - ed an - gel came;
3 "Fear not, then," said the an - gel, "Let noth - ing you af - fright;
4 Now to the Lord sing prais - es, All you with - in this place,
Re - mem - ber Christ, our Sav - ior, Was born on Christ - mas Day,
And un - to cer - tain shep - herds Brought ti - dings of the same:
This day is born a Sav - ior, Of a pure vir - gin bright,
And with true love and broth - er - hood Each oth - er now em - brace;
To save us all from Sa - tan's power When we were gone a - stray.
How that in Beth - le - hem was born The Son of God by name.
To free all those who trust in him From Sa - tan's power and might."
This ho - ly tide of Christ - mas Doth bring re - deem - ing grace.
REFRAIN
O ti - dings of com - fort and joy, com - fort and joy;

From Heaven Above to Earth I Come 133

Martin Luther, 1483-1546
Tr. Catherine Winkworth, 1827-1878

VOM HIMMEL HOCH L.M.
"Geistliche Lieder," Leipzig, 1539

O ti - dings of com - fort and joy!
1 From heav'n a - bove to earth I come, To bear good news to ev - 'ry home; Glad ti - dings of great joy I bring, Where - of I now will say and sing:
2 "To you this night is born a child Of Mar - y, cho - sen moth - er mild; This lit - tle child of low - ly birth Shall be the joy of all your earth."
3 "'Tis Christ our God who far on high Hath heard your sad and bit - ter cry; Him - self will your sal - va - tion be, Him - self from sin will make you free."
4 Wel - come to earth, thou no - ble guest, Thru whom e'en wick - ed men are blest! Thou com'st to share our mis - er - y: What can we ren - der, Lord, to thee?
5 Ah, dear - est Je - sus, ho - ly child, Make thee a bed, soft, un - de - filed, With - in my heart, that it may be A qui - et cham - ber kept for thee!
6 Glo - ry to God in high - est heav'n, Who un - to man his son hath giv'n, While an - gels sing with pi - ous mirth A glad New Year to all the earth. A - men.

BIRTH

134 Gentle Mary Laid Her Child

Joseph Simpson Cook, 1859-1933

TEMPUS ADEST FLORIDUM 7.6.7.6.D.
"Piae Cantiones," 1582
Harm. by Ernest MacMillan, 1893-

1 Gen - tle Mar - y laid her child Low - ly in a man - ger;
2 An - gels sang a - bout his birth, Wise men sought and found him;
3 Gen - tle Mar - y laid her child Low - ly in a man - ger;
There he lay, the un - de - filed, To the world a stran - ger.
Heav - en's star shone bright - ly forth, Glo - ry all a - round him.
He is still the un - de - filed, But no more a stran - ger.
Such a babe in such a place, Can he be the Sav - ior?
Shep - herds saw the won - drous sight, Heard the an - gels sing - ing;
Son of God, of hum - ble birth, Beau - ti - ful the sto - ry;
Ask the saved of all the race Who have found his fa - vor.
All the plains were lit that night, All the hills were ring - ing.
Praise his name in all the earth, Hail the King of glo - ry! A-men.

BIRTH

Go, Tell It on the Mountain

American Folk Hymn
Adapted by John W. Work, 1901-1967

GO TELL IT ON THE MOUNTAIN Irregular
American Folk Melody
Harm. by John W. Work, 1901-1967

In unison
Go, tell it on the moun - tain, O - ver the hills and ev - 'ry - where;
Fine
Go, tell it on the moun - tain That Je - sus Christ is born!
In harmony
1 While shep-herds kept their watch - ing O'er si - lent flocks by night, Be -
2 The shep-herds feared and trem-bled When lo! a - bove the earth Rang
3 Down in a low - ly man - ger The hum - ble Christ was born, And
D.C.
hold through-out the heav - ens There shone a ho - ly light.
out the an - gel cho - rus That hailed our Sav - ior's birth.
God sent us sal - va - tion That bless - ed Christ-mas morn.

136 Good Christian Men, Rejoice

Latin Carol, 14th century
Tr. John M. Neale, 1818-1866

IN DULCI JUBILO *Irregular*
German Melody, 14th century

1 Good Chris-tian men, re - joice With heart and soul and voice;
2 Good Chris-tian men, re - joice With heart and soul and voice;
3 Good Chris-tian men, re - joice With heart and soul and voice;
Give ye heed to what we say: News! news! Je-sus Christ is born to-day!
Now ye hear of end-less bliss: Joy! joy! Je-sus Christ was born for this!
Now ye need not fear the grave: Peace! peace! Je-sus Christ was born to save!
Ox and ass be-fore him bow, And he is in the man-ger now.
He has o-pened heav-en's door, And man is bless-ed ev-er-more.
Calls you one and calls you all To gain his ev-er-last-ing hall.
Christ is born to-day! Christ is born to-day!
Christ was born for this! Christ was born for this!
Christ was born to save! Christ was born to save!

Infant Holy, Infant Lowly

From the Polish
Paraphrase by Edith M. G. Reed, 1885-1933

W ZLOBIE LEZY 4.4.7.4.4.7.4.4.4.4.7.
Polish Carol
Harm. by David Hugh Jones, 1900-

1 In - fant ho - ly, In - fant low - ly, For his bed a cat - tle stall;
Ox - en low - ing, Lit - tle know-ing Christ the babe is Lord of all.
Swift are wing - ing An - gels sing - ing, No - els ring - ing,
Tid - ings bring - ing: Christ the babe is Lord of all.

2 Flocks were sleep-ing: Shep-herds keep-ing Vig - il till the morn-ing new
Saw the glo - ry, Heard the sto - ry, Ti - dings of a gos - pel true.
Thus re - joic - ing, Free from sor - row, Prais - es voic - ing
Greet the mor - row: Christ the babe was born for you.

138 Hark! the Herald Angels Sing

Charles Wesley, 1707-1788, alt.

MENDELSSOHN 7.7.7.7.D. *with Refrain*
Felix Mendelssohn, 1809-1847
Harm. by William H. Cummings, 1831-1915

1 Hark! the her - ald an - gels sing, "Glo - ry to the new - born King;
2 Christ, by high - est heaven a - dored, Christ, the ev - er - last - ing Lord:
3 Hail the heaven-born Prince of peace! Hail the Sun of right-eous - ness!
Peace on earth, and mer - cy mild— God and sin - ners rec - on - ciled!"
Late in time be - hold him come, Off - spring of the Vir - gin's womb.
Light and life to all he brings, Risen with heal - ing in his wings,
Joy - ful, all ye na - tions, rise, Join the tri - umph of the skies;
Veiled in flesh the God - head see: Hail the in - car - nate De - i - ty,
Mild he lays his glo - ry by, Born that man no more may die,
With the an - gel - ic host pro - claim, "Christ is born in Beth - le - hem!"
Pleased as man with men to dwell, Je - sus, our Em - man - u - el.
Born to raise the sons of earth, Born to give them sec - ond birth.

REFRAIN
Hark! the her-ald an-gels sing, "Glo-ry to the new-born King!"

I Heard the Bells on Christmas Day 139

Henry W. Longfellow, 1807-1882, alt.

WALTHAM L.M.
Jean Baptiste Calkin, 1827-1905

1 I heard the bells on Christmas day
Their old familiar carols play,
And wild and sweet the words repeat
Of peace on earth, good will to men.

2 I thought how, as the day had come,
The belfries of all Christendom
Had rolled along th'unbroken song
Of peace on earth, good will to men.

3 And in despair I bowed my head:
"There is no peace on earth," I said,
"For hate is strong, and mocks the song
Of peace on earth, good will to men."

4 Yet pealed the bells more loud and deep:
"God is not dead, nor does he sleep;
The wrong shall fail, the right prevail,
With peace on earth, good will to men."

5 Then ringing, singing on its way,
The world revolved from night to day—
A voice, a chime, a chant sublime,
Of peace on earth, good will to men.

140 It Came upon the Midnight Clear

Edmund H. Sears, 1810-1876, alt.
CAROL C.M.D.
Richard S. Willis, 1819-1900
1 It came up - on the mid-night clear, That glo - rious song of old,
2 Still through the clo - ven skies they come With peace-ful wings un - furled,
3 And ye, be - neath life's crush-ing load Whose forms are bend - ing low,
4 For lo, the days are has - t'ning on, By proph-et bards fore - told,
From an - gels bend - ing near the earth To touch their harps of gold:
And still their heav'n-ly mu - sic floats O'er all the wea - ry world:
Who toil a - long the climb-ing way With pain - ful steps and slow:
When with the ev - er - cir-cling years Comes round the age of gold:
"Peace on the earth, good will to men From heav'n's all gra - cious King!"
A - bove its sad and low - ly plains They bend on hov - 'ring wing,
Look now, for glad and gold - en hours Come swift - ly on the wing;
When peace shall o - ver all the earth Its an - cient splen-dors fling,
The world in sol - emn still-ness lay To hear the an - gels sing.
And ev - er o'er its Ba - bel sounds The bless - ed an - gels sing.
O rest be - side the wea - ry road And hear the an - gels sing.
And the whole world send back the song Which now the an - gels sing.

Lo, How a Rose E'er Blooming

German, 16th century
Tr. Theodore Baker, 1851-1934, Sts. 1,2
Tr. Harriet Krauth Spaeth, 1845-1925, St. 3

ES IST EIN ROS' 7.6.7.6.6.7.6.
"Geistliche Kirchengesäng," Cologne, 1599
Harm. by Michael Praetorius, 1571-1621

1 Lo, how a Rose e'er bloom-ing From ten-der stem hath sprung!
2 I - sa - iah 'twas fore-told it, The Rose I have in mind;
3 This flow'r, whose fra-grance ten-der With sweet-ness fills the air,
Of Jes-se's lin-eage com-ing As men of old have sung.
With Mar-y we be-hold it, The vir-gin moth - er kind.
Dis-pels with glo-rious splen-dor The dark-ness ev - 'ry-where.
It came, a flow-'ret bright, A - mid the cold of
To show God's love a - right She bore to men a
True man, yet ver - y God, From sin and death he
win - ter, When half - spent was the night.
Sav - ior, When half - spent was the night.
saves us And light - ens ev - 'ry load.

142 Long Ago and Far Away

Edward Traill Horn, III, 1909-
Refrain from the German, 15th century
Refrain tr. Percy Dearmer, 1867-1936

RESONET IN LAUDIBUS *Irregular*
German Carol Melody, 14th century
Harm. by Ralph Vaughan Williams, 1872-1958

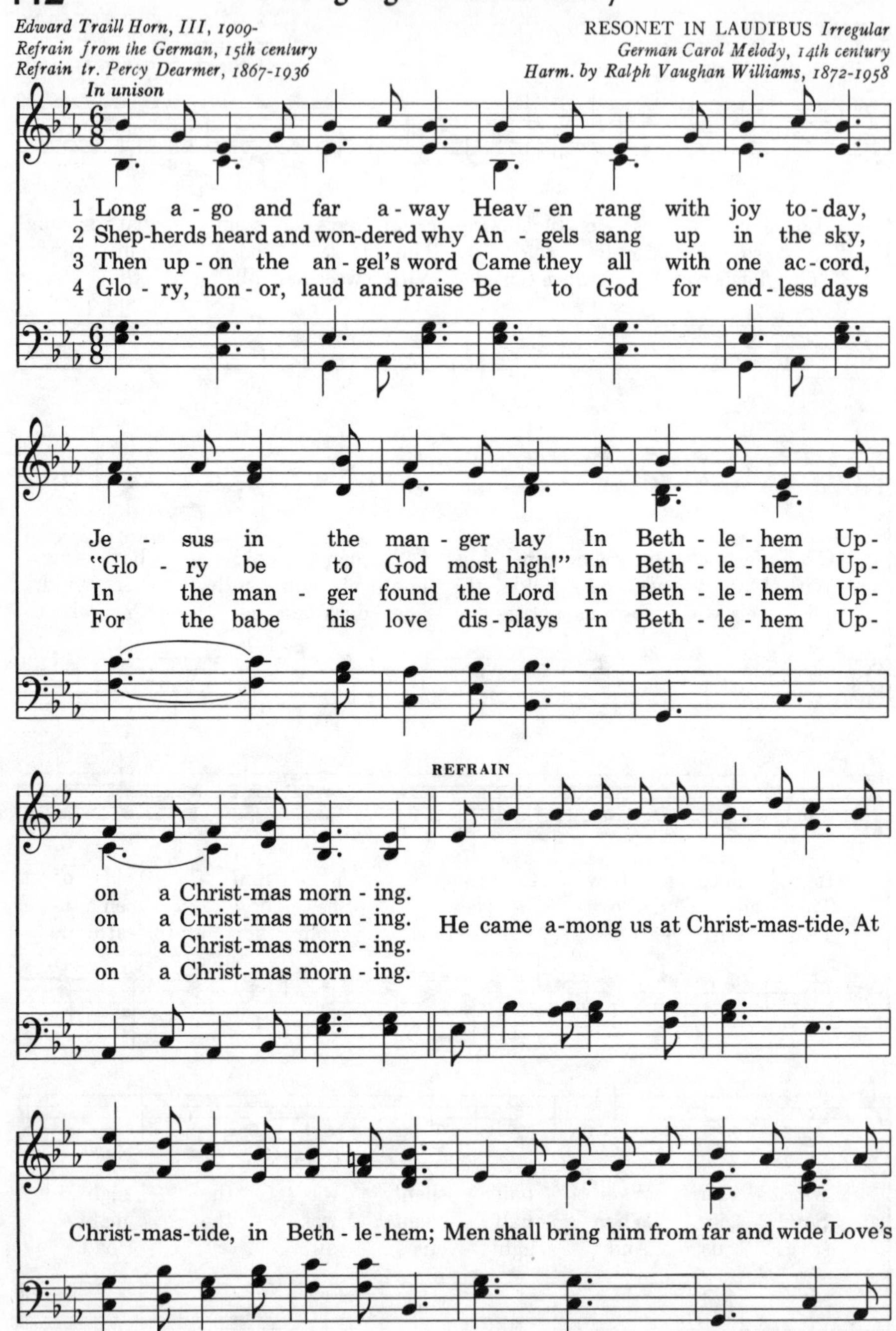

In unison
1 Long a - go and far a - way Heav - en rang with joy to - day,
2 Shep-herds heard and won-dered why An - gels sang up in the sky,
3 Then up - on the an - gel's word Came they all with one ac - cord,
4 Glo - ry, hon - or, laud and praise Be to God for end - less days
Je - sus in the man - ger lay In Beth - le - hem Up -
"Glo - ry be to God most high!" In Beth - le - hem Up -
In the man - ger found the Lord In Beth - le - hem Up -
For the babe his love dis - plays In Beth - le - hem Up -
on a Christ-mas morn - ing.
on a Christ-mas morn - ing.
on a Christ-mas morn - ing.
on a Christ-mas morn - ing.
REFRAIN
He came a-mong us at Christ-mas-tide, At
Christ-mas-tide, in Beth - le - hem; Men shall bring him from far and wide Love's

Words from *The Lutheran Service Book and Hymnal*, by permission of the Commission on the Liturgy and Hymnal. Words of refrain from *The Oxford Book of Carols* and music from *The English Hymnal* by permission of Oxford University Press.

BIRTH

di - a-dem: Je - sus, Je - sus! Lo, he comes and loves and saves and frees us.

Joy Bells Are Ringing

143

Nils Frykman, 1842-1911
Tr. E. Gustav Johnson, 1893-

JULEN ÄR INNE 5.5.6.D.
Wilhelm Theodor Söderberg, 1845-1922

1 Joy bells are ring - ing, Christ - mas is bring - ing
2 Light is as - cend - ing, Night - time is end - ing,
3 O what a treas - ure God in his pleas - ure
4 Come to the man - ger, Kin - dred and stran - ger,
5 Ban - ish all sad - ness, Fill me with glad - ness

Ti - dings of Je - sus' birth. Can - dles are gleam - ing,
Sun - shine from God ap - pears. Hope of the a - ges,
Lov - ing - ly gives to - day! Grace to the low - ly,
Hail now the new - born King! In ad - o - ra - tion,
Je - sus, whom I a - dore! All else may per - ish,

Glad - ness is stream - ing Out o - ver all the earth.
Fore - told by sag - es, Comes to dis - pel all fears.
Peace pure and ho - ly, An - gels to men con - vey.
With ju - bi - la - tion, Peo - ples and na - tions sing!
Thee will I cher - ish Now and for - ev - er - more!

144 O Thou Joyful, O Thou Wonderful

Johannes D. Falk, 1768-1826, St. 1
Anonymous, Sts. 2,3
Tr. Henry Katterjohn, 1869-1931

O SANCTISSIMA 4.5.7.6.6.7.
"Tattersall's Psalmody," 1794

1 O thou joy - ful, O thou won-der-ful Grace - re - veal - ing
2 O thou joy - ful, O thou won-der-ful Love - re - veal - ing
3 O thou joy - ful, O thou won-der-ful Peace - re - veal - ing

Christ - mas - tide! Je - sus came to win us From all sin with -
Christ - mas - tide! Loud ho - san - nas sing - ing And all prais - es
Christ - mas - tide! Dark - ness dis - ap - pear - eth, God's own light now

in us: Glo - ri - fy the ho - ly child!
bring - ing: May thy love with us a - bide.
near - eth: Peace and joy to all be - tide.

Words used by permission of the Eden Publishing House.

145 Now Shine a Thousand Candles Bright

Emmy Köhler, 1858-1925
Tr. J. Irving Erickson, 1914-
Tr. Karl A. Olsson, 1913-

CHRISTMAS CANDLES C.M.
Emmy Köhler, 1858-1925
Harm. by Norman E. Johnson, 1928-

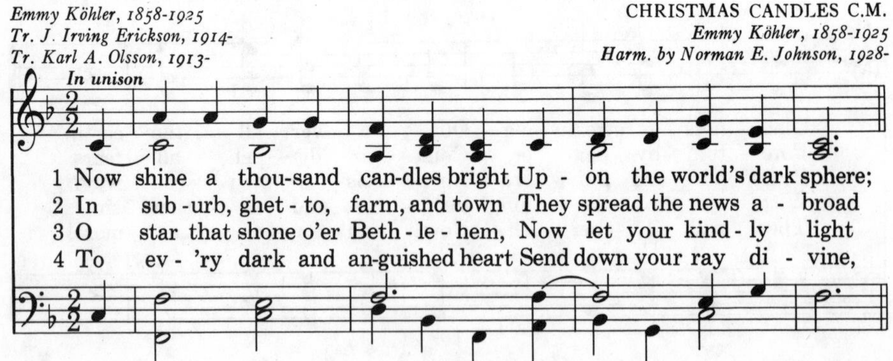
In unison
1 Now shine a thou-sand can-dles bright Up - on the world's dark sphere;
2 In sub - urb, ghet - to, farm, and town They spread the news a - broad
3 O star that shone o'er Beth - le - hem, Now let your kind - ly light
4 To ev - 'ry dark and an-guished heart Send down your ray di - vine,

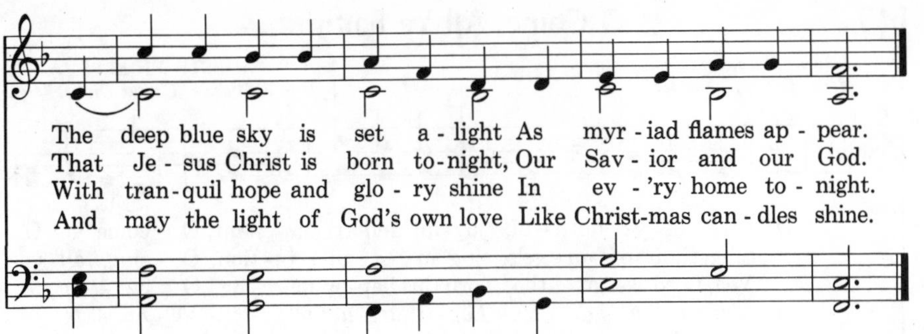
The deep blue sky is set a - light As myr - iad flames ap - pear.
That Je - sus Christ is born to-night, Our Sav - ior and our God.
With tran-quil hope and glo - ry shine In ev - 'ry home to - night.
And may the light of God's own love Like Christ-mas can - dles shine.

When Christmas Morn Is Breaking

146

Attr. to Abel Burckhardt, 19th century
Arr. by Elizabeth Ehrenborg-Posse, 1818-1880
Tr. Claude William Foss, 1855-1935, Sts. 2,3

CHRISTMAS DAWN 7.6.7.6.
German Folk Melody, 1819

1 When Christ-mas morn is break - ing, The man - ger I would seek,
2 How kind, O lov - ing Sav - ior, To come from heav'n a - bove!
3 We need thee, bless - ed Je - sus, Our dear - est friend thou art!

Where God, his throne for - sak - ing, Is rest - ing low and meek;
From sin and e - vil save us, And keep us in thy love;
For - bid that we by sin - ning Should grieve thy lov - ing heart;

Where God, his throne for - sak - ing, Is rest - ing low and meek.
From sin and e - vil save us, And keep us in thy love.
For - bid that we by sin - ning Should grieve thy lov-ing heart. A-men.

147 O Come, All Ye Faithful

Latin: John F. Wade, 1711-1786
Tr. Frederick Oakeley, 1802-1880

ADESTE FIDELES *Irregular*
John F. Wade's "Cantus Diversi," 1751

1 O come, all ye faith-ful, joy-ful and tri-um-phant, O come ye, O
2 Sing, choirs of an-gels, sing in ex-ul-ta-tion, O sing, all ye
3 Yea, Lord, we greet thee, born this hap-py morn-ing, O Je-sus, to
A-des-te fi-de-les, Lae-ti tri-um-phan-tes, Ve-ni-te, ve-
come ye to Beth-le-hem; Come and be-hold him, born the King of an-gels;
cit-i-zens of heav'n a-bove; Glo-ry to God, all glo-ry in the high-est;
thee be all glo-ry giv'n; Word of the Fa-ther, now in flesh ap-pear-ing;
ni-te in Beth-le-hem: Na-tum vi-de-te Regem an-ge-lo-rum:
REFRAIN
O come, let us a-dore him, O come, let us a-dore him,
Ve-ni-te a-do-re-mus, Ve-ni-te a-do-re-mus,
O come, let us a-dore him, Christ, the Lord. A-men.
Ve-ni-te a-do-re-mus, Do-mi-num. A-men.

O Little Town of Bethlehem

Phillips Brooks, 1835-1893

ST. LOUIS 8.6.8.6.7.6.8.6.
Lewis H. Redner, 1831-1908

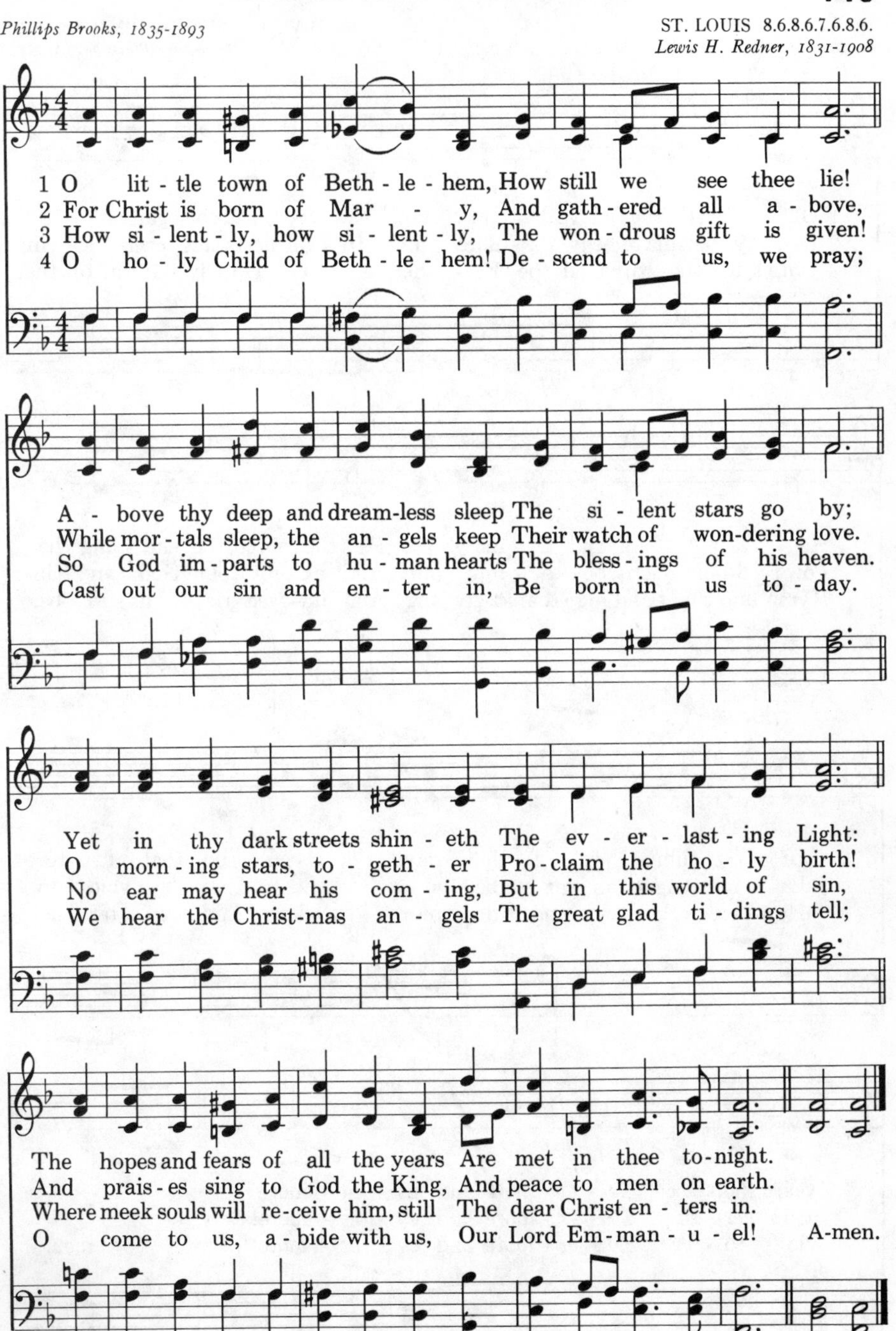

1 O lit - tle town of Beth - le - hem, How still we see thee lie!
2 For Christ is born of Mar - y, And gath - ered all a - bove,
3 How si - lent - ly, how si - lent - ly, The won - drous gift is given!
4 O ho - ly Child of Beth - le - hem! De - scend to us, we pray;
A - bove thy deep and dream-less sleep The si - lent stars go by;
While mor - tals sleep, the an - gels keep Their watch of won-dering love.
So God im - parts to hu - man hearts The bless - ings of his heaven.
Cast out our sin and en - ter in, Be born in us to - day.
Yet in thy dark streets shin - eth The ev - er - last - ing Light:
O morn - ing stars, to - geth - er Pro - claim the ho - ly birth!
No ear may hear his com - ing, But in this world of sin,
We hear the Christ-mas an - gels The great glad ti - dings tell;
The hopes and fears of all the years Are met in thee to - night.
And prais - es sing to God the King, And peace to men on earth.
Where meek souls will re - ceive him, still The dear Christ en - ters in.
O come to us, a - bide with us, Our Lord Em - man - u - el! A-men.

Alternate tune, FOREST GREEN, *No. 77*

149 Of the Father's Love Begotten

Aurelius Clemens Prudentius, 348-c.410
Tr. John M. Neale, 1818-1866, St. 1
Tr. Henry W. Baker, 1821-1877, Sts. 2,3

DIVINUM MYSTERIUM 8.7.8.7.8.7.7.
13th century Plainsong, Mode V

In unison

1 Of the Fa-ther's love be - got - ten, Ere the worlds be - gan to be,
2 O ye heights of heav'n a - dore him; An - gel hosts, his prais - es sing;
3 Christ, to thee with God the Fa - ther, And, O Ho - ly Ghost, to thee,

He is Al - pha and O - me - ga, He the source, the end - ing he,
Pow'rs, do - min - ions, bow be - fore him, And ex - tol our God and King;
Hymn and chant and high thanks-giv - ing And un - wea - ried prais - es be:

Of the things that are, that have been, And that fu - ture
Let no tongue on earth be si - lent, Ev - 'ry voice in
Hon - or, glo - ry, and do - min - ion, And e - ter - nal

years shall see, Ev - er - more and ev - er - more!
con - cert ring, Ev - er - more and ev - er - more!
vic - to - ry, Ev - er - more and ev - er - more! A - men.

BIRTH

Once in Royal David's City

150

Cecil Frances Alexander, 1818-1895

IRBY 8.7.8.7.7.7.

Henry J. Gauntlett, 1805-1876

1 Once in roy - al Da - vid's cit - y Stood a low - ly cat - tle shed, Where a moth - er laid her ba - by In a man - ger for his bed: Mar - y was that moth - er mild, Je - sus Christ her lit - tle child.
2 He came down to earth from heav-en Who is God and Lord of all, And his shel - ter was a sta - ble, And his cra - dle was a stall: With the poor and mean and low - ly, Lived on earth our Sav - ior ho - ly.
3 Je - sus is our child - hood's pat-tern, Day by day like us he grew; He was lit - tle, weak, and help - less, Tears and smiles like us he knew: And he feel - eth for our sad-ness, And he shar - eth in our glad - ness.
4 And our eyes at last shall see him, Thru his own re - deem - ing love; For that child so dear and gen - tle Is our Lord in heav'n a - bove: And he leads his chil - dren on To the place where he is gone. A - men.

151 Our Day of Joy Is Here Again

A. L. Skoog, 1856-1934

YULETIDE C.M. *with Refrain*
A. L. Skoog, 1856-1934

1 Our day of joy is here again With love and peace and song;
Come, let us join th' angelic strain With voices clear and strong.

2 When darkness lay upon this earth, A glorious light did shine;
God sent a gift of priceless worth And showed his love divine.

3 Now to the manger let us go To worship and adore
The tender babe upon the straw, Our Savior evermore.

4 How wonderful that God's own Son Should so himself abase!
He thrust the mighty from their throne And gave the lowly grace.

REFRAIN

Glory to our God, we sing, Glory to our Lord and King;
Peace, good will with all abide This holy Christmastide.

Silent Night! Holy Night!

Joseph Mohr, 1792-1848
Tr. John F. Young, 1820-1885

STILLE NACHT Irregular
Franz Gruber, 1787-1863

1 Si - lent night! ho - ly night! All is calm, all is bright 'Round yon vir - gin moth - er and child, Ho - ly in - fant, so ten - der and mild, Sleep in heav - en - ly peace, Sleep in heav - en - ly peace.
2 Si - lent night! ho - ly night! Shep - herds quake at the sight, Glo - ries stream from heav - en a - far, Heav'n - ly hosts sing al - le - lu - ia; Christ, the Sav - ior, is born! Christ, the Sav - ior, is born!
3 Si - lent night! ho - ly night! Son of God, love's pure light Ra - diant beams from thy ho - ly face, With the dawn of re - deem - ing grace, Je - sus, Lord, at thy birth, Je - sus, Lord, at thy birth.
Stil - le Nacht! hei - li - ge Nacht! Al - les schläft, ein - sam wacht Nur das trau - te, hoch - hei - li - ge Paar Hol - der Kna - be im lock - i - gen Haar, Schlaf in himm - li - scher Ruh, Schlaf in himm - li - scher Ruh!

BIRTH

153 What Child Is This, Who, Laid to Rest

William C. Dix, 1837-1898

GREENSLEEVES 8.7.8 7. *with Refrain*
English Melody
Harm. by John Stainer, 1840-1901

1 What child is this, who, laid to rest, On Mar-y's lap is sleep-ing?
Whom an-gels greet with an-thems sweet, While shep-herds watch are keep-ing?

2 Why lies he in such mean es-tate Where ox and ass are feed-ing?
Good Chris-tian, fear: for sin-ners here The si-lent Word is plead-ing.

3 So bring him in-cense, gold, and myrrh, Come peas-ant, king, to own him;
The King of kings sal-va-tion brings, Let lov-ing hearts en-throne him.

REFRAIN

This, this is Christ the King, Whom shep-herds guard and an-gels sing:
Haste, haste to bring him laud, The babe, the son of Mar-y.

While Shepherds Watched Their Flocks

Based on Luke 2:8-14
Nahum Tate, 1652-1715

WINCHESTER OLD C.M.
Thomas Este's "The Whole Book of Psalms," 1592
Based on Christopher Tye's "Acts of the Apostles," 1553
Harm. and adapted by George Kirbye, c. 1560-1634

1 While shep - herds watched their flocks by night, All seat - ed on the ground, The an - gel of the Lord came down, And glo - ry shone a - round.
2 "Fear not!" said he, for might - y dread Had seized their trou - bled mind; "Glad ti - dings of great joy I bring To you and all man - kind.
3 "To you, in Da - vid's town, this day Is born of Da - vid's line The Sav - ior, who is Christ the Lord, And this shall be the sign:
4 "The heav'n - ly babe you there shall find To hu - man view dis - played, All mean - ly wrapped in swath - ing bands, And in a man - ger laid."
5 Thus spake the ser - aph, and forth - with Ap - peared a shin - ing throng Of an - gels prais - ing God, who thus Ad - dressed their joy - ful song:

6 "All glory be to God on high,
And to the earth be peace;
Good will henceforth from heav'n to men
Begin and never cease!"

Alternate tune: CHRISTMAS, *No. 360*

155 Bright and Glorious Is the Sky

CELESTIA 7.7.8.8.7.7.

Based on Matthew 2:9
Nikolai F. S. Grundtvig, 1783-1872

Danish Melody

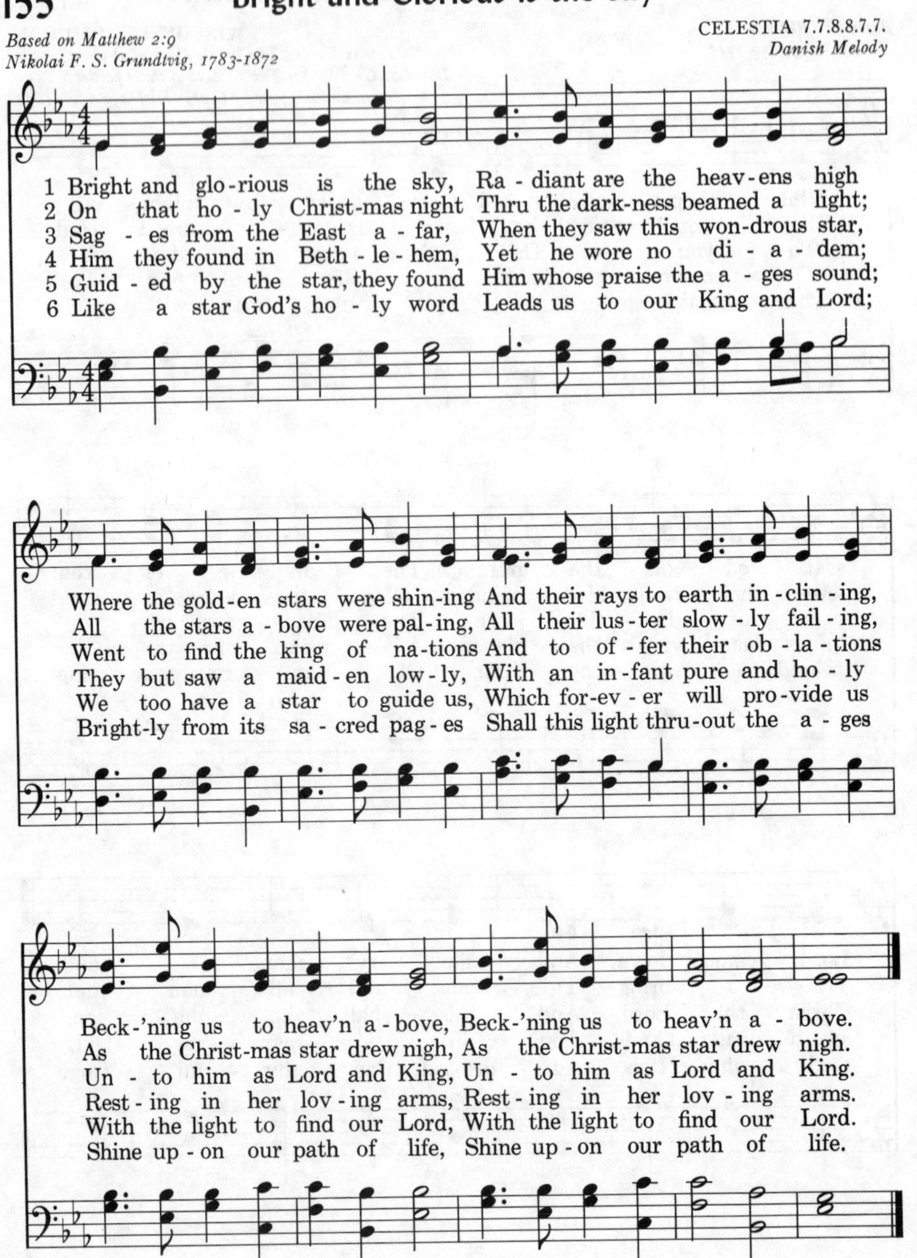

1 Bright and glo-rious is the sky, Ra-diant are the heav-ens high
2 On that ho-ly Christ-mas night Thru the dark-ness beamed a light;
3 Sag-es from the East a-far, When they saw this won-drous star,
4 Him they found in Beth-le-hem, Yet he wore no di-a-dem;
5 Guid-ed by the star, they found Him whose praise the a-ges sound;
6 Like a star God's ho-ly word Leads us to our King and Lord;
Where the gold-en stars were shin-ing And their rays to earth in-clin-ing,
All the stars a-bove were pal-ing, All their lus-ter slow-ly fail-ing,
Went to find the king of na-tions And to of-fer their ob-la-tions
They but saw a maid-en low-ly, With an in-fant pure and ho-ly
We too have a star to guide us, Which for-ev-er will pro-vide us
Bright-ly from its sa-cred pag-es Shall this light thru-out the a-ges
Beck-'ning us to heav'n a-bove, Beck-'ning us to heav'n a-bove.
As the Christ-mas star drew nigh, As the Christ-mas star drew nigh.
Un-to him as Lord and King, Un-to him as Lord and King.
Rest-ing in her lov-ing arms, Rest-ing in her lov-ing arms.
With the light to find our Lord, With the light to find our Lord.
Shine up-on our path of life, Shine up-on our path of life.

Music from *The Lutheran Service Book and Hymnal*, by permission of the Commission on the Liturgy and Hymnal.

Brightest and Best of the Sons of the Morning 156

Based on Matthew 2:11
Reginald Heber, 1783-1826

WESLEY 11.10.11.10.
Lowell Mason, 1792-1872

1 Bright - est and best of the sons of the morn - ing,
2 Cold on his cra - dle the dew - drops are shin - ing,
3 Say, shall we yield him, in cost - ly de - vo - tion,
4 Vain - ly we of - fer each am - ple ob - la - tion;
5 Bright - est and best of the sons of the morn - ing,
Dawn on our dark - ness and lend us thine aid;
Low lies his head with the beasts of the stall;
O - dors of E - dom and of - f'rings di - vine,
Vain - ly with gifts would his fa - vor se - cure;
Dawn on our dark - ness and lend us thine aid;
Star of the east, the ho - ri - zon a - dorn - ing,
An - gels a - dore him, in slum - ber re - clin - ing,
Gems of the moun - tain and pearls of the o - cean,
Rich - er by far is the heart's ad - o - ra - tion,
Star of the east, the ho - ri - zon a - dorn - ing,
Guide where our in - fant Re - deem - er is laid!
Mak - er and Mon - arch and Sav - ior of all.
Myrrh from the for - est or gold from the mine?
Dear - er to God are the prayers of the poor.
Guide where our in - fant Re - deem - er is laid!

157 O Morning Star! How Fair and Bright

Philipp Nicolai, 1556-1608
Tr. Catherine Winkworth, 1827-1878, alt.

WIE SCHÖN LEUCHTET 8.8.7.8.8.7.4.8.4.8.
Philipp Nicolai, 1556-1608
Harm. by J. S. Bach, 1685-1750

1 O Morn-ing Star! how fair and bright Thou beam-est forth in truth and light,
2 Thou heav'n-ly Bright-ness! Light di-vine! O deep with-in my heart now shine,
O Sov-'reign meek and low - ly! Thou Root of Jes - se, Da-vid's Son,
And make thee there an al - tar! Fill me with joy and strength to be
My Lord and Bride-groom, thou hast won My heart to serve thee sole - ly.
Thy mem-ber, ev - er joined to thee In love that can - not fal - ter.
Je - sus, Je - sus— Fair and glo - rious, all - vic - to - rious,
Je - sus, Je - sus— Now pos - sess me, turn and bless me!

Other harmonizations may be found at Nos. 124 and 263

Rich in bless - ing, Rule and might o'er all pos - sess - ing!
Here in sad - ness Eye and heart long for thy glad - ness! A-men.

As with Gladness Men of Old 158

William C. Dix, 1837-1898, alt.

DIX 7.7.7.7.7.7.
Adapted from a chorale by Conrad Kocher, 1786-1872

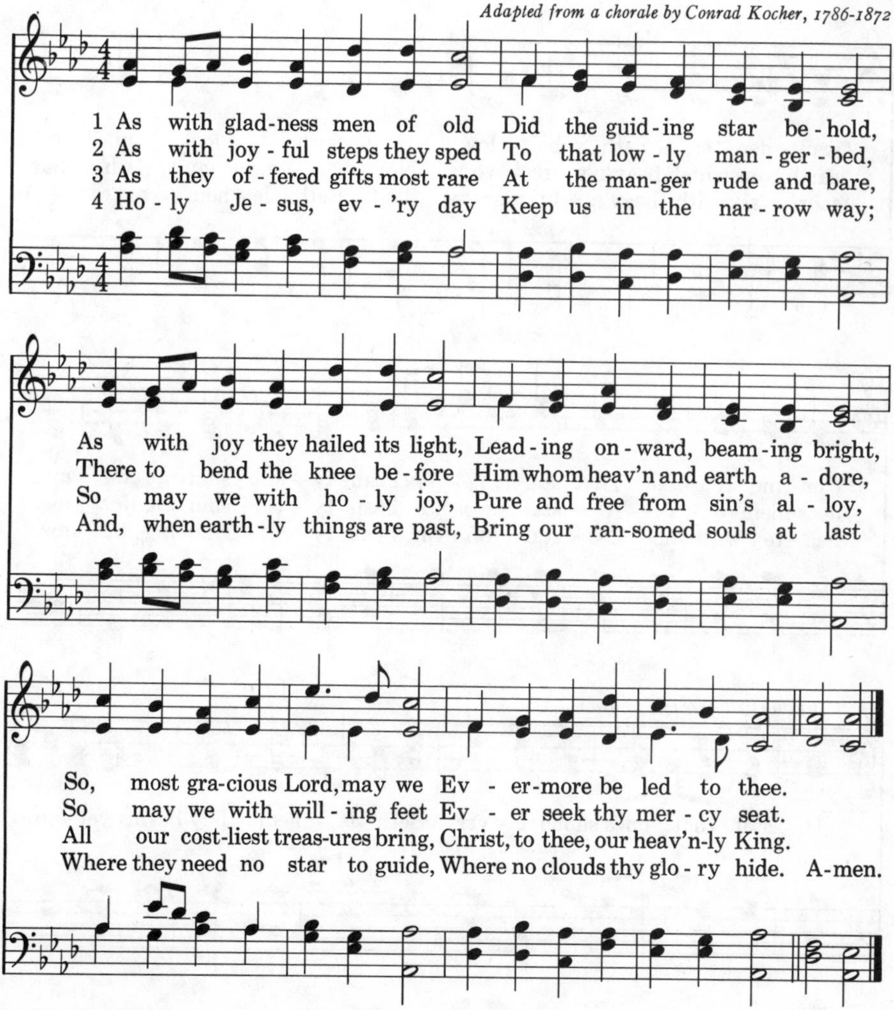

1 As with glad-ness men of old Did the guid-ing star be-hold,
2 As with joy-ful steps they sped To that low-ly man-ger-bed,
3 As they of-fered gifts most rare At the man-ger rude and bare,
4 Ho-ly Je-sus, ev-'ry day Keep us in the nar-row way;

As with joy they hailed its light, Lead-ing on-ward, beam-ing bright,
There to bend the knee be-fore Him whom heav'n and earth a-dore,
So may we with ho-ly joy, Pure and free from sin's al-loy,
And, when earth-ly things are past, Bring our ran-somed souls at last

So, most gra-cious Lord, may we Ev-er-more be led to thee.
So may we with will-ing feet Ev-er seek thy mer-cy seat.
All our cost-liest treas-ures bring, Christ, to thee, our heav'n-ly King.
Where they need no star to guide, Where no clouds thy glo-ry hide. A-men.

A lower setting may be found at No. 76

159 I Think of That Star of Long Ago

A. L. Skoog, 1856-1934

BETLEHEMS STJÄRNA 9.10.10.11. *with Refrain*
A. L. Skoog, 1856-1934

1 I think of that star of long a - go That light - ed the
2 "A child un - to us is born"– O joy! To sin-blight-ed
3 It sheds on the world its peace - ful rays, And greets ev - 'ry
wan - der - ers' path be - low; In faith I look up, and
earth comes high heav'n's en - voy; Now o - ver my path that
mor - tal with heav'n - ly grace; To Beth - le - hem's babe I
o'er me I see That star in its beau - ty— still shin - ing for me.
dear mem - o - ry— A star in its beau - ty— is shin - ing for me.
has - ten with thee, O star in thy beau - ty— still shin - ing for me.
REFRAIN (*after last stanza only*)
O star that once shone o - ver Beth - le - hem! Thy beams yet to

mor - tals great joy pro - claim; The Lord to a - dore, I
has - ten with thee, O star in thy beau - ty— still shin - ing for me.
Walk in the Light!
160
Based on I John 1:7
Bernard Barton, 1784-1849
MANOAH C.M.
Henry W. Greatorex's "Collection," 1851
1 Walk in the light! so shalt thou know That fel - low - ship of love
2 Walk in the light! and thou shalt find Thy heart made tru - ly his,
3 Walk in the light! and thou shalt own Thy dark - ness passed a - way,
4 Walk in the light! and thine shall be A path, though thorn - y, bright:
His Spir - it on - ly can be - stow, Who reigns in light a - bove.
Who dwells in cloud - less light en - shrined, In whom no dark - ness is.
Be - cause that light hath on thee shone, In which is per - fect day.
For God, by grace, shall dwell in thee, And God him - self is light.

A higher setting may be found at No. 85

161 What Star Is This, with Beams So Bright

Charles Coffin, 1676-1749
Tr. John Chandler, 1806-1876, alt.
PUER NOBIS NASCITUR L.M.
Adapted by Michael Praetorius, 1571-1621
Harm. by George R. Woodward, 1848-1934
1 What star is this, with beams so bright, More love - ly
2 'Tis now ful - filled what God de - creed, "From Ja - cob
3 O Je - sus, while the star of grace Im - pels us
4 To God the Fa - ther, heav'n - ly Light, To Christ, re -
than the noon - day light? 'Tis sent to announce a new - born
shall a star pro - ceed." And lo! the east - ern sa - ges
on to seek thy face, Let not our sloth - ful hearts re -
vealed in earth - ly night, To God the Ho - ly Ghost we
king, Glad ti - dings of our God to bring.
stand, To read in heav'n the Lord's com - mand.
fuse The guid - ance of thy light to use.
raise An end - less song of thank - ful praise! A - men.

Another harmonization may be found at No. 93

162 Immortal Love, Forever Full

John Greenleaf Whittier, 1807-1892
SERENITY C.M.
William V. Wallace, 1814-1865
1 Im - mor - tal love, for - ev - er full, For - ev - er flow - ing free, For - ev - er shared, for - ev - er whole, A nev - er - ebb - ing sea!
2 We may not climb the heav'n - ly steeps To bring the Lord Christ down; In vain we search the low - est deeps, For him no depths can drown.
3 But warm, sweet, ten - der, e - ven yet A pres - ent help is he; And faith has still its Ol - i - vet, And love its Gal - i - lee.
4 The heal - ing of his seam - less dress Is by our beds of pain; We touch him in life's throng and press, And we are whole a - gain.
5 Through him the first fond prayers are said Our lips of child - hood frame; The last low whis - pers of our dead Are bur - dened with his name.
6 O Lord and Mas - ter of us all, What - e'er our name or sign, We own thy sway, we hear thy call, We test our lives by thine. A - men.

A lower setting may be found at No. 502

Jesus of Nazareth Passes By

Anders Frostenson, 1906-
Tr. Glen V. Wiberg, 1925-

NORDQVIST 9.6.9.6.7.
Gustaf L. Nordqvist, 1886-1949

1 Je - sus of Naz - a - reth pass - es by— Now, as in an - cient time, Frees the op - pressed who for par - don cry, Giv - ing his peace sub - lime: Lo, the king - dom is near us!
2 Wealth in a - bun - dance he gives the poor, Brings to the sick re - lief; Souls that are emp - ty, in bond - age sore, Free - dom and joy re - ceive: Lo, the king - dom is near us!
3 O - pen your heart in re - pent - ant prayer, Un - lock each se - cret place; Ask him to en - ter, do not de - spair, Take of his bound - less grace: Lo, the king - dom is near us!

164 Thou Art the Way: to Thee Alone

Based on John 14:6
George W. Doane, 1799-1859

RICHMOND C.M.
Thomas Haweis, 1734-1820

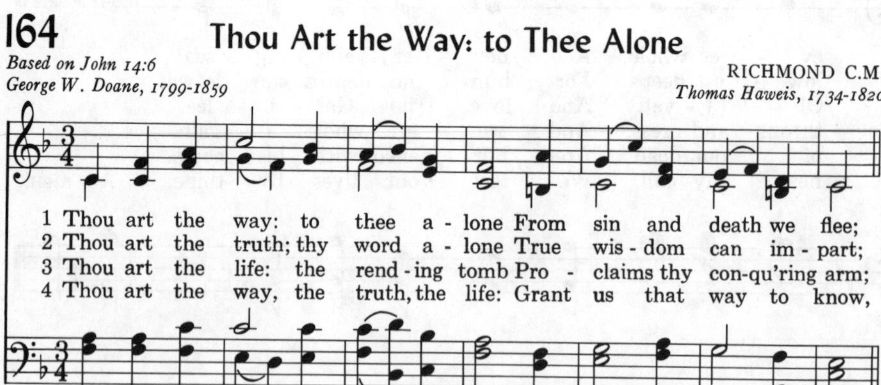
1 Thou art the way: to thee a - lone From sin and death we flee;
2 Thou art the truth; thy word a - lone True wis - dom can im - part;
3 Thou art the life: the rend - ing tomb Pro - claims thy con - qu'ring arm;
4 Thou art the way, the truth, the life: Grant us that way to know,

Another harmonization may be found at No. 471

And he who would the Fa - ther seek Must seek him, Lord, by thee.
Thou on - ly canst in - form the mind And pu - ri - fy the heart.
And those who put their trust in thee Nor death nor hell shall harm.
That truth to keep, that life to win, Whose joys e - ter - nal flow. A-men.
Strong Son of God, Immortal Love
165
Alfred Tennyson, 1809-1892
ST. CRISPIN L.M.
George J. Elvey, 1816-1893
1 Strong Son of God, im - mor - tal love, Whom we, that
2 Thou seem - est hu - man and di - vine, The high - est,
3 Our lit - tle sys - tems have their day, They have their
4 Let knowl - edge grow from more to more, But more of
have not seen thy face, By faith and faith a - lone em -
ho - liest man - hood thou; Our wills are ours— we know not
day and cease to be; They are but bro - ken lights of
rev - 'rence in us dwell, That mind and soul, ac - cord - ing
brace, Be - liev - ing where we can - not prove:
how— Our wills are ours, to make them thine.
thee, And thou, O Lord, art more than they.
well, May make one mu - sic as be - fore. A - men.

Another harmonization in a lower setting may be found at No. 91

166 My Song Is Love Unknown

Samuel Crossman, c.1624-1684
ST. JOHN 6.6.6.6.4.4.4.4.
"The Parish Choir," Vol. III, 1851
1 My song is love un - known, My Sav - ior's love to
2 He came from his blest throne Sal - va - tion to be -
3 Some - times they strew his way And his sweet prais - es
4 They rise, and needs will have My dear Lord made a -
5 Here might I stay and sing! No sto - ry so di -
me, Love to the love - less shown That they might love - ly
stow; But men made strange, and none The longed - for Christ would
sing, Re - sound - ing all the day Ho - san - nas to their
way; A mur - der - er they save, The Prince of life they
vine! Nev - er was love, dear King, Nev - er was grief like
be: O who am I, That for my sake My
know: But O my Friend, My Friend in - deed, Who
King: Then 'Cru - ci - fy!' Is all their breath, And
slay: Yet cheer - ful he To suf - f'ring goes, That
thine! This is my Friend, In whose sweet praise I
Lord should take Frail flesh and die?
at my need His life did spend!
for his death They thirst and cry.
he his foes From thence might free.
all my days Could glad - ly spend. A - men.

Thine Arm, O Lord, in Days of Old

Edward H. Plumptre, 1821-1891

FOREST GREEN C.M.D.
English Melody
Harm. by Ralph Vaughan Williams, 1872-1958

1 Thine arm, O Lord, in days of old Was strong to heal and save;
2 And lo, thy touch brought life and health, Gave speech and strength and sight;
3 Be thou our great de - liv - 'rer still, Thou Lord of life and death;

It tri-umphed o'er dis - ease and death, O'er dark - ness and the grave.
And youth re-newed and fren - zy calmed Owned thee the Lord of light.
Re - store and quick-en, soothe and bless With thine al - might-y breath.

To thee they went–the blind, the dumb, The pal - sied and the lame,
And now, O Lord, be near to bless, Al - might - y as of yore,
To hands that work and eyes that see, Give wis-dom's heav'n-ly lore,

The lep - er with his taint-ed life, The sick with fe-vered frame.
In crowd-ed street, by rest - less couch, As by Gen-nes-'ret's shore.
That whole and sick, and weak and strong, May praise thee ev - er - more. A-men.

168 O Love, How Deep, How Broad, How High

Latin: 15th century
Tr. Benjamin Webb, 1819-1885, alt.

AGINCOURT L.M.
"The Agincourt Song," 15th century

In unison
1 O love, how deep, how broad, how high, How pass - ing
2 For us bap - tized, for us he bore His ho - ly
3 For us he prayed, for us he taught, For us his
4 For us to wick - ed men be - trayed, Scourged, mocked, in
thought and fan - ta - sy, That God, the Son of God, should
fast, and hun-gered sore; For us temp - ta - tions sharp he
dai - ly works he wrought, By words and signs and ac - tions,
pur - ple robe ar - rayed, He bore the shame-ful cross and
take Our mor - tal form for mor - tals' sake.
knew, For us the temp - ter o - ver - threw.
thus Still seek - ing not him - self, but us.
death, For us gave up his dy - ing breath. A - men.

5 For us he rose from death again,
For us he went on high to reign;
For us he sent his Spirit here
To guide, to strengthen, and to cheer.

6 All glory to our Lord and God
For love so deep, so high, so broad:
The Trinity, whom we adore
For ever and for evermore. Amen.

Alternate tune: CANONBURY, *No. 534*

O Wondrous Type, O Vision Fair

Latin: 15th century
Tr. John M. Neale, 1818-1866

AGINCOURT L.M.
"The Agincourt Song," 15th century

1 O wondrous type, O vision fair
Of glory that the Church shall share,
Which Christ upon the mountain shows,
Where brighter than the sun he glows.

2 With shining face and bright array,
Christ deigns to manifest today
What glory shall be theirs above
Who joy in God with perfect love.

3 And faithful hearts are raised on high
By this great vision's mystery,
For which in joyful strains we raise
The voice of prayer, the hymn of praise.

4 O Father, with th' eternal Son,
And Holy Spirit, ever one,
Vouchsafe to bring us by thy grace
To see thy glory face to face. Amen.

A Workman in a Village Home

Author unknown, c.1930

MORNING SONG 8.6.8.6.8.6.
Wyeth's "Repository of Sacred Music, Part Second," 1813
Harm. by Austin C. Lovelace, 1919-

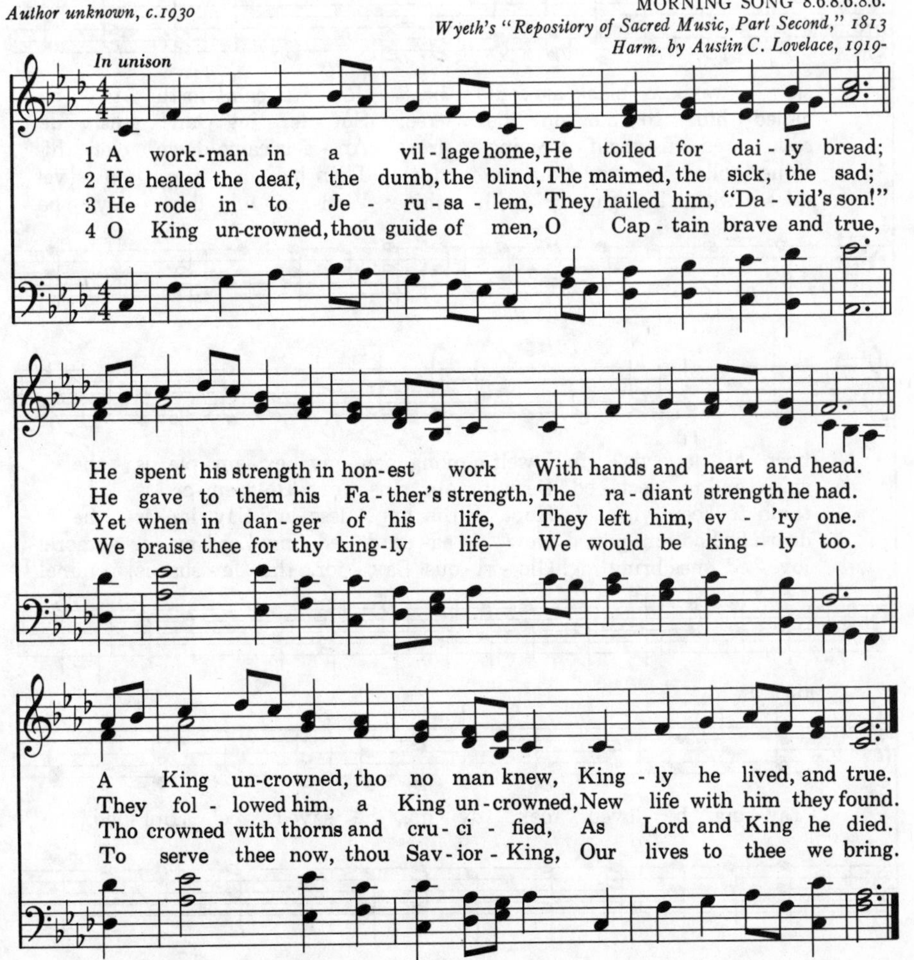

In unison
1 A work-man in a vil-lage home, He toiled for dai-ly bread;
2 He healed the deaf, the dumb, the blind, The maimed, the sick, the sad;
3 He rode in-to Je-ru-sa-lem, They hailed him, "Da-vid's son!"
4 O King un-crowned, thou guide of men, O Cap-tain brave and true,
He spent his strength in hon-est work With hands and heart and head.
He gave to them his Fa-ther's strength, The ra-diant strength he had.
Yet when in dan-ger of his life, They left him, ev-'ry one.
We praise thee for thy king-ly life— We would be king-ly too.
A King un-crowned, tho no man knew, King-ly he lived, and true.
They fol-lowed him, a King un-crowned, New life with him they found.
Tho crowned with thorns and cru-ci-fied, As Lord and King he died.
To serve thee now, thou Sav-ior-King, Our lives to thee we bring.

171 One Day!

J. Wilbur Chapman, 1859-1918

ONE DAY 11.10.11.10. with Refrain
Charles H. Marsh, 1886-1956

1 One day when heav - en was filled with his prais - es, One day when
2 One day they led him up Cal - va - ry's moun - tain, One day they
3 One day they left him a - lone in the gar - den, One day he
4 One day the grave could con - ceal him no long - er, One day the
5 One day the trum - pet will sound for his com - ing, One day the
sin was as black as could be, Je - sus came forth to be
nailed him to die on the tree; Suf - fer - ing an - guish, de -
rest - ed, from suf - fer - ing free; An - gels came down o'er his
stone rolled a - way from the door; Then he a - rose, o - ver
skies with his glo - ry will shine; Won - der - ful day, my be -
born of a vir - gin, Dwelt a - mong men—my ex - am - ple is he!
spised and re - ject - ed, Bear - ing our sins, my Re - deem - er is he!
tomb to keep vig - il—Hope of the hope - less, my Sav - ior is he!
death he had con - quered, Now is as - cend - ed, my Lord ev - er - more!
lov - ed ones bring - ing! Glo - ri - ous Sav - ior, this Je - sus is mine!
REFRAIN
Liv - ing, he loved me! dy - ing, he saved me! Bur - ied, he

car - ried my sins far a - way! Ris - ing, he jus - ti - fied
free - ly, for - ev - er! One day he's com - ing — O glo - ri - ous day!

'Tis Good, Lord, to Be Here! 172

SWABIA S.M.

Based on Luke 9:32, 33
Joseph A. Robinson, 1858-1933

Johann Martin Spiess, 1715-c.1766

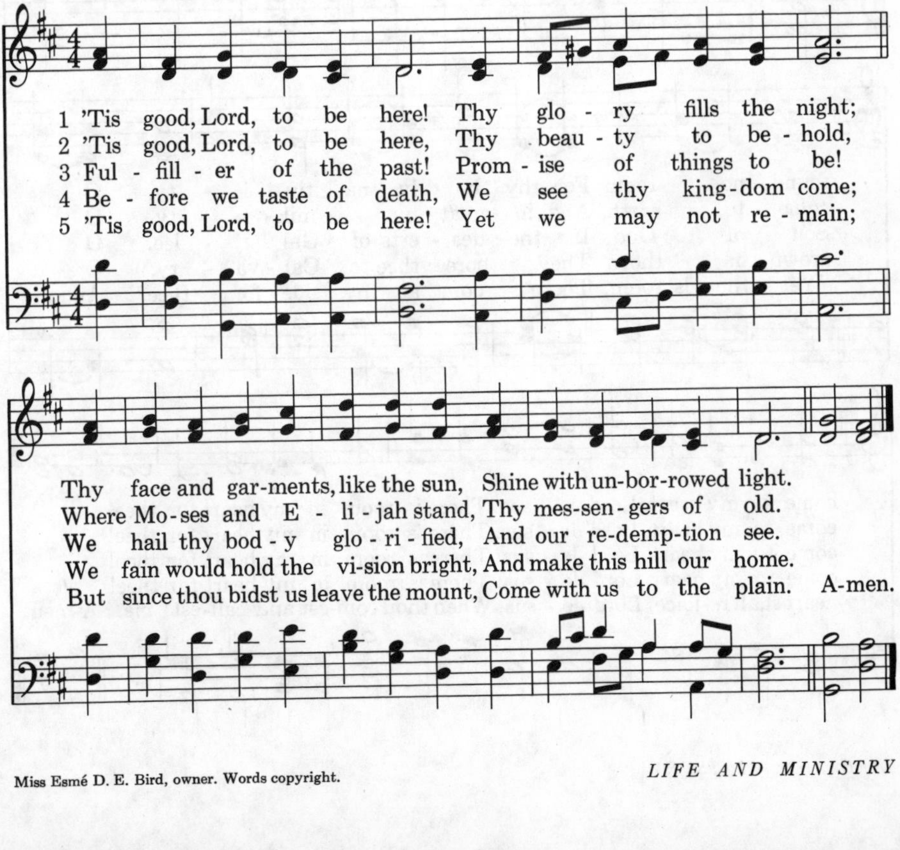

1 'Tis good, Lord, to be here! Thy glo - ry fills the night;
Thy face and gar - ments, like the sun, Shine with un - bor - rowed light.

2 'Tis good, Lord, to be here, Thy beau - ty to be - hold,
Where Mo - ses and E - li - jah stand, Thy mes - sen - gers of old.

3 Ful - fill - er of the past! Prom - ise of things to be!
We hail thy bod - y glo - ri - fied, And our re - demp - tion see.

4 Be - fore we taste of death, We see thy king - dom come;
We fain would hold the vi - sion bright, And make this hill our home.

5 'Tis good, Lord, to be here! Yet we may not re - main;
But since thou bidst us leave the mount, Come with us to the plain. A - men.

173 Thou Didst Leave Thy Throne

Emily E. S. Elliott, 1836-1897, alt.

MARGARET *Irregular*
Timothy R. Matthews, 1826-1910

1 Thou didst leave thy throne and thy king - ly crown When thou
2 Heav-en's arch - es rang when the an - gels sang, Pro -
3 The fox - es found rest, and the birds their nest In the
4 Thou cam - est, O Lord, with the liv - ing word That should
5 When the heav'ns shall ring and the an - gels sing At thy
cam - est to earth for me, But in Beth - le-hem's home there was
claim-ing thy roy - al de - gree, But in low - ly birth didst thou
shade of the for - est tree, But thy couch was the sod, O thou
set thy peo - ple free, But with mock - ing scorn and with
com - ing to vic - to - ry, Let thy voice call me home, say - ing,
found no room For thy ho - ly na - tiv - i - ty. O
come to earth, And in great hu - mil - i - ty. O
Son of God, In the des - erts of Gal - i - lee. O
crown of thorn They bore thee to Cal - va - ry. O
"Yet there is room, There is room at my side for thee." And my
come to my heart, Lord Je - sus: There is room in my heart for thee!
come to my heart, Lord Je - sus: There is room in my heart for thee!
come to my heart, Lord Je - sus: There is room in my heart for thee!
come to my heart, Lord Je - sus: There is room in my heart for thee!
heart shall re-joice, Lord Je - sus, When thou com-est and call-est me. A-men.

We Would See Jesus: Lo! His Star Is Shining

J. Edgar Park, 1879-1956

SAYRE 11.10.11.10.
Paul F. Liljestrand, 1931-

1 We would see Je - sus: lo! his star is shin - ing
2 We would see Je - sus: Mar - y's Son most ho - ly,
3 We would see Je - sus: on the moun-tain teach - ing,
4 We would see Je - sus: in his work of heal - ing,
5 We would see Je - sus: in the ear - ly morn - ing
A - bove the sta - ble while the an - gels sing;
Light of the vil - lage life from day to day;
With all the lis - t'ning peo - ple gath - ered round;
At ev - en - tide be - fore the sun was set;
Still as of old he call - eth, "Fol - low me!"
There in a man - ger on the hay re - clin - ing,
Shin - ing re - vealed through ev - 'ry task most low - ly,
While birds and flow'rs and sky a - bove are preach - ing
Di - vine and hu - man, in his deep re - veal - ing
Let us a - rise, all mean - er serv - ice scorn - ing:
Haste, let us lay our gifts be - fore the King.
The Christ of God, the Life, the Truth, the Way.
The bless - ed - ness which sim - ple trust has found.
Of God and man in lov - ing serv - ice met.
Lord, we are thine, we give our - selves to thee!

Words from *New Worship and Song.* Copyright by The Pilgrim Press.

175 O Master Workman of the Race

Jay T. Stocking, 1870-1936
KINGSFOLD C.M.D.
English Melody
Harm. by Ralph Vaughan Williams, 1872-1958
1 O Mas-ter Work-man of the race, Thou Man of Gal-i-lee,
2 O Car-pen-ter of Naz-a-reth, Build-er of life di-vine,
3 O thou who didst the vi-sion send And gives to each his task,
Who with the eyes of ear-ly youth E-ter-nal things did see,
Who shap-est man to God's own law, Thy-self the fair de-sign,
And with the task suf-fi-cient strength, Show us thy will, we ask.
We thank thee for thy boy-hood faith That shone thy whole life through;
Build us a tower of Christ-like height, That we the land may view,
Give us a con-science bold and good, Give us a pur-pose true,
"Did ye not know it is my work My Fa-ther's work to do?"
And see like thee our no-blest work Our Fa-ther's work to do.
That it may be our high-est joy Our Fa-ther's work to do. A-men.

O Sing a Song of Bethlehem

Louis F. Benson, 1855-1930

KINGSFOLD C.M.D.
English Melody
Harm. by Ralph Vaughan Williams, 1872-1958

1 O sing a song of Bethlehem,
Of shepherds watching there,
And of the news that came to them
From angels in the air:
The light that shone on Bethlehem
Fills all the world today;
Of Jesus' birth and peace on earth
The angels sing alway.

2 O sing a song of Nazareth,
Of sunny days of joy,
O sing of fragrant flowers' breath,
And of the sinless boy:
For now the flow'rs of Nazareth
In ev'ry heart may grow;
Now spreads the fame of his dear name
On all the winds that blow.

3 O sing a song of Galilee,
Of lake and woods and hill,
Of him who walked upon the sea
And bade its waves be still:
For though, like waves on Galilee,
Dark seas of trouble roll,
When faith has heard the Master's word,
Falls peace upon the soul.

4 O sing a song of Calvary,
Its glory and dismay;
Of him who hung upon the tree
And took our sins away:
For he who died on Calvary
Is risen from the grave,
And Christ, our Lord, by heav'n adored,
Is mighty now to save.

He Came to Ghettoed Lives of Men

Ralph S. Carlson, 1946-

BELMONT C.M.
William Gardiner's "Sacred Melodies," 1812

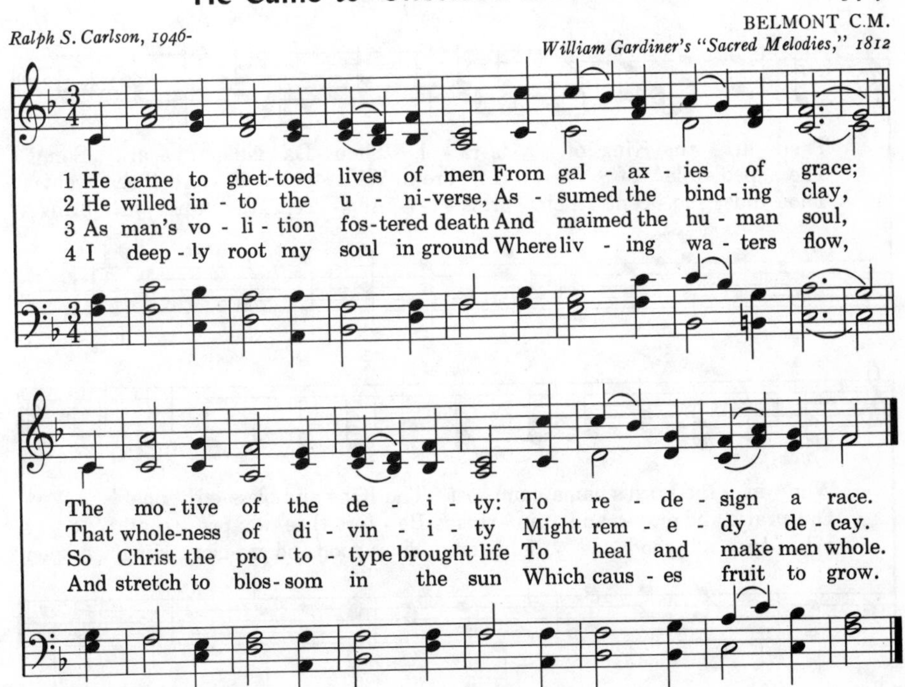
1 He came to ghet-toed lives of men From gal - ax - ies of grace;
2 He willed in - to the u - ni-verse, As - sumed the bind - ing clay,
3 As man's vo - li - tion fos-tered death And maimed the hu - man soul,
4 I deep - ly root my soul in ground Where liv - ing wa - ters flow,
The mo - tive of the de - i - ty: To re - de - sign a race.
That whole-ness of di - vin - i - ty Might rem - e - dy de - cay.
So Christ the pro - to - type brought life To heal and make men whole.
And stretch to blos - som in the sun Which caus - es fruit to grow.

A higher setting may be found at No. 59

178 All Glory, Laud, and Honor

Theodulph of Orleans, c.760-c.821
Tr. John M. Neale, 1818-1866

ST. THEODULPH 7.6.7.6.D.
Melchior Teschner, 1584-1635

1 All glo - ry, laud, and hon - or To thee, Re - deem - er, King,
2 The com - pa - ny of an - gels Are prais - ing thee on high,
3 To thee, be - fore thy pas - sion, They sang their hymns of praise;
To whom the lips of chil - dren Made sweet ho - san - nas ring:
And mor - tal men and all things Cre - at - ed make re - ply:
To thee, now high ex - alt - ed, Our mel - o - dy we raise:
Thou art the King of Is - ra - el, Thou Da - vid's roy - al Son,
The peo - ple of the He - brews With palms be - fore thee went;
Thou didst ac - cept their prais - es— Ac - cept the praise we bring,
Who in the Lord's name com - est, The King and bless - ed one!
Our praise and prayer and an - thems Be - fore thee we pre - sent.
Who in all good de - light - est, Thou good and gra - cious King! A - men.

TRIUMPHAL ENTRY

Optional free accompaniment
and descant for stanza 3
A. Royce Eckhardt, 1937-
3 Be - fore thy pas - sion they sang their hymns of praise;
Now high ex - alt - ed, our mel - o - dy we raise.
Ac - cept their prais - es; ac - cept the praise we bring,
Who in all good de - light - est, Thou good and gra - cious King. A - men.

TRIUMPHAL ENTRY

179 Ride On! Ride On in Majesty!

First Tune

Based on Matthew 21:5-11
Henry Hart Milman, 1791-1868, alt.

WINCHESTER NEW L.M.
Adapted from "Musikalisches Handbuch," Hamburg, 1690

1 Ride on! ride on in maj - es - ty! Hark! all the tribes ho - san - na cry; Thy hum - ble beast pur - sues his road With palms and scat - tered gar - ments strowed.
2 Ride on! ride on in maj - es - ty! In low - ly pomp ride on to die: O Christ, thy tri - umphs now be - gin O'er cap - tive death and con - quered sin.
3 Ride on! ride on in maj - es - ty! The an - gel ar - mies of the sky Look down with sad and won - d'ring eyes To see th' ap - proach - ing sac - ri - fice.
4 Ride on! ride on in maj - es - ty! Thy last and fierc - est strife is nigh; The Fa - ther on his sap - phire throne Ex - pects his own a - noint - ed Son. A - men.

5 Ride on! ride on in majesty!
In lowly pomp ride on to die;
Bow thy meek head to mortal pain,
Then take, O God, thy pow'r, and reign. **Amen.**

TRIUMPHAL ENTRY

Alternate tunes: OLD 100TH, *No. 4;*
TRURO, *No. 113*

Ride On! Ride On in Majesty! 180

Second Tune
Based on Matthew 21:5-11
Henry Hart Milman, 1791-1868, alt.
THE KING'S MAJESTY L.M.
Graham George, 1912-
1 Ride on! ride on in maj - es - ty! Hark! all the
2 Ride on! ride on in maj - es - ty! In low - ly
3 Ride on! ride on in maj - es - ty! The an - gel
4 Ride on! ride on in maj - es - ty! Thy last and
5 Ride on! ride on in maj - es - ty! In low - ly
tribes ho - san - na cry; Thy hum - ble beast pur - sues his
pomp ride on to die: O Christ, thy tri - umphs now be -
ar - mies of the sky Look down with sad and won - d'ring
fierc - est strife is nigh; The Fa - ther on his sap - phire
pomp ride on to die; Bow thy meek head to mor - tal
road With palms and scat - tered gar - ments strowed.
gin O'er cap - tive death and con - quered sin.
eyes To see th' ap - proach - ing sac - ri - fice.
throne Ex - pects his own a - noint - ed Son.
pain, Then take, O God, thy pow'r, and reign. A - men.

TRIUMPHAL ENTRY

181 Draw Nigh to Thy Jerusalem

Jeremy Taylor, 1613-1667, alt.

TOULON 10.10.10.10.
Adapted from "Genevan Psalter," 1551

1 Draw nigh to thy Je - ru - sa - lem, O Lord,
2 Thy road is read - y; and thy paths, made straight,
3 Ho - san - na! wel - come to our hearts! for here
Thy faith - ful peo - ple cry with one ac - cord;
With long - ing ex - pec - ta - tion seem to wait
Thou hast a tem - ple too, as Zi - on dear;
Ride on in tri - umph, Lord; be - hold we lay
The con - se - cra - tion of thy beau - teous feet,
O en - ter in, dear Lord! un - bar the door,
Our pas - sions, lusts, and proud wills in thy way!
And si - lent - ly thy prom - ised ad - vent greet!
And in that tem - ple dwell for - ev - er - more. A - men.

TRIUMPHAL ENTRY

A higher setting may be found at No. 87

From Bethany, the Master Comes

Marion Franklin Ham, 1867-1956

PASSION CHORALE 7.6.7.6.D.
Hans Leo Hassler, 1564-1612

1 From Beth - a - ny, the Mas - ter Comes down Mount Ol - ive's slope,
2 The King of love in tri - umph Rides thru the cit - y's gate,
3 Not of this world his king - dom–His pow'r is from a - bove,
And all the world is sing - ing A glad new song of hope;
Re - ject - ed, scorned, yet vic - tor—The con - quer - or of hate;
His reign is of the spir - it, His scep - ter, truth and love;
Cry out, O state - ly ce - dars A - long the rug - ged way!
O wave your green palm branch - es! Ex - tol his match-less worth!
He calls us to his serv - ice, His ban - ner is un - furled:
Ye vine-yards, shout ho - san - nas To greet this hap - py day!
This low - ly King shall con - quer The na - tions of the earth!
With thee we march, O Mas - ter, To o - ver-come the world!

Words by Marion Franklin Ham from *Hymns of the Spirit*. Used by permission of Beacon Press, publisher.

Another harmonization may be found at No. 117
Alternate tune: ST.THEODULPH, *No. 178*

TRIUMPHAL ENTRY

183 Hosanna, Loud Hosanna

Based on Matthew 21:15, 16
Jennette Threlfall, 1821-1880
ELLACOMBE 7.6.7.6.D.
"Gesangbuch der Herzogl," Wirtemberg, 1784
1 Ho - san - na, loud ho - san - na, The lit - tle chil-dren sang;
2 From Ol - i - vet they fol - lowed Mid an ex - ult - ant crowd,
3 "Ho - san - na in the high - est!" That an - cient song we sing,
Thru pil - lared court and tem - ple The love - ly an - them rang:
The vic - tor palm branch wav - ing, And chant - ing clear and loud;
For Christ is our Re - deem - er, The Lord of heav'n our King;
To Je - sus, who had blessed them Close fold - ed to his breast,
The Lord of men and an - gels Rode on in low - ly state,
O may we ev - er praise him With heart and life and voice,
The chil - dren sang their prais - es, The sim - plest and the best.
Nor scorned that lit - tle chil - dren Should on his bid - ding wait.
And in his bliss - ful pres - ence E - ter - nal - ly re - joice!

TRIUMPHAL ENTRY

A higher setting may be found at No. 80

Ride On, Ride On, O Savior-King

C. K. Solberg, 1872-1954

ALL SAINTS NEW C.M.D.
Henry S. Cutler, 1824-1902

1 Ride on, ride on, O Sav - ior-King, To set the sin - ner free!
2 Ride on, ride on, O Sav - ior-King, To claim the hearts of men!
3 Ride on, ride on, O Sav - ior-King! Ride on o'er land and sea,
To sin-cursed souls sal - va - tion bring And peace e - ter - nal - ly!
Now death has lost its dread - ful sting And hope is born a - gain.
For thou a - lone to man can bring E - ter - nal lib - er - ty.
Ride on to dark Geth - sem - a - ne, To un-told ag - o - ny,
O come, in hu-man hearts to reign, Sup - press the pow'r of sin!
Ride on to sin-bound na-tions, Lord, Un - til each heart shall own
And on the cross of Cal - va - ry Pro - cure our vic - to - ry!
Our own en-deav-or is in vain, Lord, thou must help us win!
Thy sav - ing, sanc - ti - fy - ing word And bow be - fore thy throne! A-men.

TRIUMPHAL ENTRY

185 Ah, Holy Jesus, How Hast Thou Offended

Johann Heermann, 1585-1647
Tr. Robert S. Bridges, 1844-1930

HERZLIEBSTER JESU 11.11.11.5.
Johann Crüger, 1598-1662

1 Ah, ho - ly Je - sus, how hast thou of - fend - ed,
2 Who was the guilt - y? who brought this up - on thee?
3 Lo, the good Shep - herd for the sheep is of - fered;
4 For me, kind Je - sus, was thy in - car - na - tion,
5 There - fore, kind Je - sus, since I can - not pay thee,
That man to judge thee hath in hate pre - tend - ed? By foes de -
A - las, my trea - son, Je - sus, hath un - done thee! 'Twas I, Lord
The slave hath sin - ned, and the Son hath suf - fered; For man's a -
Thy mor - tal sor - row and thy life's ob - la - tion; Thy death of
I do a - dore thee, and will ev - er pray thee, Think on thy
rid - ed, by thine own re - ject - ed, O most af - flict - ed!
Je - sus, I it was de - nied thee, I cru - ci - fied thee.
tone - ment, while he noth - ing heed - eth, God in - ter - ced - eth.
an - guish and thy bit - ter pas - sion For my sal - va - tion.
pit - y and thy love un - swerv - ing, Not my de - serv - ing. A - men.

Alas! and Did My Savior Bleed

Isaac Watts, 1674-1748

MARTYRDOM C.M.
Hugh Wilson, 1764-1824

1 A - las! and did my Sav - ior bleed And
2 Was it for sins that I have done He
3 Well might the sun in dark - ness hide And
4 Thus might I hide my blush - ing face While
5 But drops of grief can ne'er re - pay The
did my sov - ereign die? Would he de - vote that
suf - fered on the tree? A - maz - ing pit - y!
shut his glo - ries in, When Christ, the great Re -
his dear cross ap - pears, Dis - solve my heart in
debt of love I owe: Here, Lord, I give my -
sa - cred head For sin - ners such as I?
grace un - known! And love be - yond de - gree!
deem - er, died For man the crea - ture's sin.
thank - ful - ness, And melt mine eyes to tears.
self a - way— 'Tis all that I can do. A - men.

187 Beneath the Cross of Jesus

Elizabeth C. Clephane, 1830-1869

ST. CHRISTOPHER 7.6.8.6.8.6.8.6.
Frederick C. Maker, 1844-1927

1 Be - neath the cross of Je - sus I fain would take my stand:
2 Up - on that cross of Je - sus Mine eye at times can see
3 I take, O cross, thy shad - ow For my a - bid - ing place;
The shad - ow of a might - y rock With - in a wea - ry land,
The ver - y dy - ing form of one Who suf - fered there for me;
I ask no oth - er sun-shine than The sun - shine of his face,
A home with-in the wil - der - ness, A rest up - on the way,
And from my smit - ten heart, with tears, Two won - ders I con - fess—
Con - tent to let the world go by, To know no gain nor loss,
From the burn - ing of the noon-tide heat And the bur - den of the day.
The won - ders of his glo - rious love And my un - wor - thi - ness.
My sin - ful self my on - ly shame, My glo - ry all the cross.

PASSION

Come to Calvary's Holy Mountain 188

James Montgomery, 1771-1854

HOLY MOUNTAIN 8.7.8.7.7.7.
Ludvig M. Lindeman, 1812-1887

1 Come to Cal - v'ry's ho - ly moun - tain, Sin - ners ru - ined
2 Come in pov - er - ty and mean - ness, Come de - filed, with-
3 Come in sor - row and con - tri - tion, Wound - ed, im - po -
4 He that drinks shall live for - ev - er— 'Tis a soul - re -
by the fall; Here a pure and heal - ing foun - tain
out, with - in; From in - fec - tion and un - clean - ness,
tent, and blind; Here the guilt - y free re - mis - sion,
new - ing flood; God is faith - ful, God will nev - er
Flows to you, to me, to all, In a full, per -
From the lep - ro - sy of sin, Wash your robes and
Here the trou - bled peace may find: Health this foun - tain
Break his cov - e - nant of blood, Signed when our Re -
pet - ual tide, O - pened when our Sav - ior died.
make them white: Ye shall walk with God in light.
will re - store; He that drinks shall thirst no more.
deem - er died, Sealed when he was glo - ri - fied.

189
Cross of Jesus, Cross of Sorrow
William J. S. Simpson, 1860-1952
CROSS OF JESUS 8.7.8.7.
John Stainer, 1840-1901
1 Cross of Je - sus, cross of sor - row,
2 Here the King of all the a - ges,
3 Ev - er - more for hu - man fail - ure
4 Cross of Je - sus, cross of sor - row,
Where the blood of Christ was shed, Per - fect man on
Throned in light ere worlds could be, Robed in mor - tal
By his pas - sion we can plead; God has borne all
Where the blood of Christ was shed, Per - fect man on
thee did suf - fer, Per - fect God on thee has bled!
flesh, is dy - ing, Cru - ci - fied by sin for me.
mor - tal an - guish, Sure - ly he will know our need.
thee did suf - fer, Per - fect God on thee has bled! A - men.
190
In the Cross of Christ I Glory
John Bowring, 1792-1872
RATHBUN 8.7.8.7.
Ithamar Conkey, 1815-1867
1 In the cross of Christ I glo - ry, Tow'r-ing o'er the wrecks of time;
2 When the woes of life o'er-take me, Hopes de-ceive and fears an-noy,
3 When the sun of bliss is beam-ing Light and love up - on my way,
4 Bane and bless-ing, pain and pleas-ure, By the cross are sanc - ti - fied;
5 In the cross of Christ I glo - ry, Tow'r-ing o'er the wrecks of time;
PASSION

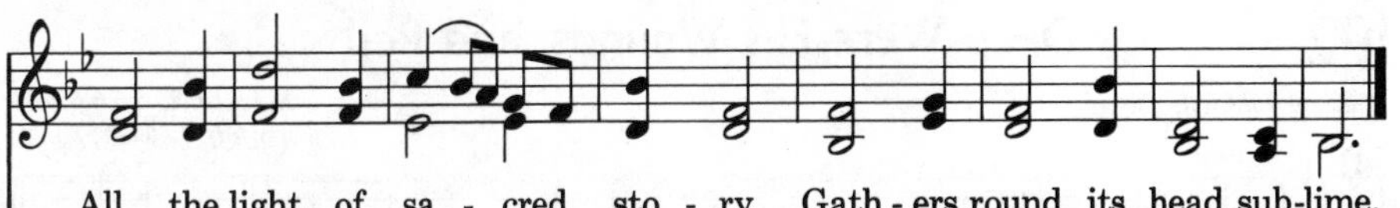

All the light of sa - cred sto - ry Gath - ers round its head sub-lime.
Nev - er shall the cross for - sake me: Lo! it glows with peace and joy.
From the cross the ra - diance stream-ing Adds more lus - ter to the day.
Peace is there that knows no meas - ure, Joys that thru all time a - bide.
All the light of sa - cred sto - ry Gath - ers round its head sub-lime.

Go to Dark Gethsemane

191

James Montgomery, 1771-1854

REDHEAD NO. 76 7.7.7.7.7.7.
Richard Redhead, 1820-1901

1 Go to dark Geth - sem - a - ne, Ye that feel the temp-ter's pow'r;
2 Fol - low to the judg - ment hall, View the Lord of life ar - raigned;
3 Cal - v'ry's mourn-ful moun - tain climb; There, a - dor - ing at his feet,

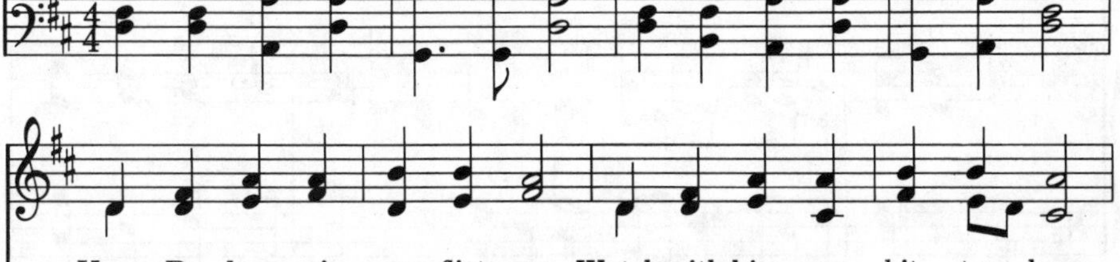

Your Re - deem - er's con - flict see, Watch with him one bit - ter hour:
O the worm-wood and the gall! O the pangs his soul sus - tained!
Mark the mir - a - cle of time, God's own sac - ri - fice com - plete:

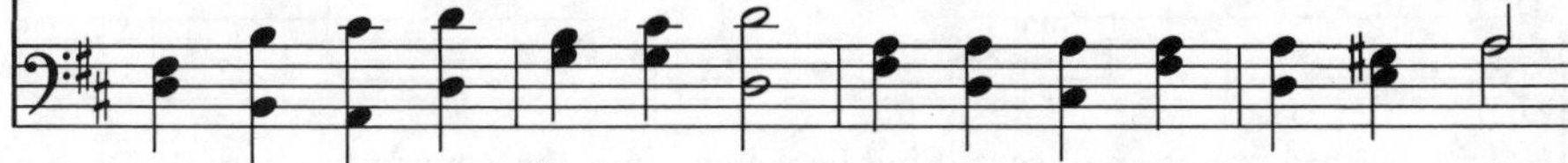

Turn not from his griefs a - way—Learn of Je - sus Christ to pray.
Shun not suf - f'ring, shame or loss—Learn of him to bear the cross.
"It is fin - ished!" hear him cry—Learn of Je - sus Christ to die.

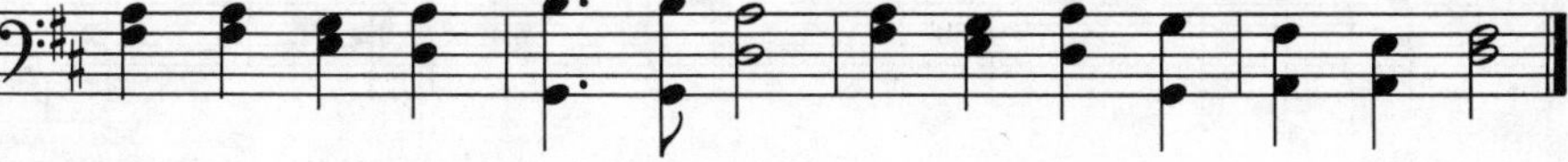

A higher setting may be found at No. 268

192 Deep Were His Wounds, and Red

William Johnson, 1906- MARLEE 6.6.6.6.8.8.

Leland B. Sateren, 1913-

In unison
1 Deep were his wounds, and red, On cru - el Cal - va - ry,
2 He suf - fered shame and scorn, And wretch-ed, dire dis - grace;
3 His life, his all, he gave When he was cru - ci - fied;
As on the cross he bled In bit - ter ag - o - ny; But they, whom
For - sak - en and for - lorn, He hung there in our place; But such as
Our bur - dened souls to save, What fear - ful death he died! But each of
sin has wound - ed sore, Find heal - ing in the wounds he bore.
would from sin be free Look to his cross for vic - to - ry.
us, though dead in sin, Thru him e - ter - nal life may win. A-men.

From *The Lutheran Service Book and Hymnal*, by permission of the Commission on the Liturgy and Hymnal.

Jesus, Refuge of the Weary

193

Girolamo Savonarola, 1454-1498
Tr. Jane Francesca Wilde, 1826-1896

WETTERLING 8.7.8.7.D.
Hampus Wetterling, 1830-1870

1 Je - sus, ref - uge of the wea - ry, Ob - ject of the Spir-it's love,
2 Do we pass that cross un - heed - ing, Breath-ing no re - pent-ant vow,
3 Je - sus, may our hearts be burn - ing With more fer - vent love for thee;
Foun - tain in life's des - ert drear - y, Sav - ior from the world a - bove:
Though we see thee wound-ed, bleed-ing, See thy thorn - en - cir - cled brow?
May our eyes be ev - er turn - ing To thy cross of ag - o - ny;
O how oft thine eyes, of - fend - ed, Gaze up - on the sin-ner's fall!
Yet thy sin - less death has brought us Life e - ter - nal, peace, and rest;
Till in glo - ry, part - ed nev - er From the bless - ed Sav - ior's side,
Yet, up - on the cross ex - tend - ed, Thou didst bear the pain of all.
On - ly what thy grace has taught us Calms the sin - ner's storm - y breast.
Grav - en in our hearts for - ev - er, Dwell the cross, the Cru - ci - fied. A - men.

194 Lord Christ, When First Thou Camest to Men

Walter Russell Bowie, 1882-1969

KIRKEN 8.7.8.7.8.8.7.
Ludvig M. Lindeman, 1812-1887

1 Lord Christ, when first thou cam'st to men, Up - on a cross they bound thee, And mocked thy sav - ing king - ship then By thorns with which they crowned thee; And still our wrongs may weave thee now New thorns to pierce that stead - y brow,
2 O awe-some love, which found no room In life where sin de - nied thee, And, doomed to death, must bring to doom The pow'r which cru - ci - fied thee, Till not a stone was left on stone, And all a na - tion's pride o'er - thrown
3 New ad - vent of the love of Christ, Shall we a - gain re - fuse thee, Till in the night of hate and war We per - ish as we lose thee? From old un - faith our souls re - lease To seek the king - dom of thy peace,
4 O wound - ed hands of Je - sus, build In us thy new cre - a - tion; Our pride is dust, our vaunt is stilled, We wait thy rev - e - la - tion. O love that tri - umphs o - ver loss, We bring our hearts be - fore thy cross,

And robe of sor - row round thee.
Went down to dust be - side thee!
By which a - lone we choose thee.
To fin - ish thy sal - va - tion. A - men.

My Crucified Savior

195

Fredrika E. Falck, 1719-1749
Tr. Claude W. Foss, 1855-1935, alt.

RUTSTRÖM 11.11.11.11.
Anders Carl Rutström, 1721-1772

1 My cru - ci - fied Sav - ior, de - spised and con - temned, Thou in - no - cent
2 Our Sav - ior thus fin - ished God's plan for our race, And laid the foun-
3 Re - stored to the bliss that was lost in the fall, Yes, great - er, for
4 Yes, come, trem - bling sin - ner, come just as thou art, Thy cares and thy

Lamb for all sin - ners con - demned, In thir - ty years' an - guish our
da - tion for par - don and grace; And then rose tri - umph - ant, the
Je - sus pre - pared for us all E - ter - nal sal - va - tion and
sor - rows to Je - sus im - part; In him seek sal - va - tion from

path thou hast trod, And di - est at last to re - deem us to God.
con - quer - ing Lord, O - beyed the Cre - a - tor and man - kind re - stored.
man - sions a - bove: Come, poor, bur - dened sin - ner, re - joice in his love.
death and the grave, For Je - sus is will - ing and might - y to save.

A higher setting may be found at No. 301

196 O Jesus, We Adore Thee

Arthur T. Russell, 1806-1874

MEIRIONYDD 7.6.7.6.D.
Welsh Melody
Attr. to William Lloyd, 1786-1852

1 O Je - sus, we a - dore thee, Up - on the cross, our King!
2 Yet doth the world dis - dain thee, Still pass - ing by the cross;
3 O glo - rious King, we bless thee, No long - er pass thee by;

We bow our hearts be - fore thee, Thy gra - cious name we sing:
Lord, may our hearts re - tain thee, All else we count but loss.
O Je - sus, we con - fess thee, The Son en - throned on high.

That name hath brought sal - va - tion, That name in life our stay,
Ah, Lord, our sins ar - raigned thee And nailed thee to the tree:
Lord, grant to us re - mis - sion, Life through thy death re - store;

Our peace, our con - so - la - tion, When life shall fade a - way.
Our pride, our Lord, dis - dained thee: Yet deign our hope to be.
Yea, grant us the fru - i - tion Of life for - ev - er - more. A-men.

A higher setting may be found at No. 575

O Sacred Head, Now Wounded 197

Latin: 12th century
German: Paul Gerhardt, 1607-1676
Tr. James W. Alexander, 1804-1859, alt.

PASSION CHORALE 7.6.7.6.D.
Hans Leo Hassler, 1564-1612
Harm. by J.S. Bach, 1685-1750

1 O sa - cred Head, now wound-ed, With grief and shame weighed down,
2 What thou, my Lord, hast suf - fered Was all for sin - ners' gain;
3 What lan-guage shall I bor - row To thank thee, dear - est friend,
Now scorn-ful - ly sur - round-ed With thorns, thy on - ly crown,
Mine, mine was the trans-gres - sion, But thine the dead-ly pain.
For this thy dy - ing sor - row, Thy pit - y with-out end?
How art thou pale with an - guish, With sore a - buse and scorn!
Lo, here I fall, my Sav - ior! 'Tis I de - serve thy place;
O make me thine for - ev - er; And, should I faint - ing be,
How does that vis - age lan - guish Which once was bright as morn!
Look on me with thy fa - vor, Vouch-safe to me thy grace.
Lord, let me nev - er, nev - er Out - live my love to thee! A-men.

198 On a Hill Far Away

George Bennard, 1873-1958 RUGGED CROSS *Irregular*
George Bennard, 1873-1958

1 On a hill far a-way stood an old rug-ged cross, The em-blem of
2 O that old rug-ged cross, so de-spised by the world, Has a won-drous at-
3 In the old rug-ged cross, stained with blood so di-vine, A won - drous
4 To the old rug-ged cross I will ev - er be true, Its shame and re -
suf - f'ring and shame; And I love that old cross where the dear-est and best
trac - tion for me; For the dear Lamb of God left his glo - ry a - bove
beau - ty I see; For 'twas on that old cross Je - sus suf-fered and died
proach glad - ly bear; Then he'll call me some day to my home far a - way,
For a world of lost sin-ners was slain.
To bear it to dark Cal-va - ry.
To par-don and sanc-ti - fy me.
Where his glo - ry for - ev - er I'll share.
REFRAIN
So I'll cher-ish the old rug-ged cross, the
cross, Till my tro-phies at last I lay down; I will cling to the
old rug-ged cross,
old rug - ged cross, And ex-change it some day for a crown.
cross, the old rug-ged cross,

PASSION

There Is a Green Hill Far Away

Cecil Frances Alexander, 1818-1895

GREEN HILL C.M. *with Refrain*
George C. Stebbins, 1846-1945
Arr. by A. Royce Eckhardt, 1937-

1 There is a green hill far a-way, Out-side a cit-y wall,
Where the dear Lord was cru-ci-fied, Who died to save us all.

2 We may not know, we can-not tell What pains he had to bear,
But we be-lieve it was for us He hung and suf-fered there.

3 He died that we might be for-giv'n, He died to make us good,
That we might go at last to heav'n, Saved by his pre-cious blood.

4 There was no oth-er good e-nough To pay the price of sin;
He on-ly could un-lock the gate Of heav'n and let us in.

REFRAIN

O dear-ly, dear-ly has he loved, And we must love him too,
And trust in his re-deem-ing blood, And try his works to do.

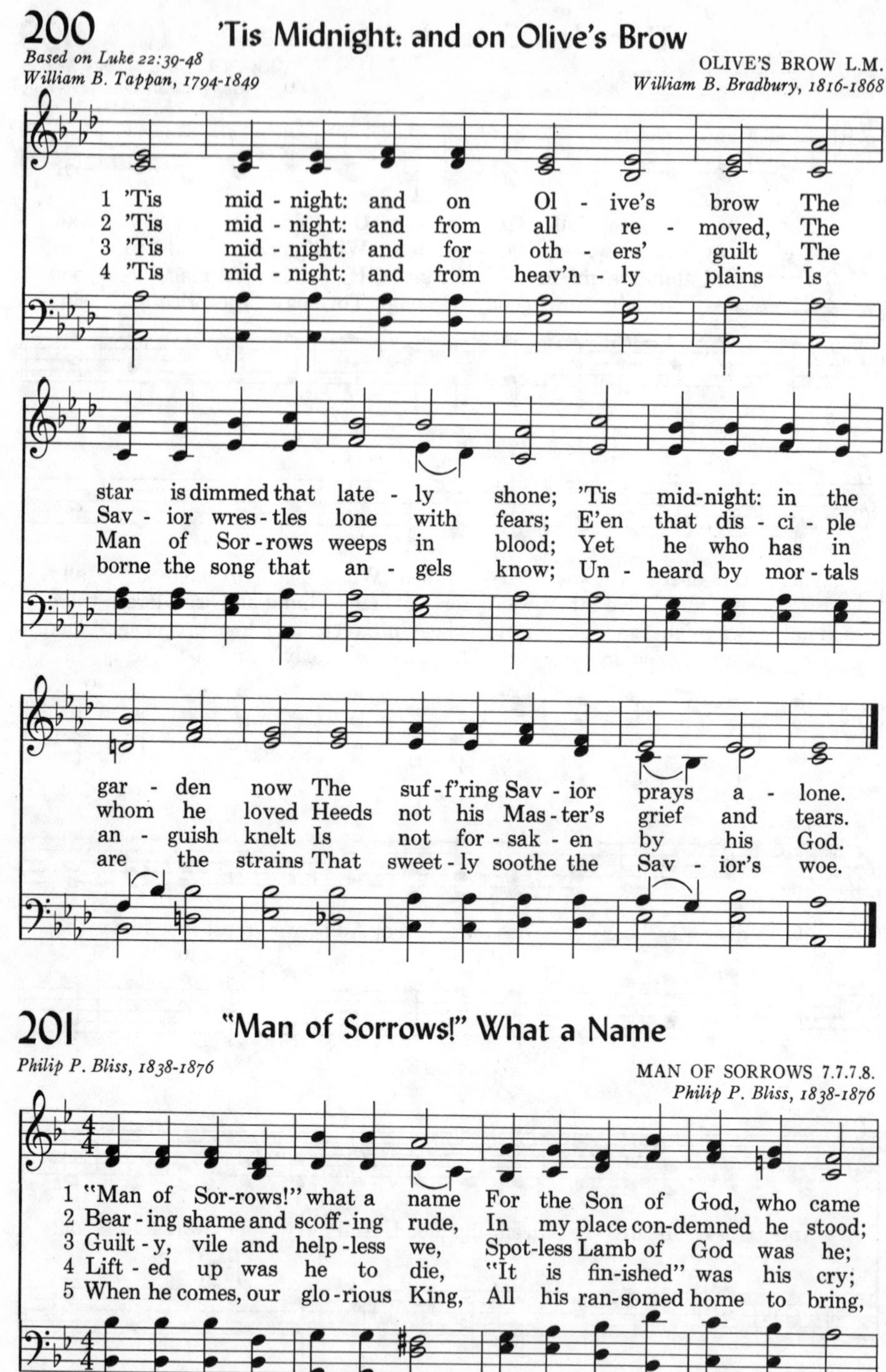
200 'Tis Midnight: and on Olive's Brow
Based on Luke 22:39-48
William B. Tappan, 1794-1849
OLIVE'S BROW L.M.
William B. Bradbury, 1816-1868
1 'Tis mid - night: and on Ol - ive's brow The star is dimmed that late - ly shone; 'Tis mid-night: in the gar - den now The suf - f'ring Sav - ior prays a - lone.
2 'Tis mid - night: and from all re - moved, The Sav - ior wres - tles lone with fears; E'en that dis - ci - ple whom he loved Heeds not his Mas - ter's grief and tears.
3 'Tis mid - night: and for oth - ers' guilt The Man of Sor - rows weeps in blood; Yet he who has in an - guish knelt Is not for - sak - en by his God.
4 'Tis mid - night: and from heav'n - ly plains Is borne the song that an - gels know; Un - heard by mor - tals are the strains That sweet - ly soothe the Sav - ior's woe.
201 "Man of Sorrows!" What a Name
Philip P. Bliss, 1838-1876
MAN OF SORROWS 7.7.7.8.
Philip P. Bliss, 1838-1876
1 "Man of Sor-rows!" what a name For the Son of God, who came
2 Bear - ing shame and scoff - ing rude, In my place con-demned he stood;
3 Guilt - y, vile and help - less we, Spot-less Lamb of God was he;
4 Lift - ed up was he to die, "It is fin-ished" was his cry;
5 When he comes, our glo - rious King, All his ran-somed home to bring,

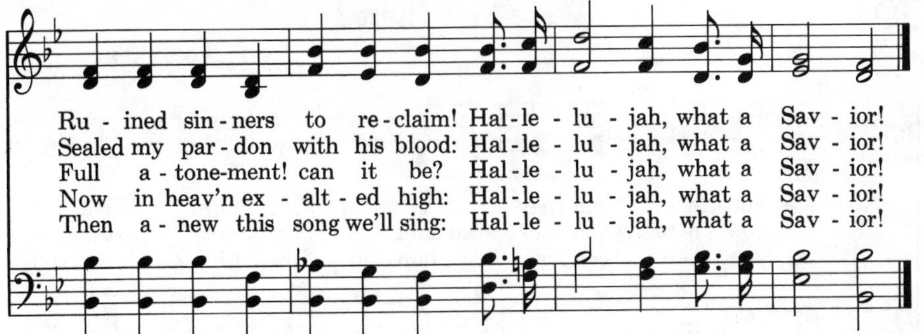
Ru - ined sin - ners to re - claim! Hal - le - lu - jah, what a Sav - ior!
Sealed my par - don with his blood: Hal - le - lu - jah, what a Sav - ior!
Full a - tone-ment! can it be? Hal - le - lu - jah, what a Sav - ior!
Now in heav'n ex - alt - ed high: Hal - le - lu - jah, what a Sav - ior!
Then a - new this song we'll sing: Hal - le - lu - jah, what a Sav - ior!

When I Survey the Wondrous Cross 202

Isaac Watts, 1674-1748

HAMBURG L.M.
Based on Gregorian Chant, Tone I
Arr. by Lowell Mason, 1792-1872

1 When I sur - vey the won - drous cross On which the
2 For - bid it, Lord, that I should boast, Save in the
3 See, from his head, his hands, his feet, Sor - row and
4 Were the whole realm of na - ture mine, That were an

Prince of glo - ry died, My rich - est gain I
death of Christ my God; All the vain things that
love flow min - gled down: Did e'er such love and
of - f'ring far too small; Love so a - maz - ing,

count but loss, And pour con - tempt on all my pride.
charm me most, I sac - ri - fice them to his blood.
sor - row meet, Or thorns com - pose so rich a crown?
so di - vine, De - mands my soul, my life, my all. A - men.

Alternate tune: ROCKINGHAM, *No. 527*

203 Were You There?

American Folk Hymn WERE YOU THERE *Irregular*
American Folk Melody

1 Were you there when they cru - ci - fied my Lord? Were you
2 Were you there when they nailed him to the tree? Were you
3 Were you there when they laid him in the tomb? Were you
there when they cru - ci - fied my Lord?
there when they nailed him to the tree? O! . . . . . .
there when they laid him in the tomb?
Some-times it caus - es me to trem - ble, trem - ble, trem - ble.
Were you there when they cru - ci - fied my Lord?
Were you there when they nailed him to the tree?
Were you there when they laid him in the tomb?

What Wondrous Love Is This

American Folk Hymn

WONDROUS LOVE 12.9.6.6.12.9.
"Southern Harmony," 1835
Harm. by Norman E. Johnson, 1928-

In unison

1 What wondrous love is this, O my soul, O my soul! What wondrous love is this, O my soul! What wondrous love is this That caused the Lord of bliss To bear the dreadful curse for my soul, for my soul, To bear the dreadful curse for my soul.

2 When I was sinking down, sinking down, sinking down, When I was sinking down, sinking down, When I was sinking down Beneath God's righteous frown, Christ laid aside his crown for my soul, for my soul, Christ laid aside his crown for my soul.

3 To God and to the Lamb I will sing, I will sing, To God and to the Lamb I will sing, To God and to the Lamb Who is the great "I Am," While millions join the theme, I will sing, I will sing, While millions join the theme, I will sing.

4 And when from death I'm free, I'll sing on, I'll sing on, And when from death I'm free, I'll sing on, And when from death I'm free, I'll sing and joyful be, And through eternity I'll sing on, I'll sing on, And through eternity I'll sing on.

205 When My Love to God Grows Weak
John R. Wreford, 1800-1881, alt.
SONG 13 7.7.7.7.
Orlando Gibbons, 1583-1625
1 When my love to God grows weak, When for deep - er
2 There I walk a - mid the shades, While the lin - g'ring
3 When my love for man grows weak, When for strong - er
4 There be - hold his ag - o - ny, Suf - fered on the
5 Then to life I turn a - gain, Learn - ing all the
faith I seek, Then in thought I go to thee,
twi - light fades; See that suf - f'ring, friend - less one
faith I seek, Hill of Cal - va - ry, I go
bit - ter tree; See his an - guish, see his faith,
worth of pain, Learn - ing all the might that lies
Gar - den of Geth - sem - a - ne.
Weep - ing, pray - ing there a - lone.
To thy scenes of fear and woe.
Love tri - um - phant still in death.
In a full self - sac - ri - fice. A - men.
PASSION
206 The Strife Is O'er, the Battle Done
Latin: 17th century
Tr. Francis Pott, 1832-1909
VICTORY 8.8.8. with Alleluia
Giovanni P. da Palestrina, c.1525-1594
Adapted by William H. Monk, 1823-1889
1 The strife is o'er, the bat - tle done, Now is the vic - tor's
2 Death's might-iest pow'rs have done their worst, And Je - sus hath his
3 The three sad days have quick - ly sped, He ris - es glo - rious
4 He broke the age - bound chains of hell, The bars from heav'n's high

RESURRECTION

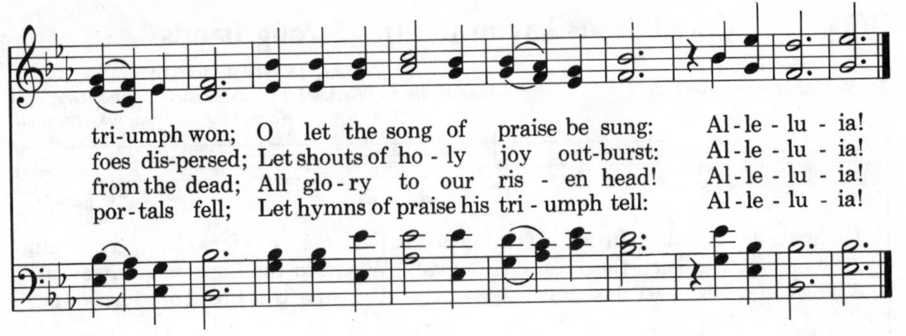
tri-umph won; O let the song of praise be sung: Al-le-lu-ia!
foes dis-persed; Let shouts of ho-ly joy out-burst: Al-le-lu-ia!
from the dead; All glo-ry to our ris-en head! Al-le-lu-ia!
por-tals fell; Let hymns of praise his tri-umph tell: Al-le-lu-ia!

Good Christian Men, Rejoice and Sing!

207

Cyril A. Alington, 1872-1955

GELOBT SEI GOTT 8.8.8. *with Alleluias*
Melchior Vulpius, c.1560-1616
Harm. by Norman E. Johnson, 1928-

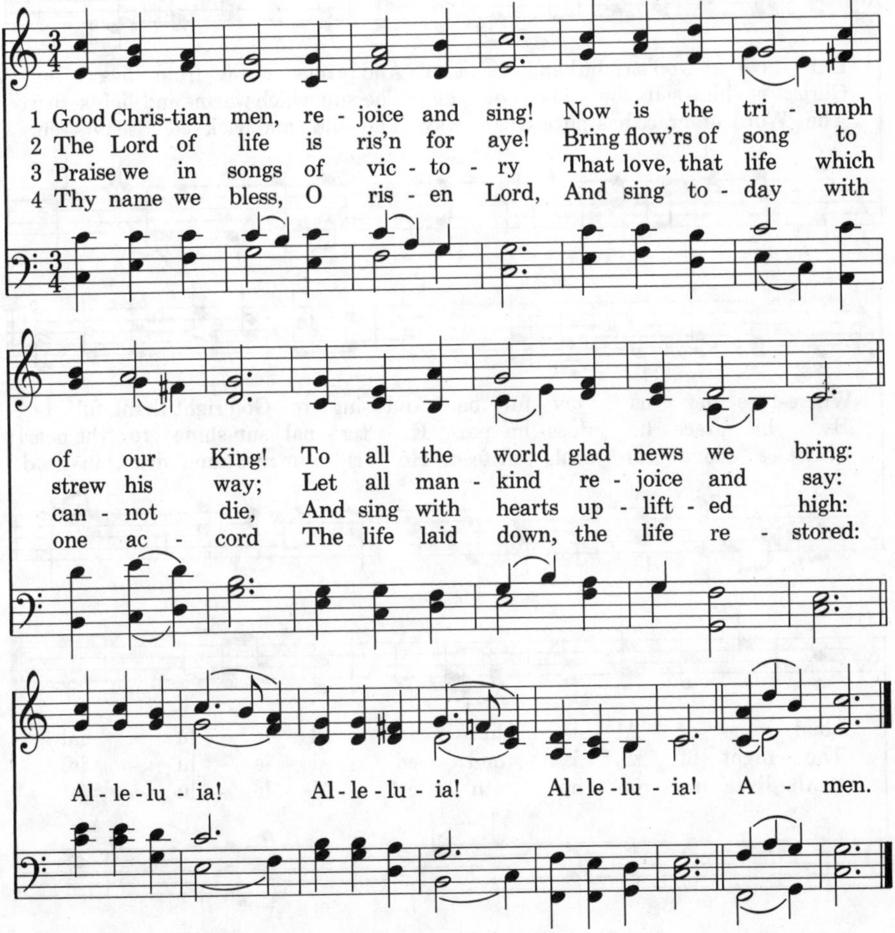

1 Good Chris-tian men, re-joice and sing! Now is the tri-umph
2 The Lord of life is ris'n for aye! Bring flow'rs of song to
3 Praise we in songs of vic-to-ry That love, that life which
4 Thy name we bless, O ris-en Lord, And sing to-day with

of our King! To all the world glad news we bring:
strew his way; Let all man-kind re-joice and say:
can-not die, And sing with hearts up-lift-ed high:
one ac-cord The life laid down, the life re-stored:

Al-le-lu-ia! Al-le-lu-ia! Al-le-lu-ia! A-men.

RESURRECTION

208 Christ Jesus Lay in Death's Strong Bands

Martin Luther, 1483-1546
Tr. Richard Massie, 1800-1887

CHRIST LAG IN TODESBANDEN 8.7.8.7.7.8.7.4.
Johann Walther's "Geistliches Gesangbüchlein," Wittenberg, 1524
Harm. by J. S. Bach, 1685-1750, alt.

1 Christ Je - sus lay in death's strong bands, For our of - fens - es giv - en;
2 So let us keep the fes - ti - val Where-to the Lord in - vites us;
3 Then let us feast this Eas - ter day On the true bread of heav - en;
But now at God's right hand he stands And brings us life from heav - en:
Christ is him-self the joy of all, The sun which warms and lights us:
The Word of grace has purged a - way The old and wick - ed leav - en:
Where-fore let us joy - ful be And sing to God right thank-ful - ly
By his grace he does im - part E - ter - nal sun-shine to the heart;
Christ a - lone our souls will feed, He is our meat and drink in - deed;
Loud songs of Al - le - lu - ia! Al - le - lu - ia!
The night of sin is end - ed! Al - le - lu - ia!
Faith lives up - on no oth - er! Al - le - lu - ia!

RESURRECTION

Christ the Lord Is Risen Today

Charles Wesley, 1707-1788, alt.

EASTER HYMN 7.7.7.7. *with Alleluias*
"Lyra Davidica," 1708

1 Christ the Lord is ris'n to - day,
2 Lives a - gain our glo - rious King,
3 Love's re - deem - ing work is done,
4 Soar we now where Christ has led,
Al - le - lu - ia!
Sons of men and an - gels say:
Where, O death, is now thy sting?
Fought the fight, the bat - tle won,
Fol - l'wing our ex - alt - ed Head,
Al - le - lu - ia!
Raise your joys and tri - umphs high,
Dy - ing once, he all doth save,
Death in vain for - bids him rise,
Made like him, like him we rise,
Al - le - lu - ia!
Sing, ye heav'ns, and earth re - ply:
Where thy vic - to - ry, O grave?
Christ has o - pened par - a - dise,
Ours the cross, the grave, the skies,
Al - le - lu - ia!

RESURRECTION

210 Come, Ye Faithful, Raise the Strain

John of Damascus, c.696-c.754
Tr. John M. Neale, 1818-1866

ST. KEVIN 7.6.7.6.D.
Arthur S. Sullivan, 1842-1900

1 Come, ye faith-ful, raise the strain Of tri-um-phant glad-ness:
2 'Tis the spring of souls to-day: Christ hath burst his pris-on,
3 "Al-le-lu-ia!" now we cry To our King im-mor-tal,
God hath brought his peo-ple forth In-to joy from sad-ness;
From the frost and gloom of death Light and life have ris-en;
Who, tri-um-phant, burst the bars Of the tomb's dark por-tal;
Now re-joice, Je-ru-sa-lem, And with true af-fec-tion
All the win-ter of our sins, Long and dark, is fly-ing
"Al-le-lu-ia!" with the Son, God the Fa-ther prais-ing,
Wel-come with un-ceas-ing praise Je-sus' res-ur-rec-tion.
From his light, to whom we give Thanks and praise un-dy-ing.
"Al-le-lu-ia!" yet a-gain To the Spir-it rais-ing. A-men.

RESURRECTION

Jesus Christ Is Risen Today

Latin: 14th century
English translation, "New Version," 1698
Charles Wesley, 1707-1788, St. 4

LLANFAIR 7.7.7.7. *with Alleluias*
Robert Williams, c.1781-1821
Harm. by John Roberts, 1822-1877

1 Je - sus Christ is ris'n to - day,
2 Hymns of praise then let us sing,
3 But the pains which he en - dured,
4 Sing we to our God a - bove,
Al - le - lu - ia!
Our tri - um - phant ho - ly day,
Un - to Christ, our heav'n - ly King,
Our sal - va - tion have pro - cured;
Praise e - ter - nal as his love;
Al - le - lu - ia!
Who did once up - on the cross,
Who en - dured the cross and grave,
Now a - bove the sky he's King,
Praise him, all ye heav'n - ly host,
Al - le - lu - ia!
Suf - fer to re - deem our loss.
Sin - ners to re - deem and save.
Where the an - gels ev - er sing.
Fa - ther, Son and Ho - ly Ghost.
Al - le - lu - ia!
A-men.

212 Low in the Grave He Lay

Robert Lowry, 1826-1899
CHRIST AROSE 6.5.6.4. with Refrain
Robert Lowry, 1826-1899
1 Low in the grave he lay, Je-sus, my Sav-ior! Wait-ing the com-ing day,
2 Vain-ly they watched his bed, Je-sus, my Sav-ior! Vain-ly they sealed the dead,
3 Death could not keep his prey, Je-sus, my Sav-ior! He tore the bars a-way,
Je-sus, my Lord!
Je-sus, my Lord!
Je-sus, my Lord!
REFRAIN
Up from the grave he a-rose,
he a-rose,
With a might-y tri-umph o'er his foes;
he a-rose;
He a-rose a vic-tor from the dark do-main, And he lives for-ev-er with his saints to reign: He a-rose!
He a-rose!
He a-rose!
He a-rose!
Hal-le-lu-jah! Christ a-rose!

Hallelujah! Jesus Lives!

Carl Bernhard Garve, 1763-1841
Tr. Jane L. Borthwick, 1813-1897

EASTER GLORY 7.7.7.7.7.7.
Ludvig M. Lindeman, 1812-1887

1 Hal - le - lu - jah! Je - sus lives! He is now the
2 Je - sus lives! let all re - joice! Praise him, ran - somed
3 Je - sus lives! and thus, my soul, Life e - ter - nal
4 Hal - le - lu - jah! an - gels, sing! Join us in our
liv - ing one! From the gloom - y house of death
ones of earth! Praise him in a no - bler song,
waits for thee! Joined to him, thy liv - ing head,
hymn of praise! Let your cho - rus swell the strain
Forth the con - quer - or has gone, Bright fore - run - ner
Cher - u - bim of heav'n - ly birth! Praise the Vic - tor -
Where he is thou too shalt be: With him - self, at
Which our fee - bler voic - es raise: Glo - ry to our
to the skies Of his peo - ple, yet to rise.
King, whose sway Sin and death and hell o - bey.
his right hand, Vic - tor o - ver death shalt stand.
God a - bove, And on earth his peace and love! A - men.

Alternate tune: DIX, *No. 158*

214 Jesus Lives, and So Shall I

Christian F. Gellert, 1715-1769
Tr. Philip Schaff, 1819-1893

JESU, MEINE ZUVERSICHT 7.8.7.8.7.7.
Johann Crüger, 1598-1662

1 Je - sus lives, and so shall I: Death, thy sting is gone for -
2 Je - sus lives and reigns su - preme: And, his king - dom still re -
3 Je - sus lives—and by his grace, Vic - t'ry o'er my pas - sions
4 Je - sus lives— I know full well Nought from him my heart can
5 Je - sus lives—and death is now But my en - trance in - to
ev - er! He for me hath deigned to die, Lives the
main - ing, I shall al - so be with him, Ev - er
giv - ing, I will cleanse my heart and ways, Ev - er
sev - er, Life nor death nor pow'rs of hell, Joy nor
glo - ry; Cour - age, then, my soul, for thou Hast a
bands of death to sev - er. He shall raise me
liv - ing, ev - er reign - ing. God has prom - ised—
to his glo - ry liv - ing. Me he rais - es
grief, hence - forth for - ev - er. None of all his
crown of life be - fore thee. Thou shalt find thy
from the dust: Je - sus is my hope and trust.
be it must: Je - sus is my hope and trust.
from the dust: Je - sus is my hope and trust.
saints is lost: Je - sus is my hope and trust.
hopes were just: Je - sus is my hope and trust. A - men.

RESURRECTION

Joy Dawned Again on Easter Day

Latin: 5th century
Tr. John M. Neale, 1818-1866, alt.

PUER NOBIS NASCITUR L.M.
Adapted by Michael Praetorius, 1571-1621
Harm. by George R. Woodward, 1848-1934

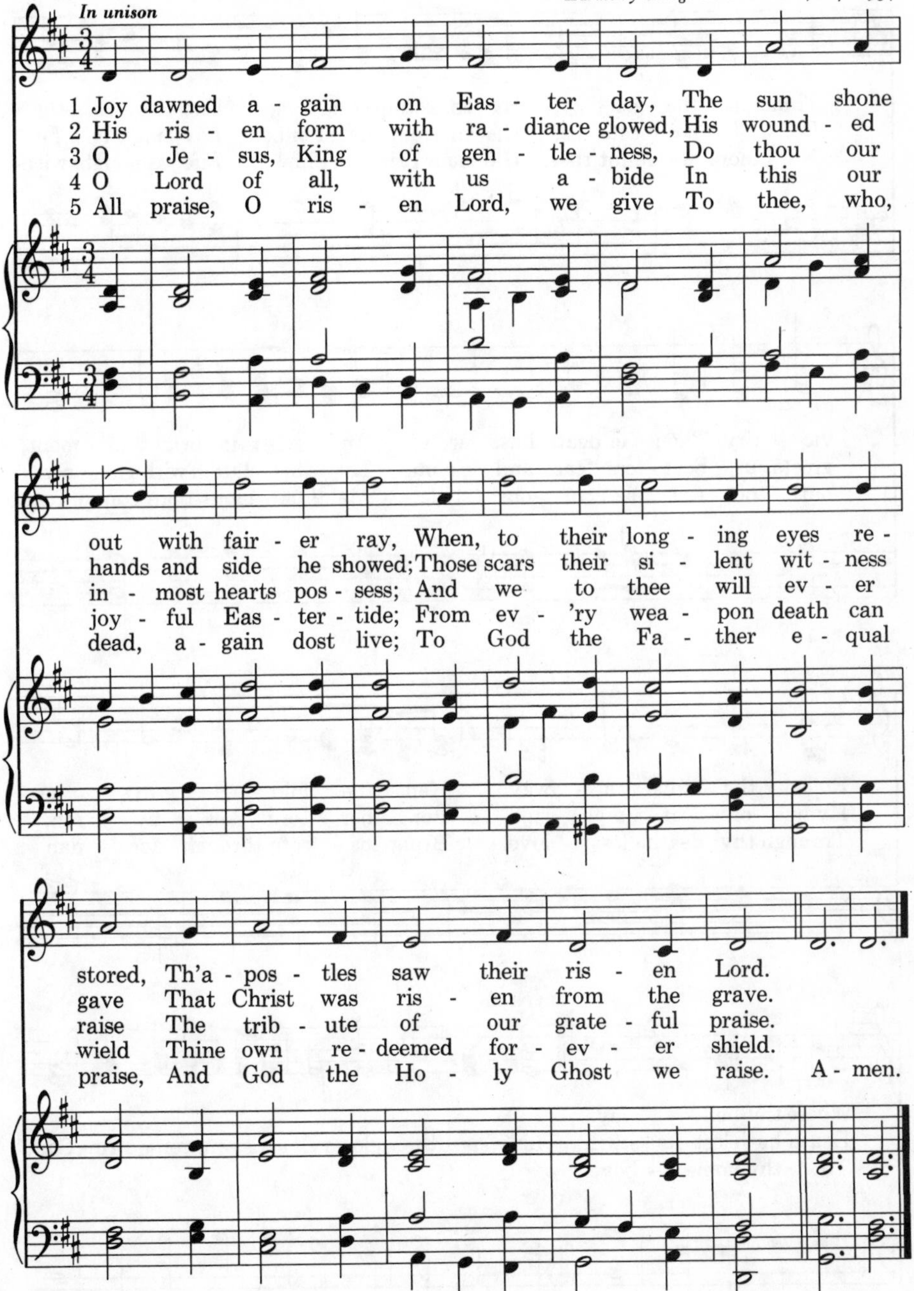

In unison

1 Joy dawned again on Easter day,
The sun shone out with fairer ray,
When, to their longing eyes restored,
Th'apostles saw their risen Lord.

2 His risen form with radiance glowed,
His wounded hands and side he showed;
Those scars their silent witness gave
That Christ was risen from the grave.

3 O Jesus, King of gentleness,
Do thou our inmost hearts possess;
And we to thee will ever raise
The tribute of our grateful praise.

4 O Lord of all, with us abide
In this our joyful Eastertide;
From ev'ry weapon death can wield
Thine own redeemed forever shield.

5 All praise, O risen Lord, we give
To thee, who, dead, again dost live;
To God the Father equal praise,
And God the Holy Ghost we raise. Amen.

216 Thine Is the Glory

Edmond L. Budry, 1854-1932
Tr. R. Birch Hoyle, 1875-1939

JUDAS MACCABEUS 5.5.6.5.6.5.6.5. *with Refrain*
George Frederick Handel, 1685-1759

1 Thine is the glo - ry, Ris - en, con-qu'ring Son; End - less is the
2 Lo! Je - sus meets us, Ris - en from the tomb; Lov - ing - ly he
3 No more we doubt thee, Glo - rious Prince of life! Life is nought with-
vic - t'ry Thou o'er death hast won. An - gels in bright rai - ment
greets us, Scat - ters fear and gloom. Let his church with glad - ness
out thee: Aid us in our strife. Make us more than con-qu'rors,
Rolled the stone a - way, Kept the fold - ed grave - clothes
Hymns of tri - umph sing, For her Lord now liv - eth:
Through thy death - less love: Bring us safe through Jor - dan
REFRAIN
Where thy bod - y lay.
Death hath lost its sting. Thine is the glo - ry, Ris - en, con-qu'ring Son;
To thy home a - bove.

RESURRECTION

End - less is the vic - t'ry Thou o'er death hast won. A - men.

Jesus Lives! Thy Terrors Now 217

Christian F. Gellert, 1715-1769
Tr. Frances E. Cox, 1812-1897

JESUS LIVES 7.8.7.8.8.8.
A. L. Skoog, 1856-1934

1 Je - sus lives! thy ter - rors now Can no long - er, death, ap - pall us;
2 Je - sus lives! hence-forth is death But the gate of life im - mor - tal;
3 Je - sus lives! for us he died: Then, a - lone to Je - sus liv - ing,
4 Je - sus lives! to him the throne O - ver all the world is giv - en;

Je - sus lives! by this we know Thou, O grave, canst not en - thrall us.
This shall calm our trem-bling breath When we pass its gloom - y por - tal.
Pure in heart may we a - bide, Glo - ry to our Sav - ior giv - ing.
May we go where he has gone, Rest and reign with him in heav - en.

Al - le - lu - ia, Al - le - lu - ia, Al - le - lu - ia, Christ is ris - en!

218 The Day of Resurrection!

John of Damascus, c.696-c.754
Tr. John M. Neale, 1818-1866, alt.

LANCASHIRE 7.6.7.6.D.
Henry T. Smart, 1813-1879

1 The day of res - ur - rec - tion! Earth, tell it out a - broad;
2 Our hearts be pure from e - vil, That we may see a - right
3 Now let the heav'ns be joy - ful, Let earth her song be - gin,
The Pass - o - ver of glad - ness, The Pass - o - ver of God.
The Lord in rays e - ter - nal Of res - ur - rec - tion light;
The round world keep high tri - umph, And all that is there - in;
From death to life e - ter - nal, From earth un - to the sky,
And, lis - t'ning to his ac - cents, May hear so calm and plain
Let all things seen and un - seen Their notes of glad - ness blend,
Our Christ hath brought us o - ver With hymns of vic - to - ry.
His own "All hail," and, hear - ing, May raise the vic - tor - strain.
For Christ the Lord is ris - en, Our joy that hath no end. A - men.

RESURRECTION

A lower setting may be found at No. 532

This Joyful Eastertide

George R. Woodward, 1848-1934

VRUECHTEN 6.7.6.7. *with Refrain*
Dutch Melody
"David's Psalmen," Amsterdam, 1685
Harm. by A. Royce Eckhardt, 1937-

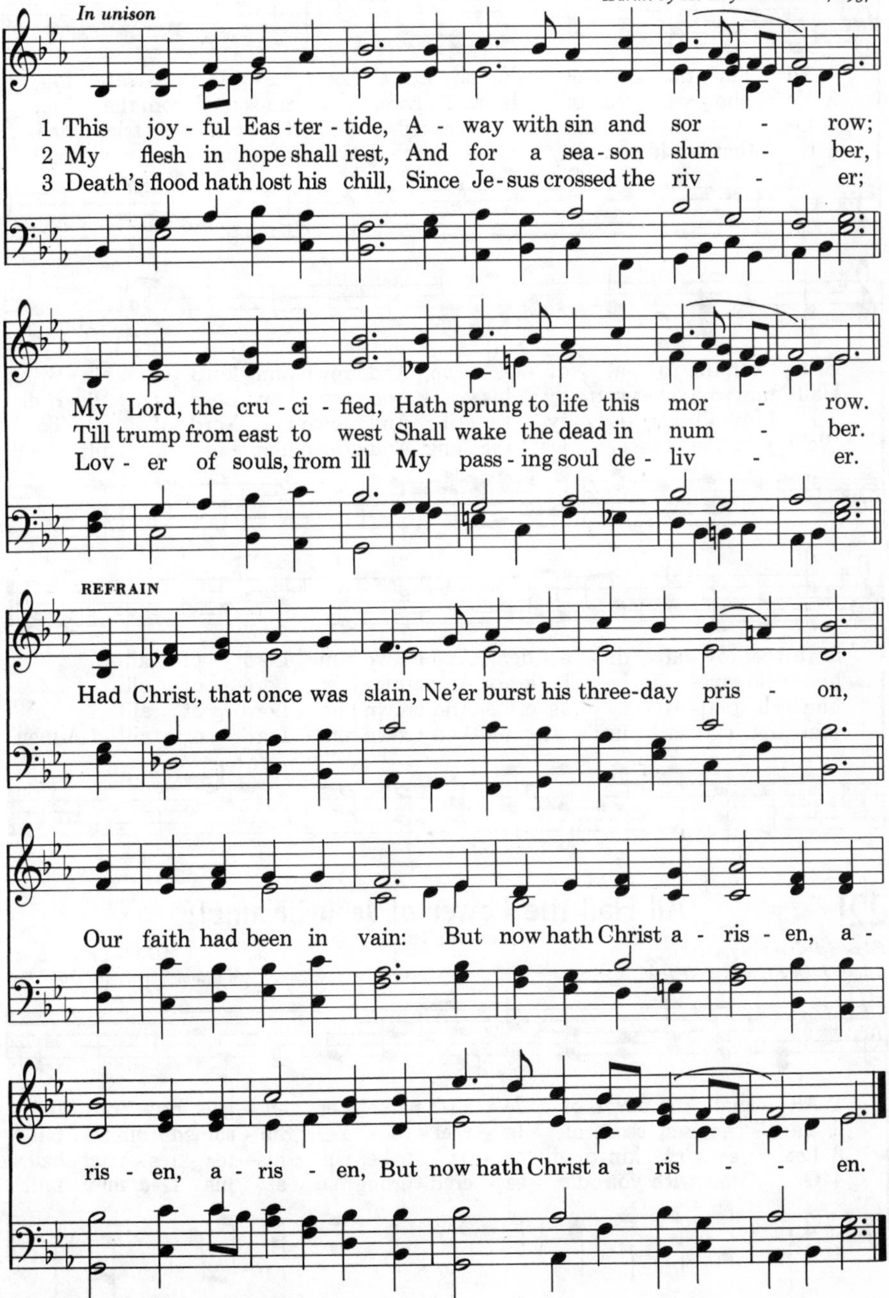

In unison

1 This joy-ful Eas-ter-tide, A-way with sin and sor-row;
2 My flesh in hope shall rest, And for a sea-son slum-ber,
3 Death's flood hath lost his chill, Since Je-sus crossed the riv-er;

My Lord, the cru-ci-fied, Hath sprung to life this mor-row.
Till trump from east to west Shall wake the dead in num-ber.
Lov-er of souls, from ill My pass-ing soul de-liv-er.

REFRAIN

Had Christ, that once was slain, Ne'er burst his three-day pris-on,
Our faith had been in vain: But now hath Christ a-ris-en, a-ris-en, a-ris-en, But now hath Christ a-ris-en.

RESURRECTION

220 All Hail the Power of Jesus' Name!

First Tune

Edward Perronet, 1726-1792
Alt. by John Rippon, 1751-1836

CORONATION C.M.
Oliver Holden, 1765-1844

1 All hail the pow'r of Je - sus' name! Let an - gels pros-trate fall;
2 Ye cho - sen seed of Is - rael's race, Ye ran-somed from the fall,
3 Let ev - 'ry kin-dred, ev - 'ry tribe, On this ter - res - trial ball,
4 O that with yon - der sa - cred throng We at his feet may fall!

Bring forth the roy - al di - a - dem, And crown him Lord of all; Bring
Hail him who saves you by his grace, And crown him Lord of all; Hail
To him all maj - es - ty as - cribe, And crown him Lord of all; To
We'll join the ev - er - last - ing song, And crown him Lord of all; We'll

forth the roy - al di - a - dem, And crown him Lord of all!
him who saves you by his grace, And crown him Lord of all!
him all maj - es - ty as - cribe, And crown him Lord of all!
join the ev - er - last - ing song, And crown him Lord of all! A-men.

221 All Hail the Power of Jesus' Name!

Second Tune

Edward Perronet, 1726-1792
Alt. by John Rippon, 1751-1836

MILES LANE C.M.
William Shrubsole, 1760-1806

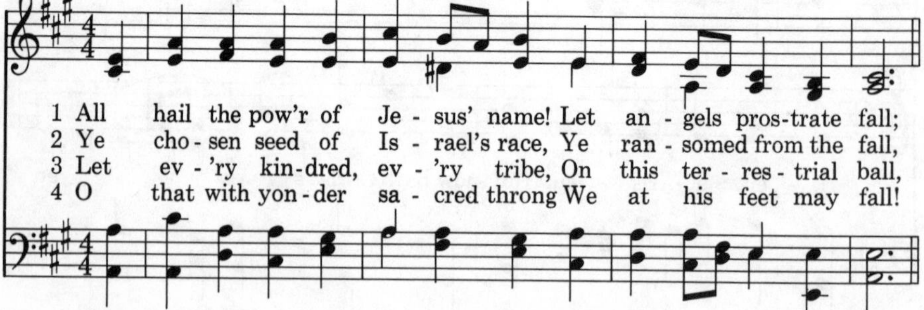

1 All hail the pow'r of Je - sus' name! Let an - gels pros-trate fall;
2 Ye cho - sen seed of Is - rael's race, Ye ran - somed from the fall,
3 Let ev - 'ry kin-dred, ev - 'ry tribe, On this ter - res - trial ball,
4 O that with yon - der sa - cred throng We at his feet may fall!

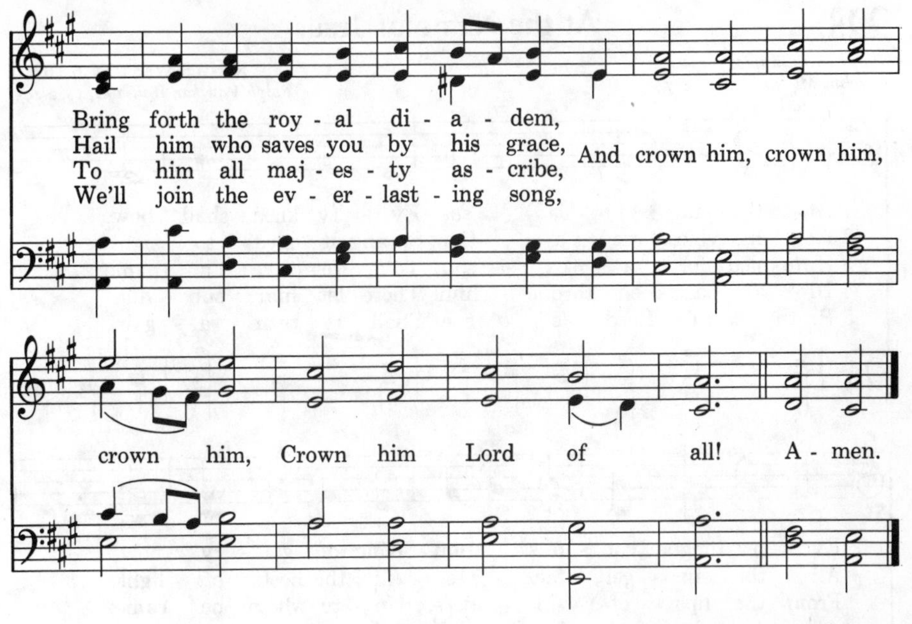
Bring forth the roy - al di - a - dem,
Hail him who saves you by his grace,
To him all maj - es - ty as - cribe,
We'll join the ev - er - last - ing song,
And crown him, crown him,
crown him, Crown him Lord of all! A - men.

Jesus Shall Reign Where'er the Sun 222

Based on Psalm 72
Isaac Watts, 1674-1748

DUKE STREET L.M.
John Hatton, c.1710-1793

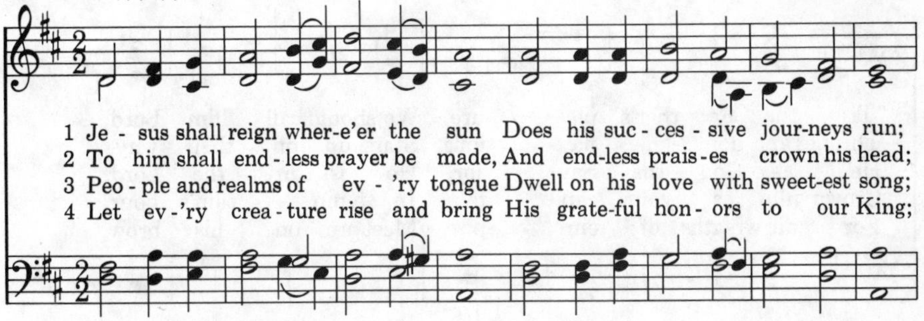

1 Je - sus shall reign wher-e'er the sun Does his suc - ces - sive jour-neys run;
2 To him shall end - less prayer be made, And end-less prais - es crown his head;
3 Peo - ple and realms of ev - 'ry tongue Dwell on his love with sweet-est song;
4 Let ev - 'ry crea - ture rise and bring His grate-ful hon - ors to our King;

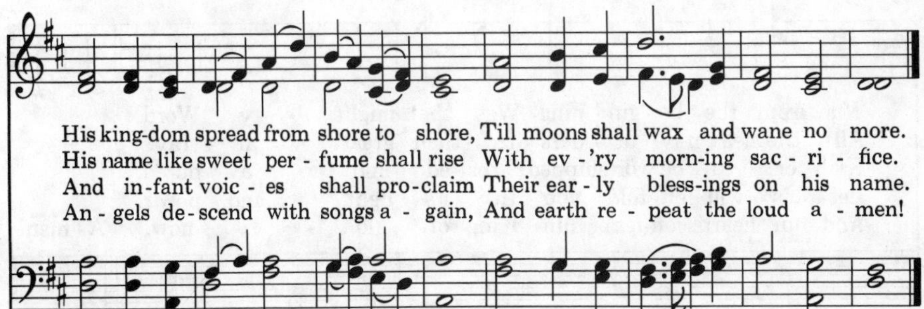

His king-dom spread from shore to shore, Till moons shall wax and wane no more.
His name like sweet per - fume shall rise With ev - 'ry morn-ing sac - ri - fice.
And in-fant voic - es shall pro-claim Their ear - ly bless-ings on his name.
An - gels de - scend with songs a - gain, And earth re - peat the loud a - men!

Another harmonization may be found at No. 6
A higher setting may be found at No. 362

223 At the Name of Jesus

Based on Philippians, 2:5-11
Caroline M. Noel, 1817-1877

KING'S WESTON 6.5.6.5.D.
Ralph Vaughan Williams, 1872-1958

In unison
1 At the name of Je - sus Ev - 'ry knee shall bow,
2 At his voice cre - a - tion Sprang at once to sight,
3 Hum-bled for a sea - son, To re-ceive a name
4 In your hearts en-throne him: There let him sub-due
5 Broth-ers, this Lord Je - sus Shall re-turn a - gain,
Ev - 'ry tongue con - fess him King of glo - ry now;
All the an - gel fac - es, All the hosts of light,
From the lips of sin - ners, Un - to whom he came;
All that is not ho - ly, All that is not true;
With his Fa - ther's glo - ry, With his an - gel train;
'Tis the Fa - ther's pleas - ure We should call him Lord,
Thrones and dom - i - na - tions, Stars up - on their way,
He is God the Sav - ior, He is Christ the Lord,
Crown him as your cap - tain In temp - ta - tion's hour,
For all wreaths of em - pire Meet up - on his brow,
Who from the be - gin - ning Was the might - y Word.
All the heav'n-ly or - ders In their great ar - ray.
Ev - er to be wor-shipped, Trust-ed and a - dored.
Let his will en - fold you In its light and pow'r.
And our hearts con - fess him King of glo - ry now. A - men.

ASCENSION AND REIGN

Crown Him with Many Crowns 224

Matthew Bridges, 1800-1894
Godfrey Thring, 1823-1903, St. 3

DIADEMATA S.M.D.
George J. Elvey, 1816-1893

1 Crown him with man - y crowns, The Lamb up - on his throne:
2 Crown him the Lord of love: Be - hold his hands and side,
3 Crown him the Lord of life: Who tri - umphed o'er the grave,
4 Crown him the Lord of heav'n: One with the Fa - ther known,
5 Crown him the Lord of years: The po - ten - tate of time,

Hark! how the heav'n-ly an - them drowns All mu - sic but its own!
Rich wounds, yet vis - i - ble a - bove, In beau - ty glo - ri - fied;
Who rose vic - to - rious to the strife For those he came to save;
One with the Spir - it through him giv'n From yon - der glo - rious throne.
Cre - a - tor of the roll - ing spheres, In - ef - fa - bly sub - lime.

A - wake, my soul, and sing Of him who died for thee; And
No an - gel in the sky Can ful - ly bear that sight, But
His glo - ries now we sing, Who died and rose on high, Who
To thee be end - less praise, For thou for us hast died; Be
All hail, Re - deem - er, hail! For thou hast died for me; Thy

hail him as thy match - less King Thru all e - ter - ni - ty.
down - ward bends his won - d'ring eye At mys - ter - ies so bright.
died e - ter - nal life to bring, And lives that death may die.
thou, O Lord, thru end - less days A - dored and mag - ni - fied.
praise and glo - ry shall not fail Thru - out e - ter - ni - ty. A - men.

A higher setting may be found at No. 523

225 See the Conqueror Mounts in Triumph

Christopher Wordsworth, 1807-1885

IN BABILONE 8.7.8.7.D.
Dutch Melody
Harm. by Norman E. Johnson, 1928-

In unison
1 See the Con-qu'ror mounts in tri-umph; See the King in roy - al state,
2 He who on the cross did suf-fer, He who from the grave a - rose,
3 Thou hast raised our hu - man na-ture On the clouds to God's right hand:
Rid - ing on the clouds, his char-iot, To his heav'n-ly pal - ace gate!
He has van-quish'd sin and Sa-tan, He by death has spoiled his foes.
There we sit in heav'n-ly plac-es, There with thee in glo - ry stand.
Hark! the choirs of an-gel voic-es Joy-ful al - le - lu - ias sing,
While he lifts his hands in bless-ing, He is part-ed from his friends;
Je - sus reigns, a - dored by an-gels; Man with God is on the throne;
And the por-tals high are lift-ed To re-ceive their heav'n-ly King.
While their ea-ger eyes be-hold him, He up-on the clouds as-cends.
Might-y Lord, in thine as-cen-sion, We by faith be - hold our own.

The Lord Is King!

Norman E. Johnson, 1928-
Freely adapted from Josiah Conder, 1789-1855

ALL IS WELL 10.6.10.6.8.8.8.6.
J. T. White's "Sacred Harp," 1844
Harm. by Norman E. Johnson, 1928-

1 The Lord is King! Lift up, lift up thy voice— Sing his praise, sing his praise!
2 The Lord is King! Let all his worth de-clare— Great is he, great is he!
3 The Lord is King! And bow to him ye must— God is great, God is good!
4 The Lord is King! Thru-out his vast do-main He is all, all in all!

All heav'n and earth be-fore him now re-joice—Sing his praise, sing his praise!
Bow to his will and trust his ten-der care—Great is he, great is he!
The Judge of all to all is ev-er just—God is great, God is good!
The Lord Je-ho-vah ev-er-more shall reign—He is all, all in all!

From world to world the joy shall ring, For he a-lone is God and King;
Nor mur-mur at his wise de-crees, Nor doubt his stead-fast prom-is-es;
Ho-ly and true are all his ways: Let ev-'ry crea-ture shout his praise;
Thru earth and heav'n one song shall ring, From grate-ful hearts this an-them spring:

From sky to sky his ban-ners fling—Sing his praise, sing his praise!
In hum-ble faith fall on thy knees—Great is he, great is he!
The Lord of Hosts, An-cient of Days—God is great, God is good!
A-rise, ye saints, sa-lute thy King—All thy days, sing his praise!

227 Look, Ye Saints! the Sight Is Glorious

Thomas Kelly, 1769-1855

CORONAE 8.7.8.7.4.7.
William H. Monk, 1823-1889

1 Look, ye saints! the sight is glo - rious: See the Man of
2 Crown the Sav - ior! an - gels, crown him! Rich the tro - phies
3 Sin - ners in de - ri - sion crowned him, Mock-ing thus Mes -
4 Hark! those bursts of ac - cla - ma - tion! Hark! those loud tri -
Sor - rows now! From the fight re - turned vic - to - rious,
Je - sus brings; In the seat of pow'r en - throne him,
si - ah's claim; Saints and an - gels throng a - round him,
um - phant chords! Je - sus takes the high - est sta - tion—
Ev - 'ry knee to him shall bow: Crown him!
While the vault of heav - en rings: Crown him!
Own his ti - tle, praise his name: Crown him!
O what joy the sight af - fords! Crown him!
crown him! Crowns be - come the vic - tor's brow.
crown him! Crown the Sav - ior, King of kings.
crown him! Spread a - broad the vic - tor's fame!
crown him! King of kings and Lord of lords.

Rejoice, the Lord Is King! 228

Based on Philippians 4:4
Charles Wesley, 1707-1788

DARWALL'S 148th 6.6.6.6.8.8.
John Darwall, 1731-1789

1 Re - joice, the Lord is King! Your Lord and King a - dore!
2 The Lord, our Sav - ior, reigns, The God of truth and love;
3 His king - dom can - not fail, He rules o'er earth and heav'n;
4 Re - joice in glo - rious hope! Our Lord the judge shall come
Re - joice, give thanks, and sing, And tri - umph ev - er -
When he had purged our stains, He took his seat a -
The keys of death and hell Are to our Je - sus
And take his serv - ants up To their e - ter - nal
more:
bove:
giv'n:
home:
Lift up your heart, lift up your voice! Re -
joice, a - gain I say, re - joice! A - men.

229 The Head That Once Was Crowned with Thorns

Based on Hebrews 2:9 — ST. MAGNUS C.M.
Thomas Kelly, 1769-1855 — *Jeremiah Clark, c.1670-1707*

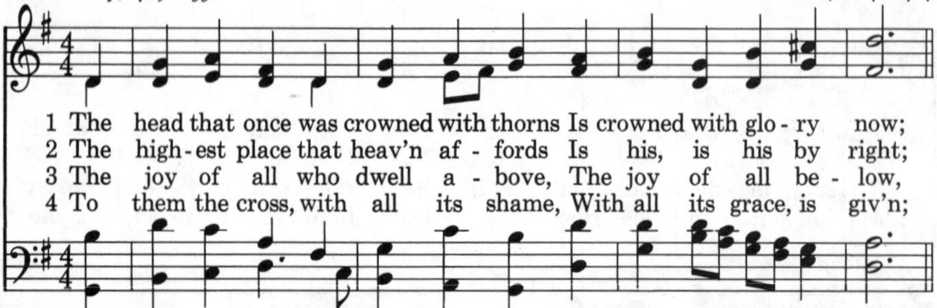

1 The head that once was crowned with thorns Is crowned with glo - ry now;
2 The high - est place that heav'n af - fords Is his, is his by right;
3 The joy of all who dwell a - bove, The joy of all be - low,
4 To them the cross, with all its shame, With all its grace, is giv'n;

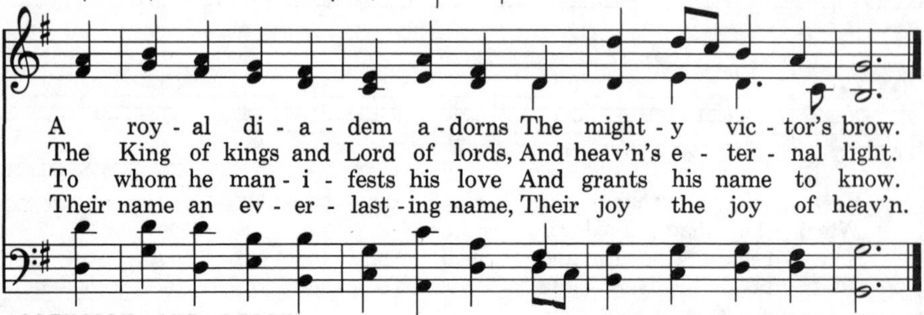

A roy - al di - a - dem a - dorns The might - y vic - tor's brow.
The King of kings and Lord of lords, And heav'n's e - ter - nal light.
To whom he man - i - fests his love And grants his name to know.
Their name an ev - er - last - ing name, Their joy the joy of heav'n.

ASCENSION AND REIGN

A lower setting may be found at No. 598

230 We Wait for a Great and Glorious Day

A. L. Skoog, 1856-1934 — SKOOG 10.7.10.7. *with Refrain*
A. L. Skoog, 1856-1934

1 We wait for a great and glo - ri - ous day, As
2 In glo - ry and pow'r our King shall ap - pear And
3 For cross - es we've borne then crowns will be giv'n, For
4 We know not the day, we know not the hour When
Snart ran - das en dag så här - lig och stor För
man - y as love the Lord, When shad - ows shall flee, and
call to him - self his own; No dis - tance nor death shall
tem - pests e - ter - nal calm; For path - way of thorns rich
sounds the last trump so clear; But loud rings a cry from
al - la, som äls - ka Gud; Dess sol ald - rig skyms av

COMING IN GLORY

clouds pass a - way, And weep - ing no more be heard.
part them as here, Nor sin with its pains be known.
man - sions in heav'n, For war - fare the vic - tor's palm.
truth's loft - y tow'r, "The day of the Lord is near."
skug - gor - nas flor, Och ald - rig hörs kla - gans ljud.
REFRAIN (after last stanza only)
O won - der - ful day that soon may be here!
O här - li - ga dag som ran - das för mig!
O beau - ti - ful hope the pil - grim to cheer!
O här - li - ga mål på pil - gri - mens stig!
Thy com - ing we hail in tune - ful ac - cord,
Min läng - tan och blick allt mer till dig drag,
Thou glo - ri - ous day of Christ, our Lord.
Du här - li - ga Je - su Kri - sti dag!

231 Christ Is Coming! Let Creation

John R. MacDuff, 1818-1895

BRYN CALFARIA 8.7.8.7.4.7.
William Owen, 1814-1893
Harm. by Carlton R. Young, 1926-

1 Christ is com - ing! let cre - a - tion From her groans and trav - ail cease;
Let the glo - rious proc - la - ma - tion Hope re - store and faith in - crease:
Christ is com - ing, Christ is com - ing, Christ is com - ing—
Come, thou bless-ed Prince of Peace! Come, thou bless-ed Prince of Peace!

2 Earth can now but tell the sto - ry Of thy bit - ter cross and pain;
She shall yet be - hold thy glo - ry When thou com - est back to reign:
Christ is com - ing, Christ is com - ing, Christ is com - ing—
Let each heart re - peat the strain! Let each heart re - peat the strain!

3 Long thine ex - iles have been pin - ing, Far from rest and home and thee;
But, in heav'n-ly ves-tures shin - ing, They their lov - ing Lord shall see:
Christ is com - ing, Christ is com - ing, Christ is com - ing—
Haste the joy - ous ju - bi - lee! Haste the joy - ous ju - bi - lee!

4 With that bless - ed hope be - fore us, Let no harp re - main un-strung;
Let the might - y ad - vent cho - rus On - ward roll from tongue to tongue:
Christ is com - ing, Christ is com - ing, Christ is com - ing—
Come, Lord Je - sus, quick - ly come! Come, Lord Je - sus, quick-ly come! A - men.

COMING IN GLORY

Lo! He Comes, with Clouds Descending 232

Based on Revelation 1:7
Charles Wesley, 1707-1788

HOLYWOOD 8.7.8.7.8.7.
John F. Wade's "Cantus Diversi," 1751

1 Lo! he comes, with clouds de - scend - ing, Once for our sal -
2 Ev - 'ry eye shall now be - hold him, Robed in dread - ful
3 Yea, A - men! Let all a - dore thee, High on thine e -
va - tion slain; Thou - sand thou - sand saints at - tend - ing
maj - es - ty; Those who set at naught and sold him,
ter - nal throne; Sav - ior, take the pow'r and glo - ry,
Swell the tri - umph of his train: Al - le - lu - ia!
Pierced and nailed him to the tree, With great an - guish,
Claim the king - dom for thine own: Al - le - lu - ia!
Al - le - lu - ia! God ap - pears on earth to reign.
with great an - guish, Shall the true Mes - si - ah see.
Al - le - lu - ia! Thou shalt reign and thou a - lone. A - men.

233 Day of Judgment! Day of Wonders!

John Newton, 1725-1807

PRAISE MY SOUL 8.7.8.7.8.7.
John Goss, 1800-1880

1 Day of judg-ment! day of won - ders! Hark, the trum-pet's
2 See the Judge, our na - ture wear - ing, Clothed in maj - es -
3 At his call the dead a - wak - en, Rise to life from
4 Then to all who have con - fess - ed, Loved and served the
aw - ful sound, Loud - er than a thou-sand thun-ders,
ty di - vine; Ye who love the Lord's ap - pear ing
earth and sea; All the pow'rs of na - ture, shak - en,
Lord be - low, He will say, "Come near, ye bless - ed,
Shakes the vast cre - a - tion round: How the sum-mons,
Then shall say, "This God is mine!" Gra - cious Sav - ior,
At his call pre - pare to flee: Care - less sin - ner,
See the king-dom I be - stow: You for ev - er,
how the sum-mons Will the sin-ner's heart con - found!
gra - cious Sav - ior, Own me on that day as thine.
care - less sin - ner, What will then be - come of thee?
you for - ev - er Shall my love and glo - ry know."

Great God, What Do I See and Hear!

Based on 1 Thessalonians 4:16
William B. Collyer, 1782-1854
Alt. by Thomas Cotterill, 1779-1823

NUN FREUT EUCH 8.7.8.7.8.8.7.
Joseph Klug's "Geistliche Lieder," Wittenberg, 1535

1 Great God, what do I see and hear! The end of things cre - at - ed!
2 The dead in Christ shall first a - rise At the last trum-pet's sound - ing,
3 Great God, what do I see and hear! The end of things cre - at - ed!

The Judge of man-kind doth ap-pear, On clouds of glo - ry seat - ed!
Caught up to meet him in the skies, With joy their Lord sur - round - ing;
The Judge of man-kind doth ap-pear, On clouds of glo - ry seat - ed!

The trum-pet sounds–the graves re - store The dead which they con -
No gloom-y fears their souls dis - may; His pres - ence sheds e -
Be - neath his cross I view the day When heav'n and earth shall

tained be - fore: Pre - pare, my soul, to meet him.
ter - nal day On those pre - pared to meet him.
pass a - way, And thus pre - pare to meet him. A - men.

235 Hide Not Thy Face, O My Savior

Lina Sandell, 1832-1903
Tr. Joseph E. Anderson, 1890-1954

LOST IN THE NIGHT 11.11. *with Refrain*
Finnish Folk Melody
"Karelen," 1857

1 Hide not thy face, O my Sav - ior— be near me;
2 Still far re - moved from my home - land, I wan - der;
3 While thou dost tar - ry, my path wouldst thou bright - en;
4 Grant, then, O Lord, that I fear thee, a - dore thee;
5 Help me the bur - den to bear thou hast giv - en;
Com - fort and bless— while I pray, wilt thou hear me:
Here but a pil - grim and stran - ger, I pon - der:
Sor - rows and cares of my heart wouldst thou light - en.
Hum - bly in spir - it I bow down be - fore thee.
Give me at last, Lord, a crown in thy heav - en.
REFRAIN
Bless - ed Re - deem - er, my Sav - ior and Com - fort - er,
Art thou com - ing soon? Art thou com - ing soon? A - men.

It May Be at Morn

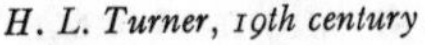
H. L. Turner, 19th century

CHRIST RETURNETH 12.12.12.8. *with Refrain*
James McGranahan, 1840-1907

1 It may be at morn, when the day is a - wak - ing, When sun-light thru
dark - ness and shad - ow is break - ing, That Je - sus will come in the
full - ness of glo - ry, To re - ceive from the world his own.

2 It may be at mid - day, it may be at twi-light, It may be, per -
chance, that the black-ness of mid-night Will burst in - to light in the
blaze of his glo - ry, When Je - sus re - ceives his own.

3 O joy! O de - light! should we go with-out dy - ing, No sick - ness, no
sad - ness, no dread and no cry - ing, Caught up thru the clouds with our
Lord in - to glo - ry, When Je - sus re - ceives his own.

REFRAIN

O Lord Je - sus, how long, how long Ere we shout the glad song: Christ re -
turn - eth, hal - le - lu - jah! Hal - le - lu - jah! A - men, Hal - le - lu - jah! A - men.

237 The King Shall Come When Morning Dawns

From the Greek
Tr. John Brownlie, 1859-1925

ST. MICHEL'S C.M.D.
William Gawler's "Hymns and Psalms," c. 1788

1 The King shall come when morn-ing dawns And light tri - um-phant breaks,
2 O bright - er than the ris - ing morn When he, vic - to - rious, rose
3 The King shall come when morn-ing dawns And light tri - um-phant breaks,
When beau - ty gilds the east - ern hills And life to joy a - wakes.
And left the lone-some place of death, De - spite the rage of foes—
When beau - ty gilds the east - ern hills And life to joy a - wakes.
Not as of old a lit - tle child, To bear and fight and die,
O bright - er than the glo-rious morn Shall this fair morn - ing be,
The King shall come when morn-ing dawns And light and beau - ty brings;
But crowned with glo - ry like the sun That lights the morn - ing sky.
When Christ our King in beau - ty comes And we his face shall see!
Hail, Christ the Lord! thy peo - ple pray, Come quick-ly, King of kings!

COMING IN GLORY

Alternate tune: ALL SAINTS NEW, *No. 184*

My Lord, What a Morning! 238

American Folk Hymn

WHAT A MORNING *Irregular*
American Folk Melody
Harm. by James P. Davies, 1913-

In unison
My Lord, what a morn-ing! My Lord, what a morn-ing!
Fine
My Lord, what a morn-ing, When the stars be-gin to fall!
1 You'll hear the trum-pet sound,
2 You'll hear the sin-ner mourn, To wake the na-tions un-der-ground;
3 You'll hear the Chris-tian shout,
D.C.
Look-ing to my God's right hand, When the stars be-gin to fall.

239 All Praise to Thee, for Thou, O King Divine

Based on Philippians 2:5-11
F. Bland Tucker, 1895-

SARUM 10.10.10. *with Alleluias*
Joseph Barnby, 1838-1896
Harm. by Norman E. Johnson, 1928-

In unison
1 All praise to thee, for thou, O King di - vine,
2 Thou cam'st to us in low - li - ness of thought,
3 Let this mind be in us which was in thee,
4 Where - fore, by God's e - ter - nal pur - pose, thou
5 Let ev - 'ry tongue con - fess with one ac - cord
Didst yield the glo - ry that of right was thine,
By thee the out - cast and the poor were sought,
Who wast a serv - ant that we might be free,
Art ex - alt - ed o'er all crea - tures now,
In heav'n and earth that Je - sus Christ is Lord,
That in our dark - ened hearts thy grace might shine:
And by thy death was God's sal - va - tion wrought:
Hum - bling thy - self to death on Cal - va - ry:
And giv'n the name to which all knees shall bow:
And God the Fa - ther be by all a - dored:
Al - le - lu - ia! Al - le - lu - ia!
Al - le - lu - ia! Al - le - lu - ia!
Al - le - lu - ia! Al - le - lu - ia!
Al - le - lu - ia! Al - le - lu - ia!
Al - le - lu - ia! Al - le - lu - ia! A - men.

Alternate tune: SINE NOMINE, *No. 602*

All Praise to Him Who Reigns Above 240

W. H. Clark, 19th century
Refrain added by Ralph E. Hudson, 1843-1901

BLESSED BE THE NAME C.M. *with Refrain*
Ralph E. Hudson, 1843-1901
Harm. by William J. Kirkpatrick, 1838-1921

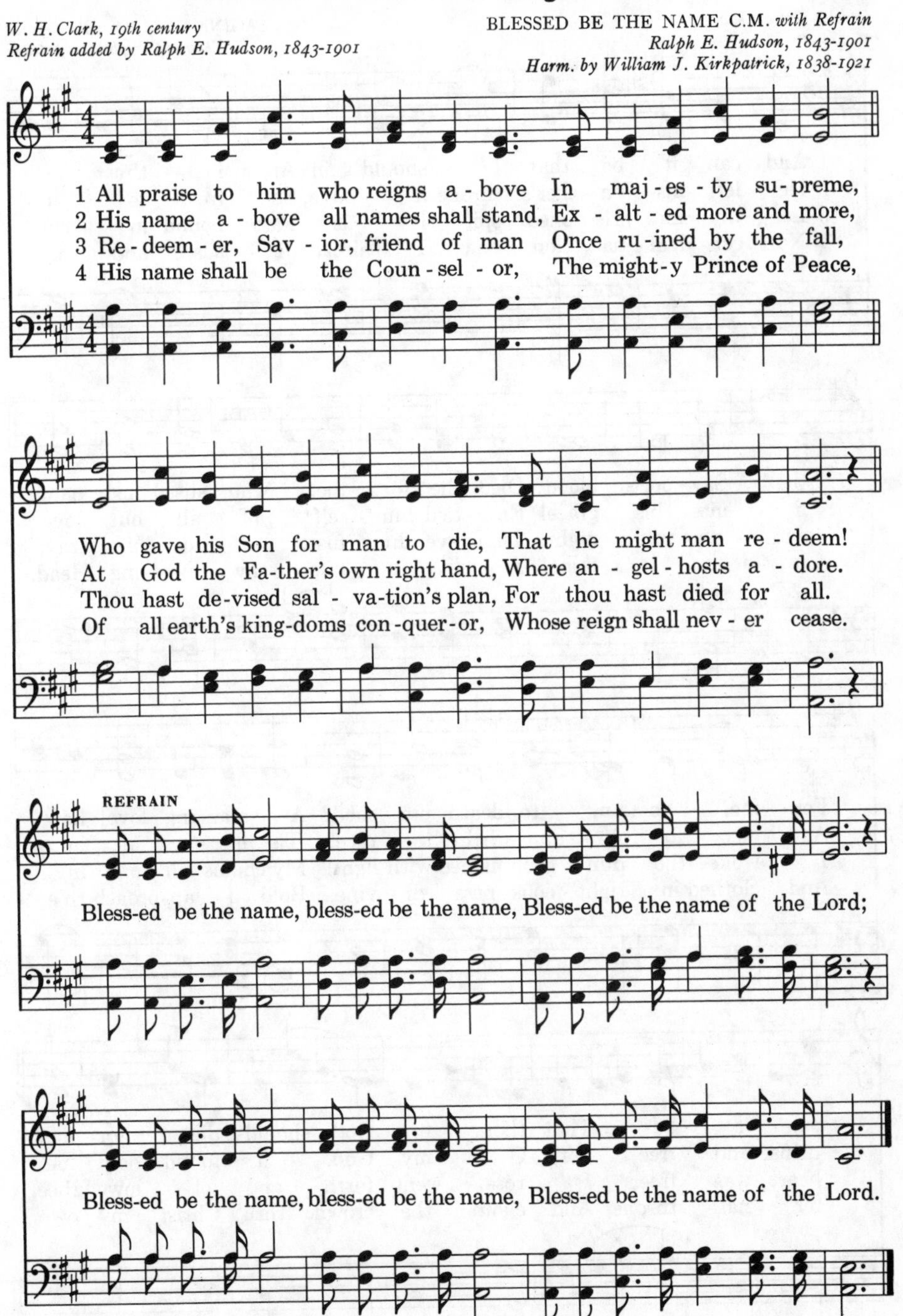
1 All praise to him who reigns a - bove In maj - es - ty su - preme,
2 His name a - bove all names shall stand, Ex - alt - ed more and more,
3 Re - deem - er, Sav - ior, friend of man Once ru - ined by the fall,
4 His name shall be the Coun - sel - or, The might - y Prince of Peace,
Who gave his Son for man to die, That he might man re - deem!
At God the Fa - ther's own right hand, Where an - gel - hosts a - dore.
Thou hast de - vised sal - va - tion's plan, For thou hast died for all.
Of all earth's king - doms con - quer - or, Whose reign shall nev - er cease.
REFRAIN
Bless - ed be the name, bless - ed be the name, Bless - ed be the name of the Lord;
Bless - ed be the name, bless - ed be the name, Bless - ed be the name of the Lord.

241 And Can It Be That I Should Gain

Charles Wesley, 1707-1788

SAGINA 8.8.8.8.8.8. *with Refrain*
Thomas Campbell, 1777-1844

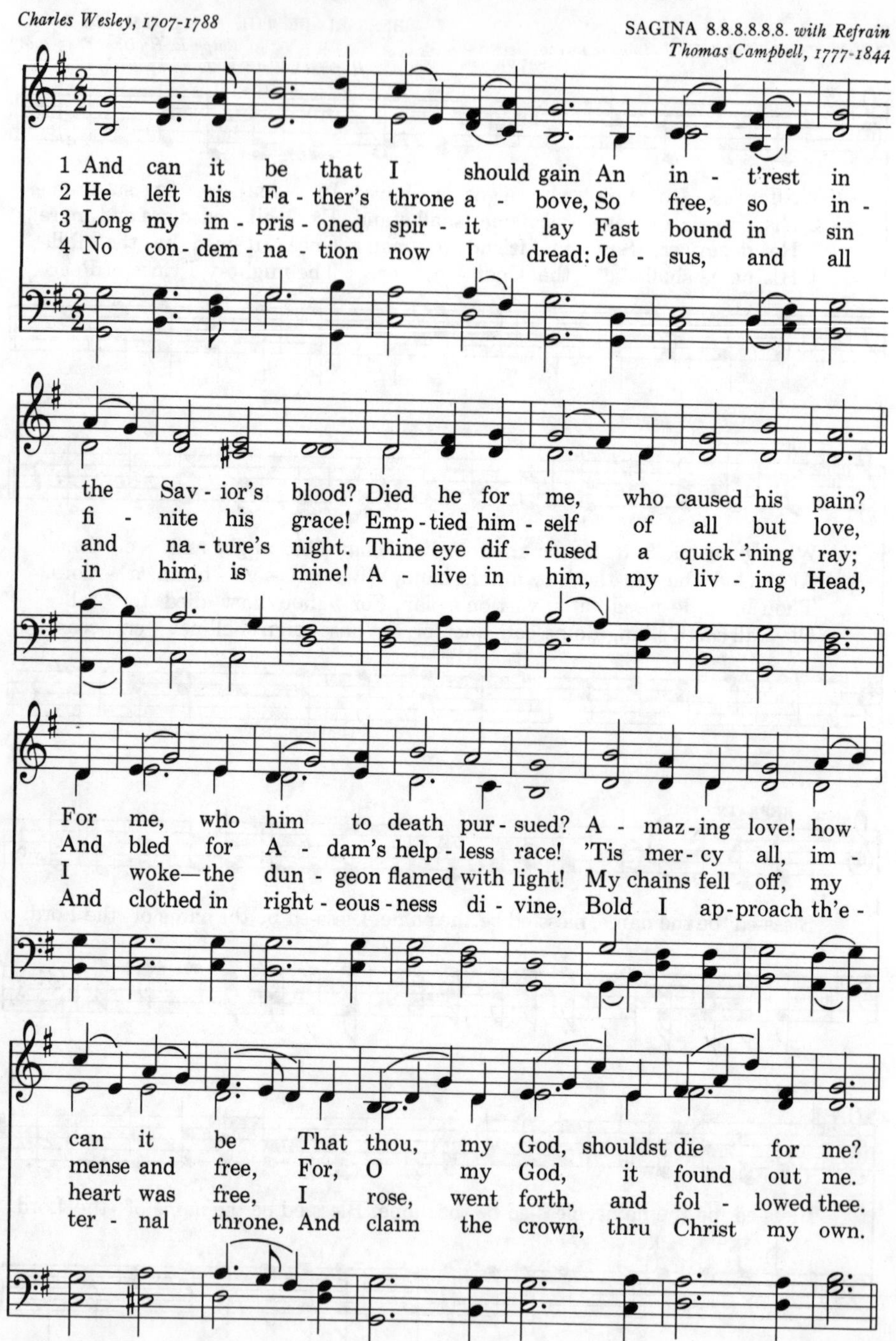
1 And can it be that I should gain An in - t'rest in
2 He left his Fa - ther's throne a - bove, So free, so in -
3 Long my im - pris - oned spir - it lay Fast bound in sin
4 No con - dem - na - tion now I dread: Je - sus, and all
the Sav - ior's blood? Died he for me, who caused his pain?
fi - nite his grace! Emp - tied him - self of all but love,
and na - ture's night. Thine eye dif - fused a quick - 'ning ray;
in him, is mine! A - live in him, my liv - ing Head,
For me, who him to death pur - sued? A - maz - ing love! how
And bled for A - dam's help - less race! 'Tis mer - cy all, im -
I woke—the dun - geon flamed with light! My chains fell off, my
And clothed in right - eous - ness di - vine, Bold I ap - proach th'e -
can it be That thou, my God, shouldst die for me?
mense and free, For, O my God, it found out me.
heart was free, I rose, went forth, and fol - lowed thee.
ter - nal throne, And claim the crown, thru Christ my own.

REFRAIN
A - maz - ing love! how can it be
A-maz-ing love! how can it be
That thou, my God, shouldst die for me! A - men.
O for a Thousand Tongues to Sing
242
Charles Wesley, 1707-1788
AZMON C.M.
Carl G. Gläser, 1784-1829
Mason's "Modern Psalmody," 1839
1 O for a thou-sand tongues to sing My great Re-deem-er's praise,
2 My gra-cious Mas-ter and my God, As - sist me to pro-claim,
3 Je - sus! the name that charms our fears, That bids our sor - rows cease,
4 He breaks the pow'r of can-celled sin, He sets the pris - 'ner free;
5 Hear him, ye deaf; his praise, ye dumb, Your loos-ened tongues em-ploy;
6 Glo - ry to God and praise and love Be ev - er, ev - er giv'n
The glo-ries of my God and King, The tri-umphs of his grace!
To spread thru all the earth a-broad The hon-ors of thy name.
'Tis mu-sic in the sin-ner's ears, 'Tis life and health and peace.
His blood can make the foul-est clean, His blood a-vailed for me.
Ye blind, be-hold your Sav-ior come; And leap, ye lame, for joy.
By saints be-low and saints a-bove, The Church in earth and heav'n. A-men.

Alternate tune: RICHMOND, *No. 164*

243 Come, Christians, Join to Sing

Christian Henry Bateman, 1813-1889

SPANISH HYMN 6.6.6.6.D.
Source unknown
Harm. by A. Royce Eckhardt, 1937-

1 Come, Chris-tians, join to sing— Al - le - lu - ia! A - men!
2 Come, lift your hearts on high— Al - le - lu - ia! A - men!
3 Praise yet our Christ a - gain— Al - le - lu - ia! A - men!
Loud praise to Christ our King— Al - le - lu - ia! A - men!
Let prais - es fill the sky— Al - le - lu - ia! A - men!
Life shall not end the strain— Al - le - lu ia! A - men!
Let all, with heart and voice, Be - fore his throne re - joice;
He is our guide and friend, To us he'll con - de - scend;
On heav - en's bliss - ful shore His good - ness we'll a - dore,
Praise is his gra - cious choice: Al - le - lu - ia! A - men!
His love shall nev - er end: Al - le - lu - ia! A - men!
Sing - ing for - ev - er - more, "Al - le - lu - ia! A - men!"

244 Come, Let Us Praise Him

Lina Sandell, 1832-1903
Tr. Karl A. Olsson, 1913-

LÅTOM OSS SJUNGA 5.6.5.6.6.
Ahnfelt's "Sånger," 1868
Harm. by A. Royce Eckhardt, 1937-

1 Come, let us praise him, Sing - ing of grace di - vine; Youths now and
2 Earth and the heav - ens Show forth his glo - ry bright; Yet he was
3 Will - ing - ly stoop - ing Un - der my bur - den, he Pa - tient - ly
4 Bear - ing our an - guish, Nailed to a shame-ful tree, He died to
5 All this he suf - fered For his be - lov - ed bride, That she for -
6 Let us be sing - ing Al - ways of him, our friend, Ev - er a -
eld - ers Prais - ing his love's de - sign, Laud - ing his acts be - nign.
hum - bled, Stripped of his won-drous might, Shar - ing our hu - man plight.
car - ried All that op-press - es me, Set - ting the cap - tive free.
save us From an e - ter - ni - ty Of deep-est mis - er - y.
ev - er, By his death sanc - ti - fied, Might in his house a - bide.
dor - ing Mer - cies with-out an end: Christ, we our prais - es lend.
1 Je - sus! name of won-drous love, Name all oth - er names a - bove,
2 Je - sus! name of price - less worth To the fall - en sons of earth,
3 Je - sus! on - ly name that's giv'n Un - der all the might - y heav'n
4 Je - sus! name of won-drous love, Hu - man name of God a - bove:
Un - to which must ev - 'ry knee Bow in deep hu - mil - i - ty.
For the prom - ise that it gave, "Je - sus shall his peo - ple save."
Where-by man, to sin en-slaved, Bursts his fet - ters and is saved.
Plead-ing on - ly this we flee, Help-less, O our God, to thee. A-men.

245 Jesus! Name of Wondrous Love

Based on Philippians 2:9, 10
William Walsham How, 1823-1897

ST. BEES 7.7.7.7.
John B. Dykes, 1823-1876

A lower setting may be found at No. 329

246 I Will Sing of My Redeemer

Philip P. Bliss, 1838-1876

MY REDEEMER 8.7.8.7. *with Refrain*
James McGranahan, 1840-1907
Harm. by A. Royce Eckhardt, 1937-

1 I will sing of my Re-deem-er And his won-drous love to me;
2 I will tell the won-drous sto-ry, How my lost es-tate to save,
3 I will praise my dear Re-deem-er, His tri-um-phant pow'r I'll tell,
4 I will sing of my Re-deem-er And his heav'n-ly love to me;
On the cru-el cross he suf-fered, From the curse to set me free.
In his bound-less love and mer-cy, He the ran-som free-ly gave.
How the vic-to-ry he giv-eth O-ver sin and death and hell.
He from death to life hath brought me, Son of God with him to be.
REFRAIN
Sing, O sing of my Re-deem-er, With his blood he pur-chased me;
On the cross he sealed my par-don, Paid the debt and made me free.

Alternate tune: HYFRYDOL, *No. 247*

I Will Sing the Wondrous Story

HYFRYDOL 8.7.8.7.D.

Francis H. Rowley, 1854-1952

Rowland H. Prichard, 1811-1887
Harm. by James P. Davies, 1913-

In unison
1 I will sing the won-drous sto - ry Of the Christ who died for me,
2 I was lost, but Je - sus found me, Found the sheep that went a - stray,
3 I was bruised, but Je - sus healed me, Faint was I from man - y a fall;
4 Days of dark - ness still come o'er me, Sor - row's paths I oft - en tread,
How he left his home in glo - ry For the cross of Cal - va - ry.
Threw his lov - ing arms a - round me, Drew me back in - to the way.
Sight was gone, and fears pos - sessed me, But he freed me from them all.
But the Sav - ior still is with me, By his hand I'm safe - ly led.
REFRAIN
Yes, I'll sing the won-drous sto - ry Of the Christ who died for me,
Sing it with the saints in glo - ry, Gath-ered by the crys - tal sea.

Another harmonization in a higher setting may be found at No. 248

248 Jesus! What a Friend for Sinners!

J. Wilbur Chapman, 1859-1918

HYFRYDOL 8.7.8.7.D.
Rowland H. Prichard, 1811-1887
Harm. by Robert Harkness, 1880-1961

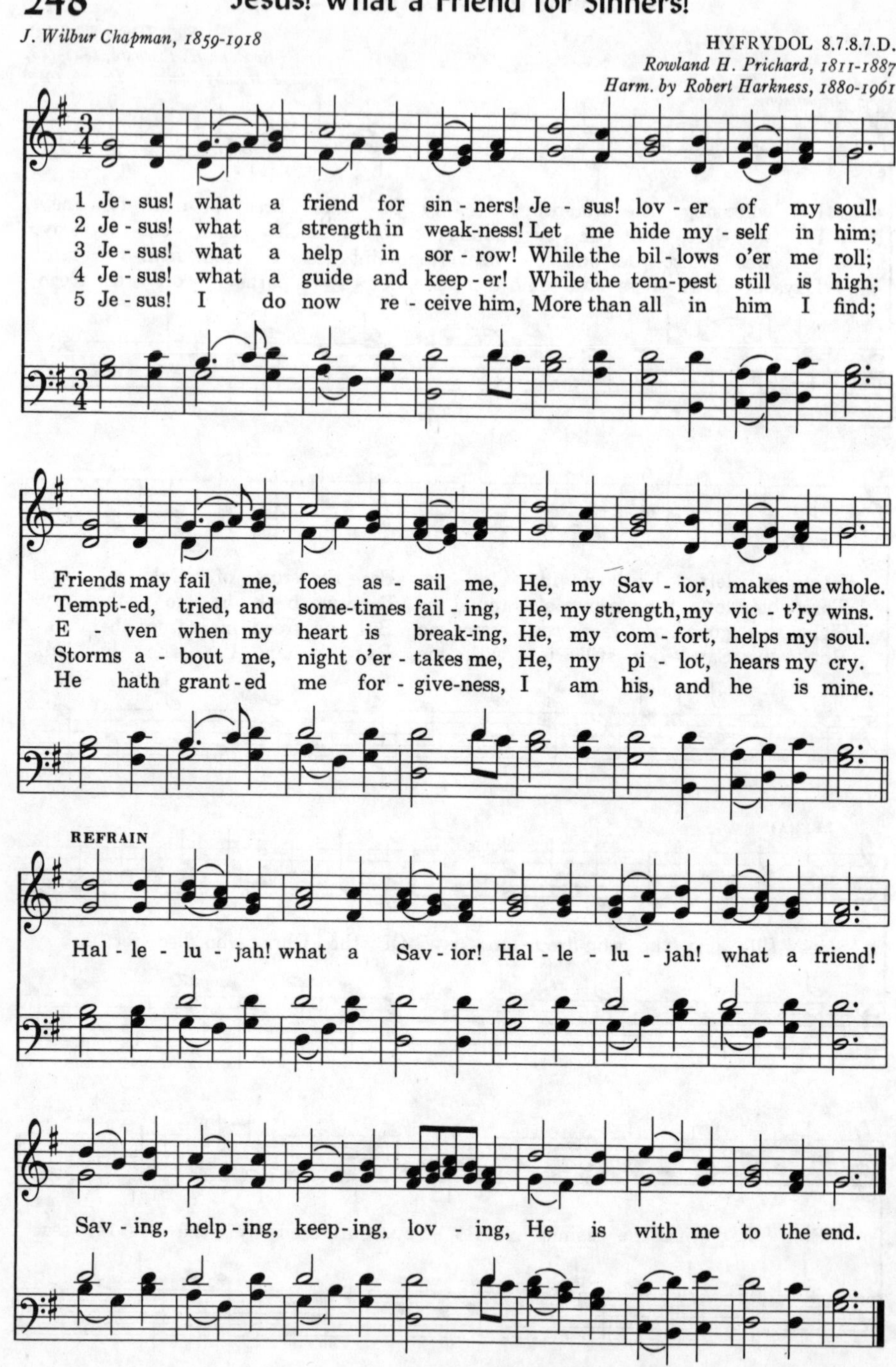

1 Je - sus! what a friend for sin - ners! Je - sus! lov - er of my soul!
2 Je - sus! what a strength in weak-ness! Let me hide my - self in him;
3 Je - sus! what a help in sor - row! While the bil - lows o'er me roll;
4 Je - sus! what a guide and keep - er! While the tem-pest still is high;
5 Je - sus! I do now re - ceive him, More than all in him I find;
Friends may fail me, foes as - sail me, He, my Sav - ior, makes me whole.
Tempt-ed, tried, and some-times fail - ing, He, my strength, my vic - t'ry wins.
E - ven when my heart is break-ing, He, my com - fort, helps my soul.
Storms a - bout me, night o'er - takes me, He, my pi - lot, hears my cry.
He hath grant - ed me for - give-ness, I am his, and he is mine.
REFRAIN
Hal - le - lu - jah! what a Sav - ior! Hal - le - lu - jah! what a friend!
Sav - ing, help - ing, keep - ing, lov - ing, He is with me to the end.

Other harmonizations in a lower setting may be found at Nos. 247, 260, and 335

Join All the Glorious Names

Isaac Watts, 1674-1748

DARWALL'S 148th 6.6.6.6.8.8.
John Darwall, 1731-1789

1 Join all the glo-rious names Of wis-dom, love, and pow'r,
2 Great Proph-et of my God, My tongue would bless thy name;
3 Je - sus, thou great High Priest, Thou gav'st thy blood and died;
4 Di - vine, al-might-y Lord, My Con-qu'ror and my King,
5 Now let my soul a - rise And tread the tempt-er down;
That ev-er mor-tals knew, That an-gels ev - er bore:
By thee the joy-ful news Of our sal - va - tion came:
My guilt-y con-science seeks No sac-ri-fice be - side:
Thy scep-ter and thy sword, Thy reign-ing grace I sing:
My cap-tain leads me forth To con-quest and a crown:
All are too poor to speak his worth,
The joy - ful news of sins for - giv'n,
Thy pow'r - ful blood didst once a - tone
Thine is the pow'r! be - hold I sit
A fee - ble saint shall win the day,
Too poor to set my Sav - ior forth.
Of hell sub-dued, and peace with heav'n.
And now it pleads be - fore the throne.
In will - ing bonds be - neath thy feet.
Though death and hell ob - struct the way.

Another harmonization in a lower setting may be found at No. 256

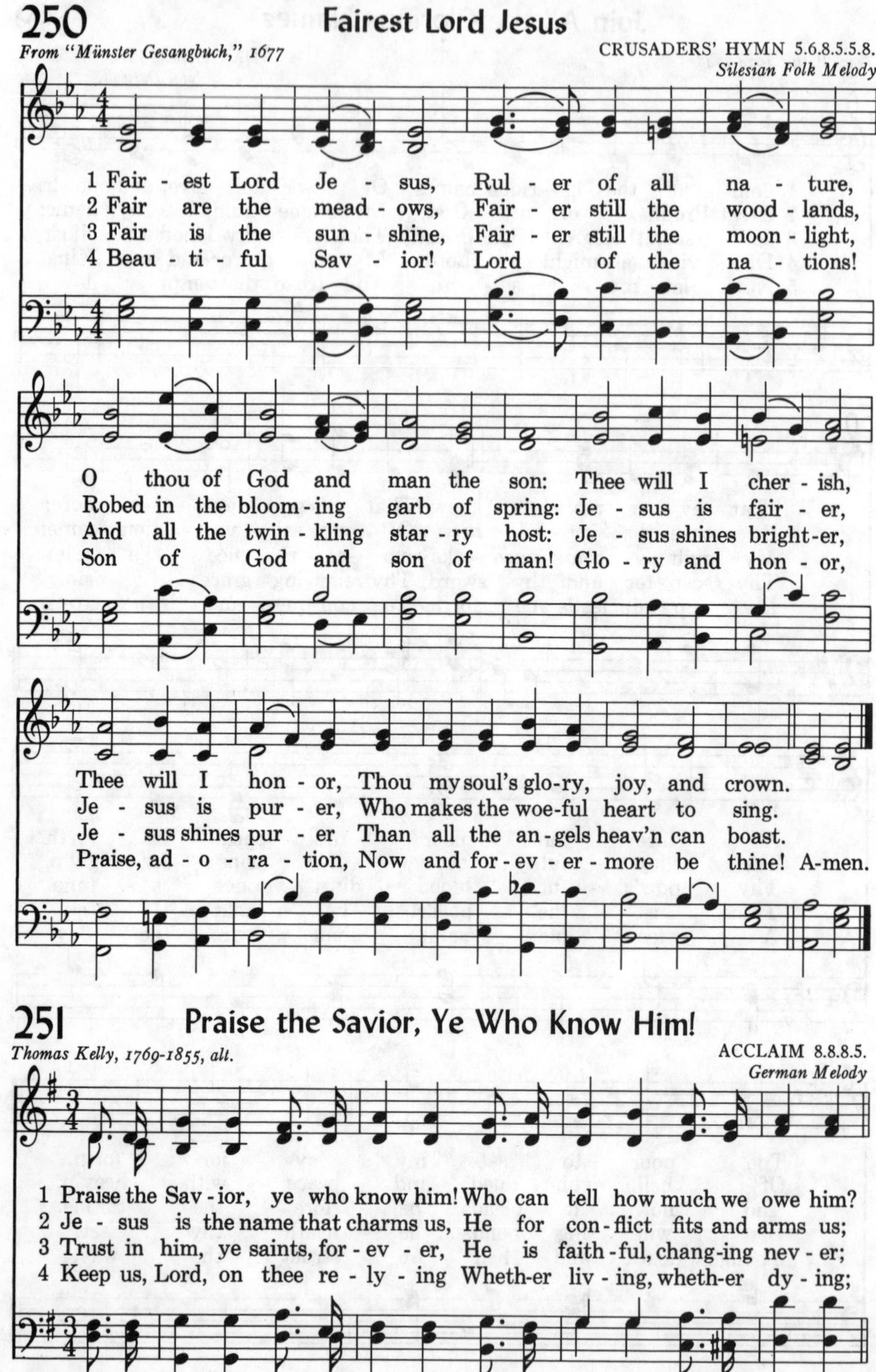
250 Fairest Lord Jesus
From "Münster Gesangbuch," 1677
CRUSADERS' HYMN 5.6.8.5.5.8.
Silesian Folk Melody
1 Fair - est Lord Je - sus, Rul - er of all na - ture,
2 Fair are the mead - ows, Fair - er still the wood - lands,
3 Fair is the sun - shine, Fair - er still the moon - light,
4 Beau - ti - ful Sav - ior! Lord of the na - tions!
O thou of God and man the son: Thee will I cher - ish,
Robed in the bloom - ing garb of spring: Je - sus is fair - er,
And all the twin - kling star - ry host: Je - sus shines bright - er,
Son of God and son of man! Glo - ry and hon - or,
Thee will I hon - or, Thou my soul's glo - ry, joy, and crown.
Je - sus is pur - er, Who makes the woe - ful heart to sing.
Je - sus shines pur - er Than all the an - gels heav'n can boast.
Praise, ad - o - ra - tion, Now and for - ev - er - more be thine! A - men.
251 Praise the Savior, Ye Who Know Him!
Thomas Kelly, 1769-1855, alt.
ACCLAIM 8.8.8.5.
German Melody
1 Praise the Sav - ior, ye who know him! Who can tell how much we owe him?
2 Je - sus is the name that charms us, He for con - flict fits and arms us;
3 Trust in him, ye saints, for - ev - er, He is faith - ful, chang - ing nev - er;
4 Keep us, Lord, on thee re - ly - ing Wheth - er liv - ing, wheth - er dy - ing;

Jesus, Jesus, Name Most Precious 252

Carl Boberg, 1859-1940
Tr. Karl A. Olsson, 1913-

JESU NAMN 8.7.8.7.8.7.
Amanda S. Waesterberg, 1842-1918
Harm. by A. Royce Eckhardt, 1937-

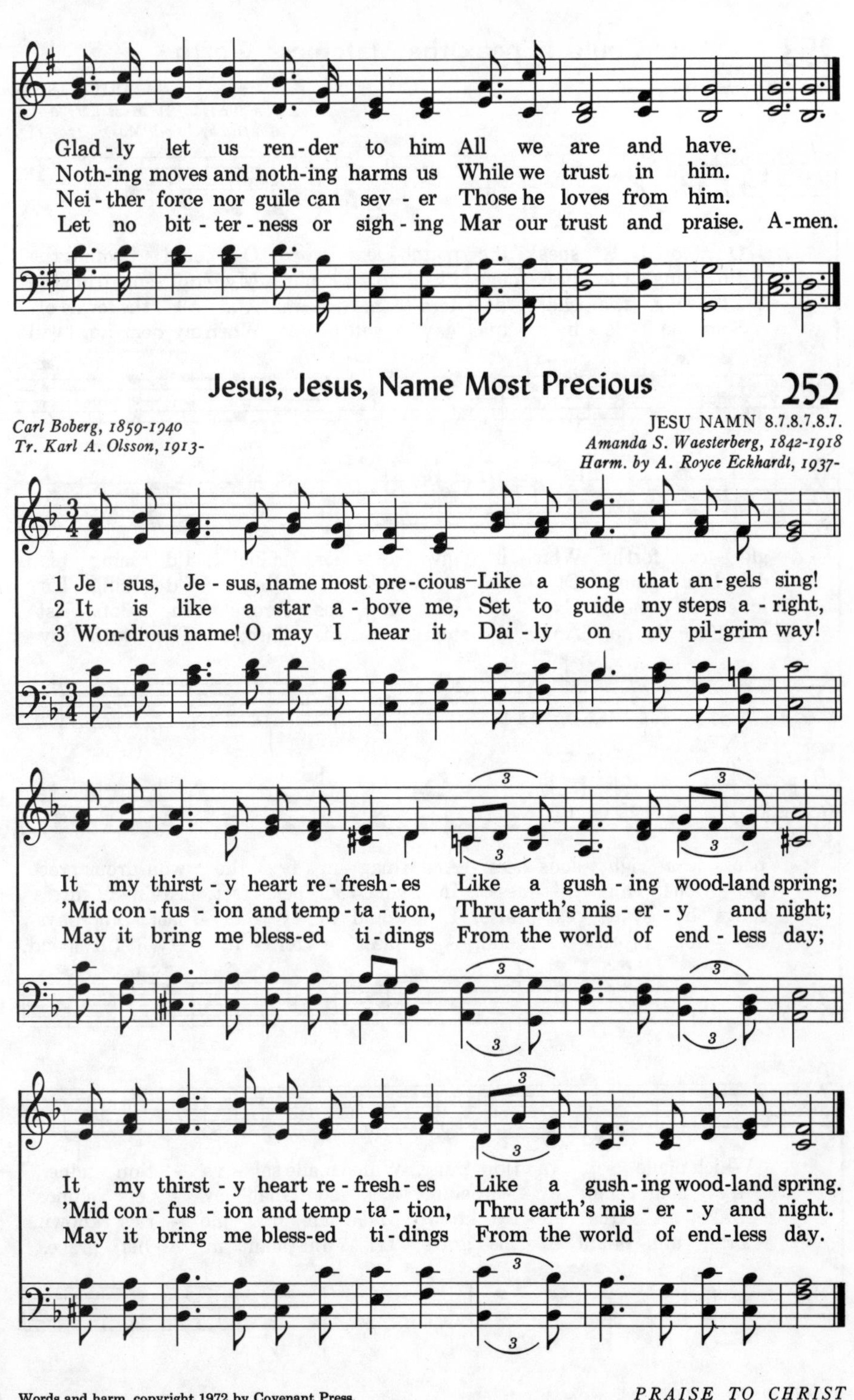
Glad-ly let us ren-der to him All we are and have.
Noth-ing moves and noth-ing harms us While we trust in him.
Nei-ther force nor guile can sev-er Those he loves from him.
Let no bit-ter-ness or sigh-ing Mar our trust and praise. A-men.
1 Je-sus, Je-sus, name most pre-cious–Like a song that an-gels sing!
2 It is like a star a-bove me, Set to guide my steps a-right,
3 Won-drous name! O may I hear it Dai-ly on my pil-grim way!
It my thirst-y heart re-fresh-es Like a gush-ing wood-land spring;
'Mid con-fu-sion and temp-ta-tion, Thru earth's mis-er-y and night;
May it bring me bless-ed ti-dings From the world of end-less day;
It my thirst-y heart re-fresh-es Like a gush-ing wood-land spring.
'Mid con-fus-ion and temp-ta-tion, Thru earth's mis-er-y and night.
May it bring me bless-ed ti-dings From the world of end-less day.

253 O Could I Speak the Matchless Worth

Samuel Medley, 1738-1799, alt.

ARIEL 8.8.6.D.
Attr. to Wolfgang A. Mozart, 1756-1791
Adapted by Lowell Mason, 1792-1872

1 O could I speak the match-less worth, O could I sound the
2 I'd sing the pre-cious blood he spilt, My ran-som from the
3 I'd sing the char-ac-ters he bears, And all the forms of
4 Soon the de-light-ful day will come When my dear Lord will
glo-ries forth Which in my Sav-ior shine! I'd sing his
dread-ful guilt Of sin, and wrath di-vine; I'd sing his
love he wears, Ex-alt-ed on his throne; In loft-iest
bring me home, And I shall see his face; Then with my
per-fect right-eous-ness, And mag-ni-fy the won-drous grace
glo-rious ho-li-ness, In which all-per-fect, heav'n-ly dress
songs of sweet-est praise, I would to ev-er-last-ing days
Sav-ior, broth-er, friend, A blest e-ter-ni-ty I'll spend,
Which made sal-va-tion mine, Which made sal-va-tion mine.
My soul shall ev-er shine, My soul shall ev-er shine.
Make all his glo-ries known, Make all his glo-ries known.
Tri-um-phant in his grace, Tri-um-phant in his grace.

O Savior, Precious Savior

Frances Ridley Havergal, 1836-1879

ANGEL'S STORY 7.6.7.6.D.
Arthur H. Mann, 1850-1929

1 O Sav - ior, pre - cious Sav - ior, Whom yet un - seen we love,
2 O bring - er of sal - va - tion, Who won - drous - ly hast wrought,
3 In thee all full - ness dwell - eth, All grace and pow'r di - vine,
4 O grant the con - sum - ma - tion Of this our song a - bove,
O Name of might and fa - vor, All oth - er names a - bove:
Thy - self the rev - e - la - tion Of love be - yond our thought:
The glo - ry that ex - cel - leth, O Son of God, is thine:
In end - less ad - o - ra - tion And ev - er - last - ing love:
We wor - ship thee, we bless thee, To thee, O Christ, we sing,
We wor - ship thee, we bless thee, To thee, O Christ, we sing,
We wor - ship thee, we bless thee, To thee, O Christ, we sing,
Then shall we praise and bless thee Where per - fect prais - es ring,
We praise thee and con - fess thee, Our ho - ly Lord and King.
We praise thee and con - fess thee, Our gra - cious Lord and King.
We praise thee and con - fess thee, Our glo - rious Lord and King.
And ev - er - more con - fess thee, Our Sav - ior and our King. A - men.

255 Sing the Glad Carol of Jesus, Our Lord

A. L. Skoog, 1856-1934 — GLAD CAROL 10.4.4.10.6. *with Refrain*
Tr. E. Gustav Johnson, 1893- — *A. L. Skoog, 1856-1934*

1 Sing the glad car-ol of Je-sus, our Lord, Sing it a-gain, sing it a-gain!
2 Faith and new cour-age are in this re-frain, Sing it a-gain, sing it a-gain!
3 Sing it for all who God's love hold in scorn, Sing it a-gain, sing it a-gain!
4 Sing with God's chil-dren a-round you to-day, Sing it a-gain, sing it a-gain!
No oth-er song can such bless-ing af-ford, Sing it a-gain, a-gain!
Free-dom it of-fers, it breaks ev-'ry chain, Sing it a-gain, a-gain!
For through its pow-er can souls be re-born, Sing it a-gain, a-gain!
Let us our joy in the Sav-ior dis-play, Sing it a-gain, a-gain!
REFRAIN
Je-sus, our friend! Hap-py and bless-ed cho-rus!
Je-sus, our friend! our friend!
O-ver the earth let its mes-sage ex-tend, Sing it a-gain, a-gain!

We Come, O Christ, to Thee

E. Margaret Clarkson, 1915-
DARWALL'S 148th 6.6.6.6.8.8.
John Darwall, 1731-1789
1 We come, O Christ, to thee, True son of God and
2 Thou art the way to God, Thy blood our ran - som
3 Thou art the liv - ing truth! All wis - dom dwells in
4 Thou on - ly art true life, To know thee is to
5 We wor - ship thee, Lord Christ, Our Sav - ior and our
man, By whom all things con - sist, In whom all
paid; In thee we face our Judge And Mak - er
thee, Thou source of ev - 'ry skill, E - ter - nal
live The more a - bun - dant life That earth can
King, To thee our youth and strength A - dor - ing -
life be - gan: In thee a - lone we live and move
un - a - fraid: Be - fore the throne ab - solved we stand,
Ver - i - ty: Thou great "I am!" in thee we rest,
nev - er give: O ris - en Lord! we live in thee
ly we bring: So fill our hearts, that men may see
And have our be - ing, in thy love.
Thy love has met thy law's de - mand.
True an - swer to our ev - 'ry quest.
And thou in us e - ter - nal - ly!
Thy life in us and turn to thee! A - men!

A higher setting may be found at No. 249

257 Ye Servants of God, Your Master Proclaim

Charles Wesley, 1707-1788, alt. HANOVER 10.10.11.11.
Attr. to William Croft, 1678-1727

1 Ye serv - ants of God, your Mas - ter pro - claim,
2 God rul - eth on high, al - might - y to save,
3 "Sal - va - tion to God, who sits on the throne!"
4 Then let us a - dore and give him his right—
And pub - lish a - broad his won - der - ful name;
And still he is nigh, his pres - ence we have;
Let all cry a - loud and hon - or the Son;
All glo - ry and pow'r, all wis - dom and might,
The name, all - vic - to - rious, of Je - sus ex - tol:
The great con - gre - ga - tion his tri - umph shall sing,
The prais - es of Je - sus the an - gels pro - claim,
All hon - or and bless - ing, with an - gels a - bove,
His king - dom is glo - rious, he rules o - ver all.
As - crib - ing sal - va - tion to Je - sus, our King.
Fall down on their fac - es and wor - ship the Lamb.
And thanks nev - er - ceas - ing, and in - fi - nite love.

O Praise Ye the Lord!

258

Henry W. Baker, 1821-1877

HANOVER 10.10.11.11.
Attr. to William Croft, 1678-1727

1 O praise ye the Lord!
Praise him in the height;
Rejoice in his word,
Ye angels of light:
Ye heavens, adore him
By whom ye were made,
And worship before him
In brightness arrayed.

2 O praise ye the Lord!
Praise him upon earth
In tuneful accord,
Ye sons of new birth:
Praise him who hath brought you
His grace from above,
Praise him who hath taught you
To sing of his love.

3 O praise ye the Lord,
All things that give sound;
Each jubilant chord
Re-echo around:
Loud organs, his glory
Forth-tell in deep tone,
And sweet harp, the story
Of what he hath done.

4 O praise ye the Lord!
Thanksgiving and song
To him be outpoured
All ages along:
For love in creation,
For heaven restored,
For grace of salvation,
O praise ye the Lord!

PRAISE TO CHRIST

Breathe on Me, Breath of God

259

Edwin Hatch, 1835-1889

TRENTHAM S.M.
Robert Jackson, 1842-1914

1 Breathe on me, Breath of God, Fill me with life a - new,
2 Breathe on me, Breath of God, Un - til my heart is pure,
3 Breathe on me, Breath of God, Till I am whol - ly thine,
4 Breathe on me, Breath of God, So shall I nev - er die,
That I may love what thou dost love, And do what thou wouldst do.
Un - til with thee I will one will To do and to en - dure.
Un - til this earth-ly part of me Glows with thy fire di - vine.
But live with thee the per - fect life Of thine e - ter - ni - ty. A - men.

HOLY SPIRIT

260 Holy Ghost, Dispel Our Sadness

Paul Gerhardt, 1607-1676
Tr. John C. Jacobi, 1670-1750
HYFRYDOL 8.7.8.7.D.
Rowland H. Prichard, 1811-1887
1 Ho - ly Ghost, dis - pel our sad - ness, Pierce the clouds of na - ture's night;
2 Au - thor of the new cre - a - tion, Come with unc - tion and with pow'r;
Come, thou source of joy and glad - ness, Breathe thy life and spread thy light.
Make our hearts thy hab - i - ta - tion, On our souls thy grac - es show'r.
From the height which knows no meas - ure, As a gra - cious show'r de - scend,
Hear, O hear our sup - pli - ca - tion, Bless - ed Spir - it, God of peace!
Bring - ing down the rich - est treas - ure Man can wish or God can send.
Rest up - on this con - gre - ga - tion With the full - ness of thy grace. A - men.

Another harmonization in a higher setting may be found at No. 248

Thou, Whose Purpose Is to Kindle 261

Based on Luke 12:49
David Elton Trueblood, 1900-

HYFRYDOL 8.7.8.7.D.
Rowland H. Prichard, 1811-1887

1. Thou, whose purpose is to kindle:
Now ignite us with thy fire;
While the earth awaits thy burning
With thy passion us inspire.
Overcome our sinful calmness,
Rouse us with redemptive shame;
Baptize with thy fiery Spirit,
Crown our lives with tongues of flame.

2. Thou, who in thy holy gospel
Wills that man should truly live:
Make us sense our share of failure,
Our tranquillity forgive.
Teach us courage as we struggle
In all liberating strife;
Lift the smallness of our vision
By thine own abundant life.

3. Thou, who still a sword delivers
Rather than a placid peace:
With thy sharpened word disturb us,
From complacency release!
Save us now from satisfaction
When we privately are free,
Yet are undisturbed in spirit
By our brother's misery. Amen.

Come, Holy Spirit, Heavenly Dove 262

Isaac Watts, 1674-1748

GRÄFENBERG C.M.
"Praxis Pietatis Melica," Berlin, 1653
Johann Crüger, 1598-1662

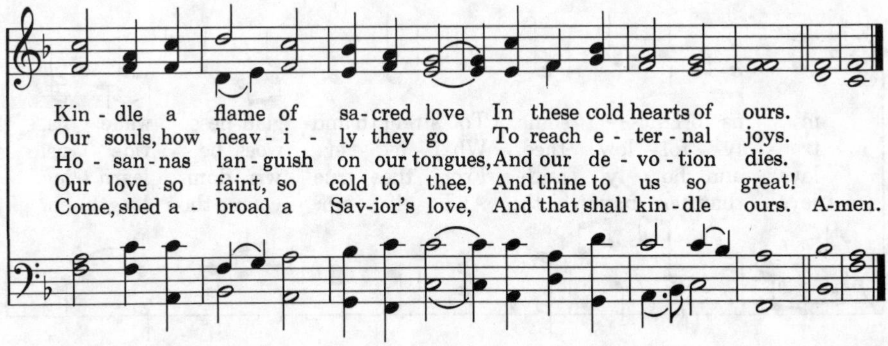

1 Come, Ho - ly Spir - it, heav'n-ly Dove, With all thy quick-'ning pow'rs;
2 See how we tri - fle here be - low, Fond of these earth - ly toys;
3 In vain we tune our for - mal songs, In vain we strive to rise;
4 Dear Lord, and shall we ev - er live At this poor, dy - ing rate?
5 Come, Ho - ly Spir - it, heav'n-ly Dove, With all thy quick-'ning pow'rs;

Kin - dle a flame of sa - cred love In these cold hearts of ours.
Our souls, how heav - i - ly they go To reach e - ter - nal joys.
Ho - san - nas lan - guish on our tongues, And our de - vo - tion dies.
Our love so faint, so cold to thee, And thine to us so great!
Come, shed a - broad a Sav-ior's love, And that shall kin - dle ours. A-men.

263 O Holy Spirit, Enter In

Michael Schirmer, 1606-1673
Tr. Catherine Winkworth, 1827-1878

WIE SCHÖN LEUCHTET 8.8.7.8.8.7.4.8.4.8.
Philipp Nicolai, 1556-1608
Harm. by J. S. Bach, 1685-1750

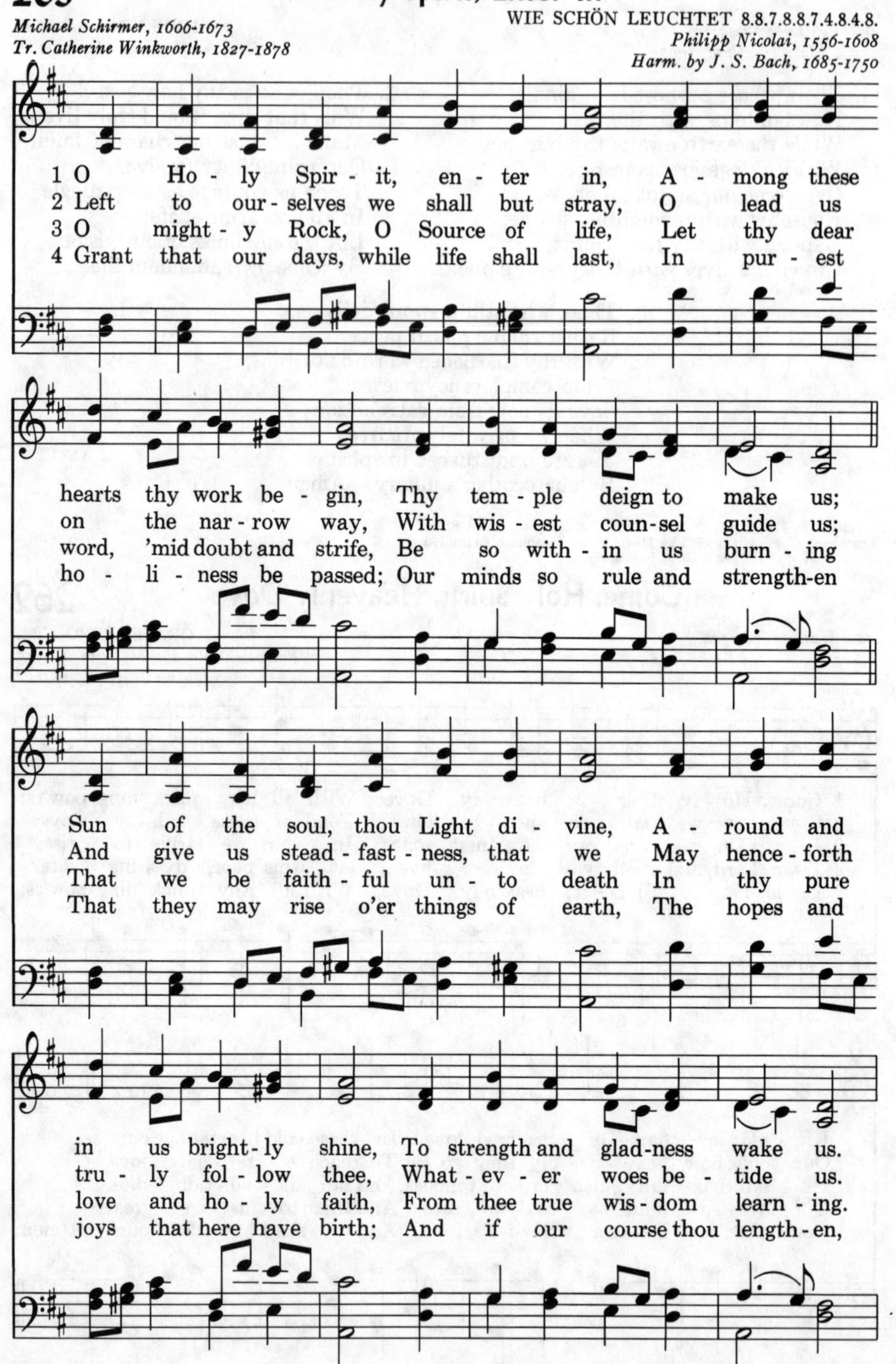
1 O Ho - ly Spir - it, en - ter in, A - mong these
2 Left to our - selves we shall but stray, O lead us
3 O might - y Rock, O Source of life, Let thy dear
4 Grant that our days, while life shall last, In pur - est
hearts thy work be - gin, Thy tem - ple deign to make us;
on the nar - row way, With wis - est coun - sel guide us;
word, 'mid doubt and strife, Be so with - in us burn - ing
ho - li - ness be passed; Our minds so rule and strength - en
Sun of the soul, thou Light di - vine, A - round and
And give us stead - fast - ness, that we May hence - forth
That we be faith - ful un - to death In thy pure
That they may rise o'er things of earth, The hopes and
in us bright - ly shine, To strength and glad - ness wake us.
tru - ly fol - low thee, What - ev - er woes be - tide us.
love and ho - ly faith, From thee true wis - dom learn - ing.
joys that here have birth; And if our course thou length - en,

Other harmonizations may be found at Nos. 124 and 157

Where thou shin - est, Life from heav - en there is giv - en;
Heal thou gen - tly Hearts now bro - ken, give some to - ken
Lord, thy grac - es On us show - er; by thy pow - er
Keep thou pure, Lord, From of - fens - es, heart and sens - es;
We be - fore thee For that pre-cious gift im - plore thee.
Thou art near us, Whom we trust to light and cheer us.
Christ con - fess - ing, Let us win his grace and bless - ing.
Bless - ed Spir - it, Bid us thus true life in - her - it. A-men.

Spirit Divine, Attend Our Prayers 264

Andrew Reed, 1787-1862

SHELL LAKE C.M.
Harry P. Opel, 1921-

1 Spir - it di - vine, at - tend our prayers And make our hearts thy home; De -
2 Come as the light: to us re - veal Our sin - ful - ness and woe; And
3 Come as the fire, and purge our hearts Like sac - ri - fi - cial flame; Let
4 Come as the wind, with rush - ing sound, With pen - te - cos - tal grace; And
5 Come as the dove, and spread thy wings, The wings of peace-ful love; And
scend with all thy gra - cious pow'r, Come, Ho - ly Spir - it, come!
lead us in those paths of life Where all the right-eous go.
our whole soul an of - f'ring be To our Re - deem-er's name.
make the great sal - va - tion known Wide as the hu - man race.
let thy Church on earth be - come Blest as thy Church a - bove. A-men.

265 Spirit of God, Descend upon My Heart

George Croly, 1780-1860

MORECAMBE 10.10.10.10.
Frederick C. Atkinson, 1841-1897

1 Spir - it of God, de - scend up - on my heart;
2 I ask no dream, no proph - et - ec - sta - cies,
3 Hast thou not bid us love thee, God and King?
4 Teach me to feel that thou art al - ways nigh;
5 Teach me to love thee as thine an - gels love,
Wean it from earth, through all its puls - es move;
No sud - den rend - ing of the veil of clay,
All, all thine own— soul, heart and strength and mind!
Teach me the strug - gles of the soul to bear;
One ho - ly pas - sion fill - ing all my frame;
Stoop to my weak - ness, might - y as thou art,
No an - gel vis - i - tant, no o - p'ning skies:
I see thy cross— there teach my heart to cling;
To check the ris - ing doubt, the reb - el sigh,
The bap - tism of the heav'n - de - scend - ed Dove:
And make me love thee as I ought to love.
But take the dim - ness of my soul a - way.
O let me seek thee, and O let me find!
Teach me the pa - tience of un - an - swered prayer.
My heart an al - tar, and thy love the flame. A - men.

Come, Holy Ghost, Our Hearts Inspire 266

Charles Wesley, 1707-1788

WINCHESTER OLD C.M.
Thomas Este's "The Whole Book of Psalms," 1592

1 Come, Ho - ly Ghost, our hearts in-spire, Let us thine in-fluence prove: Source
2 Come, Ho - ly Ghost, for moved by thee The proph-ets wrote and spoke; Un -
3 Ex - pand thy wings, ce - les - tial Dove, Brood o'er our na-ture's night; On
4 God, thru him-self, we then shall know If thou with - in us shine, And
of the old pro - phet - ic fire, Foun - tain of life and love.
lock the truth, thy - self the key, Un - seal the sa - cred book.
our dis - or - dered spir - its move, And let there now be light.
sound with all thy saints be - low The depths of love di - vine. A-men.
1 Ho - ly Ghost, with light di - vine, Shine up - on this heart of mine;
2 Ho - ly Ghost, with pow'r di - vine, Cleanse this guilt - y heart of mine;
3 Ho - ly Ghost, with joy di - vine, Cheer this sad-dened heart of mine;
4 Ho - ly Spir - it, all di - vine, Dwell with - in this heart of mine;
Chase the shades of night a - way, Turn my dark-ness in - to day.
Long hath sin with-out con - trol Held do - min - ion o'er my soul.
Bid my man - y woes de - part, Heal my wound-ed, bleed-ing heart.
Cast down ev - 'ry i - dol-throne, Reign su - preme and reign a - lone. A-men.

Holy Ghost, with Light Divine 267

Andrew Reed, 1787-1862

MERCY 7.7.7.7.
Louis M. Gottschalk, 1829-1869
Adapted by Edwin P. Parker, 1836-1925

268 Gracious Spirit, Dwell with Me

Thomas Toke Lynch, 1818-1871

REDHEAD NO. 76 7.7.7.7.7.7.
Richard Redhead, 1820-1901

1 Gra - cious Spir - it, dwell with me: I my - self would gra-cious be,
2 Truth-ful Spir - it, dwell with me: I my - self would truth-ful be,
3 Ho - ly Spir - it, dwell with me: I my - self would ho - ly be;

And with words that help and heal Would thy life in mine re - veal,
And with wis - dom kind and clear Let thy life in mine ap - pear,
Sep - 'rate from all sin, I would Choose and cher - ish all things good,

And with ac - tions bold and meek Would for Christ my Sav - ior speak.
And with ac - tions broth - er - ly Speak my Lord's sin - cer - i - ty.
And what - ev - er I can be Give to him who gave me thee! A - men.

A lower setting may be found at No. 191

269 Heavenly Spirit, Gentle Spirit

Joel Blomqvist, 1840-1930
Tr. Gerhard W. Palmgren, 1880-1959

HEAVENLY DOVE 8.7.8.7.
Joel Blomqvist, 1840-1930
Harm. by A. Royce Eckhardt, 1937-

In unison
1 Heav'n-ly Spir - it, gen - tle Spir - it, O de - scend on us, we pray;
2 Hear us plead-ing, in - ter - ced - ing, Thou in - ter - pre - ter of love;
3 Come to cheer us, be thou near us, Kin - dle in us heav-en's love;
4 Pil - grims, stran-gers, 'mid life's dan - gers, We on thee would e'er de - pend;

Come, con-sole us and con-trol us, Christ most fair to us por-tray.
With thy fire— us in-spire,— Ho-ly flame from God a-bove.
Keep us burn-ing, hum-ble, yearn-ing, Dwell in us, O heav'n-ly Dove.
Spir-it ten-der, our de-fend-er, Guide us, keep us to the end. A-men.

HOLY SPIRIT

We Believe in One True God 270

Tobias Clausnitzer, 1619-1684
Tr. Catherine Winkworth, 1827-1878

RATISBON 7.7.7.7.7.7.
Johann G. Werner's "Choralbuch," 1815
Harm. by W. H. Monk, 1823-1889

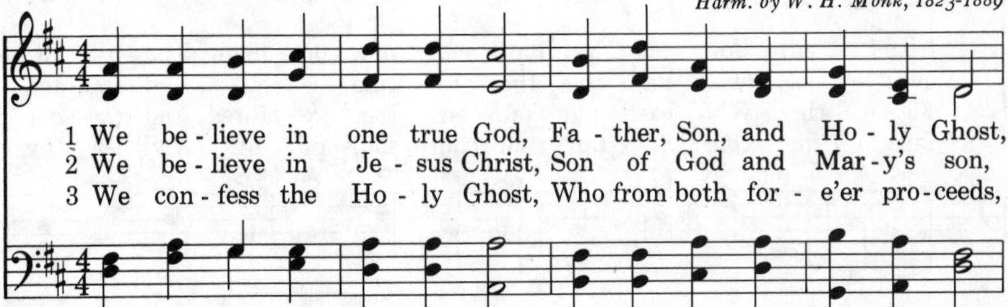

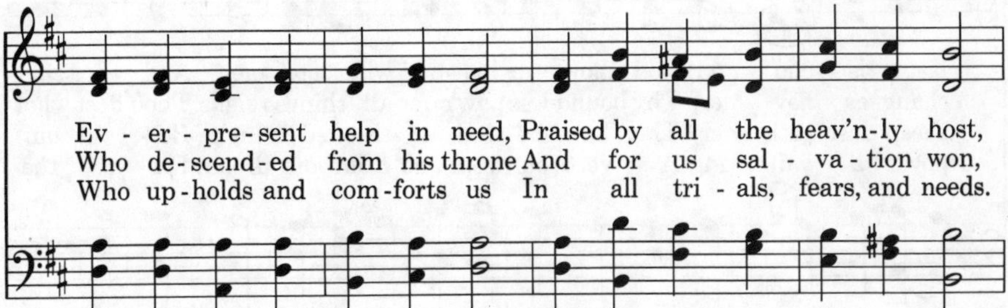

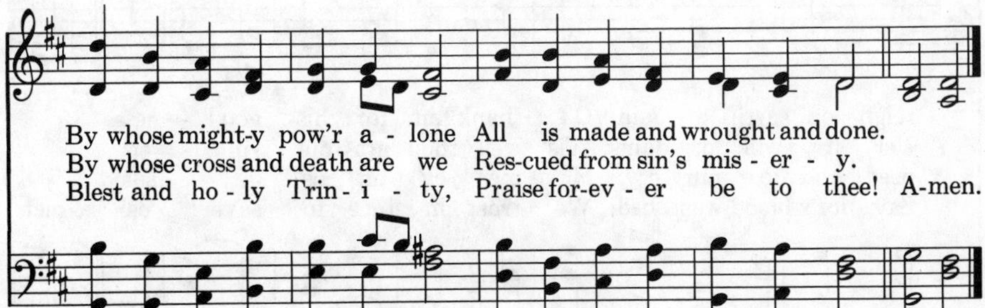

1 We be-lieve in one true God, Fa-ther, Son, and Ho-ly Ghost,
Ev-er-pre-sent help in need, Praised by all the heav'n-ly host,
By whose might-y pow'r a-lone All is made and wrought and done.

2 We be-lieve in Je-sus Christ, Son of God and Mar-y's son,
Who de-scend-ed from his throne And for us sal-va-tion won,
By whose cross and death are we Res-cued from sin's mis-er-y.

3 We con-fess the Ho-ly Ghost, Who from both for-e'er pro-ceeds,
Who up-holds and com-forts us In all tri-als, fears, and needs.
Blest and ho-ly Trin-i-ty, Praise for-ev-er be to thee! A-men.

HOLY TRINITY

271 All Glory Be to God on High

Nikolaus Decius, c.1490-1541
Tr. Catherine Winkworth, 1827-1878, alt.

ALLEIN GOTT IN DER HÖH 8.7.8.7.8.8.7.
"Geistliche Lieder," Leipzig, 1539

1 All glo - ry be to God on high, Who hath our race be - friend - ed; To us no harm shall now come nigh, The strife at last is end - ed; God show - eth his good will to men, And peace shall reign on earth a - gain: O thank him for his good - ness.
2 We praise, we wor - ship thee, we trust, And give thee thanks for - ev - er, O Fa - ther, that thy rule is just And wise, and chang - es nev - er; Thy bound - less pow'r o'er all things reigns, Thou dost what - e'er thy will or - dains: 'Tis well thou art our rul - er!
3 O Je - sus Christ, our God and Lord, Be - got - ten of the Fa - ther, Who hast our fall - en race re - stored And stray - ing sheep dost gath - er, Thou Lamb of God, en - throned on high, Be - hold our need and hear our cry: Have mer - cy on us, Je - sus!
4 O Ho - ly Spir - it, pre - cious gift, Thou Com - fort - er un - fail - ing, O'er Sa - tan's snares our souls up - lift, And let thy pow'r a - vail - ing A - vert our woes and calm our dread; For us the Sav - ior's blood was shed: We trust in thee to save us! A - men.

HOLY TRINITY

Ancient of Days, Who Sittest Throned in Glory 272

William C. Doane, 1832-1913
ANCIENT OF DAYS 11.10.11.10.
J. Albert Jeffery, 1854-1929
Harm. by A. Royce Eckhardt, 1937-
In unison
1 An - cient of Days, who sit - test throned in glo - ry,
2 O ho - ly Fa - ther, who hast led thy chil - dren
3 O ho - ly Je - sus, Prince of Peace and Sav - ior,
4 O Ho - ly Ghost, the Lord and the Life - giv - er,
5 O Tri - une God, with heart and voice a - dor - ing,
To thee all knees are bent, all voic - es pray;
In all the a - ges with the fire and cloud,
To thee we owe the peace that shall pre - vail,
Thine is the quick - 'ning pow'r that gives in - crease:
Praise we the good - ness that doth crown our days;
Thy love has blessed the wide world's won - drous sto - ry
Through seas dry - shod, through wea - ry wastes be - wil - d'ring,
Still - ing the rude wills of men's wild be - hav - ior,
From thee have flowed, as from a might - y riv - er,
Pray we that thou wilt hear us, still im - plor - ing
With light and life since E - den's dawn - ing day.
To thee in rev - 'rent love our hearts are bowed.
And calm - ing pas - sion's fierce and storm - y gale.
Our faith and hope, our fel - low - ship and peace.
Thy love and fav - or, kept to us al - ways. A - men.

A lower setting may be found at No. 464

273 Holy, Holy, Holy! Lord God Almighty!

Reginald Heber, 1783-1826

NICAEA *Irregular*
John B. Dykes, 1823-1876
Descant by David McK. Williams, 1887-

Descant for stanza 4

Ho - - - - - - ly,

1 Ho - ly, ho - ly, ho - ly! Lord God Al - might - y!
2 Ho - ly, ho - ly, ho - ly! all the saints a - dore thee,
3 Ho - ly, ho - ly, ho - ly! tho the dark-ness hide thee,
4 Ho - ly, ho - ly, ho - ly! Lord God Al - might - y!

Ho - - - - - - ly,

Ear - ly in the morn - ing our song shall rise to thee;
Cast - ing down their gold - en crowns a - round the glass - y sea;
Tho the eye of sin - ful man thy glo - ry may not see;
All thy works shall praise thy name in earth and sky and sea;

Ho - - - - - - ly,

Ho - ly, ho - ly, ho - ly! mer - ci - ful and might - y!
Cher - u - bim and ser - a - phim fall - ing down be - fore thee,
On - ly thou art ho - ly— there is none be - side thee
Ho - ly, ho - ly, ho - ly! mer - ci - ful and might - y!

HOLY TRINITY

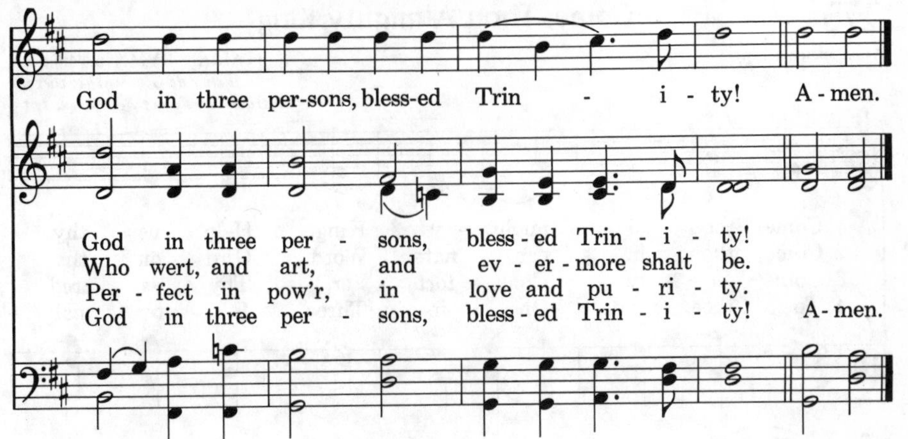
God in three per-sons, bless-ed Trin - i - ty! A-men.
God in three per - sons, bless-ed Trin - i - ty!
Who wert, and art, and ev - er - more shalt be.
Per - fect in pow'r, in love and pu - ri - ty.
God in three per - sons, bless-ed Trin - i - ty! A-men.

Praise Ye the Father

274

Elizabeth Rundle Charles, 1828-1896

FLEMMING 11.11.11.5.
Friedrich F. Flemming, 1778-1813

1 Praise ye the Fa - ther for his lov - ing - kind - ness; Ten - der - ly cares he for his err - ing chil - dren; Praise him, ye an - gels, praise him in the heav - ens, Praise ye Je - ho - vah!

2 Praise ye the Sav - ior— great is his com - pas - sion; Gra - cious - ly cares he for his cho - sen peo - ple; Young men and maid - ens, ye old men and chil - dren, Praise ye the Sav - ior!

3 Praise ye the Spir - it, Com - fort - er of Is - rael, Sent of the Fa - ther and the Son to bless us; Praise ye the Fa - ther, Son, and Ho - ly Spir - it, Praise ye the Tri - une God! A-men.

A lower setting may be found at No. 370

275 Come, Thou Almighty King

Anonymous, c.1757

ITALIAN HYMN 6.6.4.6.6.6.4.
Felice de Giardini, 1716-1796
Harm. by James P. Davies, 1913-

1 Come, thou al - might - y King, Help us thy
2 Come, thou in - car - nate Word, Gird on thy
3 Come, ho - ly Com - fort - er, Thy sa - cred
4 To thee, great One in Three, E - ter - nal

name to sing, Help us to praise: Fa - ther all -
might - y sword, Our prayer at - tend: Come, and thy
wit - ness bear In this glad hour: Thou who al -
prais - es be Hence, ev - er - more: Thy sov - 'reign

glo - ri - ous, O'er all vic - to - ri - ous,
peo - ple bless, And give thy word suc - cess;
might - y art, Now rule in ev - 'ry heart,
maj - es - ty May we in glo - ry see,

Come, and reign o - ver us, An - cient of Days!
Spir - it of ho - li - ness, On us de - scend!
And ne'er from us de - part, Spir - it of pow'r!
And to e - ter - ni - ty Love and a - dore! A - men.

HOLY TRINITY

Another harmonization in a higher setting may be found at No. 557

276 Glory to the Father Give

James Montgomery, 1771-1854

SABBATSDAG 7.7.7.7.
Joel Blomqvist, 1840-1930

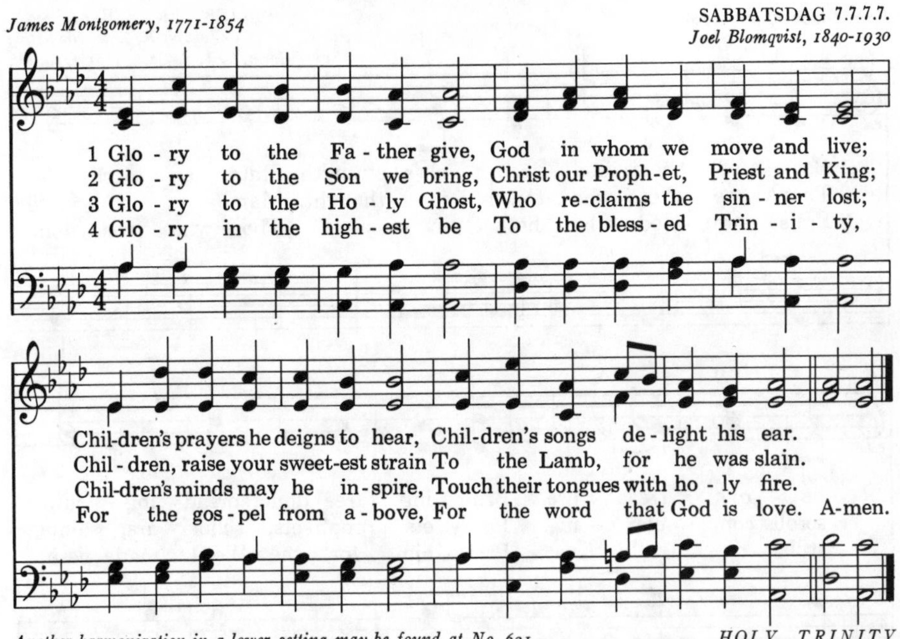

1 Glo - ry to the Fa - ther give, God in whom we move and live;
2 Glo - ry to the Son we bring, Christ our Proph - et, Priest and King;
3 Glo - ry to the Ho - ly Ghost, Who re - claims the sin - ner lost;
4 Glo - ry in the high - est be To the bless - ed Trin - i - ty,
Chil - dren's prayers he deigns to hear, Chil - dren's songs de - light his ear.
Chil - dren, raise your sweet - est strain To the Lamb, for he was slain.
Chil - dren's minds may he in - spire, Touch their tongues with ho - ly fire.
For the gos - pel from a - bove, For the word that God is love. A - men.

Another harmonization in a lower setting may be found at No. 621

HOLY TRINITY

277 Almighty God, Thy Word Is Cast

Based on Luke 8:11-15
John Cawood, 1775-1852

BELMONT C.M.
William Gardiner's "Sacred Melodies," 1812

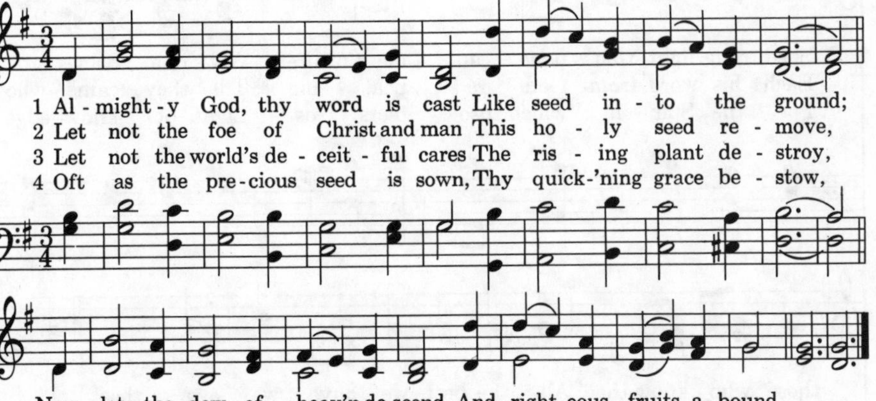

1 Al - might - y God, thy word is cast Like seed in - to the ground;
2 Let not the foe of Christ and man This ho - ly seed re - move,
3 Let not the world's de - ceit - ful cares The ris - ing plant de - stroy,
4 Oft as the pre - cious seed is sown, Thy quick - 'ning grace be - stow,
Now let the dew of heav'n de - scend, And right - eous fruits a - bound.
But give it root in ev - 'ry heart, To bring forth fruits of love.
But let it yield a hun - dred - fold The fruits of peace and joy.
That all whose souls the truth re - ceive Its sav - ing pow'r may know. A - men.

A lower setting may be found at No. 177

HOLY SCRIPTURES

278 Book of Books, Our People's Strength

Percy Dearmer, 1867-1936

LIEBSTER JESU 7.8.7.8.8.8.
Johann R. Ahle, 1625-1673
Harm. by J. S. Bach, 1685-1750, alt.

1 Book of books, our peo - ple's strength, States-man's, teach - er's,
2 Thank we those who toiled in thought, Man - y di - verse
3 Praise we God, who hath in - spired Those whose wis - dom
he - ro's treas - ure, Bring - ing free - dom, spread - ing truth,
scrolls com - plet - ing, Po - ets, proph - ets, schol - ars, saints,
still di - rects us; Praise him for the Word made flesh,
Shed - ding light that none can meas - ure: Wis - dom comes to
Each his word from God re - peat - ing, Till they came, who
For the Spir - it which pro - tects us. Light of knowl - edge,
those who know thee, All the best we have we owe thee.
told the sto - ry Of the Word, and showed his glo - ry.
ev - er burn - ing, Shed on us thy death - less learn - ing. A-men.

O Word of God Incarnate

William W. How, 1823-1897

MUNICH 7.6.7.6.D.
"Neu-vermehrtes Gesangbuch," Meiningen, 1693
Harm. by Felix Mendelssohn, 1809-1847

1 O Word of God in - car - nate, O Wis - dom from on high,
2 The Church from her dear Mas - ter Re-ceived the gift di - vine,
3 It float - eth like a ban - ner Be - fore God's host un - furled;
4 O make thy Church, dear Sav - ior, A lamp of bur-nished gold,
O Truth un-changed, un - chang - ing, O Light of our dark sky,
And still that light she lift - eth O'er all the earth to shine.
It shin-eth like a bea - con A - bove the dark - ling world.
To bear a - mong the na - tions Thy true light as of old.
We praise thee for the ra - diance That from the hal - lowed page,
It is the gold - en cas - ket Where gems of truth are stored;
It is the chart and com - pass That o'er life's surg - ing sea,
O teach thy wan-dering pil - grims By this their path to trace,
A lan - tern to our foot - steps, Shines on from age to age.
It is the heaven-drawn pic - ture Of Christ, the liv - ing Word.
'Mid mists, and rocks, and quick-sands, Still guides, O Christ, to thee.
Till, clouds and dark - ness end - ed, They see thee face to face! A-men.

280 O God of Light, Thy Word, a Lamp Unfailing

Sarah E. Taylor, 1883-1954

CHARTERHOUSE 11.10.11.10.

David Evans, 1874-1948

In unison
1 O God of light, thy Word, a lamp un - fail - ing,
2 From days of old, thru swift - ly roll - ing a - ges,
3 Un-dimmed by time, the Word is still re - veal - ing
4 To all the world the mes - sage thou art send - ing,
Shines thru the dark - ness of our earth - ly way,
Thou hast re - vealed thy will to mor - tal men,
To sin - ful men thy jus - tice and thy grace;
To ev - 'ry land, to ev - 'ry race and clan;
O'er fear and doubt, o'er black de - spair pre - vail - ing,
Speak - ing to saints, to proph - ets, kings, and sag - es,
And quest - ing hearts that long for peace and heal - ing
And myr - iad tongues, in one great an - them blend - ing,

A simpler accompaniment may be found at No. 573

Guid - ing our steps to thine e - ter - nal day.
Who wrote the mes - sage with im - mor - tal pen.
See thy com - pas - sion in the Sav - ior's face.
Ac - claim with joy thy won - drous gift to man. A - men.

Break Thou the Bread of Life

281

Based on Matthew 14:19
Mary A. Lathbury, 1841-1913, Sts. 1, 2
Alexander Groves, 1842-1909, Sts. 3, 4

BREAD OF LIFE 6.4.6.4.D.
William F. Sherwin, 1826-1888

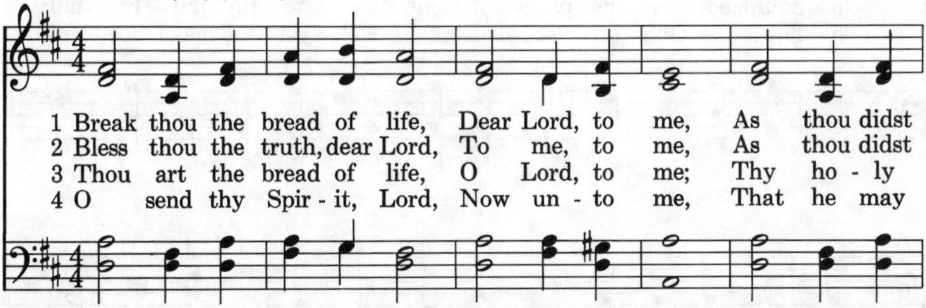

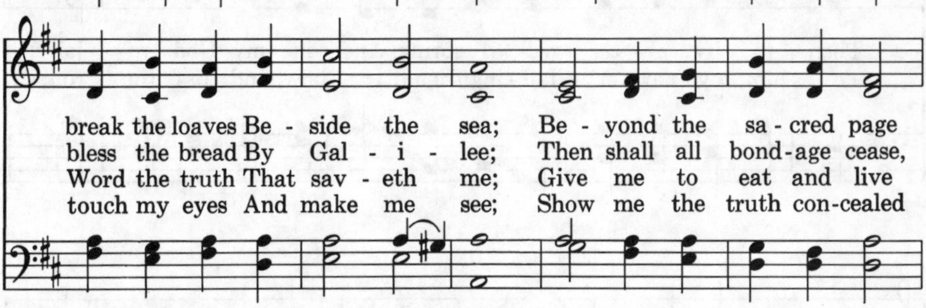

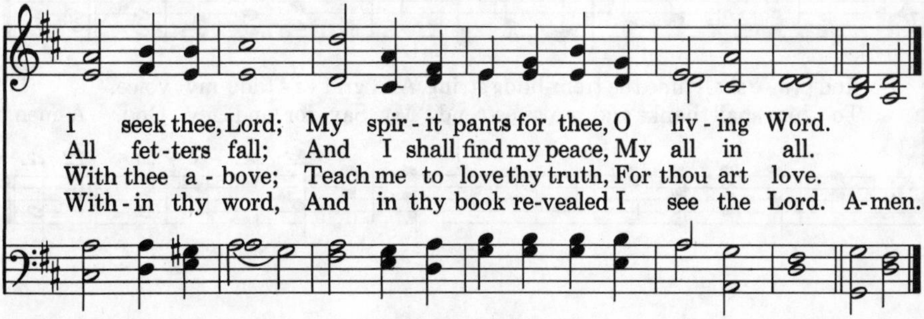

1 Break thou the bread of life, Dear Lord, to me, As thou didst break the loaves Be - side the sea; Be - yond the sa - cred page I seek thee, Lord; My spir - it pants for thee, O liv - ing Word.

2 Bless thou the truth, dear Lord, To me, to me, As thou didst bless the bread By Gal - i - lee; Then shall all bond - age cease, All fet - ters fall; And I shall find my peace, My all in all.

3 Thou art the bread of life, O Lord, to me; Thy ho - ly Word the truth That sav - eth me; Give me to eat and live With thee a - bove; Teach me to love thy truth, For thou art love.

4 O send thy Spir - it, Lord, Now un - to me, That he may touch my eyes And make me see; Show me the truth con - cealed With - in thy word, And in thy book re - vealed I see the Lord. A - men.

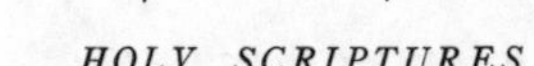

282 Send Forth, O God, Thy Light and Truth

Based on Psalm 43
John Quincy Adams, 1767-1848

BETHLEHEM C.M.D.
Gottfried W. Fink, 1783-1846

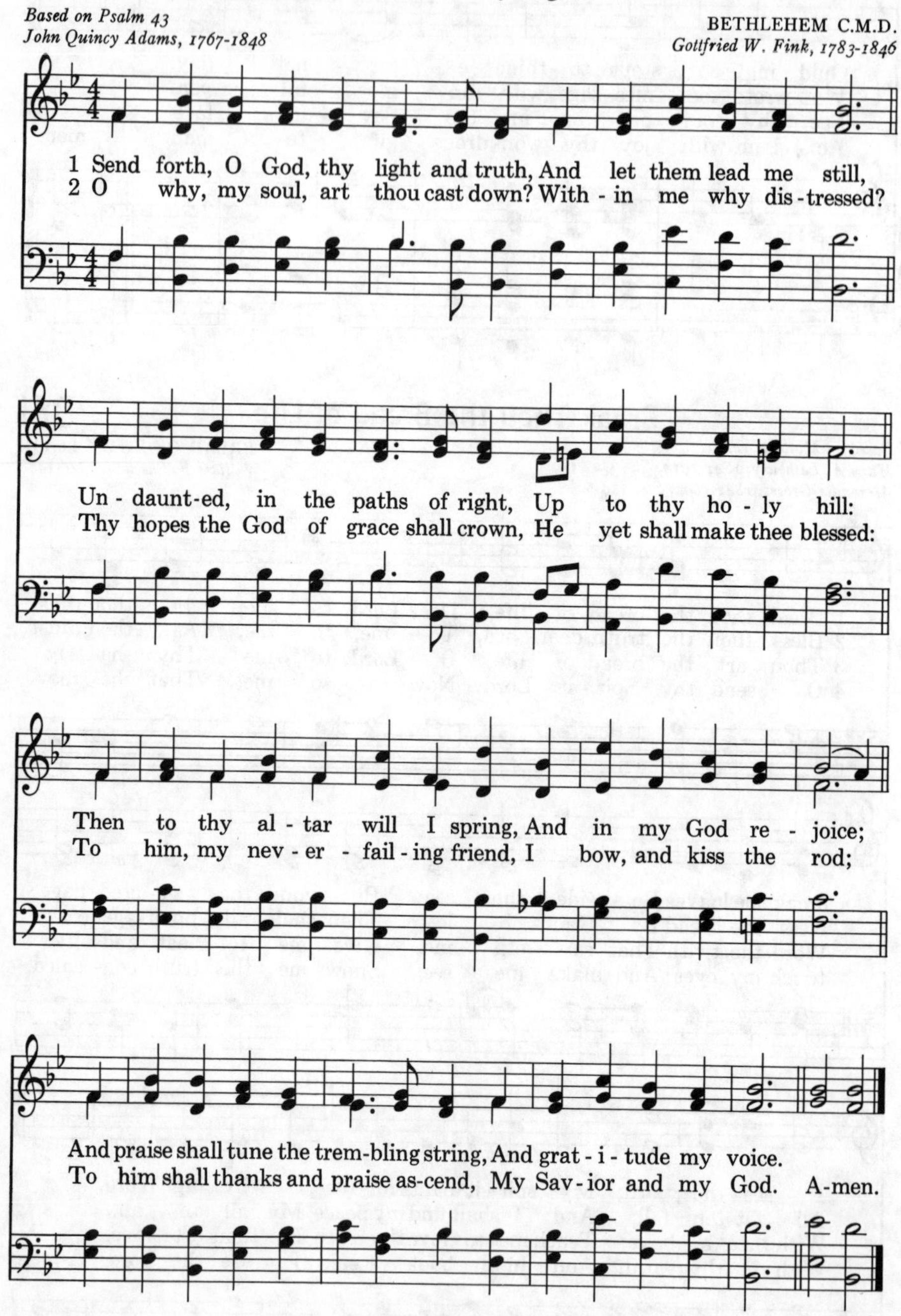

1 Send forth, O God, thy light and truth, And let them lead me still,
2 O why, my soul, art thou cast down? With - in me why dis - tressed?
Un - daunt-ed, in the paths of right, Up to thy ho - ly hill:
Thy hopes the God of grace shall crown, He yet shall make thee blessed:
Then to thy al - tar will I spring, And in my God re - joice;
To him, my nev - er - fail - ing friend, I bow, and kiss the rod;
And praise shall tune the trem-bling string, And grat - i - tude my voice.
To him shall thanks and praise as-cend, My Sav - ior and my God. A-men.

Another harmonization in a lower setting may be found at No. 78

The Highest Joy That Can Be Known

Nils Frykman, 1842-1911
Tr. Signe L. Bennett, 1900-
Tr. Andrew T. Frykman, 1875-1943

HIGHEST JOY 8.6.8.6.8.6.
Amanda S. Waesterberg, 1842-1918

1 The high - est joy that can be known By those who
2 The Word doth give me wealth un - told, All good it
3 How oft - en when in deep de - spair My soul has
4 It tells me of a love di - vine, How Je - sus'
5 When stars a - bove shall shine no more, God's Word is
heav'n - ward wend— It is the Word of Life to
has in store; My deep - est sor - rows yield their
been re - stored; And when the tempt - er would en -
blood was shed; Each day this joy - ous song is
still my light; When pleas - ures of this world are
own, And God to have as friend; It is the
hold To joys for - ev - er - more; My deep - est
snare 'Twould strength to stand af - ford; And when the
mine As paths of grace I tread; Each day this
o'er, My joys will reach their height; When pleas - ures
Word of Life to own, And God to have as friend.
sor - rows yield their hold To joys for - ev - er - more.
tempt - er would en - snare 'Twould strength to stand af - ford.
joy - ous song is mine As paths of grace I tread.
of this world are o'er, My joys will reach their height.

284 The Spirit Breathes upon the Word
William Cowper, 1731-1800
ORTONVILLE C.M.
Thomas Hastings, 1784-1872
1 The Spirit breathes upon the Word, And brings the truth to sight; Precepts and promises afford A sanctifying light, A sanctifying light.
2 A glory gilds the sacred page, Majestic like the sun; It gives a light to ev'ry age— It gives, but borrows none, It gives, but borrows none.
3 The hand that gave it still supplies The gracious light and heat; His truths upon the nations rise— They rise, but never set, They rise, but never set.
4 Let everlasting thanks be thine For such a bright display As makes a world of darkness shine With beams of heav'nly day, With beams of heav'nly day.
5 My soul rejoices to pursue The steps of him I love, Till glory breaks upon my view In brighter worlds above, In brighter worlds above.
285 Tell Me the Old, Old Story
Katherine Hankey, 1834-1911
EVANGEL 7.6.7.6.D. with Refrain
William H. Doane, 1832-1915
Harm. by James P. Davies, 1913-
1 Tell me the old, old story Of unseen things above,
2 Tell me the story slowly That I may take it in—
3 Tell me the story softly With earnest tones and grave;
4 Tell me the same old story When you have cause to fear

Of Je - sus and his glo - ry, Of Je - sus and his love;
That won - der - ful re - demp - tion, God's rem - e - dy for sin;
Re - mem - ber I'm the sin - ner Whom Je - sus came to save;
That this world's emp - ty glo - ry Is cost - ing me too dear;
Tell me the sto - ry sim - ply, As to a lit - tle child,
Tell me the sto - ry oft - en, For I for - get so soon;
Tell me the sto - ry al - ways, If you would real - ly be,
Yes, and when that world's glo - ry Is dawn - ing on my soul,
For I am weak and wea - ry, And help - less and de - filed.
The ear - ly dew of morn - ing Has passed a - way at noon.
In an - y kind of trou - ble, A com - fort - er to me.
Tell me the old, old sto - ry: "Christ Je - sus makes thee whole."
REFRAIN
Tell me the old, old sto - ry, Tell me the old, old sto - ry,
Tell me the old, old sto - ry Of Je - sus and his love.

HOLY SCRIPTURES

286 Thy Word Is Like a Garden, Lord

Edwin Hodder, 1837-1904

FOREST GREEN C.M.D.
English Melody
Harm. by Ralph Vaughan Williams, 1872-1958

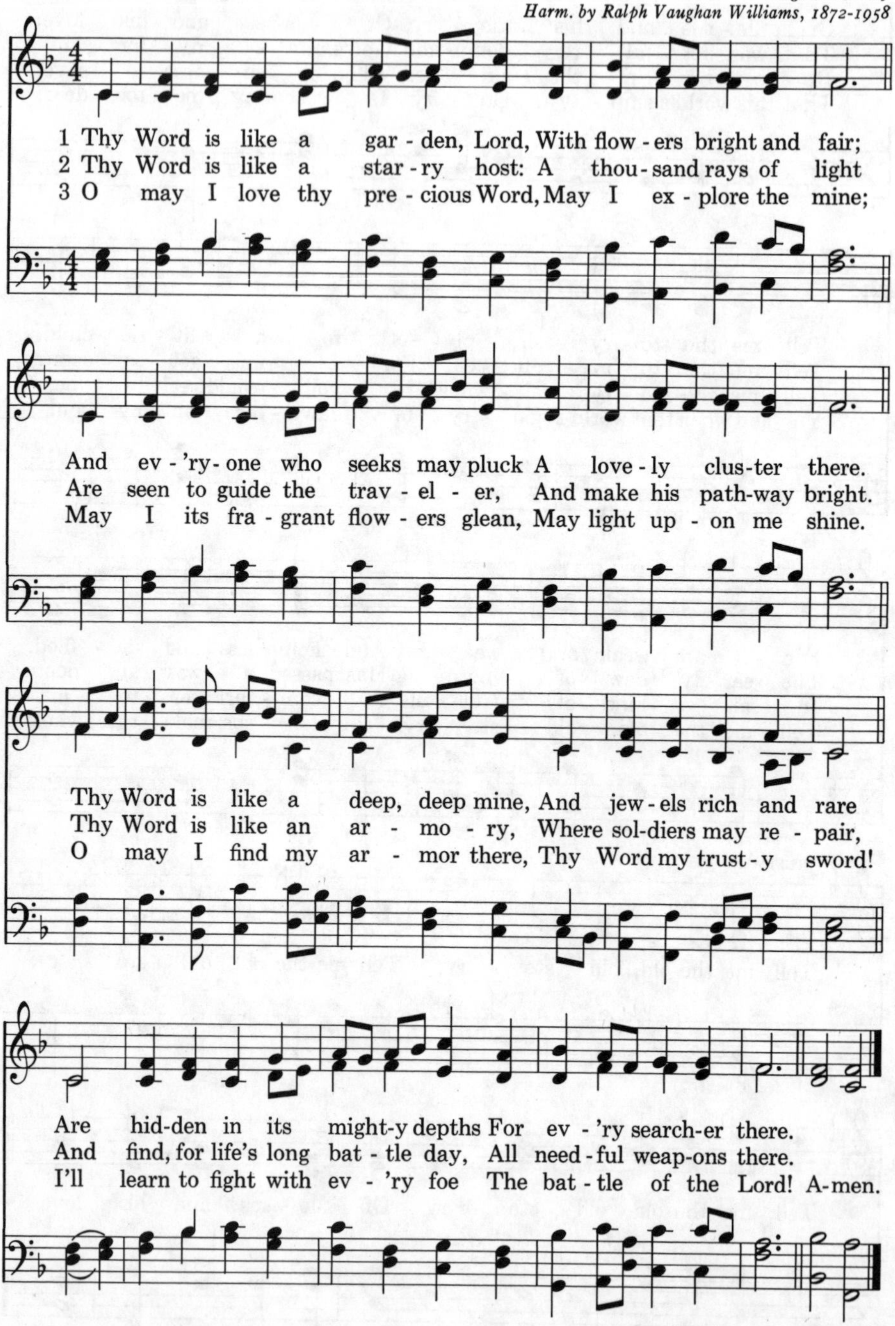

1 Thy Word is like a gar - den, Lord, With flow - ers bright and fair;
2 Thy Word is like a star - ry host: A thou - sand rays of light
3 O may I love thy pre - cious Word, May I ex - plore the mine;

And ev - 'ry - one who seeks may pluck A love - ly clus - ter there.
Are seen to guide the trav - el - er, And make his path - way bright.
May I its fra - grant flow - ers glean, May light up - on me shine.

Thy Word is like a deep, deep mine, And jew - els rich and rare
Thy Word is like an ar - mo - ry, Where sol - diers may re - pair,
O may I find my ar - mor there, Thy Word my trust - y sword!

Are hid - den in its might - y depths For ev - 'ry search - er there.
And find, for life's long bat - tle day, All need - ful weap - ons there.
I'll learn to fight with ev - 'ry foe The bat - tle of the Lord! A - men.

Alternate tune: BETHLEHEM, *No. 282*

287 Come, Every Soul by Sin Oppressed

John H. Stockton, 1813-1877
STOCKTON C.M. with Refrain
John H. Stockton, 1813-1877
1 Come, ev - 'ry soul by sin op-pressed, There's mer - cy with the Lord,
2 For Je - sus shed his pre - cious blood Rich bless-ings to be - stow;
3 Yes, Je - sus is the truth, the way That leads you in - to rest;
4 Come, then, and join this ho - ly band And on to glo - ry go,
And he will sure - ly give you rest By trust - ing in his Word.
Plunge now in - to the crim - son flood That wash - es white as snow.
Be - lieve in him with - out de - lay And you are ful - ly blest.
To dwell in that ce - les - tial land Where joys im - mor - tal flow.
REFRAIN
On - ly trust him, on - ly trust him, On - ly trust him now;
He will save you, he will save you, He will save you now.

288 Come to the Savior Now

John M. Wigner, 1844-1911

INVITATION 6.6.6.6.D.
Frederick C. Maker, 1844-1927

1 Come to the Sav - ior now, He gent - ly call - eth thee;
2 Come to the Sav - ior now, Ye who have wan - dered far;
3 Come to the Sav - ior, all, What - e'er your bur - dens be;
In true re - pent - ance bow, Be - fore him bend the knee.
Re - new your sol - emn vow, For his by right you are.
Hear now his lov - ing call, "Cast all your care on me."
He wait - eth to be - stow Sal - va - tion, peace, and love,
Come, like poor wan - d'ring sheep Re - turn - ing to his fold;
Come, and for ev - 'ry grief In Je - sus you will find
True joy on earth be - low, A home in heav'n a - bove.
His arm will safe - ly keep, His love will ne'er grow cold.
A sure and safe re - lief, A lov - ing friend, and kind.

Come, Ye Sinners, Poor and Needy

Joseph Hart, 1712-1768

BEACH SPRING 8.7.8.7.D.
"The Sacred Harp," 1844
Harm. by A. Royce Eckhardt, 1937-

1 Come, ye sin - ners, poor and need - y, Bruised and bro - ken by the fall;
2 Let not con - science make you lin - ger, Nor of fit - ness fond - ly dream;
3 Lo! th' in - car - nate God, as - cend - ed, Pleads the mer - it of his blood;

Je - sus read - y stands to save you, Full of par - d'ning love for all.
All that he re - quires of sin - ners Is to turn and trust in him.
Ven - ture on him, ven - ture whol - ly Let no oth - er trust in - trude:

He is a - ble, he is a - ble, He is will - ing, doubt no more;
He will save you, he will save you, 'Tis the gos - pel's con - stant theme.
None but Je - sus, none but Je - sus Can do help - less sin - ners good.

He is a - ble, he is a - ble, He is will - ing, doubt no more.
He will save you, he will save you, 'Tis the gos - pel's con - stant theme.
None but Je - sus, none but Je - sus Can do help - less sin - ners good.

290 "Follow Me!" a Call So Tender

Based on John 10:27, 28
A. L. Skoog, 1856-1934

TENDER CALL 8.7.8.7. *with Refrain*
A. L. Skoog, 1856-1934

1 "Fol-low me!" a call so ten-der Falls up-on my lis-t'ning ear;
2 In-to pas-tures green he lead-eth, His own sheep he calls by name;
3 Lit-tle flock, fear not! he shields you From the dan-gers of the land;
4 In his steps, then, I would fol-low, Seek in him my all in all;
'Tis the voice of Christ, my Sav-ior, 'Tis the Shep-herd's call I hear.
When their feet are sore and wea-ry, In his arms he car-ries them.
Hear his pro-mise: none shall ev-er Pluck you from his might-y hand.
I am safe, what-e'er be-falls me, When I heed his ten-der call.
REFRAIN (*after last stanza only*)
O that call! lov-ing call! 'Tis the sweet-est voice of all! How it
draws me near-er to him, When I hear my Shep-herd's call.
draws me near-er hear my Shep-herd's call.

Hush, My Soul, What Voice Is Pleading? 291

John H. Lester, 19th century

UPSALA 8.7.8.7.D.
Gunnar Wennerberg, 1817-1901

1 Hush, my soul, what voice is plead-ing? Thou canst feel its si - lent pow'r;
2 Hark! it is a voice of sweet-ness, Ten - der - ly it speaks, and true!
3 What is this that steals be - side me? Can it be that at my side,
4 Hush, my soul! it is thy Sav - ior! And he seeks his lost one now;
Who is this that speaks so gen - tly In this sol - emn, qui - et hour?
Dark and sad, yet strange-ly yearn-ing For a peace I nev - er knew,
In his own mys - ter - ious pres-ence, Stands the won-drous Cru - ci - fied?
He is wait - ing– flee not from him, Ven - ture near, be - fore him bow.
"Stay, poor sin - ner, life is fleet - ing, And thy soul is dark with - in;
Half - in - clined to stay and lis - ten, Half - in - clined to go a - way,
"Why, poor sin - ner, wilt thou lin - ger? I am wait - ing to for - give;
Tell thy sins– he will for - give thee, And he will not love thee less;
Wilt thou wait till out - er dark - ness Close in gloom thy life of sin?"
Still I lin - ger, for it whis - pers, "Hard-en not thy heart to - day."
See the mean-ing of these wound-prints: I have died that thou may'st live!"
For the hu - man heart of Je - sus O - ver - flows with ten - der - ness.

292 Jesus Stands Outside the Door

Based on Revelation 3:20
Source unknown
Tr. Herbert E. Palmquist, 1896-

RÖSLEIN 7.6.7.7.6.7.6.
Heinrich Werner, 1800-1833
Harm. by A. Royce Eckhardt, 1937-

1 Je - sus stands out - side the door—Why not bid him en - ter?
2 With a wea - ry, trou - bled race Hear the Sav - ior plead - ing:
3 Come to me, O Je - sus good, O - pen now your treas - ure,
Though your weight of sin be sore, He can life and
"Come to me and my em - brace, I am meek and
Cleanse me in your pre - cious blood, That life - giv - ing,
strength re - store: Hear his voice so ten - der. Trou - bled soul, I
full of grace That your souls are need - ing." Sons of men, what-
heal - ing flood Flow - ing with - out meas - ure. Je - sus, Je - sus,
do im - plore, Will you let him en - ter?
e'er your place, Will you spurn his plead - ing?
Je - sus good, Be my last - ing treas - ure. A - men.

List to the Gospel Resounding

Nils Frykman, 1842-1911
Tr. Andrew T. Frykman, 1875-1943

HEAVENLY VOICE 8.7.8.7. *with Refrain*
Carl M. Frykman, 1880-1930

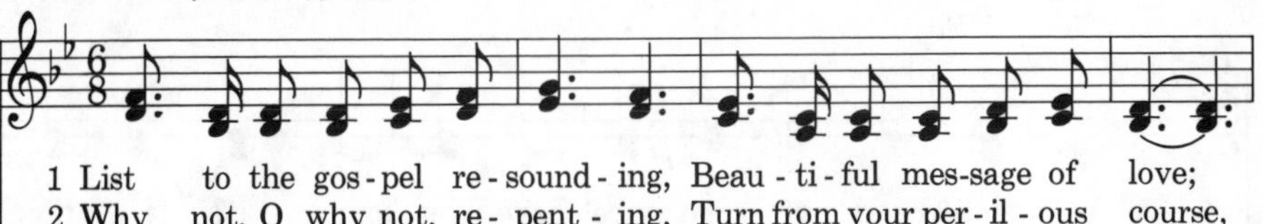

1 List to the gos-pel re-sound-ing, Beau-ti-ful mes-sage of love;
2 Why not, O why not, re-pent-ing, Turn from your per-il-ous course,
3 Life, like the dew of the morn-ing, Van-ish-eth quick-ly a-way;
4 Touch'd by the Spir-it so ten-der, Call-ing as ev-er be-fore,

Je-sus, in mer-cy a-bound-ing, Call-eth for you from a-bove.
End-ing in woe un-re-lent-ing, An-guish, dis-grace and re-morse?
Death bring-eth sor-row and mourn-ing, Wail-ing for-ev-er and aye.
Will-ing-ly, free-ly sur-ren-der, O-pen, yes, o-pen your door.

REFRAIN

List to the heav-en-ly voice Ten-der-ly urg-ing your choice;

Yield to the love of your Sav-ior, Lis-ten, be-lieve, and re-joice.

CALL OF CHRIST

294 O That Pearl of Great Price!

Based on Matthew 13:45, 46
From the Swedish
Tr. A. L. Skoog, 1856-1934

PEARL OF GREAT PRICE 10.9.10.9.D.
A. L. Skoog, 1856-1934

1 O that Pearl of great price! have you found it? Is the
2 Have you come to the liv - ing Re - deem - er, Him that
3 Has the Sav - ior, the right - eous, the ho - ly, Cast the
Sav - ior su-preme in your love? O con - sid - er it well, ere you
bore all your sins on the tree? Has he gra - cious - ly par-doned and
beams of his all-search-ing light In - to all of your heart's deep re -
an - swer, As you hope for a wel - come a - bove. Have you
cleansed you In the blood shed for you and for me? At his
cess - es, And trans-formed in - to day their dark night? O then
giv - en up all for this Treas - ure? Have you count - ed past
feet as one dead, have you fall - en, And been quick - ened a -
an - swer these ques - tions so press - ing, Be - fore God, ere time's

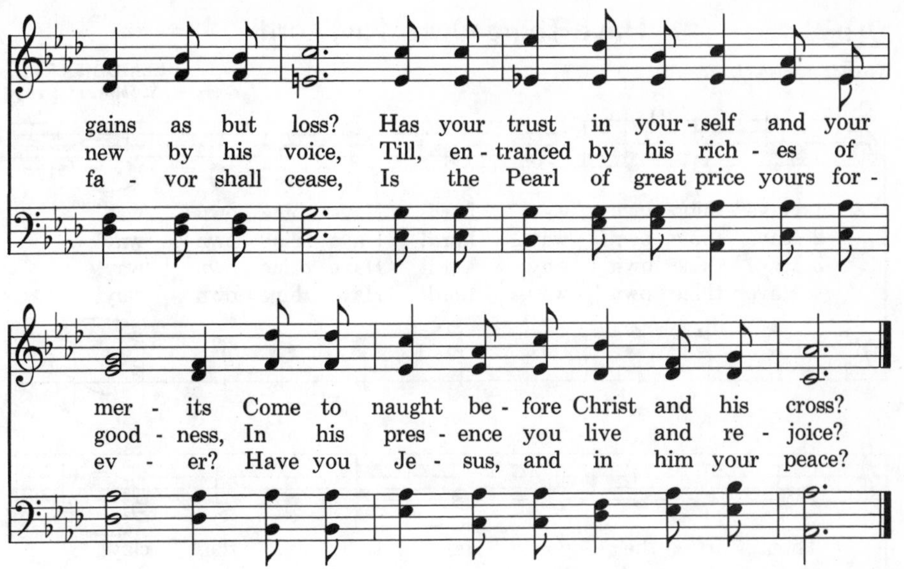
gains as but loss? Has your trust in your-self and your
new by his voice, Till, en-tranced by his rich-es of
fa-vor shall cease, Is the Pearl of great price yours for-
mer-its Come to naught be-fore Christ and his cross?
good-ness, In his pres-ence you live and re-joice?
ev-er? Have you Je-sus, and in him your peace?

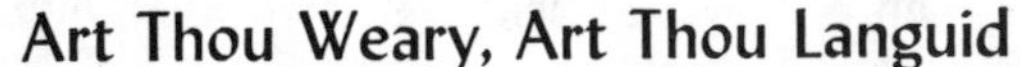

Art Thou Weary, Art Thou Languid 295

John M. Neale, 1818-1866
Based on Stephen the Sabaite, 725-794

STEPHANOS 8.5.8.3.
Henry W. Baker, 1821-1877

1 Art thou wea-ry, art thou lan-guid, Art thou sore dis-tressed?
"Come to me," saith One, "and com-ing, Be at rest."

2 Hath he marks to lead me to him, If he be my guide?
"In his feet and hands are wound-prints, And his side."

3 Is there di-a-dem, as mon-arch, That his brow a-dorns?
"Yea, a crown, in ver-y sure-ty, But of thorns."

4 If I find him, if I fol-low, What my hon-ors here?
"Man-y a sor-row, man-y a la-bor, Man-y a tear."

5 If I still hold close-ly to him, What hath he at last?
"Sor-row van-quished, la-bor end-ed, Jor-dan passed."

6 Find-ing, fol-l'wing, keep-ing, strug-gling, Is he sure to bless?
Saints, a-pos-tles, proph-ets, mar-tyrs, An-swer, "Yes!"

296 Have Thine Own Way, Lord!

Adelaide A. Pollard, 1862-1934

ADELAIDE 5.4.5.4.D.
George C. Stebbins, 1846-1945

1 Have thine own way, Lord! Have thine own way!
2 Have thine own way, Lord! Have thine own way!
3 Have thine own way, Lord! Have thine own way!
4 Have thine own way, Lord! Have thine own way!
Thou art the pot - ter, I am the clay!
Search me and try me, Mas - ter, to - day!
Wound - ed and wea - ry, Help me, I pray!
Hold o'er my be - ing Ab - so - lute sway!
Mold me and make me Aft - er thy will,
Whit - er than snow, Lord, Wash me just now,
Pow - er— all pow - er— Sure - ly is thine!
Fill with thy Spir - it Till all shall see
While I am wait - ing, Yield - ed and still.
As in thy pres - ence Hum - bly I bow.
Touch me and heal me, Sav - ior di - vine!
Christ on - ly, al - ways, Liv - ing in me! A - men.

I Heard the Voice of Jesus Say

Horatius Bonar, 1808-1889

VOX DILECTI C.M.D.
John B. Dykes, 1823-1876

1 I heard the voice of Je - sus say, "Come un - to me and rest;
2 I heard the voice of Je - sus say, "Be - hold, I free - ly give
3 I heard the voice of Je - sus say, "I am this dark world's light;
Lay down, thou wea - ry one, lay down Thy head up - on my breast."
The liv - ing wa - ter—thirst - y one, Stoop down, and drink, and live."
Look un - to me—thy morn shall rise, And all thy day be bright."
I came to Je - sus as I was, Wea - ry, and worn, and sad;
I came to Je - sus, and I drank Of that life - giv - ing stream;
I looked to Je - sus, and I found In him my star, my sun;
I found in him a rest - ing place, And he has made me glad.
My thirst was quenched, my soul re - vived, And now I live in him.
And in that light of life I'll walk, Till trav-'ling days are done.

Alternate tunes: GREEN HILL, *No. 199,* NO OTHER PLEA, *No. 391*

298 In the Springtime Fair

Lina Sandell, 1832-1903
Tr. Karl A. Olsson, 1913-

SPRINGTIME 8.7.8.7. *with Refrain*
Swedish Folk Melody
Harm. by Norman E. Johnson, 1928-

In unison
1 In the spring-time fair but mor - tal, In the day of frag - ile flow'rs,
2 Though at ev - 'ry mo-ment near you, Is the Lord un - heed - ed still?
Christ is wait - ing at your por - tal, Faith-ful thru the pass - ing hours.
For how long will he con - tin - ue Speak-ing to your shut-tered will?
REFRAIN
O - pen now, be - fore the au - tumn Sweeps the sum-mer's flow'rs a - way;
O - pen while the sun is shin - ing—All too brief our earth - ly day!

My Jesus, As Thou Wilt! 299

Benjamin Schmolck, 1672-1737
Tr. Jane L. Borthwick, 1813-1897

JEWETT 6.6.6.6.D.
Carl Maria von Weber, 1786-1826
Adapted by Joseph P. Holbrook, 1822-1888

1 My Je - sus, as thou wilt! O may thy will be mine!
2 My Je - sus, as thou wilt! Though seen thru man - y a tear,
3 My Je - sus, as thou wilt! All shall be well for me;
In - to thy hand of love I would my all re - sign.
Let not my star of hope Grow dim or dis - ap - pear.
Each chang-ing fu - ture scene I glad - ly trust with thee.
Thru sor - row or thru joy, Con - duct me as thine own;
Since thou on earth hast wept, And sor - rowed oft a - lone,
Straight to my home a - bove I trav - el calm - ly on,
And help me still to say, "My Lord, thy will be done."
If I must weep with thee, "My Lord, thy will be done."
And sing, in life or death, "My Lord, thy will be done." A-men.

300 Out of My Bondage, Sorrow, and Night

William T. Sleeper, 1819-1904

JESUS I COME *Irregular*
George C. Stebbins, 1846-1945

1 Out of my bond - age, sor - row, and night, Je - sus, I come,
2 Out of my shame - ful fail - ure and loss, Je - sus, I come,
3 Out of un - rest and ar - ro - gant pride, Je - sus, I come,
4 Out of the fear and dread of the tomb, Je - sus, I come,
Je - sus, I come; In - to thy free - dom, glad - ness and light,
Je - sus, I come; In - to the glo - rious gain of thy cross,
Je - sus, I come; In - to thy bless - ed will to a - bide,
Je - sus, I come; In - to the joy and light of thy home,
Je - sus, I come to thee. Out of my sick - ness
Je - sus, I come to thee. Out of earth's sor - rows
Je - sus, I come to thee. Out of my - self to
Je - sus, I come to thee. Out of the depths of
in - to thy health, Out of my want and in - to thy wealth,
in - to thy balm, Out of life's storms and in - to thy calm,
dwell in thy love, Out of de - spair in - to rap - tures a - bove,
ru - in un - told, In - to the peace of thy shel - ter - ing fold,

Out of my sin and in - to thy-self, Je - sus, I come to thee.
Out of dis-tress to ju - bi-lant psalm, Je - sus, I come to thee.
Up-ward for aye on wings like a dove, Je - sus, I come to thee.
Ev - er thy glo-rious face to be-hold, Je - sus, I come to thee. A-men.

Lord Jesus, I Long to Be Perfectly Whole 301

Based on Psalm 51
James Nicholson, c.1828-1896

RUTSTRÖM 11.11.11.11.
Anders Carl Rutström, 1721-1772

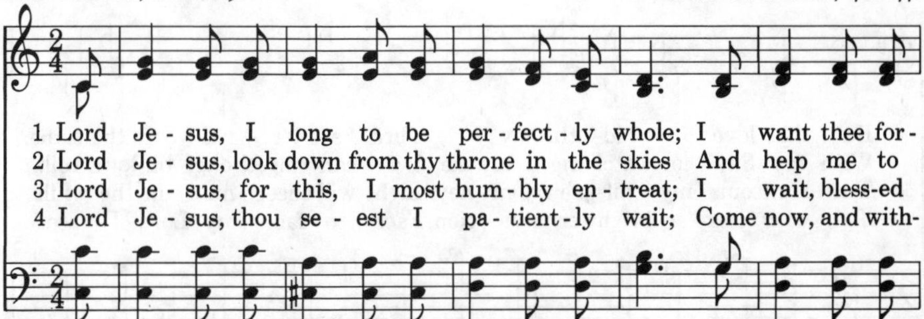

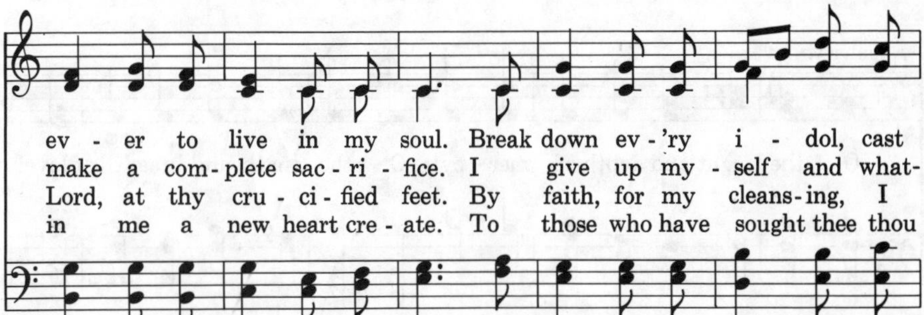

1 Lord Je - sus, I long to be per - fect - ly whole; I want thee for - ev - er to live in my soul. Break down ev - 'ry i - dol, cast out ev - 'ry foe— Now wash me, and I shall be whit - er than snow.

2 Lord Je - sus, look down from thy throne in the skies And help me to make a com - plete sac - ri - fice. I give up my - self and what - ev - er I know— Now wash me, and I shall be whit - er than snow.

3 Lord Je - sus, for this, I most hum - bly en - treat; I wait, bless-ed Lord, at thy cru - ci - fied feet. By faith, for my cleans - ing, I see thy blood flow— Now wash me, and I shall be whit - er than snow.

4 Lord Je - sus, thou se - est I pa - tient - ly wait; Come now, and with - in me a new heart cre - ate. To those who have sought thee thou nev - er saidst "No"— Now wash me, and I shall be whit - er than snow. A-men.

A lower setting may be found at No. 195

302 Take the World, but Give Me Jesus

Fanny J. Crosby, 1820-1915

STILLA STUNDER 8.7.8.7. *with Refrain*
J. A. Hulman, 1861-1942

1 Take the world, but give me Je-sus—All its joys are but a name;
2 Take the world, but give me Je-sus—Sweet-est com-fort of my soul;
3 Take the world, but give me Je-sus—Let me view his con-stant smile;
4 Take the world, but give me Je-sus—In his cross my trust shall be;
But his love a-bid-eth ev-er, Thru e-ter-nal years the same.
With my Sav-ior watch-ing o'er me, I can sing, though bil-lows roll.
Then thru-out my pil-grim jour-ney Light will cheer me all the while.
Till, with clear-er, bright-er vi-sion, Face to face my Lord I see.
REFRAIN
O the height and depth of mer-cy! O the length and breadth of love!
O the full-ness of re-demp-tion, Pledge of end-less life a-bove!

I Lay My Sins on Jesus

Horatius Bonar, 1808-1889

CRUCIFIX 7.6.7.6.D.
Greek Melody
Harm. by A. Royce Eckhardt, 1937-

1 I lay my sins on Je - sus, The spot - less Lamb of God;
2 I lay my wants on Je - sus—All full - ness dwells in him;
3 I long to be like Je - sus—Meek, lov - ing, low - ly, mild;
He bears them all, and frees us From the ac - curs - ed load.
He heals all my dis - eas - es, He doth my soul re - deem.
I long to be like Je - sus—The Fa - ther's ho - ly child.
I bring my guilt to Je - sus, To wash my crim - son stains
I lay my griefs on Je - sus, My bur - dens and my cares;
I long to be with Je - sus, A - mid the heav'n - ly throng,
White in his blood most pre - cious, Till not a spot re - mains.
He from them all re - leas - es, He all my sor - rows shares.
To sing with saints his prais - es, To learn the an - gels' song.

Alternate tune: ST. HILDA, No. 308

304 Just As I Am, Without One Plea

Charlotte Elliott, 1789-1871

WOODWORTH L.M.
William B. Bradbury, 1816-1868

1 Just as I am, with - out one plea But
2 Just as I am, though tossed a - bout With
3 Just as I am, poor, wretch - ed, blind— Sight,
4 Just as I am, thou wilt re - ceive, Wilt

that thy blood was shed for me, And that thou bidd'st me
man - y a con - flict, man - y a doubt, Fight - ings and fears with-
rich - es, heal - ing of the mind, Yea, all I need in
wel - come, par - don, cleanse, re - lieve; Be - cause thy prom - ise

come to thee, O Lamb of God, I come, I come!
in, with - out, O Lamb of God, I come, I come!
thee to find, O Lamb of God, I come, I come!
I be - lieve, O Lamb of God, I come, I come! A-men.

Alternate tune: ST. CRISPIN, *No. 165*

305 Amazing Grace! How Sweet the Sound

John Newton, 1725-1807
John P. Rees c.1859-?, St. 5

AMAZING GRACE C.M.
American Melody
Carrell and Clayton's "Virginia Harmony," 1831
Harm. by Edwin O. Excell, 1851-1921

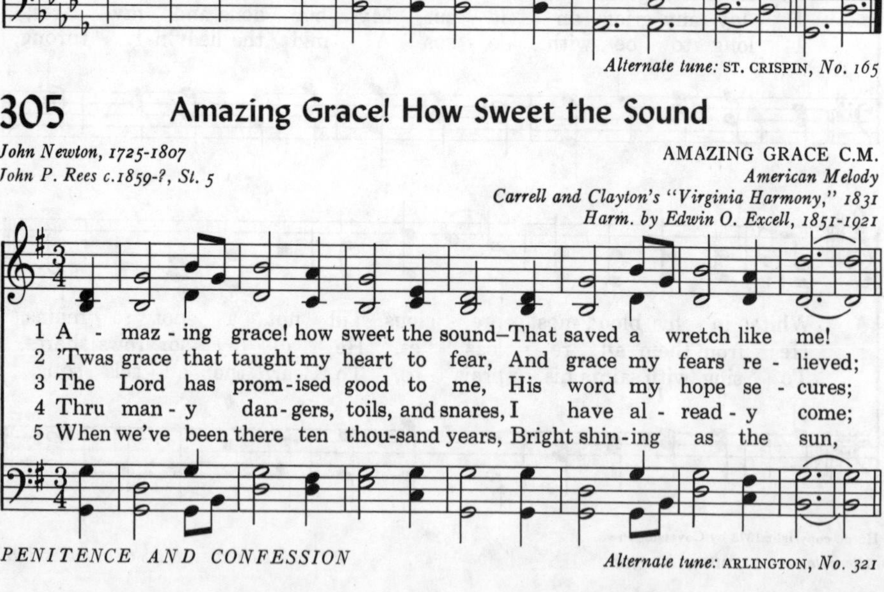
1 A - maz - ing grace! how sweet the sound–That saved a wretch like me!
2 'Twas grace that taught my heart to fear, And grace my fears re - lieved;
3 The Lord has prom - ised good to me, His word my hope se - cures;
4 Thru man - y dan - gers, toils, and snares, I have al - read - y come;
5 When we've been there ten thou - sand years, Bright shin - ing as the sun,

Alternate tune: ARLINGTON, *No. 321*

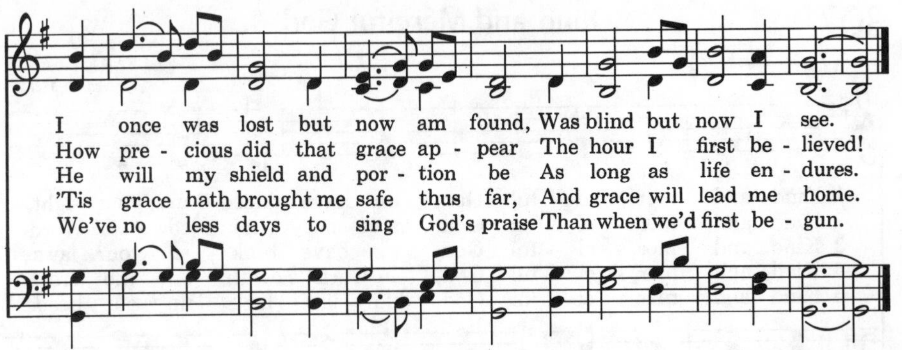
I once was lost but now am found, Was blind but now I see.
How pre - cious did that grace ap - pear The hour I first be - lieved!
He will my shield and por - tion be As long as life en - dures.
'Tis grace hath brought me safe thus far, And grace will lead me home.
We've no less days to sing God's praise Than when we'd first be - gun.

My Faith Looks Up to Thee

306

Ray Palmer, 1808-1887

OLIVET 6.6.4.6.6.6.4.
Lowell Mason, 1792-1872

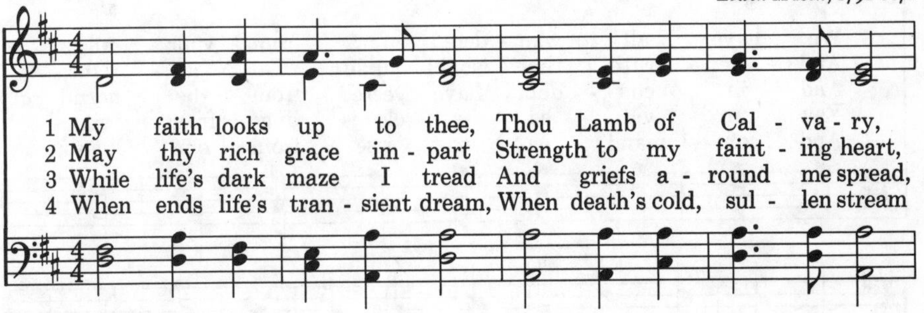

1 My faith looks up to thee, Thou Lamb of Cal - va - ry,
2 May thy rich grace im - part Strength to my faint - ing heart,
3 While life's dark maze I tread And griefs a - round me spread,
4 When ends life's tran - sient dream, When death's cold, sul - len stream

Sav - ior di - vine! Now hear me while I pray, Take all my
My zeal in - spire; As thou has died for me, O may my
Be thou my guide; Bid dark-ness turn to day, Wipe sor-row's
Shall o'er me roll, Blest Sav - ior, then, in love, Fear and dis -

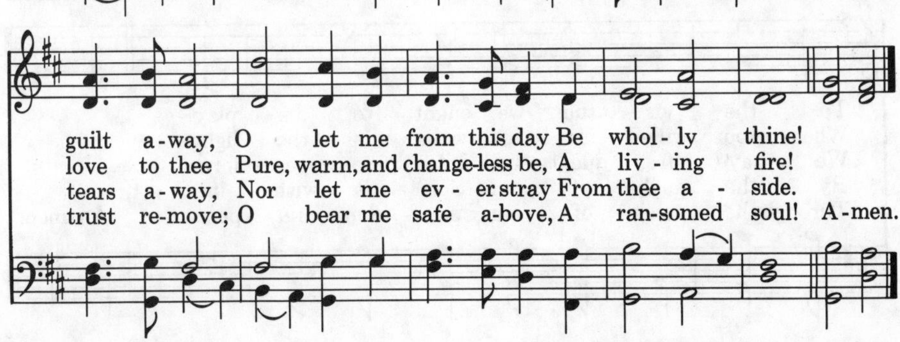

guilt a-way, O let me from this day Be whol - ly thine!
love to thee Pure, warm, and change-less be, A liv - ing fire!
tears a-way, Nor let me ev - er stray From thee a - side.
trust re-move; O bear me safe a-bove, A ran-somed soul! A-men.

307 Kind and Merciful God

Bryan Jeffery Leech, 1931-

ELFÅKER 6.6.9.D.
Swedish Melody

1 Kind and mer - ci - ful God, we have sinned in your sight,
2 Kind and mer - ci - ful God, we've ne - glect - ed your Word
3 Kind and mer - ci - ful God, we have brok - en your laws
4 Kind and mer - ci - ful God, in Christ's death on the cross
5 Kind and mer - ci - ful God, bid us lift up our heads
We have all wan - dered far from your way;
And the truth that would guide us a - right;
And in con - duct have veered from the norm;
You pro - vid - ed a cleans - ing from sin;
And com - mand us to rise from our knees;
We have fol - lowed de - sire, We have failed to as - pire
We have lived in the shade Of the dark we have made,
We have dreamed of the good, But the good that we could
Speak the words that for - give That hence - forth we may live
May our hearts now be changed And no long - er es - tranged,
To the vir - tue we ought to dis - play.
When you willed us to walk in the light.
We have fre - quent - ly failed to per - form.
By the might of your Spir - it with - in.
Through the pow'r of your par - don and peace. A - men.

PENITENCE AND CONFESSION

O Jesus, Thou Art Standing

William W. How, 1823-1897

ST. HILDA 7.6.7.6.D.
Justin H. Knecht, 1752-1817, and
Edward Husband, 1843-1908

1 O Je - sus, thou art stand - ing Out - side the fast-closed door,
2 O Je - sus, thou art knock - ing, And lo! that hand is scarred,
3 O Je - sus, thou art plead - ing In ac - cents meek and low:
In low - ly pa - tience wait - ing To pass the thresh - old o'er.
And thorns thy brow en - cir - cle, And tears thy face have marred.
"I died for you, my chil - dren, And will ye treat me so?"
Shame on us, Chris - tian broth - ers, His name and sign who bear;
O love that pass - eth knowl - edge, So pa - tient - ly to wait!
O Lord, with shame and sor - row We o - pen now the door;
O shame, thrice shame up - on us, To keep him stand - ing there!
O sin that hath no e - qual, So fast to bar the gate!
Dear Sav - ior, en - ter, en - ter, And leave us nev - er - more! A-men.

309 Rock of Ages, Cleft for Me

Augustus M. Toplady, 1740-1778
TOPLADY 7.7.7.7.7.7.
Thomas Hastings, 1784-1872
1 Rock of A - ges, cleft for me, Let me hide my-self in thee;
2 Could my tears for - ev - er flow, Could my zeal no lan-guor know,
3 While I draw this fleet-ing breath, When my eyes shall close in death,
Let the wa - ter and the blood, From thy wound-ed side which flowed,
These for sin could not a - tone – Thou must save, and thou a - lone:
When I rise to worlds un-known, And be - hold thee on thy throne,
Be of sin the dou-ble cure, Save from wrath and make me pure.
In my hand no price I bring, Sim-ply to thy cross I cling.
Rock of A - ges, cleft for me, Let me hide my-self in thee. A-men.
Alternate tune: REDHEAD NO. 76, No. 311
310 There Is a Fountain Filled with Blood
William Cowper, 1731-1800
BELMONT C.M.
William Gardiner's "Sacred Melodies," 1812
1 There is a foun-tain filled with blood Drawn from Em - man-uel's veins,
2 The dy - ing thief re - joiced to see That foun-tain in his day,
3 Dear dy - ing Lamb, thy pre - cious blood Shall nev - er lose its pow'r,
4 E'er since by faith I saw the stream Thy flow-ing wounds sup-ply,
5 When this poor lisp - ing, stamm'ring tongue Lies si - lent in the grave,

A lower setting may be found at No. 177

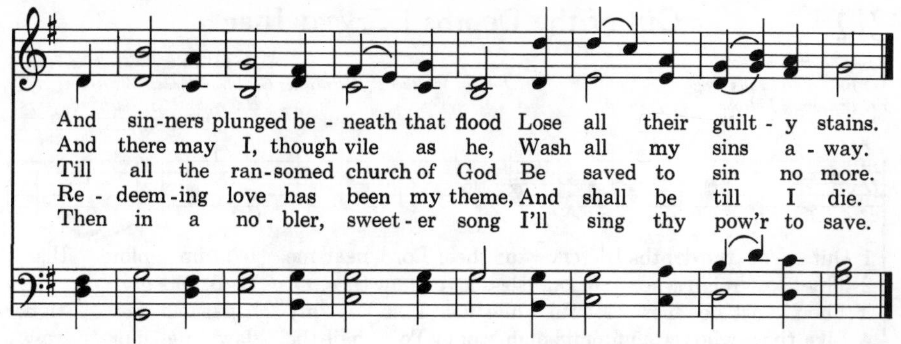
And sin-ners plunged be - neath that flood Lose all their guilt - y stains.
And there may I, though vile as he, Wash all my sins a - way.
Till all the ran-somed church of God Be saved to sin no more.
Re - deem-ing love has been my theme, And shall be till I die.
Then in a no-bler, sweet - er song I'll sing thy pow'r to save.

Sinners Jesus Will Receive

311

Erdmann Neumeister, 1671-1756
Tr. Emma Frances Bevan, 1827-1909

REDHEAD NO. 76 7.7.7.7.7.7.
Richard Redhead, 1820-1901

1 Sin - ners Je - sus will re-ceive: Tell this word of grace to all
2 Shep-herds seek their wan-d'ring sheep O'er the moun-tains bleak and cold;
3 Sick and sor - row - ful and blind, I with all my sins draw nigh;
4 Christ re - ceiv - eth sin - ful men, E - ven me with all my sin;

Who the heav'n-ly path-way leave, All who lin - ger, all who fall!
Je - sus such a watch doth keep O'er the lost ones of his fold,
O my Sav - ior, thou canst find Help for sin - ners such as I!
O - p'neth to me heav'n a - gain— With him I may en - ter in!

This can bring them back a - gain: 'Christ re - ceiv - eth sin - ful men.'
Seek - ing them o'er moor and fen: Christ re - ceiv - eth sin - ful men.
Speak that word of love a - gain: 'Christ re - ceiv - eth sin - ful men.'
Death hath no more sting nor pain: Christ re - ceiv - eth sin - ful men.

A lower setting may be found at No. 191

312 Out of the Depths I Cry to Thee

Based on Psalm 130 — AUS TIEFER NOT 8.7.8.7.8.8.7.
Martin Luther, 1483-1546 — *Johann Walther's "Geistliches Gesangbüchlein," Wittenberg, 1524*
Tr. Benjamin Latrobe, 1725-1786, alt. — *Harm. by J. S. Bach, 1685-1750*

1 Out of the depths I cry to thee: Lord, hear me, I im - plore thee;
2 Thy sov-'reign grace and bound-less love Show thee, O Lord, for - giv - ing;
3 Thou canst be mer - ci - ful while just, This is my hope's foun-da - tion;
4 Like those who watch for mid-night's hour To hail the dawn-ing mor - row,

Bend down thy gra - cious ear to me, Let my prayer come be - fore thee!
My pur-est thoughts and deeds but prove Sin in my heart is liv - ing:
In thy re-deem-ing grace I trust, O grant me thy sal-va - tion.
I wait for thee, I trust thy pow'r, Un-moved by doubt or sor - row.

On my mis - deeds in mer - cy look, O deign to blot them
None guilt - less in thy sight ap - pear, All who ap - proach thy
Up - held by thee, I stand se - cure: Thy word is firm, thy
So let thy peo - ple hope in thee, And they shall find thy

from thy book, And let me come be - fore thee.
throne must fear, And hum - bly trust thy mer - cy.
prom - ise sure, And I re - ly up - on thee.
mer - cy free, And thy re - demp-tion plen - teous. A-men.

Alternate tune: NUN FREUT EUCH, *No. 461*

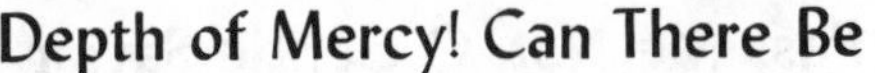
Depth of Mercy! Can There Be

313

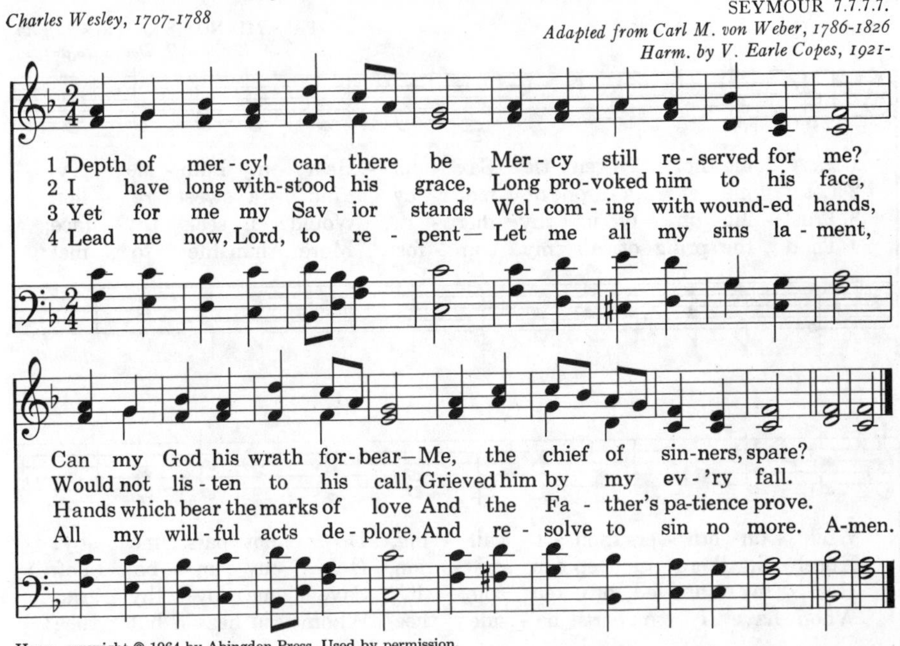
Charles Wesley, 1707-1788
SEYMOUR 7.7.7.7.
Adapted from Carl M. von Weber, 1786-1826
Harm. by V. Earle Copes, 1921-
1 Depth of mer-cy! can there be Mer-cy still re-served for me?
2 I have long with-stood his grace, Long pro-voked him to his face,
3 Yet for me my Sav-ior stands Wel-com-ing with wound-ed hands,
4 Lead me now, Lord, to re-pent— Let me all my sins la-ment,
Can my God his wrath for-bear—Me, the chief of sin-ners, spare?
Would not lis-ten to his call, Grieved him by my ev-'ry fall.
Hands which bear the marks of love And the Fa-ther's pa-tience prove.
All my will-ful acts de-plore, And re-solve to sin no more. A-men.

Lord Jesus, Think on Me

314

Synesius of Cyrene, c.375-430
Tr. Allen W. Chatfield, 1808-1896

SOUTHWELL S.M.
Adapt. from "Damon's Psalmes," 1579

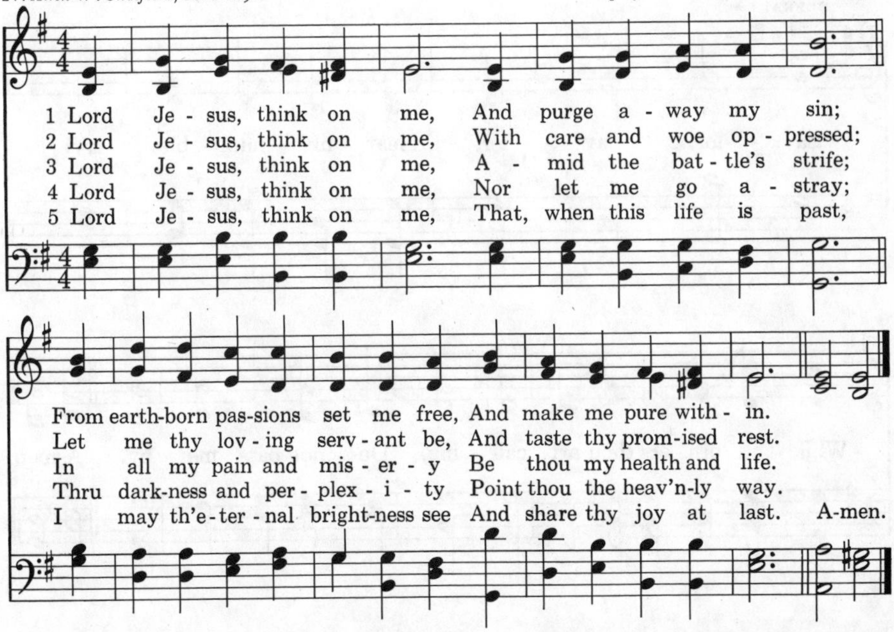

1 Lord Je-sus, think on me, And purge a-way my sin;
From earth-born pas-sions set me free, And make me pure with-in.

2 Lord Je-sus, think on me, With care and woe op-pressed;
Let me thy lov-ing serv-ant be, And taste thy prom-ised rest.

3 Lord Je-sus, think on me, A-mid the bat-tle's strife;
In all my pain and mis-er-y Be thou my health and life.

4 Lord Je-sus, think on me, Nor let me go a-stray;
Thru dark-ness and per-plex-i-ty Point thou the heav'n-ly way.

5 Lord Je-sus, think on me, That, when this life is past,
I may th'e-ter-nal bright-ness see And share thy joy at last. A-men.

315 Pass Me Not, O Gentle Savior

Fanny J. Crosby, 1820-1915

PASS ME NOT 8.5.8.5. *with Refrain*
William H. Doane, 1832-1915

1 Pass me not, O gen - tle Sav - ior— Hear my hum - ble cry!
2 Let me at a throne of mer - cy Find a sweet re - lief;
3 Trust - ing on - ly in thy mer - it, Would I seek thy face;
4 Thou the spring of all my com - fort, More than life to me!
While on oth - ers thou art call - ing, Do not pass me by.
Kneel - ing there in deep con - tri - tion, Help my un - be - lief.
Heal my wound - ed, bro - ken spir - it, Save me by thy grace.
Whom have I on earth be - side thee? Whom in heav'n but thee?
REFRAIN
Sav - ior, Sav - ior, Hear my hum - ble cry!
While on oth - ers thou art call - ing, Do not pass me by. A-men.

Years I Spent in Vanity and Pride 316

William R. Newell, 1868-1956

CENTERWOOD 9.9.9.4.
A. Royce Eckhardt, 1937-

1 Years I spent in van-i-ty and pride, Car-ing not my Lord was
2 By God's Word at last my sin I learned–Then I trem-bled at the
3 Mer-cy there was great, and grace was free, Par-don there was mul-ti-
4 Now I've giv'n to Je-sus ev-'ry-thing, Now I glad-ly own him
5 O the love that drew sal-va-tion's plan! O the grace that bro't it
cru-ci-fied, Know-ing not it was for me he died On Cal-va-ry.
law I'd spurned, Till my guil-ty soul im-plor-ing turned To Cal-va-ry.
plied to me; There my bur-dened soul found lib-er-ty— At Cal-va-ry.
as my King, Now my rap-tured soul can on-ly sing Of Cal-va-ry.
down to man! O the might-y gulf that God did span At Cal-va-ry!

PENITENCE AND CONFESSION

A Charge to Keep I Have 317

Charles Wesley, 1707-1788

BOYLSTON S.M.
Lowell Mason, 1792-1872

1 A charge to keep I have, A God to glo-ri-fy,
2 To serve the pres-ent age, My call-ing to ful-fill:
3 Arm me with jeal-ous care, As in thy sight to live;
4 Help me to watch and pray, And on thy-self re-ly;
A nev-er-dy-ing soul to save And fit it for the sky.
O may it all my pow'rs en-gage To do my Mas-ter's will!
And O thy serv-ant, Lord, pre-pare A strict ac-count to give!
O let me not my trust be-tray, But press to realms on high. A-men.

CONSECRATION

318 I Am Thine, O Lord

Fanny J. Crosby, 1820-1915

I AM THINE 10.7.10.7. *with Refrain*
William H. Doane, 1832-1915

1 I am thine, O Lord— I have heard thy voice, And it told thy love to me; But I long to rise in the arms of faith And be clos - er drawn to thee.
2 Con - se - crate me now to thy serv - ice, Lord, By the pow'r of grace di - vine; Let my soul look up with a stead - fast hope And my will be lost in thine.
3 O the pure de - light of a sin - gle hour That be - fore thy throne I spend, When I kneel in prayer and with thee, my God, I com - mune as friend with friend.
4 There are depths of love that I can - not know Till I cross the nar - row sea; There are heights of joy that I may not reach Till I rest in peace with thee.
REFRAIN
Draw me near - er, near - er, bless - ed Lord, To the cross where thou hast died; Draw me near - er, near - er, near - er, bless - ed Lord, To thy pre - cious, bleed - ing side. A - men.

CONSECRATION

I Have Heard Thy Voice, Lord Jesus

UPSALA 8.7.8.7.D.

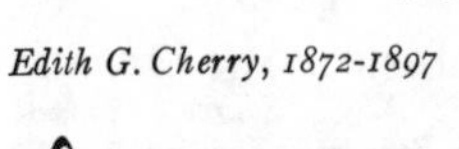
Edith G. Cherry, 1872-1897

Gunnar Wennerberg, 1817-1901

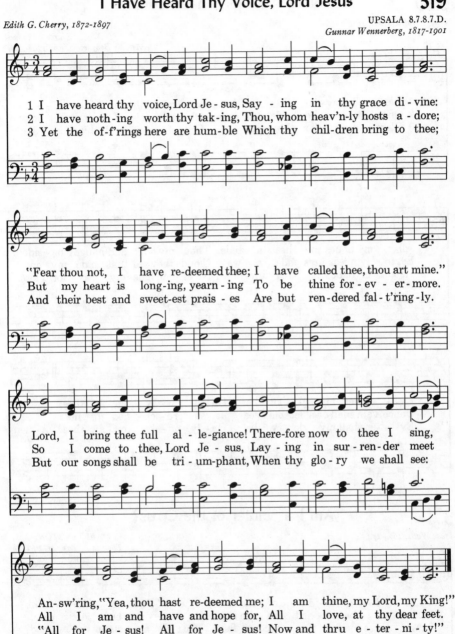

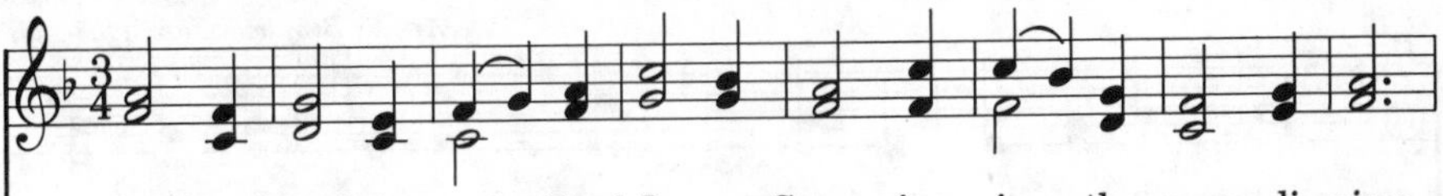

1 I have heard thy voice, Lord Je - sus, Say - ing in thy grace di - vine:
2 I have noth - ing worth thy tak - ing, Thou, whom heav'n-ly hosts a - dore;

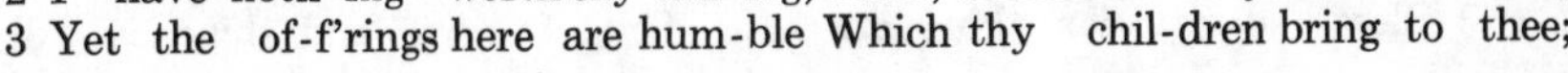
3 Yet the of-f'rings here are hum - ble Which thy chil - dren bring to thee;

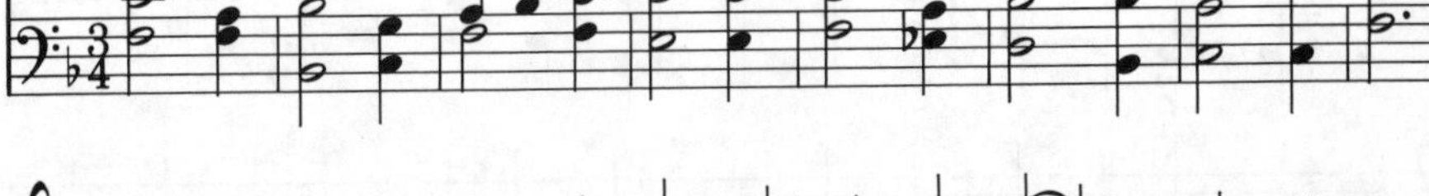

"Fear thou not, I have re-deemed thee; I have called thee, thou art mine."
But my heart is long - ing, yearn - ing To be thine for - ev - er - more.
And their best and sweet-est prais - es Are but ren - dered fal - t'ring - ly.

Lord, I bring thee full al - le - giance! There-fore now to thee I sing,
So I come to thee, Lord Je - sus, Lay - ing in sur - ren - der meet
But our songs shall be tri - um-phant, When thy glo - ry we shall see:

An - sw'ring, "Yea, thou hast re-deemed me; I am thine, my Lord, my King!"
All I am and have and hope for, All I love, at thy dear feet.
"All for Je - sus! All for Je - sus! Now and thru e - ter - ni - ty!"

Alternate tune: HYFRYDOL, *No. 247, No. 260*

320 Blessed Savior, Thee I Love

George Duffield, Jr., 1818-1888

SPANISH HYMN 7.7.7.7.7.7.
Source unknown
Arr. by Benjamin Carr, 1768-1831

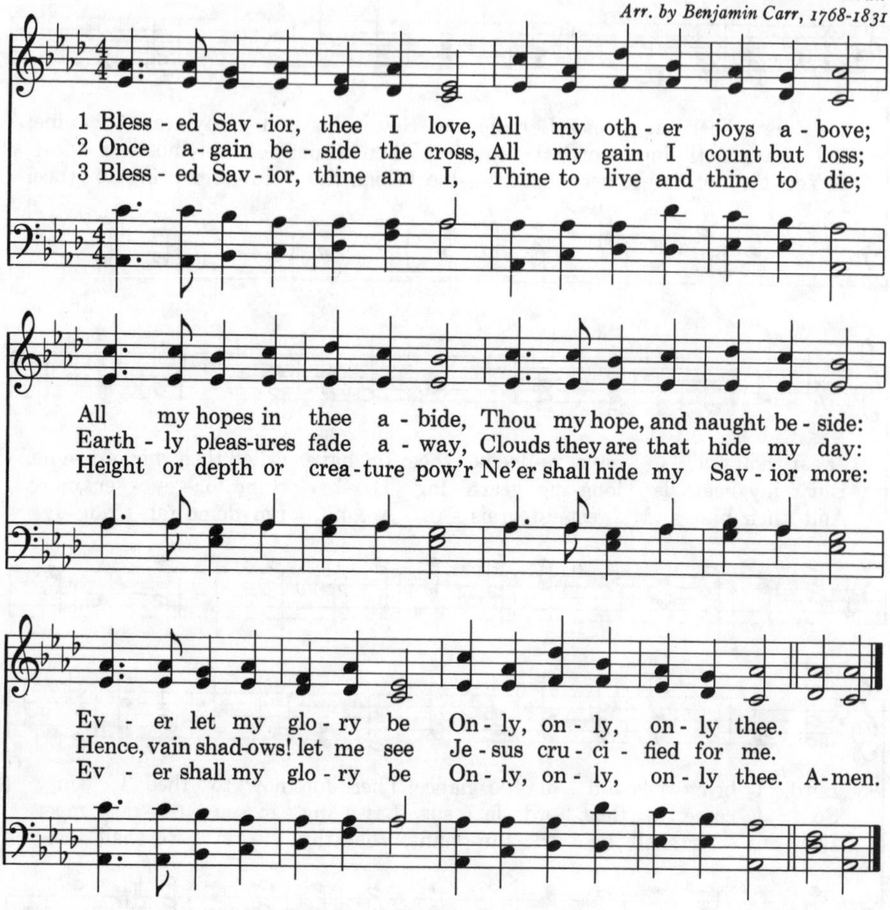

1 Bless - ed Sav - ior, thee I love, All my oth - er joys a - bove;
2 Once a - gain be - side the cross, All my gain I count but loss;
3 Bless - ed Sav - ior, thine am I, Thine to live and thine to die;

All my hopes in thee a - bide, Thou my hope, and naught be - side:
Earth - ly pleas-ures fade a - way, Clouds they are that hide my day:
Height or depth or crea - ture pow'r Ne'er shall hide my Sav - ior more:

Ev - er let my glo - ry be On - ly, on - ly, on - ly thee.
Hence, vain shad-ows! let me see Je - sus cru - ci - fied for me.
Ev - er shall my glo - ry be On - ly, on - ly, on - ly thee. A-men.

321 Am I a Soldier of the Cross?

Isaac Watts, 1674-1748

ARLINGTON C.M.
Thomas A. Arne, 1710-1778

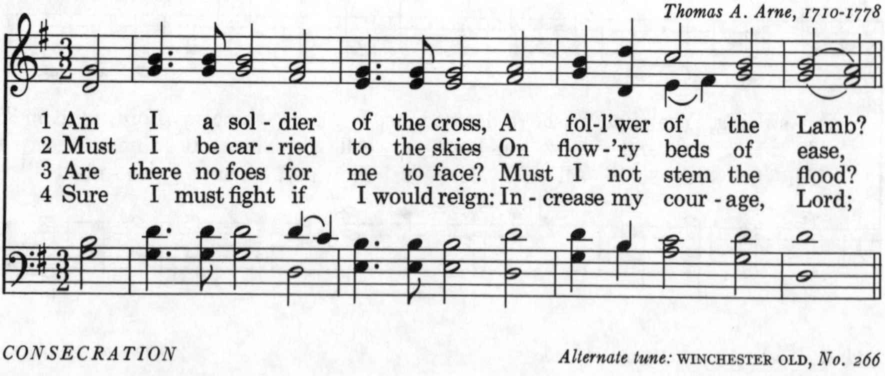

1 Am I a sol - dier of the cross, A fol-l'wer of the Lamb?
2 Must I be car - ried to the skies On flow - 'ry beds of ease,
3 Are there no foes for me to face? Must I not stem the flood?
4 Sure I must fight if I would reign: In - crease my cour - age, Lord;

Alternate tune: WINCHESTER OLD, No. 266

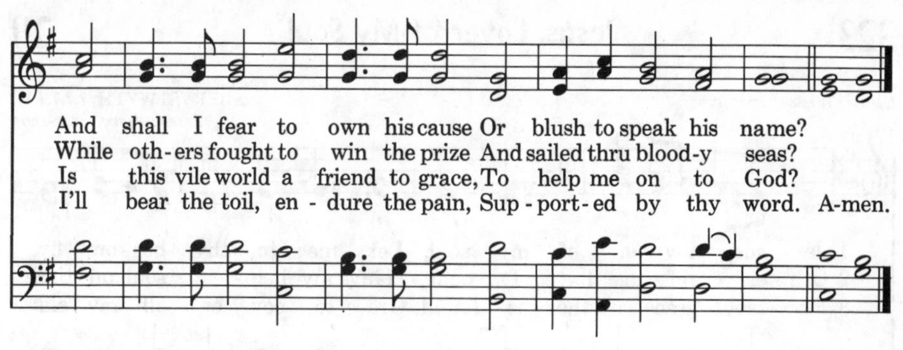
And shall I fear to own his cause Or blush to speak his name?
While oth-ers fought to win the prize And sailed thru blood-y seas?
Is this vile world a friend to grace, To help me on to God?
I'll bear the toil, en - dure the pain, Sup - port-ed by thy word. A-men.

More Love to Thee, O Christ 322

Elizabeth P. Prentiss, 1818-1878

MORE LOVE TO THEE 6.4.6.4.6.6.4.
William H. Doane, 1832-1915

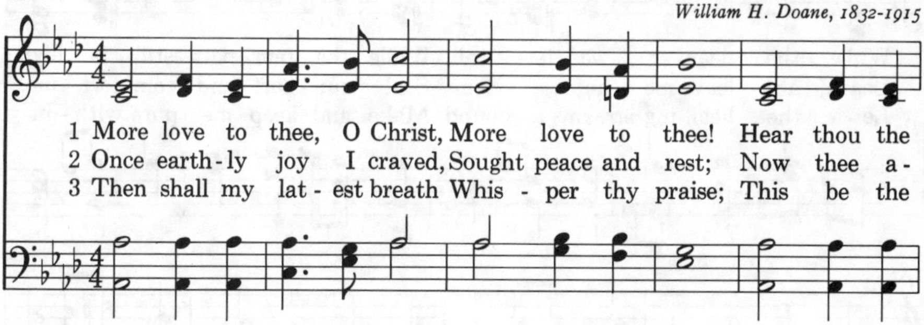

1 More love to thee, O Christ, More love to thee! Hear thou the
2 Once earth-ly joy I craved, Sought peace and rest; Now thee a -
3 Then shall my lat - est breath Whis - per thy praise; This be the

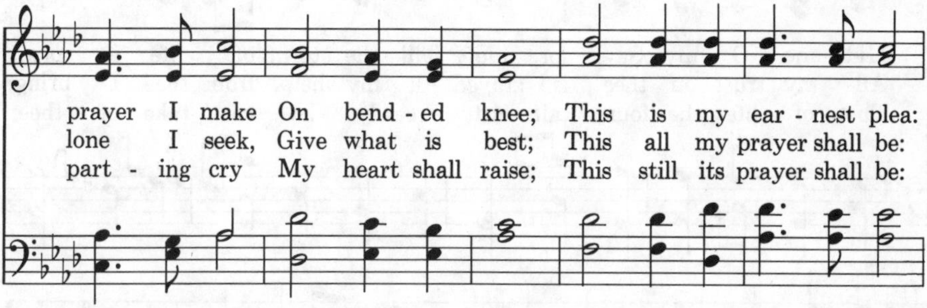

prayer I make On bend - ed knee; This is my ear - nest plea:
lone I seek, Give what is best; This all my prayer shall be:
part - ing cry My heart shall raise; This still its prayer shall be:

More love, O Christ, to thee, More love to thee, More love to thee! A-men.

323 Jesus, Lover of My Soul

Charles Wesley, 1707-1788
ABERYSTWYTH 7.7.7.7.D.
Joseph Parry, 1841-1903
1 Je - sus, lov - er of my soul, Let me to thy bos - om fly,
2 Oth - er ref - uge have I none, Hangs my help - less soul on thee;
3 Plen - teous grace with thee is found, Grace to cov - er all my sin;
While the near - er wa - ters roll, While the tem - pest still is high.
Leave, ah! leave me not a - lone, Still sup - port and com - fort me.
Let the heal - ing streams a - bound, Make and keep me pure with - in.
Hide me, O my Sav - ior, hide, Till the storm of life is past;
All my trust on thee is stayed, All my help from thee I bring;
Thou of life the foun - tain art, Free - ly let me take of thee;
Safe in - to the ha - ven guide, O re - ceive my soul at last!
Cov - er my de - fense - less head With the shad - ow of thy wing.
Spring thou up with - in my heart, Rise to all e - ter - ni - ty. A - men.

King of My Life I Crown Thee Now

Jennie Evelyn Hussey, 1874-1958

LEAD ME TO CALVARY C.M. *with Refrain*
William J. Kirkpatrick, 1838-1921

1 King of my life I crown thee now– Thine shall the glo - ry be;
2 Show me the tomb where thou wast laid, Ten - der-ly mourned and wept;
3 Let me like Mar - y, thru the gloom, Come with a gift to thee;
4 May I be will - ing, Lord, to bear Dai - ly my cross for thee;

Lest I for-get thy thorn-crowned brow, Lead me to Cal - va - ry.
An - gels in robes of light ar - rayed Guard-ed thee whilst thou slept.
Show to me now the emp - ty tomb– Lead me to Cal - va - ry.
E - ven thy cup of grief to share– Thou hast borne all for me.

REFRAIN

Lest I for-get Geth-sem - a - ne, Lest I for-get thine ag - o - ny,

Lest I for-get thy love for me, Lead me to Cal - va - ry. A-men.

325 Jesus Calls Us o'er the Tumult

First Tune

Cecil Frances Alexander, 1818-1895

GALILEE 8.7.8.7.

William H. Jude, 1851-1922

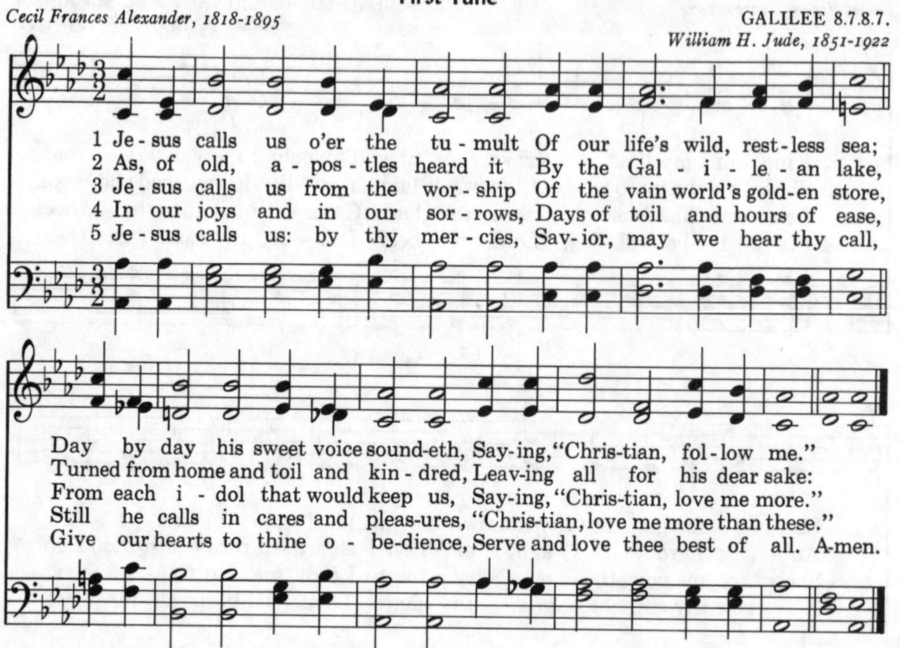
1 Je-sus calls us o'er the tu-mult Of our life's wild, rest-less sea;
2 As, of old, a-pos-tles heard it By the Gal-i-le-an lake,
3 Je-sus calls us from the wor-ship Of the vain world's gold-en store,
4 In our joys and in our sor-rows, Days of toil and hours of ease,
5 Je-sus calls us: by thy mer-cies, Sav-ior, may we hear thy call,
Day by day his sweet voice sound-eth, Say-ing, "Chris-tian, fol-low me."
Turned from home and toil and kin-dred, Leav-ing all for his dear sake:
From each i-dol that would keep us, Say-ing, "Chris-tian, love me more."
Still he calls in cares and pleas-ures, "Chris-tian, love me more than these."
Give our hearts to thine o-be-dience, Serve and love thee best of all. A-men.

326 Jesus Calls Us o'er the Tumult

Second Tune

Cecil Frances Alexander, 1818-1895

PLEADING SAVIOR 8.7.8.7.D.

"The Christian Lyre," 1831

Harm. by Norman E. Johnson, 1928-

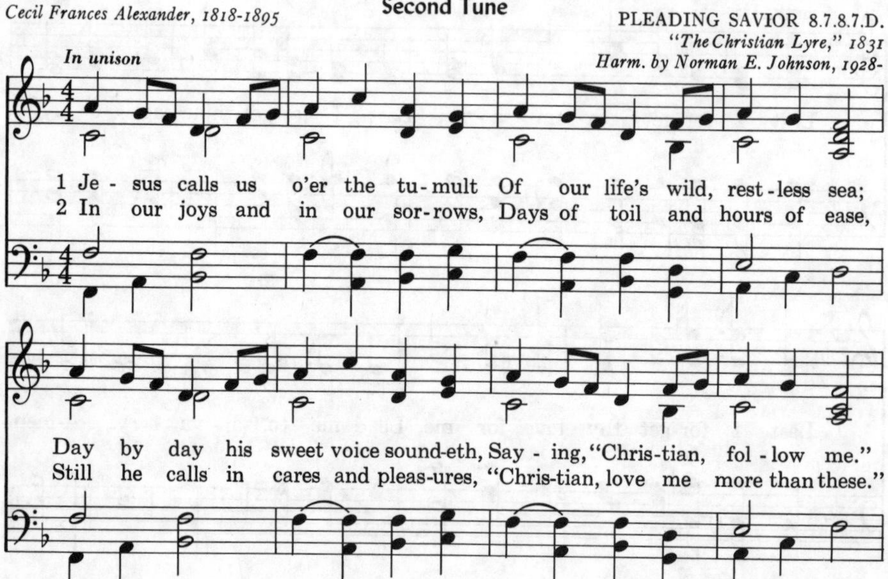
In unison
1 Je-sus calls us o'er the tu-mult Of our life's wild, rest-less sea;
2 In our joys and in our sor-rows, Days of toil and hours of ease,
Day by day his sweet voice sound-eth, Say-ing, "Chris-tian, fol-low me."
Still he calls in cares and pleas-ures, "Chris-tian, love me more than these."

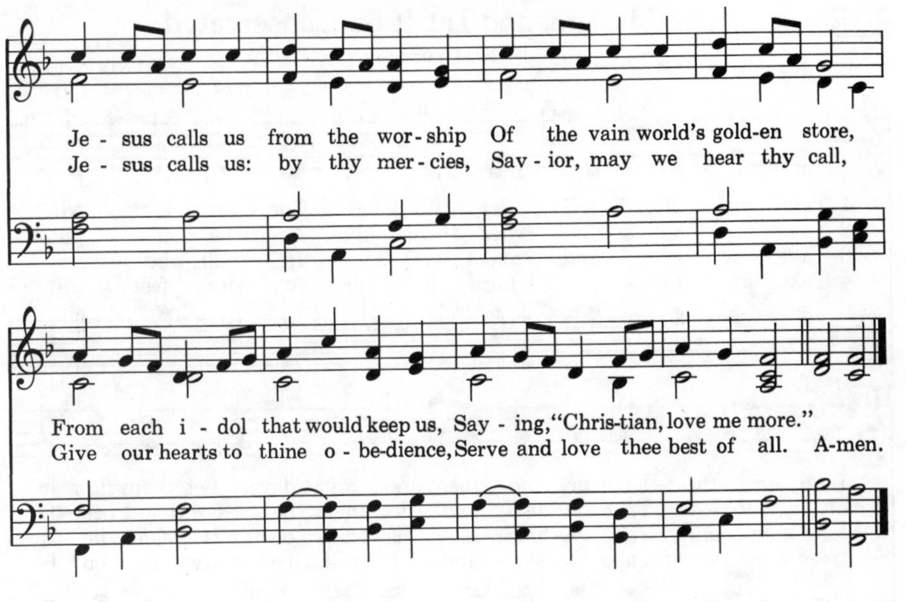
Je - sus calls us from the wor - ship Of the vain world's gold-en store,
Je - sus calls us: by thy mer - cies, Sav - ior, may we hear thy call,
From each i - dol that would keep us, Say - ing, "Chris-tian, love me more."
Give our hearts to thine o - be-dience, Serve and love thee best of all. A-men.

Jesus, in Stillness, Longing I Wait

327

Lina Sandell, 1832-1903
Tr. E. Gustav Johnson, 1893-

STILLNESS 5.7.5.7.
Carl Erik Sjögren, 1799-1877

1 Je - sus, in still - ness, Long - ing I wait for thy peace;
2 Hope - ful and yearn - ing Ev - er to be at thy side—
3 Je - sus, O lead me Forth on my fal - ter - ing way;
4 Safe from temp - ta - tion Keep me and hide me, O Lord;
5 Keep me, dear Sav - ior, Bless me and sanc - ti - fy me;

Heal my soul's ill - ness, Bid thou my an - guish to cease.
Keep me from turn - ing, Help me in grace to a - bide.
Teach me to heed thee Will - ing - ly, al - ways, I pray.
In trib - u - la - tion Sol - ace and glad - ness af - ford.
In lov - ing fa - vor Let me thy coun - te - nance see. A - men.

328 Take My Life, and Let It Be Consecrated

First Tune

Frances Ridley Havergal, 1836-1879

HENDON 7.7.7.7.
H. A. César Malan, 1787-1864

1 Take my life, and let it be
Consecrated, Lord, to thee;
Take my moments and my days,
Let them flow in ceaseless praise,
Let them flow in ceaseless praise.

2 Take my hands, and let them move
At the impulse of thy love;
Take my feet, and let them be
Swift and beautiful for thee,
Swift and beautiful for thee.

3 Take my will, and make it thine—
It shall be no longer mine;
Take my heart—it is thine own,
It shall be thy royal throne,
It shall be thy royal throne.

4 Take my love—my Lord, I pour
At thy feet its treasure store;
Take myself, and I will be
Ever, only, all for thee,
Ever, only, all for thee. Amen.

A lower setting may be found at No. 424

329 Take My Life, and Let It Be Consecrated

Second Tune

Frances Ridley Havergal, 1836-1879

ST. BEES 7.7.7.7.
John B. Dykes, 1823-1876

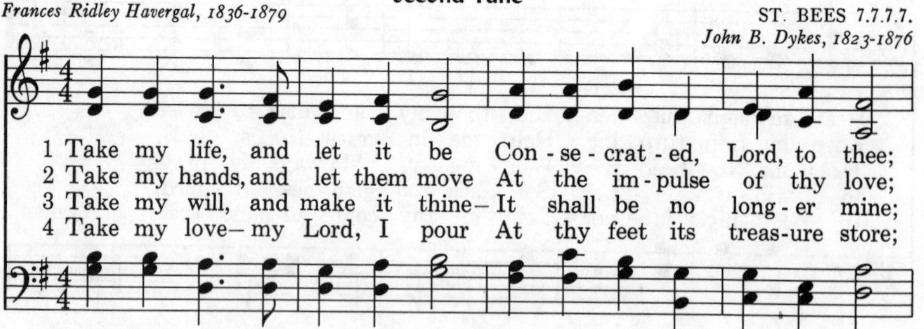
1 Take my life, and let it be Con-se-crat-ed, Lord, to thee;
2 Take my hands, and let them move At the im-pulse of thy love;
3 Take my will, and make it thine– It shall be no long-er mine;
4 Take my love– my Lord, I pour At thy feet its treas-ure store;

A higher setting may be found at No. 245

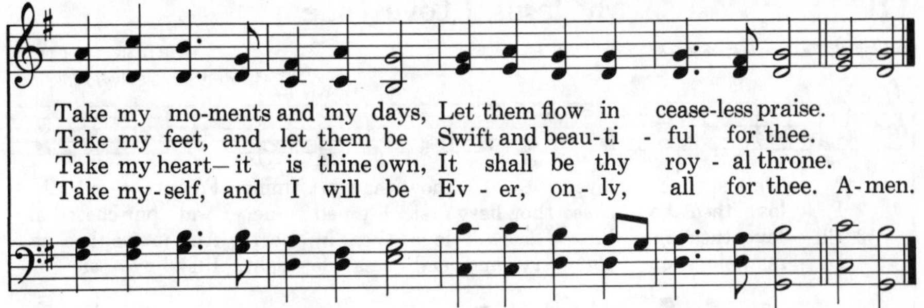

Take my mo-ments and my days, Let them flow in cease-less praise.
Take my feet, and let them be Swift and beau-ti - ful for thee.
Take my heart– it is thine own, It shall be thy roy - al throne.
Take my-self, and I will be Ev - er, on - ly, all for thee. A-men.

O Thou Who Hast Thy Servants Taught 330

Henry Alford, 1810-1871

ST. PETER C.M.
Alexander R. Reinagle, 1799-1877

1 O thou who hast thy serv - ants taught That
2 While in the house of prayer we meet And
3 When we our voic - es lift in praise, Give
4 And, in the dan - g'rous path of life Up -

not by words a - lone, But by the fruits of
call thee God and Lord, Give us a heart to
thou us grace to bring An of - f'ring of un -
hold us as we go, That with our lips and

ho - li - ness, The life of God is shown:
fol - low thee, O - be - dient to thy word.
feign - ed thanks, And with the spir - it sing.
in our lives Thy glo - ry we may show. A - men.

A higher setting may be found at No. 485

331 My Jesus, I Love Thee
William R. Featherston, 1846-1873
GORDON 11.11.11.11.
Adoniram J. Gordon, 1836-1895
1 My Je - sus, I love thee, I know thou art mine; For thee all the
2 I love thee be - cause thou hast first lov - ed me, And pur-chased my
3 I'll love thee in life, I will love thee in death, And praise thee as
4 In man-sions of glo - ry and end - less de - light, I'll ev - er a -
fol - lies of sin I re - sign; My gra - cious Re - deem - er, my
par - don on Cal - va - ry's tree; I love thee for wear - ing the
long as thou lend - est me breath; And say when the death - dew lies
dore thee in heav - en so bright; I'll sing with the glit - ter - ing
Sav - ior art thou: If ev - er I loved thee, my Je - sus, 'tis now.
thorns on thy brow: If ev - er I loved thee, my Je - sus, 'tis now.
cold on my brow: If ev - er I loved thee, my Je - sus, 'tis now.
crown on my brow: If ev - er I loved thee, my Je - sus, 'tis now. A-men.
332 Take Time to Be Holy
William D. Longstaff, 1822-1894
LONGSTAFF 6.5.6.5.D.
George C. Stebbins, 1846-1945
1 Take time to be ho - ly, Speak oft with thy Lord; A - bide in him
2 Take time to be ho - ly, The world rush-es on; Much time spend in
3 Take time to be ho - ly, Let him be thy guide, And run not be -

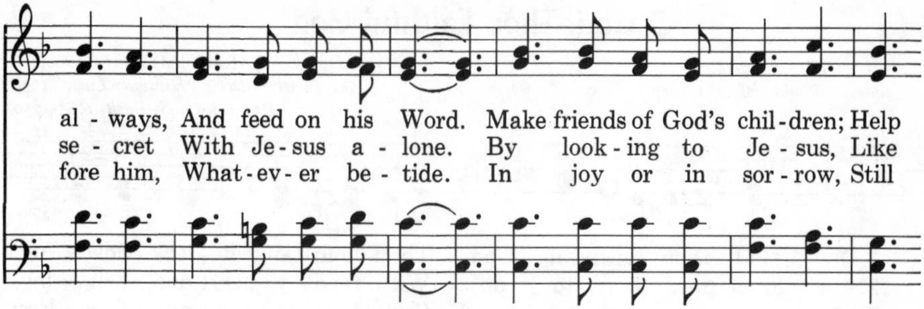

al - ways, And feed on his Word. Make friends of God's chil-dren; Help
se - cret With Je - sus a - lone. By look - ing to Je - sus, Like
fore him, What-ev-er be - tide. In joy or in sor-row, Still

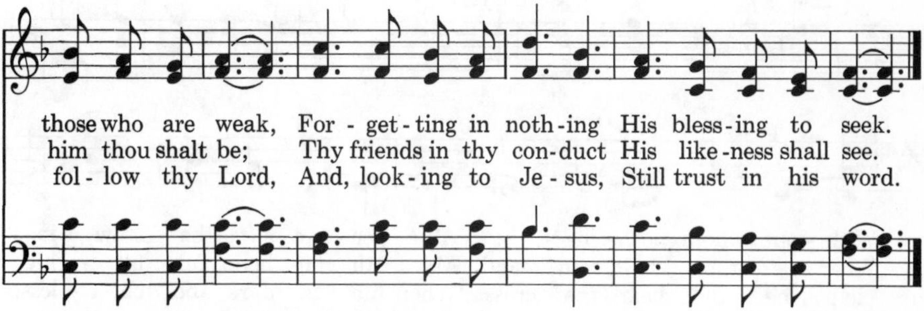

those who are weak, For - get - ting in noth-ing His bless-ing to seek.
him thou shalt be; Thy friends in thy con-duct His like-ness shall see.
fol - low thy Lord, And, look-ing to Je - sus, Still trust in his word.

More Holiness Give Me

333

Philip P. Bliss, 1838-1876

LONGSTAFF 6.5.6.5.D.
George C. Stebbins, 1846-1945

1 More holiness give me, More striving within,
More patience in suff'ring, More sorrow for sin;
More faith in my Savior, More sense of his care,
More joy in his service, More purpose in prayer.

2 More gratitude give me, More trust in the Lord,
More pride in his glory, More hope in his word;
More tears for his sorrows, More pain at his grief,
More meekness in trial, More praise for relief.

3 More purity give me, More strength to o'ercome,
More freedom from earth stains, More longings for home;
More fit for the kingdom, More used would I be,
More blessed and holy, More, Savior, like thee. Amen.

A - men.

334 O God, Thou Faithful God

Johann Heermann, 1585-1647
Tr. Catherine Winkworth, 1827-1878

DARMSTADT 6.7.6.7.6.6.6.6.
Ahasuerus Fritsch's "Himmels-Lust," 1679
Harm. by J. S. Bach, 1685-1750

1 O God, thou faith-ful God, Thou foun-tain ev - er flow - ing,
2 And grant me, Lord, to do, With read - y heart, and will - ing,
3 If dan - gers gath - er round, Still keep me calm and fear - less;
With - out whom noth - ing is, All per - fect gifts be - stow - ing,
What - e'er thou shalt com - mand, My call - ing here ful - fill - ing,
Help me to bear the cross When life is dark and cheer - less,
Grant me a health-y frame, And give me, Lord, with - in,
And do it when I ought, With zeal and joy - ful - ness:
To o - ver - come my foe With words and ac - tions kind;
A con-science free from blame, A soul un - hurt by sin.
And bless the work I've wrought, For thou must give suc - cess.
When coun - sel I would know, Good coun - sel let me find. A-men.

CONSECRATION

Savior, While My Heart Is Tender

John Burton, Jr., 1803-1877

HYFRYDOL 8.7.8.7.D.
Rowland H. Prichard, 1811-1887

1 Sav - ior, while my heart is ten - der, I would yield that heart to thee;
2 Send me, Lord, where thou wilt send me, On - ly do thou guide my way;
3 May this sol - emn con - se - cra - tion Nev - er once for - got - ten be;

All my pow'rs to thee sur - ren - der, Thine and on - ly thine to be.
May thy grace thru life at - tend me, Glad - ly then shall I o - bey.
Let it know no rev - o - ca - tion, Reg - is - tered, con - firmed by thee.

Take me now, Lord Je - sus, take me, Let my heart be ev - er thine;
Let me do thy will, or bear it, I would know no will but thine;
Thine I am, O Lord, for - ev - er To thy serv - ice set a - part;

Thy de - vot - ed ser - vant make me, Fill my soul with love di - vine.
Shouldst thou take my life, or spare it, I that life to thee re - sign.
Suf - fer me to leave thee nev - er, Seal thine im - age on my heart. A-men.

Another harmonization in a higher setting may be found at No. 248

336 More About Jesus Would I Know

Eliza E. Hewitt, 1851-1920
PENTECOST L.M.
William Boyd, 1847-1928
1 More a-bout Je-sus would I know, More of his grace to oth-ers show,
2 More a-bout Je-sus let me learn, More of his ho-ly will dis-cern;
3 More a-bout Je-sus— in his Word Hold-ing com-mun-ion with my Lord,
4 More a-bout Je-sus on his throne, Rich-es in glo-ry all his own,
More of his sav-ing full-ness see, More of his love who died for me.
Spir-it of God, my teach-er be, Show-ing the things of Christ to me.
Hear-ing his voice in ev-'ry line, Mak-ing each faith-ful say-ing mine.
More of his king-dom's sure in-crease, More of his com-ing, Prince of Peace.
CONSECRATION
Higher settings may be found Nos. 372 and 501
337 Father, Hear the Prayer We Offer
Love Maria Willis, 1824-1908
STUTTGART 8.7.8.7.
Attr. to Christian F. Witt, 1660-1716
"Psalmodia Sacra," Gotha, 1715
1 Fa-ther, hear the prayer we of-fer: Not for ease that prayer shall be,
2 Not for-ev-er in green pas-tures Do we ask our way to be;
3 Not for-ev-er by still wa-ters Would we i-dly qui-et stay,
4 Be our strength in hours of weak-ness, In our wan-d'rings be our guide;
But for strength, that we may ev-er Live our lives cou-ra-geous-ly.
But the steep and rug-ged path-way May we tread re-joic-ing-ly.
But would smite the liv-ing foun-tains From the rocks a-long the way.
Thru en-deav-or, fail-ure, dan-ger, Fa-ther, be thou at our side. A-men.

PRAYER AND INTERCESSION

A higher setting may be found at No. 658

In the Hour of Trial 338

James Montgomery, 1771-1854, alt.

PENITENCE 6.5.6.5.D.
Spencer Lane, 1843-1903

1 In the hour of tri - al, Je - sus, plead for me,
2 With for - bid - den pleas - ures Would this vain world charm,
3 Should thy mer - cy send me Sor - row, toil, or woe,
Lest by base de - ni - al I de - part from thee;
Or its sor - did treas - ures Spread to work me harm:
Or should pain at - tend me On my path be - low,
When thou seest me wa - ver, With a look re - call,
Bring to my re - mem - brance Sad Geth-sem - a - ne,
Grant that I may nev - er Fail thy hand to see;
Nor for fear or fa - vor Suf - fer me to fall.
Or, in dark - er sem-blance, Cross-crowned Cal - va - ry.
Grant that I may ev - er Cast my care on thee. A - men.

339 Lord, I Hear of Showers of Blessing

Based on Ezekiel 34:26
Elizabeth Codner, 1824-1919

EVEN ME 8.7.8.7. *with Refrain*
William B. Bradbury, 1816-1868
Harm. by Norman E. Johnson, 1928-

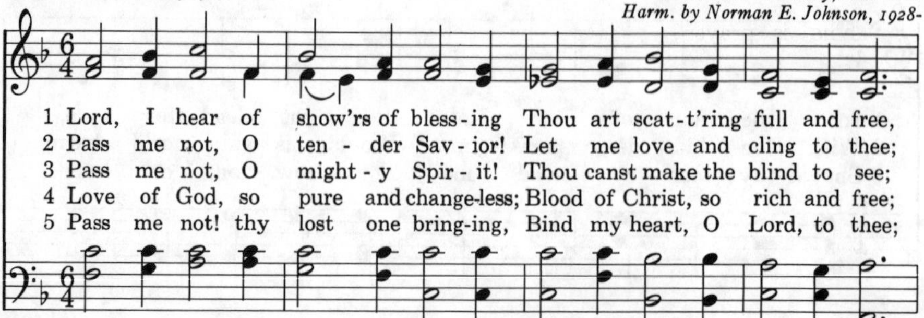

1 Lord, I hear of show'rs of bless-ing Thou art scat-t'ring full and free,
2 Pass me not, O ten - der Sav-ior! Let me love and cling to thee;
3 Pass me not, O might-y Spir-it! Thou canst make the blind to see;
4 Love of God, so pure and change-less; Blood of Christ, so rich and free;
5 Pass me not! thy lost one bring-ing, Bind my heart, O Lord, to thee;

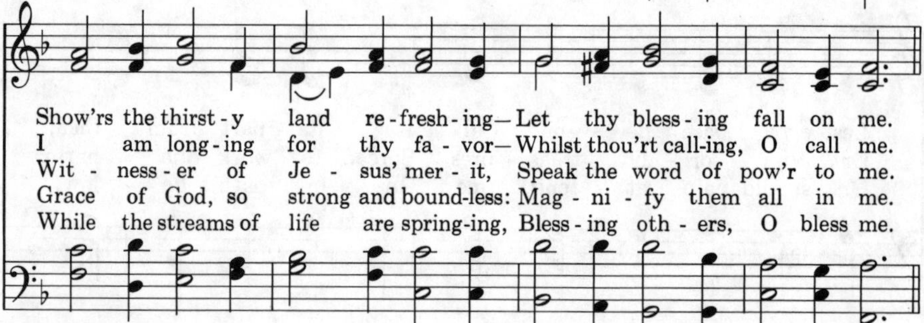

Show'rs the thirst-y land re-fresh-ing—Let thy bless-ing fall on me.
I am long-ing for thy fa-vor—Whilst thou'rt call-ing, O call me.
Wit - ness-er of Je - sus' mer-it, Speak the word of pow'r to me.
Grace of God, so strong and bound-less: Mag - ni - fy them all in me.
While the streams of life are spring-ing, Bless-ing oth-ers, O bless me.

REFRAIN

E - ven me, e - ven me, Let thy bless-ing fall on me. A-men.

340 Jesus, Kneel Beside Me

Allen Eastman Cross, 1864-1943

EUDOXIA 6.5.6.5.
Sabine Baring-Gould, 1834-1924

1 Je - sus, kneel be - side me In the dawn of day;
2 Mas - ter, work be - side me In the shin - ing sun;
3 Sav - ior, watch be - side me In the clos - ing light;
4 Birds are wing - ing home - ward, Sun and shad - ow cease;

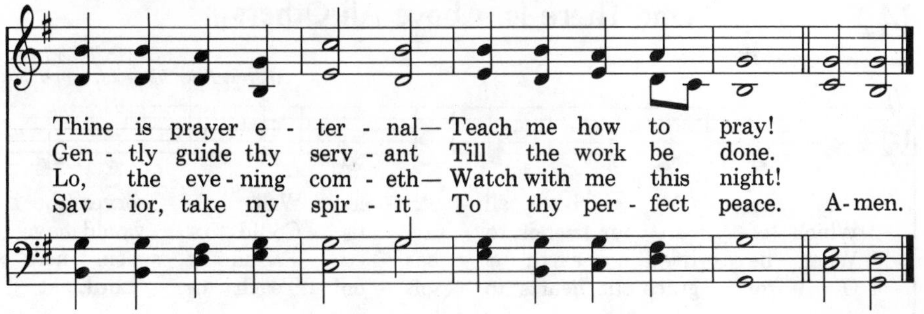
Thine is prayer e - ter - nal— Teach me how to pray!
Gen - tly guide thy serv - ant Till the work be done.
Lo, the eve - ning com - eth— Watch with me this night!
Sav - ior, take my spir - it To thy per - fect peace. A-men.

Dear Lord and Father of Mankind

341

John Greenleaf Whittier, 1807-1892

REST 8.6.8.8.6.
Frederick C. Maker, 1844-1927

1 Dear Lord and Fa - ther of man - kind, For - give our fev - 'rish ways!
2 In sim - ple trust like theirs who heard, Be - side the Syr - ian sea,
3 O sab - bath rest by Gal - i - lee! O calm of hills a - bove!
4 Drop thy still dews of qui - et - ness, Till all our striv - ings cease;
5 Breathe thru the puls - es of de - sire Thy cool - ness and thy balm;

Re - clothe us in our right - ful mind; In pur - er lives thy
The gra - cious call - ing of the Lord, Let us, like them, with -
Where Je - sus knelt to share with thee The si - lence of e -
Take from our souls the strain and stress, And let our or - dered
Let sense be dumb, let flesh re - tire; Speak thru the earth-quake,

serv - ice find, In deep - er rev - 'rence, praise.
out a word, Rise up and fol - low thee.
ter - ni - ty, In - ter - pret - ed by love:
lives con - fess The beau - ty of thy peace.
wind, and fire, O still, small voice of calm. A - men.

342 One There Is, Above All Others

John Newton, 1725-1807

DANA 8.7.8.7.7.7.
Andreas Peter Berggren, 1801-1880

1 One there is, a - bove all oth - ers, Well de - serves the
2 Which of all our friends, to save us, Could or would have
3 When he lived on earth a - bas - ed, 'Friend of sin - ners'
4 O for grace our hearts to soft - en! Teach us, Lord, at
name of friend; His is love be - yond a broth - er's,
shed his blood? But this Sav - ior died to have us
was his name; Now, a - bove all glo - ry rais - ed,
length to love! We, a - las, for - get too oft - en
Cost - ly, free, and knows no end: They who once his kind - ness
Re - con - ciled in him to God: This was bound-less love in -
He re - joic - es in the same: Still he calls them breth - ren,
What a friend we have a - bove: But when home our souls are
prove Find it ev - er - last - ing love.
deed! Je - sus is a friend in need.
friends, And to all their wants at - tends.
brought We will love thee as we ought. A - men.

Sweet Hour of Prayer

William W. Walford, 1772-1850

SWEET HOUR L.M.D.
William B. Bradbury, 1816-1868

1 Sweet hour of prayer, sweet hour of prayer, That calls me from a world of care,
2 Sweet hour of prayer, sweet hour of prayer, Thy wings shall my pe - ti - tion bear
And bids me at my Fa-ther's throne Make all my wants and wish - es known:
To him whose truth and faith - ful-ness En - gage the wait - ing soul to bless:
In sea - sons of dis - tress and grief My soul has oft - en found re - lief,
And since he bids me seek his face, Be - lieve his Word, and trust his grace,
And oft es-caped the tempt-er's snare By thy re - turn, sweet hour of prayer.
I'll cast on him my ev - 'ry care, And wait for thee, sweet hour of prayer.

344 Heavenly Father, Hear My Supplication

Joel Blomqvist, 1840-1930
Tr. Carl E. Backstrom, 1901-

FLEMMING 11.11.11.6.
Friedrich F. Flemming, 1778-1813

1 Heav - en - ly Fa - ther, hear my sup - pli - ca - tion;
2 Draw me, Re - deem - er, I would seek thee sole - ly,
3 Dwell thou, O Sav - ior, in my heart for - ev - er,

I bow be - fore thee in thy con - gre - ga - tion Hum - ble and
Help me to cher - ish, love, o - bey thee whol - ly, Ful - ly sur -
Thou who hast prom - ised noth - ing shall us sev - er, Com - fort and

need - y, seek - ing thy sal - va - tion, Hear thou my prayer, O God!
ren - dered, live a life that's ho - ly, Hear thou my prayer, O God!
lead me, I would leave thee nev - er, Hear thou my prayer, O God! A-men.

A higher setting may be found at No. 274

345 Prayer Is the Soul's Sincere Desire

James Montgomery, 1771-1854

SHADDICK C.M.
Bates G. Burt, 1878-1948

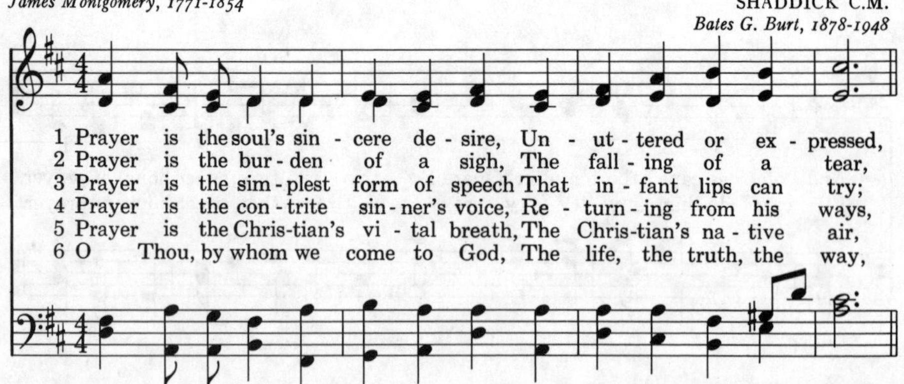
1 Prayer is the soul's sin - cere de - sire, Un - ut - tered or ex - pressed,
2 Prayer is the bur - den of a sigh, The fall - ing of a tear,
3 Prayer is the sim - plest form of speech That in - fant lips can try;
4 Prayer is the con - trite sin - ner's voice, Re - turn - ing from his ways,
5 Prayer is the Chris - tian's vi - tal breath, The Chris - tian's na - tive air,
6 O Thou, by whom we come to God, The life, the truth, the way,

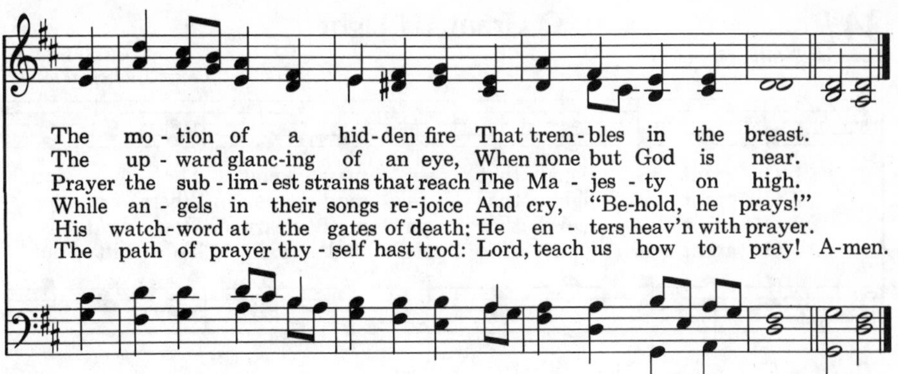
The mo - tion of a hid-den fire That trem-bles in the breast.
The up - ward glanc-ing of an eye, When none but God is near.
Prayer the sub - lim - est strains that reach The Ma - jes - ty on high.
While an - gels in their songs re-joice And cry, "Be-hold, he prays!"
His watch-word at the gates of death: He en - ters heav'n with prayer.
The path of prayer thy - self hast trod: Lord, teach us how to pray! A-men.

Our Father in Heaven, We Hallow Thy Name 346

Based on Matthew 6:9-13
Sarah J. Hale, 1795-1879

ST. DENIO 11.11.11.11.
Welsh Melody
John Roberts' "Caniadau y Cyssegr," 1839

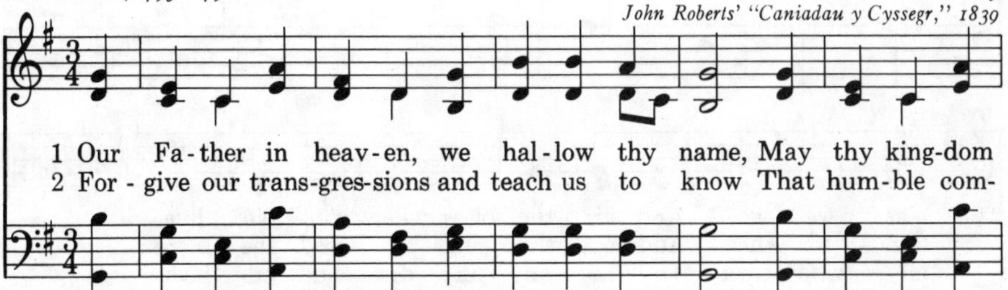

1 Our Fa-ther in heav-en, we hal-low thy name, May thy king-dom
2 For - give our trans-gres-sions and teach us to know That hum-ble com-

ho - ly on earth be the same; O give to us dai - ly our
pas - sion which par - dons each foe; Keep us from temp - ta - tion, from

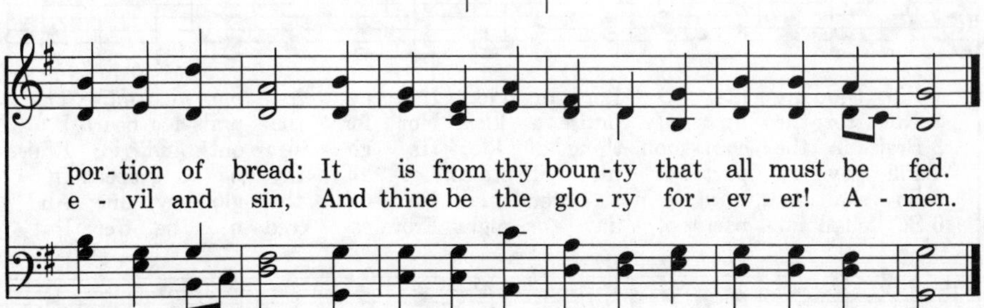

por - tion of bread: It is from thy boun-ty that all must be fed.
e - vil and sin, And thine be the glo - ry for - ev - er! A - men.

Another harmonization in a higher setting may be found at No. 15

347

O Grant Us Light

Lawrence Tuttiett, 1825-1897

ST. CRISPIN L.M.
George J. Elvey, 1816-1893

1 O grant us light, that we may know The wis - dom
2 O grant us light, that we may see Where er - ror
3 O grant us light, that we may learn How dead is
4 O grant us light, in grief and pain, To lift our

thou a - lone canst give, That truth may guide wher-
lurks in hu - man lore, And turn our doubt - ing
life from thee a - part, How sure is joy for
bur - dened hearts a - bove, And count the ver - y

e'er we go, And vir - tue bless wher - e'er we live.
minds to thee, And love thy sim - ple word the more.
all who turn To thee an un - di - vid - ed heart.
cross a gain, And bless our Fa - ther's hid - den love. A - men.

PRAYER AND INTERCESSION

Another harmonization in a lower setting may be found at No. 91

348 Fill Thou My Life, O Lord My God

Horatius Bonar, 1808-1889

RICHMOND C.M.
Thomas Haweis, 1734-1820

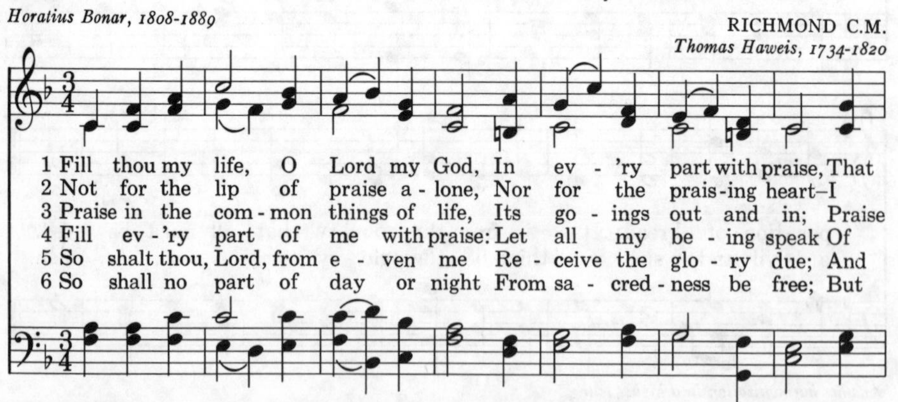
1 Fill thou my life, O Lord my God, In ev - 'ry part with praise, That
2 Not for the lip of praise a - lone, Nor for the prais-ing heart–I
3 Praise in the com - mon things of life, Its go - ings out and in; Praise
4 Fill ev - 'ry part of me with praise: Let all my be - ing speak Of
5 So shalt thou, Lord, from e - ven me Re - ceive the glo - ry due; And
6 So shall no part of day or night From sa - cred - ness be free; But

ASPIRATION

Another harmonization may be found at No. 471

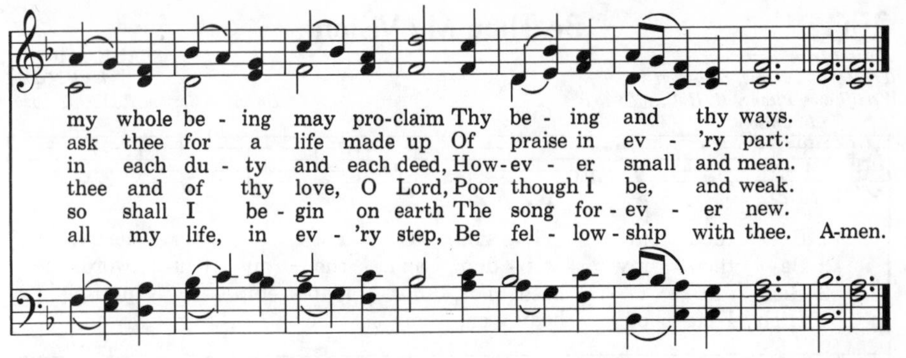
my whole be - ing may pro-claim Thy be - ing and thy ways.
ask thee for a life made up Of praise in ev - 'ry part:
in each du - ty and each deed, How-ev - er small and mean.
thee and of thy love, O Lord, Poor though I be, and weak.
so shall I be - gin on earth The song for - ev - er new.
all my life, in ev - 'ry step, Be fel - low - ship with thee. A-men.

Lead Us, O Father, in the Paths of Peace 349

William H. Burleigh, 1812-1871

MINNEHAHA 10.10.10.10.
Harry P. Opel, 1921-

In unison

1 Lead us, O Fa - ther, in the paths of peace; With-out thy guid-ing
2 Lead us, O Fa - ther, in the paths of truth; Un-helped by thee, in
3 Lead us, O Fa - ther, in the paths of right; Blind-ly we stum-ble
4 Lead us, O Fa - ther, to thy heav'n-ly rest, How-ev - er rough and

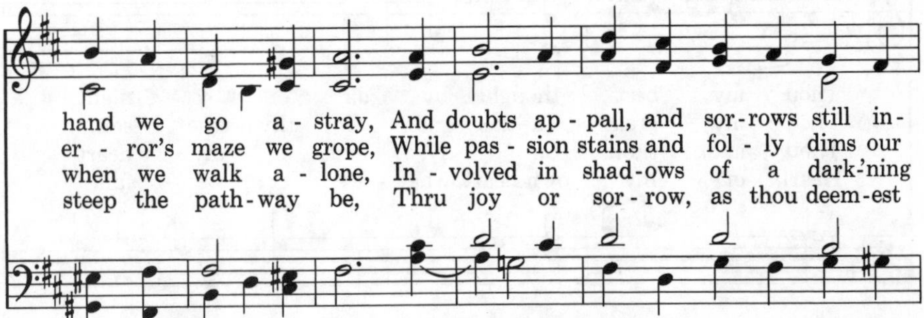

hand we go a - stray, And doubts ap - pall, and sor - rows still in -
er - ror's maze we grope, While pas - sion stains and fol - ly dims our
when we walk a - lone, In - volved in shad - ows of a dark-'ning
steep the path - way be, Thru joy or sor - row, as thou deem - est

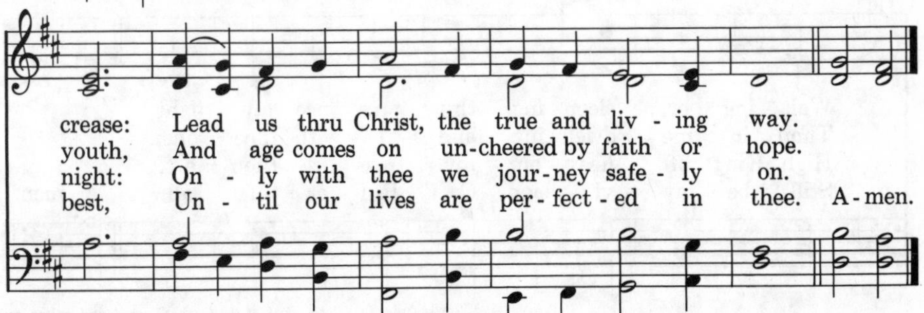

crease: Lead us thru Christ, the true and liv - ing way.
youth, And age comes on un - cheered by faith or hope.
night: On - ly with thee we jour - ney safe - ly on.
best, Un - til our lives are per - fect - ed in thee. A - men.

350 Be Thou My Vision

Ancient Irish
Tr. Mary E. Byrne, 1880-1931
Versified by Eleanor H. Hull, 1860-1935

SLANE 10.10.9.10.
Irish Melody
Harm. by Carlton R. Young, 1926-

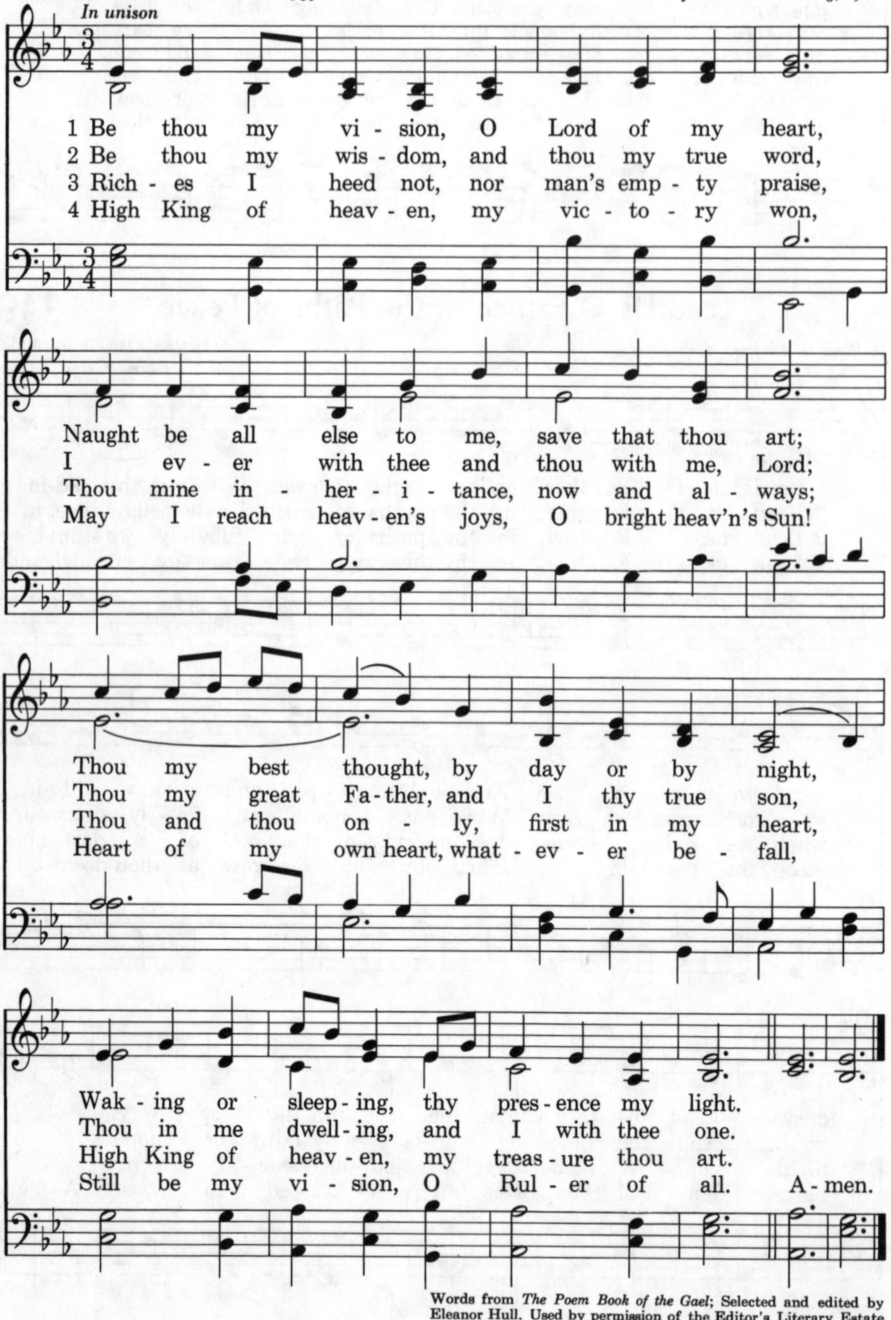

In unison

1 Be thou my vi - sion, O Lord of my heart,
2 Be thou my wis - dom, and thou my true word,
3 Rich - es I heed not, nor man's emp - ty praise,
4 High King of heav - en, my vic - to - ry won,

Naught be all else to me, save that thou art;
I ev - er with thee and thou with me, Lord;
Thou mine in - her - i - tance, now and al - ways;
May I reach heav - en's joys, O bright heav'n's Sun!

Thou my best thought, by day or by night,
Thou my great Fa - ther, and I thy true son,
Thou and thou on - ly, first in my heart,
Heart of my own heart, what - ev - er be - fall,

Wak - ing or sleep - ing, thy pres - ence my light.
Thou in me dwell - ing, and I with thee one.
High King of heav - en, my treas - ure thou art.
Still be my vi - sion, O Rul - er of all. A - men.

Declare, O Heavens, the Lord of Space

Robert Lansing Edwards, 1915-

LASST UNS ERFREUEN 8.8.4.4.8.8. *with Alleluias*
"Geistliche Kirchengesäng," Cologne, 1623
Arr. by Ralph Vaughan Williams, 1872-1958

In unison

1 De - clare, O heav'ns, the Lord of space, Re - ply, broad lands in ev - 'ry
2 Launch forth, O man, and bold - ly rise, Be - yond our plan - et pierce the
3 Yet see this world with pro - blems filled, Earth longs for life the Mas - ter
4 O Lord, whose pow'r all space ex - tols, Draw near our lives, en - large our

place: Tell his splen - dor! Al - le - lu - ia! New realms we find he first hath
skies: Bound - less ven - ture! Al - le - lu - ia! No soar - ing flight can e'er out -
willed: Light its dark - ness! Al - le - lu - ia! Reach out all bro - ken lives to
souls: Dwell with - in us! Al - le - lu - ia! Stir deeds of grace to serve thy

made, All be - ing is his pow'r dis - played: Al - le - lu - ia!
run Truth God has shown us in his Son: Al - le - lu - ia!
mend, In Christ win peace no war will end: Al - le - lu - ia!
plan, Wake joy the morn - ing stars be - gan: Al - le - lu - ia!

Al - le - lu - ia! Al - le - lu - ia! Al - le - lu - ia! Al - le - lu - ia! A - men.

Another harmonization in a higher setting may be found at No. 2

ASPIRATION

352 God, Who Stretched the Spangled Heavens

Catherine C. Arnott, 1927-

HYMN TO JOY 8.7.8.7.D.
Ludwig van Beethoven, 1770-1827
Adapted by Edward Hodges, 1796-1867

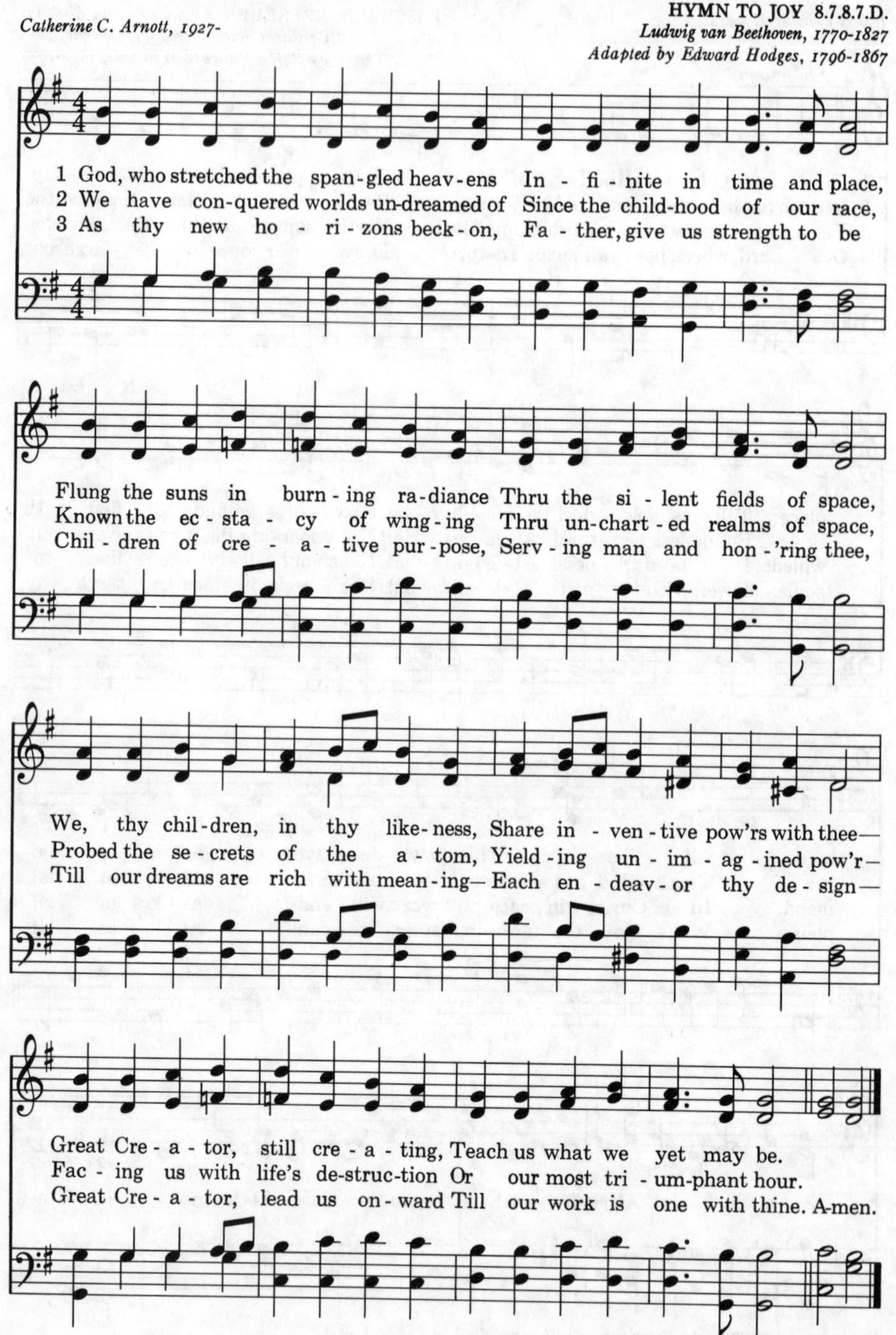
1 God, who stretched the spangled heavens Infinite in time and place,
Flung the suns in burning radiance Thru the silent fields of space,
We, thy children, in thy likeness, Share inventive pow'rs with thee—
Great Creator, still creating, Teach us what we yet may be.
2 We have conquered worlds undreamed of Since the childhood of our race,
Known the ecstacy of winging Thru uncharted realms of space,
Probed the secrets of the atom, Yielding unimagined pow'r—
Facing us with life's destruction Or our most triumphant hour.
3 As thy new horizons beckon, Father, give us strength to be
Children of creative purpose, Serving man and hon-'ring thee,
Till our dreams are rich with meaning—Each endeavor thy design—
Great Creator, lead us onward Till our work is one with thine. Amen.

ASPIRATION

Words used by permission of Catherine C. Arnott.
Alternate tune: FRANKLIN SQUARE, *No. 564*

I with Thee Would Begin

Lina Sandell, 1832-1903
Tr. A. Samuel Wallgren, 1885-1940

BEGYNNELSE 12.9.12.9.9.
Wilhelm Theodor Söderberg, 1845-1922
Harm. by James P. Davies, 1913-

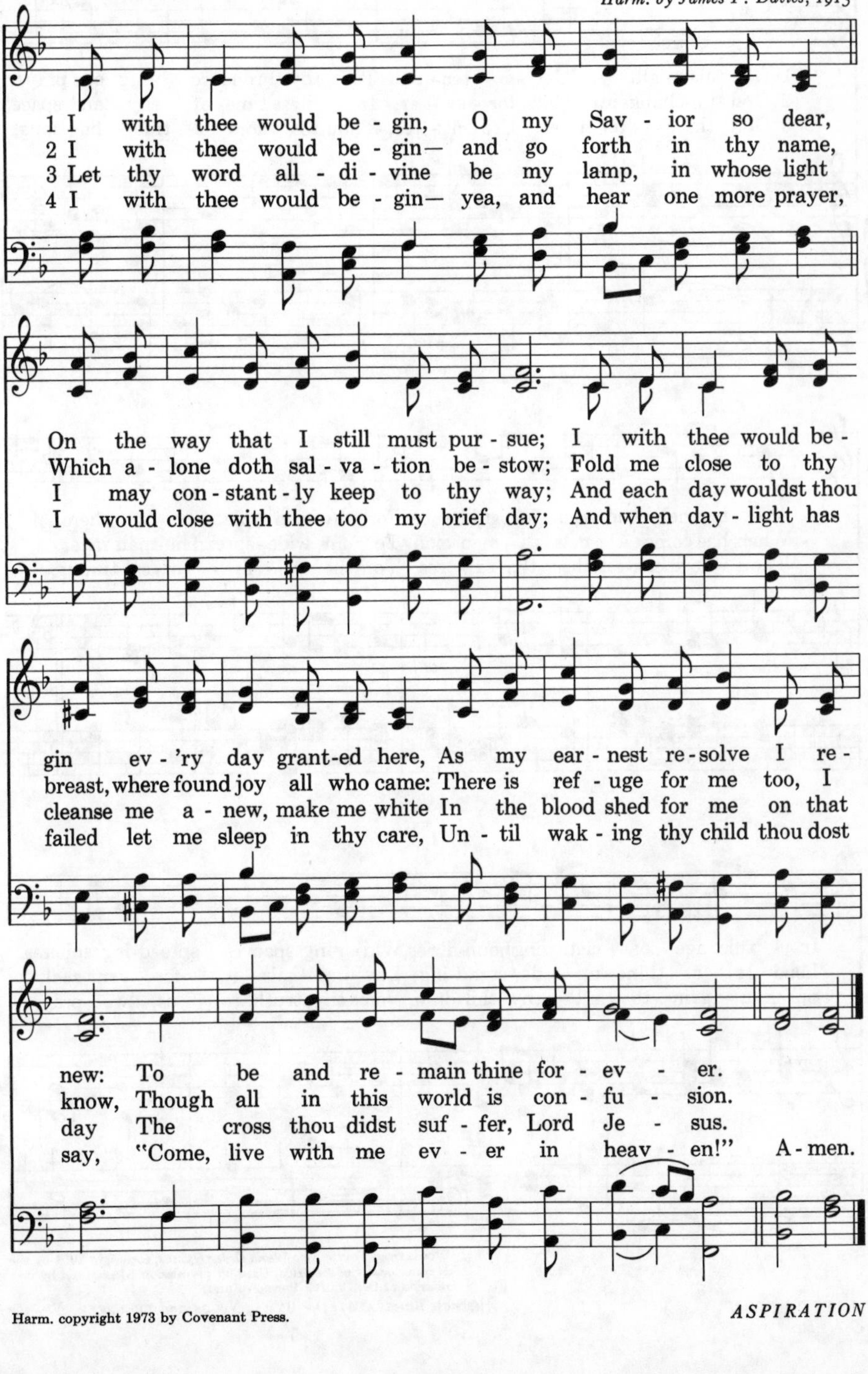

1 I with thee would be - gin, O my Sav - ior so dear,
2 I with thee would be - gin— and go forth in thy name,
3 Let thy word all - di - vine be my lamp, in whose light
4 I with thee would be - gin— yea, and hear one more prayer,

On the way that I still must pur - sue; I with thee would be -
Which a - lone doth sal - va - tion be - stow; Fold me close to thy
I may con - stant - ly keep to thy way; And each day wouldst thou
I would close with thee too my brief day; And when day - light has

gin ev - 'ry day grant - ed here, As my ear - nest re - solve I re -
breast, where found joy all who came: There is ref - uge for me too, I
cleanse me a - new, make me white In the blood shed for me on that
failed let me sleep in thy care, Un - til wak - ing thy child thou dost

new: To be and re - main thine for - ev - er.
know, Though all in this world is con - fu - sion.
day The cross thou didst suf - fer, Lord Je - sus.
say, "Come, live with me ev - er in heav - en!" A - men.

ASPIRATION

354 God Almighty, God Eternal

Mary Jackson Cathey, 1926- GENEVA 8.7.8.7.D.

George Henry Day, 1883-

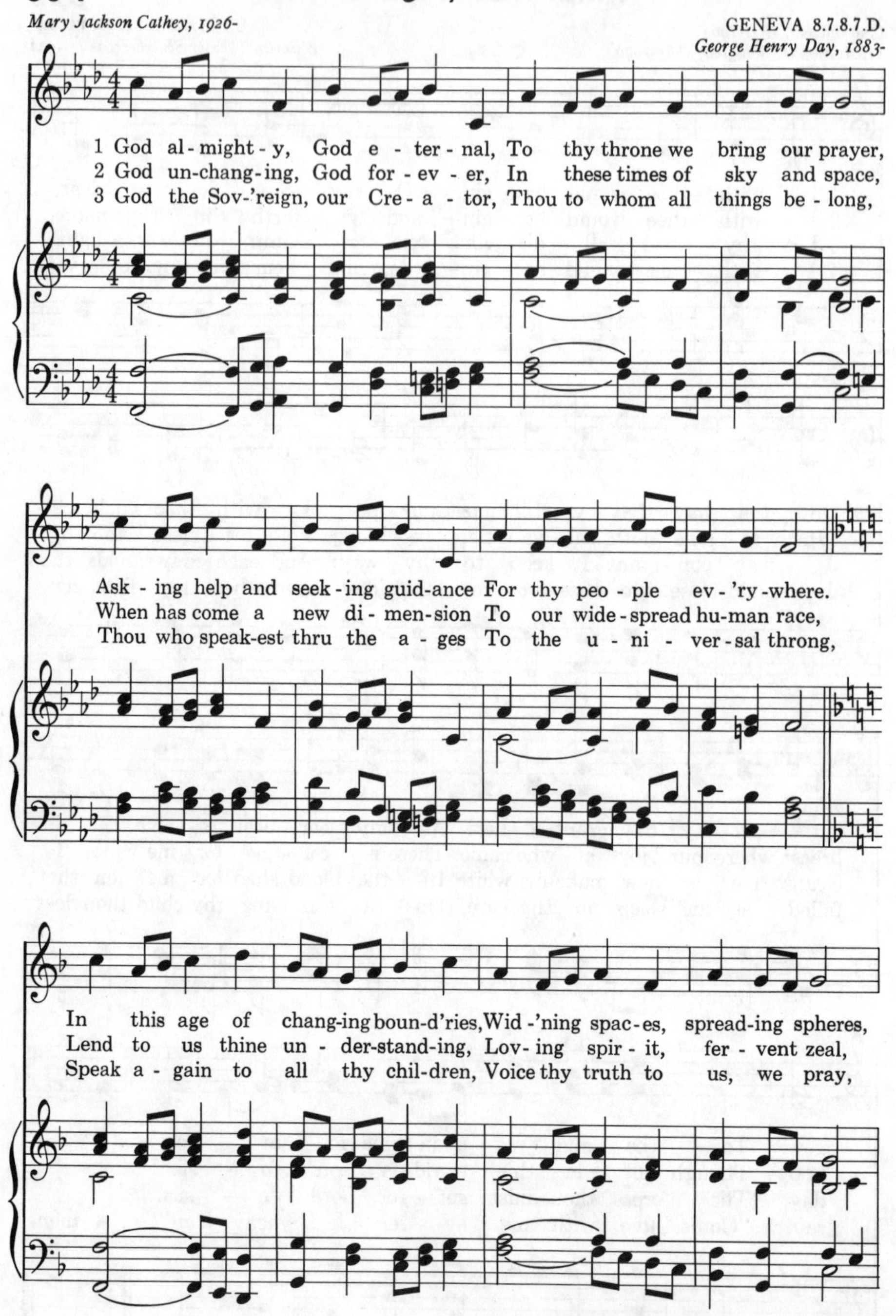

1 God al-might-y, God e-ter-nal, To thy throne we bring our prayer,
2 God un-chang-ing, God for-ev-er, In these times of sky and space,
3 God the Sov-'reign, our Cre-a-tor, Thou to whom all things be-long,
Ask-ing help and seek-ing guid-ance For thy peo-ple ev-'ry-where.
When has come a new di-men-sion To our wide-spread hu-man race,
Thou who speak-est thru the a-ges To the u-ni-ver-sal throng,
In this age of chang-ing boun-d'ries, Wid-'ning spac-es, spread-ing spheres,
Lend to us thine un-der-stand-ing, Lov-ing spir-it, fer-vent zeal,
Speak a-gain to all thy chil-dren, Voice thy truth to us, we pray,

ASPIRATION

Alternate tunes: AUSTRIAN HYMN, *No. 25 and* EBENEZER, *No. 367*

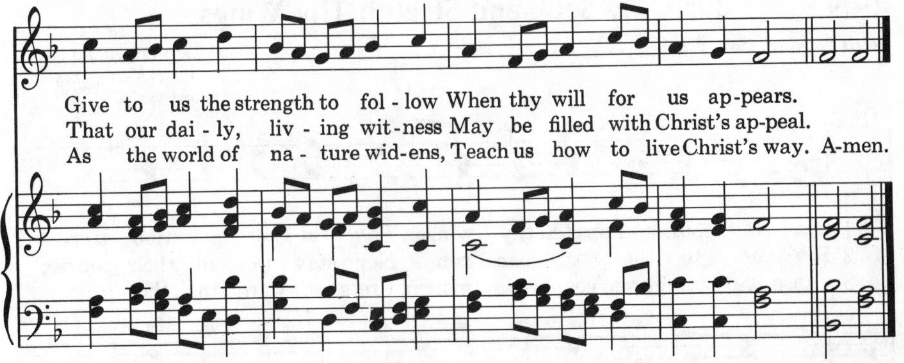

Give to us the strength to fol - low When thy will for us ap-pears.
That our dai - ly, liv - ing wit-ness May be filled with Christ's ap-peal.
As the world of na - ture wid-ens, Teach us how to live Christ's way. A-men.

Teach Me Thy Way, O Lord

355

B. Mansell Ramsey, 1849-1923

CAMACHA 6.4.6.4.6.6.6.4.
B. Mansell Ramsey, 1849-1923

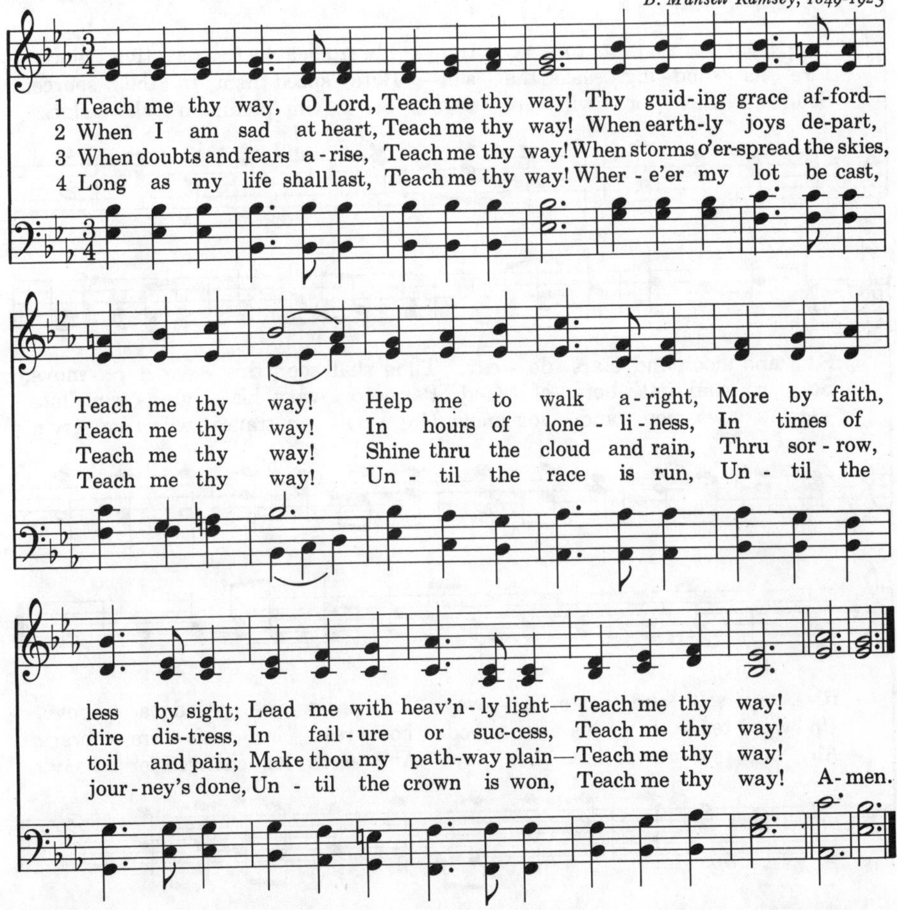

1 Teach me thy way, O Lord, Teach me thy way! Thy guid-ing grace af-ford—
2 When I am sad at heart, Teach me thy way! When earth-ly joys de-part,
3 When doubts and fears a-rise, Teach me thy way! When storms o'er-spread the skies,
4 Long as my life shall last, Teach me thy way! Wher - e'er my lot be cast,

Teach me thy way! Help me to walk a-right, More by faith,
Teach me thy way! In hours of lone - li-ness, In times of
Teach me thy way! Shine thru the cloud and rain, Thru sor - row,
Teach me thy way! Un - til the race is run, Un - til the

less by sight; Lead me with heav'n-ly light—Teach me thy way!
dire dis-tress, In fail - ure or suc-cess, Teach me thy way!
toil and pain; Make thou my path-way plain—Teach me thy way!
jour-ney's done, Un - til the crown is won, Teach me thy way! A-men.

ASPIRATION

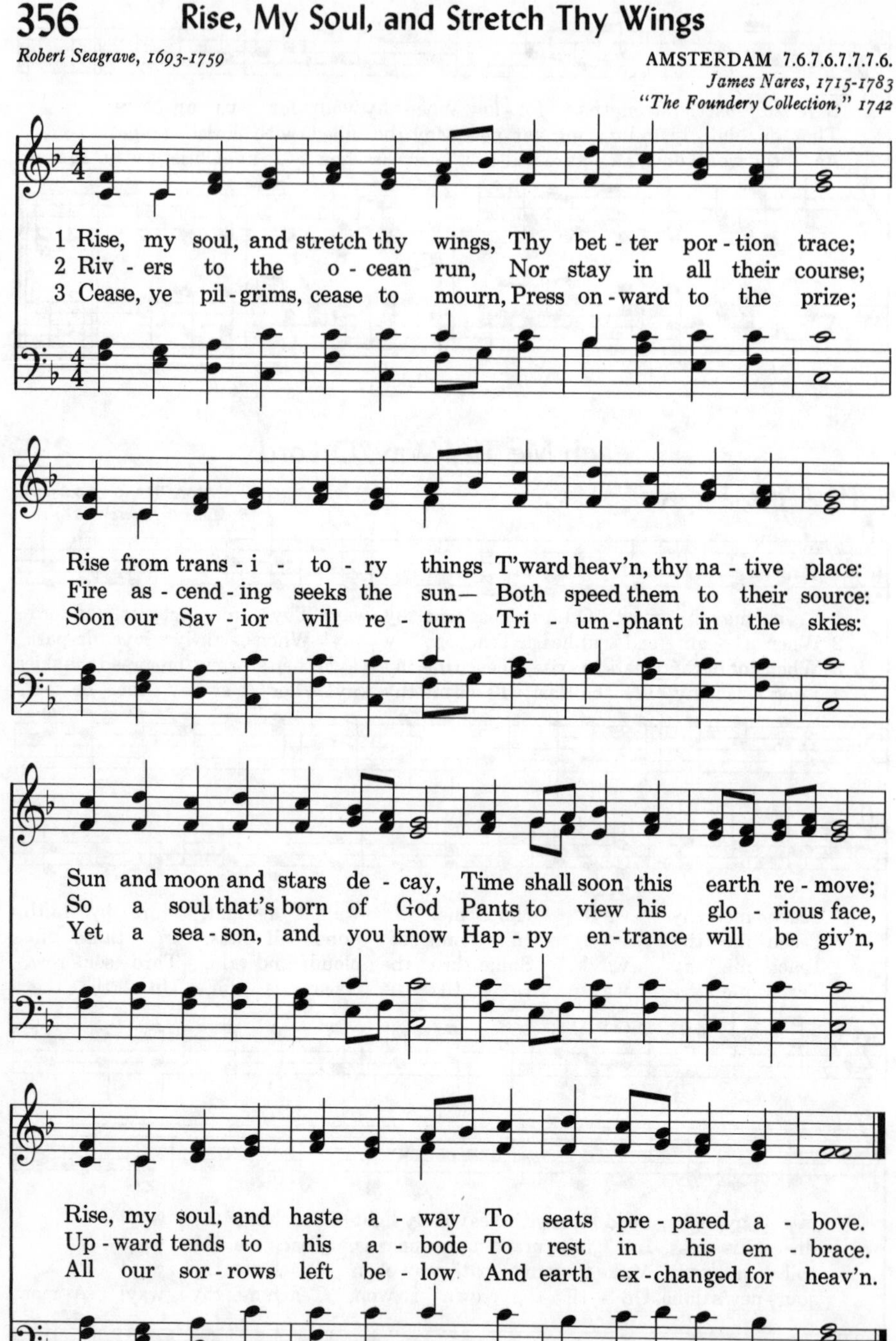
356 Rise, My Soul, and Stretch Thy Wings
Robert Seagrave, 1693-1759
AMSTERDAM 7.6.7.6.7.7.7.6.
James Nares, 1715-1783
"The Foundery Collection," 1742
1 Rise, my soul, and stretch thy wings, Thy bet - ter por - tion trace;
2 Riv - ers to the o - cean run, Nor stay in all their course;
3 Cease, ye pil - grims, cease to mourn, Press on - ward to the prize;
Rise from trans - i - to - ry things T'ward heav'n, thy na - tive place:
Fire as - cend - ing seeks the sun— Both speed them to their source:
Soon our Sav - ior will re - turn Tri - um - phant in the skies:
Sun and moon and stars de - cay, Time shall soon this earth re - move;
So a soul that's born of God Pants to view his glo - rious face,
Yet a sea - son, and you know Hap - py en - trance will be giv'n,
Rise, my soul, and haste a - way To seats pre - pared a - bove.
Up - ward tends to his a - bode To rest in his em - brace.
All our sor - rows left be - low And earth ex - changed for heav'n.

357 When in His Own Image

WHITWORTH 6.5.6.5.D.

Frederik Herman Kaan, 1929-

Walter MacNutt, 1910-

In unison

1 When in his own im - age God cre - at - ed man,
2 God to man en - trust - ed Life as gift and aim;
3 Then in time, our Mak - er Chose to in - ter - vene,
4 Choose we now in free - dom Where we should be - long;

He in - clud - ed free - dom In cre - a - tion's plan.
Sin be - came our pris - on, Turn - ing hope to shame.
Set his love in per - son In the hu - man scene.
Let us turn to Je - sus, Let our choice be strong.

For he loved us e - ven From be - fore our birth;
Man a - gainst his broth - er Lift - ed hand and sword,
Je - sus broke the cir - cle Of re - peat - ed sin,
May the great o - be - dience Which in Christ we see

By his grace he made us Free - men of this earth.
And the Fa - ther's plead - ing Went un - seen, un - heard.
So that man's de - vo - tion New - ly might be - gin.
Per - fect all our serv - ice: Then we shall be free!

ASPIRATION

358 O for a Faith That Will Not Shrink

William H. Bathurst, 1796-1877

EVAN C.M.

William H. Havergal, 1793-1870

1 O for a faith that will not shrink Though
2 That will not mur - mur nor com - plain Be -
3 A faith that shines more bright and clear When
4 Lord, give me such a faith as this, And

pressed by man - y a foe, That will not trem - ble
neath the chas - t'ning rod, But in the hour of
tem - pests rage with - out, That when in dan - ger
then, what - e'er may come, I'll taste e'en here the

on the brink Of pov - er - ty or woe;
grief or pain Can lean up - on its God;
knows no fear, In dark - ness feels no doubt.
hal - lowed bliss Of an e - ter - nal home. A - men.

A lower setting may be found at No. 92

359 May the Mind of Christ, My Savior

Kate B. Wilkinson, 1859-1928

ST. LEONARDS 8.7.8.5.

A. Cyril Barham-Gould, 1891-1953

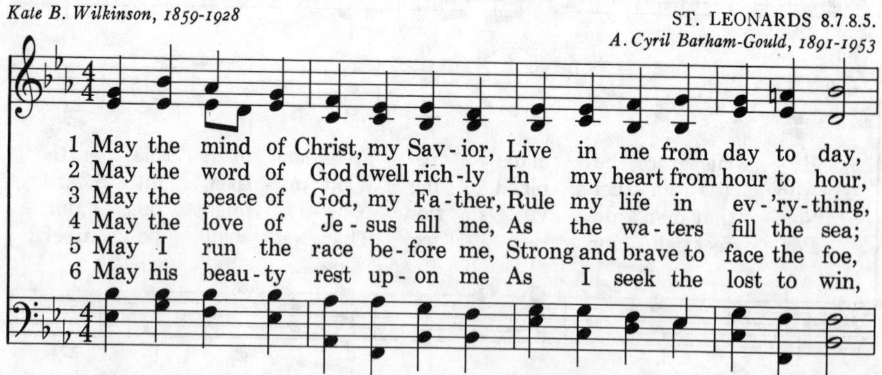
1 May the mind of Christ, my Sav - ior, Live in me from day to day,
2 May the word of God dwell rich - ly In my heart from hour to hour,
3 May the peace of God, my Fa - ther, Rule my life in ev - 'ry - thing,
4 May the love of Je - sus fill me, As the wa - ters fill the sea;
5 May I run the race be - fore me, Strong and brave to face the foe,
6 May his beau - ty rest up - on me As I seek the lost to win,

ASPIRATION

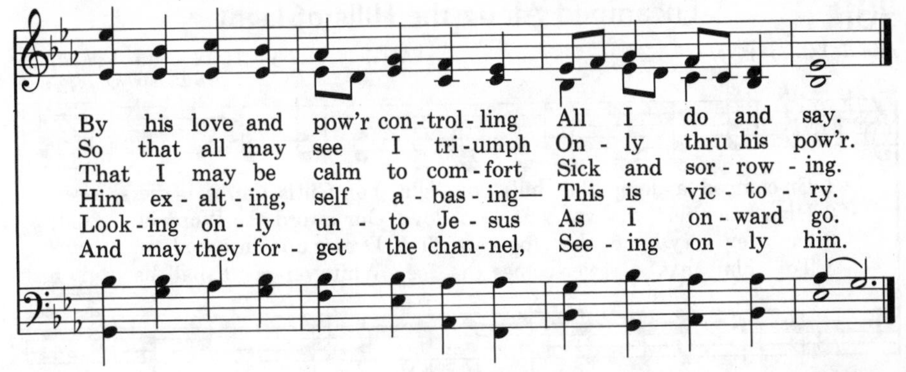
By his love and pow'r con-trol-ling All I do and say.
So that all may see I tri-umph On-ly thru his pow'r.
That I may be calm to com-fort Sick and sor-row-ing.
Him ex-alt-ing, self a-bas-ing— This is vic-to-ry.
Look-ing on-ly un-to Je-sus As I on-ward go.
And may they for-get the chan-nel, See-ing on-ly him.

Awake, My Soul, Stretch Every Nerve 360

Based on Hebrews 12:1
Philip Doddridge, 1702-1751

CHRISTMAS C.M.
Weyman's "Melodia Sacra," 1815
Arr. from George Frederick Handel, 1685-1759

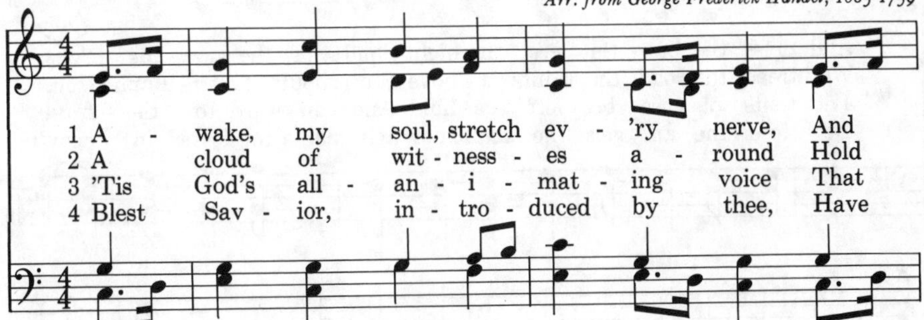

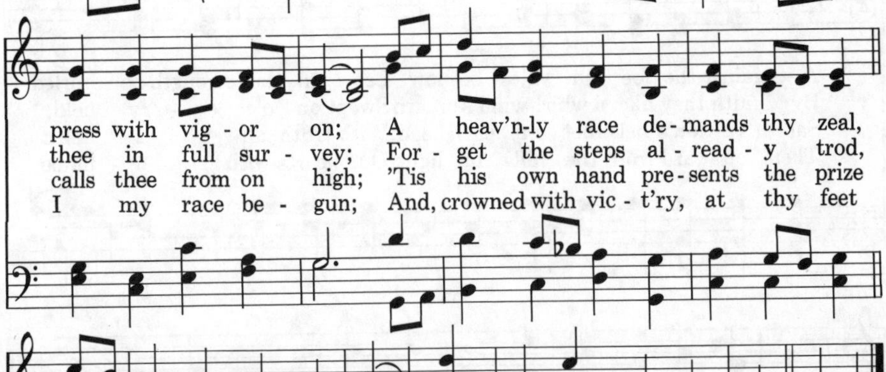

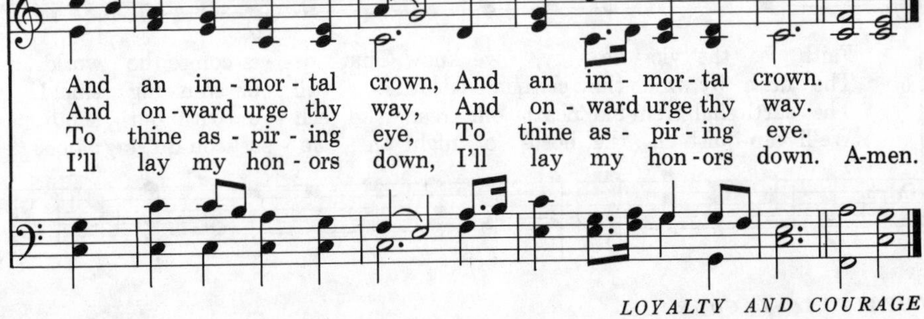

1 A - wake, my soul, stretch ev - 'ry nerve, And press with vig - or on;
A heav'n-ly race de-mands thy zeal, And an im-mor-tal crown, And an im-mor-tal crown.

2 A cloud of wit - ness - es a - round Hold thee in full sur - vey;
For - get the steps al - read - y trod, And on-ward urge thy way, And on - ward urge thy way.

3 'Tis God's all - an - i - mat - ing voice That calls thee from on high;
'Tis his own hand pre-sents the prize To thine as - pir - ing eye, To thine as - pir - ing eye.

4 Blest Sav - ior, in - tro - duced by thee, Have I my race be - gun;
And, crowned with vic - t'ry, at thy feet I'll lay my hon - ors down, I'll lay my hon-ors down. A-men.

361 Encamped Along the Hills of Light

John H. Yates, 1837-1900
FAITH IS THE VICTORY C.M.D. with Refrain
Ira D. Sankey, 1840-1908
1 En-camped a-long the hills of light, Ye Chris-tian sol-diers, rise,
2 His ban-ner o-ver us is love, Our sword the Word of God;
3 On ev-'ry hand the foe we find Drawn up in dread ar-ray;
4 To him that o-ver-comes the foe White rai-ment shall be giv'n;
And press the bat-tle ere the night Shall veil the glow-ing skies.
We tread the road the saints a-bove With shouts of tri-umph trod.
Let tents of ease be left be-hind, And on-ward to the fray!
Be-fore the an-gels he shall know His name con-fessed in heav'n.
A-gainst the foe in vales be-low Let all our strength be hurled;
By faith they like a whirl-wind's breath Swept on o'er ev-'ry field;
Sal-va-tion's hel-met on each head, With truth all girt a-bout:
Then on-ward from the hills of light, Our hearts with love a-flame;
Faith is the vic-to-ry, we know, That o-ver-comes the world.
The faith by which they con-quered death Is still our shin-ing shield.
The earth shall trem-ble 'neath our tread And ech-o with our shout.
We'll van-quish all the hosts of night In Je-sus' con-qu'ring name.

REFRAIN (*after last stanza only*)

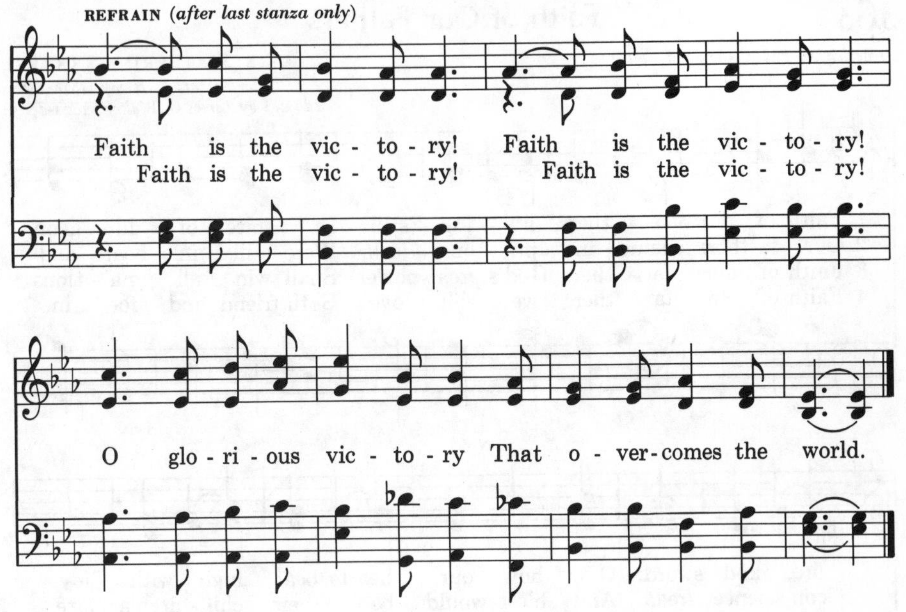
Faith is the vic - to - ry! Faith is the vic - to - ry!
Faith is the vic - to - ry! Faith is the vic - to - ry!
O glo - ri - ous vic - to - ry That o - ver - comes the world.

God Send Us Men of Steadfast Will 362

Frederick J. Gillman, 1866-1949, alt.

DUKE STREET L.M.
John Hatton, c.1710-1793

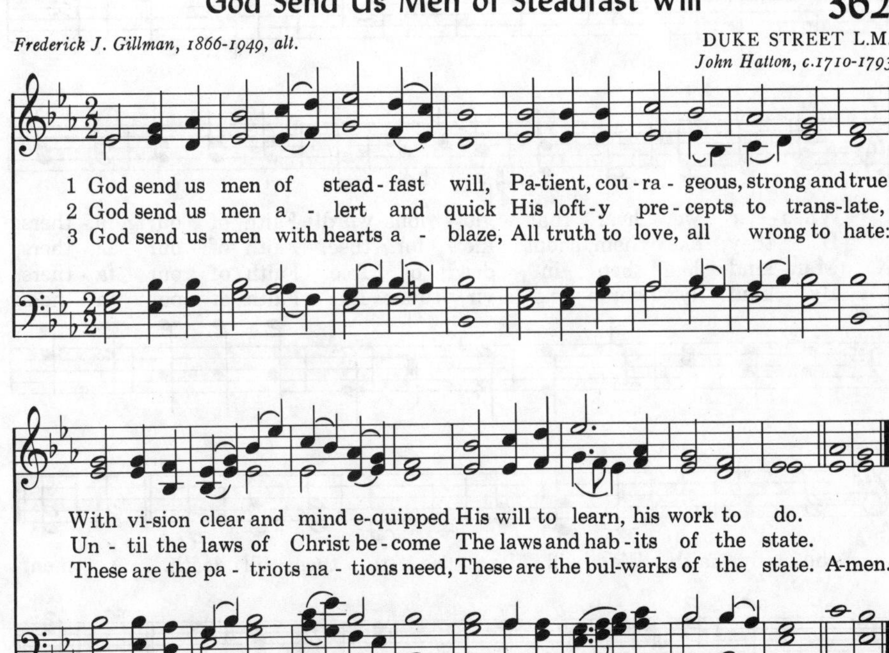
1 God send us men of stead - fast will, Pa-tient, cou - ra - geous, strong and true,
2 God send us men a - lert and quick His loft - y pre - cepts to trans-late,
3 God send us men with hearts a - blaze, All truth to love, all wrong to hate:
With vi-sion clear and mind e-quipped His will to learn, his work to do.
Un - til the laws of Christ be - come The laws and hab - its of the state.
These are the pa - triots na - tions need, These are the bul-warks of the state. A-men.

Words used by permission of the *Trustees of the Fellowship Hymn Book.*
Another harmonization in a lower setting may be found at No. 6

363 Faith of Our Fathers

Frederick W. Faber, 1814-1863, alt.

ST. CATHERINE 8.8.8.8.8.8.
Henri F. Hemy, 1818-1888
Adapted by James G. Walton, 1821-1905

1 Faith of our fa - thers, liv - ing still In spite of dun - geon,
2 Our fa-thers, chained in pris - ons dark, Were still in heart and
3 Faith of our fa - thers, God's great power Shall win all na - tions
4 Faith of our fa - thers, we will love Both friend and foe in

fire, and sword, O how our hearts beat high with joy
con-science free, And blest would be their chil - dren's fate,
un - to thee, And through the truth that comes from God,
all our strife, And preach thee too as love knows how,

When - e'er we hear that glo - rious word! Faith of our fa - thers,
If they, like them, should die for thee. Faith of our fa - thers,
Man - kind shall then in - deed be free. Faith of our fa - thers,
By kind - ly words and vir - tuous life. Faith of our fa - thers,

ho - ly faith, We will be true to thee till death. A - men.

God of Grace and God of Glory

Harry Emerson Fosdick, 1878-1969

CWM RHONDDA 8.7.8.7.8.7.
John Hughes, 1873-1932

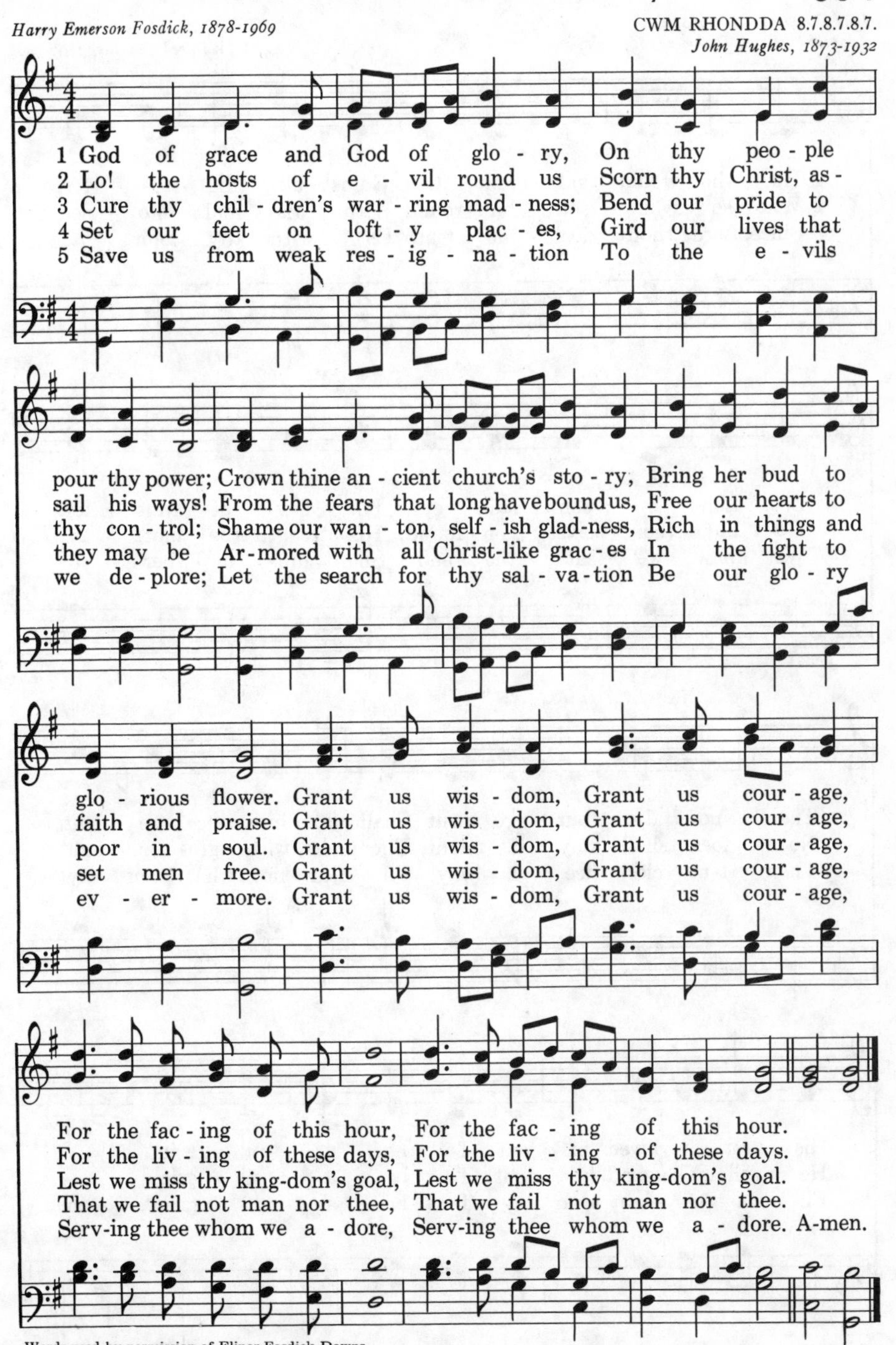
1 God of grace and God of glo - ry, On thy peo - ple
2 Lo! the hosts of e - vil round us Scorn thy Christ, as -
3 Cure thy chil - dren's war - ring mad - ness; Bend our pride to
4 Set our feet on loft - y plac - es, Gird our lives that
5 Save us from weak res - ig - na - tion To the e - vils
pour thy power; Crown thine an - cient church's sto - ry, Bring her bud to
sail his ways! From the fears that long have bound us, Free our hearts to
thy con - trol; Shame our wan - ton, self - ish glad-ness, Rich in things and
they may be Ar-mored with all Christ-like grac - es In the fight to
we de - plore; Let the search for thy sal - va - tion Be our glo - ry
glo - rious flower. Grant us wis - dom, Grant us cour - age,
faith and praise. Grant us wis - dom, Grant us cour - age,
poor in soul. Grant us wis - dom, Grant us cour - age,
set men free. Grant us wis - dom, Grant us cour - age,
ev - er - more. Grant us wis - dom, Grant us cour - age,
For the fac - ing of this hour, For the fac - ing of this hour.
For the liv - ing of these days, For the liv - ing of these days.
Lest we miss thy king-dom's goal, Lest we miss thy king-dom's goal.
That we fail not man nor thee, That we fail not man nor thee.
Serv-ing thee whom we a - dore, Serv-ing thee whom we a - dore. A-men.

365 He Who Would Valiant Be

John Bunyan, 1628-1688, alt.
Adapted by Percy Dearmer, 1867-1936

ST. DUNSTAN'S 6.5.6.5.6.6.6.5.
C. Winfred Douglas, 1867-1944

1 He who would val - iant be 'Gainst all dis - as - ter,
2 Who so be - set him round With dis - mal sto - ries,
3 Since, Lord, thou dost de - fend Us with thy Spir - it,
Let him in con - stan - cy Fol - low the Mas - ter.
Do but them - selves con - found; His strength the more is.
We know we at the end Shall life in - her - it.
There's no dis - cour - age - ment Shall make him once re - lent
No foes shall stay his might, Though he with gi - ants fight;
Then fan - cies, flee a - way! I'll fear not what men say;
His first a - vowed in - tent To be a pil - grim.
He will make good his right To be a pil - grim.
I'll la - bor night and day To be a pil - grim. A - men.

O Jesus, I Have Promised

John E. Bode, 1816-1874

DAY OF REST 7.6.7.6.D.
James W. Elliott, 1833-1915

1 O Je - sus, I have prom-ised To serve thee to the end;
2 O let me feel thee near me! The world is ev - er near;
3 O let me hear thee speak-ing In ac - cents clear and still,
4 O Je - sus, thou hast prom-ised To all who fol - low thee
Be thou for - ev - er near me, My Mas - ter and my Friend.
I see the sights that daz - zle, The tempt-ing sounds I hear.
A - bove the storms of pas - sion, The mur-murs of self - will.
That where thou art in glo - ry There shall thy serv - ant be.
I shall not fear the bat - tle If thou art by my side,
My foes are ev - er near me, A - round me and with - in;
O speak to re - as - sure me, To has - ten or con - trol!
And, Je - sus, I have prom - ised To serve thee to the end;
Nor wan-der from the path-way If thou wilt be my guide.
But, Je - sus, draw thou near - er, And shield my soul from sin.
O speak, and make me lis - ten, Thou guard-ian of my soul.
O give me grace to fol - low, My Mas - ter and my Friend. A-men.

Alternate tune: MUNICH, *No. 279*

367 Once to Every Man and Nation

James Russell Lowell, 1819-1891

EBENEZER 8.7.8.7.D.
Thomas J. Williams, 1869-1944

1 Once to ev - 'ry man and na - tion Comes the
2 Then to side with truth is no - ble, When we
3 By the light of burn - ing mar - tyrs, Christ, thy
4 Though the cause of e - vil pros - per, Yet 'tis
mo - ment to de - cide, In the strife of
share her wretch - ed crust, Ere her cause bring
bleed - ing feet we track, Toil - ing up new
truth a - lone is strong; Though her por - tion
truth with false - hood, For the good or e - vil side;
fame and prof - it And 'tis pros - perous to be just;
Cal - v'ries ev - er With the cross that turns not back;
be the scaf - fold And up - on the throne be wrong;
Some great cause, God's new Mes - si - ah, Of - f'ring
Then it is the brave man choos - es, While the
New oc - ca - sions teach new du - ties, Time makes
Yet that scaf - fold sways the fu - ture, And, be -

A lower setting may be found at No. 432

each the bloom or blight, And the choice goes
cow - ard stands a - side, Till the mul - ti -
an - cient good un - couth; They must up - ward
hind the dim un - known, Stand - eth God with -
by for - ev - er 'Twixt that dark - ness and that light.
tude make vir - tue Of the faith they had de - nied.
still, and on - ward, Who would keep a - breast of truth.
in the shad - ow, Keep - ing watch a - bove his own.
My Soul, Be on Thy Guard
368
George Heath, 1750-1822
LABAN S.M.
Lowell Mason, 1792-1872
1 My soul, be on thy guard— Ten thou - sand foes a - rise;
2 O watch and fight and pray, The bat - tle ne'er give o'er;
3 Ne'er think the vic - t'ry won, Nor lay thine ar - mor down;
4 Fight on, my soul, till death Shall bring thee to thy God;
The hosts of sin are press - ing hard To draw thee from the skies.
Re - new it bold - ly ev - 'ry day, And help di - vine im - plore.
The work of faith will not be done Till thou ob - tain the crown.
He'll take thee, at thy part - ing breath, To his di - vine a - bode.

369 Onward, Christian Soldiers

Sabine Baring-Gould, 1834-1924
ST. GERTRUDE 6.5.6.5.D. with Refrain
Arthur S. Sullivan, 1842-1900
1 On-ward, Chris-tian sol - diers, March-ing as to war, With the cross of
2 At the sign of tri - umph Sa-tan's host doth flee; On, then, Chris-tian
3 Like a might-y ar - my Moves the Church of God; Broth-ers, we are
4 On-ward, then, ye peo - ple, Join our hap-py throng; Blend with ours your
Je - sus Go - ing on be - fore! Christ, the roy - al Mas - ter,
sol - diers, On to vic - to - ry! Hell's foun-da - tions quiv - er
tread - ing Where the saints have trod. We are not di - vid - ed,
voic - es In the tri-umph song. Glo - ry, laud, and hon - or
Leads a - gainst the foe; For - ward in - to bat - tle
At the shout of praise; Broth-ers, lift your voic - es,
All one bod - y we: One in hope and doc - trine,
Un - to Christ the King: This thru count-less a - ges
See his ban - ner go!
Loud your an - thems raise!
One in char - i - ty.
Men and an - gels sing.
REFRAIN
On-ward, Chris-tian sol - diers,

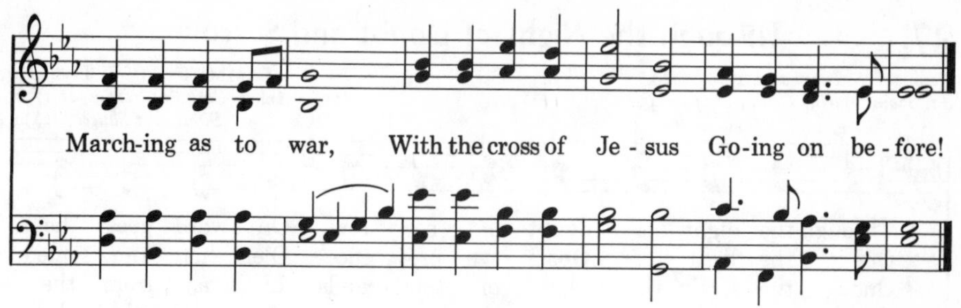
March-ing as to war, With the cross of Je - sus Go-ing on be - fore!

Lord of Our Life 370

Matthäus von Löwenstern, 1594-1648
Tr. Philip Pusey, 1799-1855

FLEMMING 11.11.11.5.
Friedrich F. Flemming, 1778-1813

1 Lord of our life and God of our sal - va - tion,
2 Lord, thou canst help when earth - ly ar - mor fail - eth;
3 Peace in our hearts, our e - vil thoughts as - suag - ing;
4 Grant us thy help till back - ward they are driv - en;

Star of our night and hope of ev - 'ry na - tion, Hear and re -
Lord, thou canst save when sin it - self as - sail - eth; Lord, o'er thy
Peace in thy Church where broth-ers are en - gag - ing; Peace when the
Grant them thy truth, that they may be for - giv - en; Grant peace on

ceive thy Church's sup-pli - ca - tion—Lord God al - might - y.
rock nor death nor hell pre - vail - eth—Grant us thy peace, Lord:
world its bus - y war is wag - ing—Calm thy foes' rag - ing!
earth, or, aft - er we have striv - en, Peace in thy heav - en. A-men.

A higher setting may be found at No. 274

371 Through the Night of Doubt and Sorrow

Bernhardt S. Ingemann, 1789-1862
Tr. Sabine Baring-Gould, 1834-1924

LAMMETS FOLK 8.7.8.7.D.
Attr. to Anders Carl Rutström, 1721-1772
"Sions Nya Sånger," 1854

1 Through the night of doubt and sorrow On-ward goes the
2 One the light of God's own pres-ence O'er his ran-somed
3 One the strain that lips of thou-sands Lift as from the
4 On-ward, there-fore, pil-grim broth-ers, On-ward, with the
pil-grim band, Sing-ing songs of ex-pec-ta-tion,
peo-ple shed, Chas-ing far the gloom and ter-ror,
heart of one; One the con-flict, one the per-il,
cross our aid; Bear its shame and fight its bat-tle,
March-ing to the prom-ised land. Clear be-fore us
Bright-'ning all the path we tread; One the ob-ject
One the march in God be-gun; One the glad-ness
Till we rest be-neath its shade. Soon shall come the
through the dark-ness Gleams and burns the guid-ing light; Broth-er
of our jour-ney, One the faith which nev-er tires, One the
of re-joic-ing On the far e-ter-nal shore, Where the
great a-wak-ing, Soon the rend-ing of the tomb, Then the

Alternate tune: AUSTRIAN HYMN, *No. 25*

clasps the hand of broth - er, Step - ping fear - less through the night.
ear - nest look - ing for - ward, One the hope our God in - spires.
one Al - might - y Fath - er Reigns in love for - ev - er - more.
scat - t'ring of all shad - ows And the end of toil and gloom.
Fight the Good Fight
372
John S. B. Monsell, 1811-1875, alt.
PENTECOST L.M.
William Boyd, 1847-1928
1 Fight the good fight with all thy might! Christ is thy
2 Run the straight race through God's good grace; Lift up thine
3 Cast care a - side, lean on thy guide; His bound - less
4 Faint not nor fear, his arms are near; He chang - eth
strength, and Christ thy right. Lay hold on life, and
eyes, and seek his face. Life with its way be -
mer - cy will pro - vide. Trust, and thy trust - ing
not, and thou art dear. On - ly be - lieve, and
it shall be Thy joy and crown e - ter - nal - ly.
fore us lies; Christ is the path, and Christ the prize.
soul shall prove Christ is its life, and Christ its love.
thou shalt see That Christ is all in all to thee. A - men.

373 Stand Fast for Christ Thy Savior

Walter J. Mathams, 1853-1932

ALFORD 7.6.8.6.D.
John B. Dykes, 1823-1876

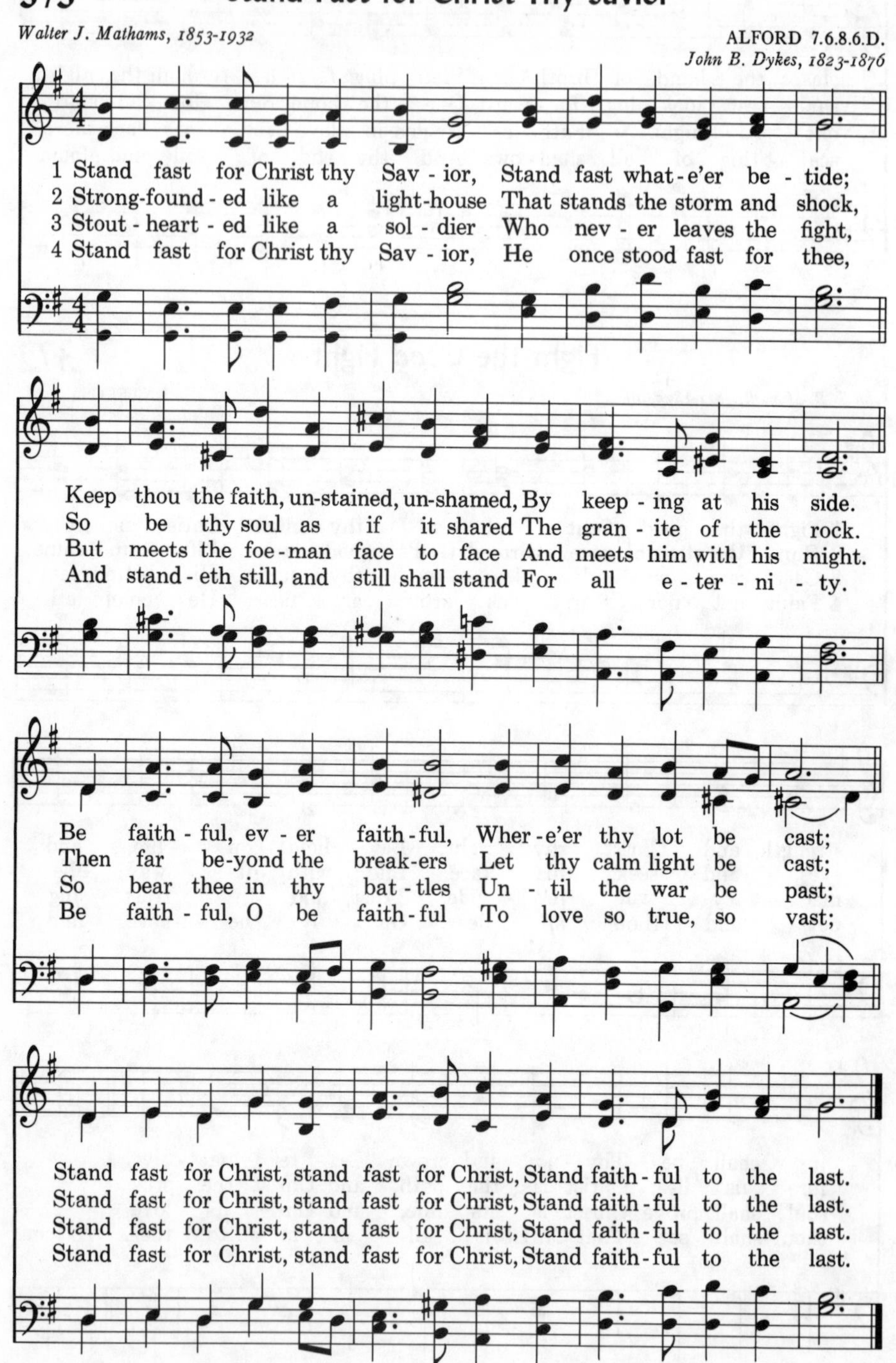

1 Stand fast for Christ thy Sav - ior, Stand fast what - e'er be - tide;
2 Strong-found - ed like a light-house That stands the storm and shock,
3 Stout - heart - ed like a sol - dier Who nev - er leaves the fight,
4 Stand fast for Christ thy Sav - ior, He once stood fast for thee,
Keep thou the faith, un-stained, un-shamed, By keep - ing at his side.
So be thy soul as if it shared The gran - ite of the rock.
But meets the foe - man face to face And meets him with his might.
And stand - eth still, and still shall stand For all e - ter - ni - ty.
Be faith - ful, ev - er faith - ful, Wher - e'er thy lot be cast;
Then far be-yond the break - ers Let thy calm light be cast;
So bear thee in thy bat - tles Un - til the war be past;
Be faith - ful, O be faith - ful To love so true, so vast;
Stand fast for Christ, stand fast for Christ, Stand faith - ful to the last.
Stand fast for Christ, stand fast for Christ, Stand faith - ful to the last.
Stand fast for Christ, stand fast for Christ, Stand faith - ful to the last.
Stand fast for Christ, stand fast for Christ, Stand faith - ful to the last.

Stand Up, Stand Up for Jesus

George Duffield, 1818-1888

WEBB 7.6.7.6.D.
George J. Webb, 1803-1887

1 Stand up, stand up for Je - sus, Ye sol - diers of the cross;
2 Stand up, stand up for Je - sus, The trum - pet call o - bey;
3 Stand up, stand up for Je - sus, Stand in his strength a - lone;
4 Stand up, stand up for Je - sus, The strife will not be long;
Lift high his roy - al ban - ner, It must not suf - fer loss.
Forth to the might - y con - flict, In this his glo - rious day.
The arm of flesh will fail you, Ye dare not trust your own.
This day the noise of bat - tle, The next the vic - tor's song.
From vic - t'ry un - to vic - t'ry His ar - my shall he lead,
Ye that are men now serve him A - gainst un - num - bered foes;
Put on the gos - pel ar - mor, Each piece put on with prayer;
To him that o - ver - com - eth A crown of life shall be:
Till ev - 'ry foe is van - quished And Christ is Lord in - deed.
Let cour - age rise with dan - ger And strength to strength op - pose.
Where du - ty calls, or dan - ger, Be nev - er want - ing there.
He with the King of glo - ry Shall reign e - ter - nal - ly.

A lower setting may be found at No. 533

375 The Son of God Goes Forth to War

Reginald Heber, 1783-1826

ALL SAINTS NEW C.M.D.
Henry S. Culler, 1824-1902

1 The Son of God goes forth to war, A king - ly crown to gain;
2 The mar - tyr first, whose ea - gle - eye Could pierce be - yond the grave,
3 A glo - rious band, the cho - sen few On whom the Spir - it came,
4 A no - ble ar - my, men and boys, The ma - tron and the maid,
His blood - red ban - ner streams a - far— Who fol - lows in his train?
Who saw his Mas - ter in the sky And called on him to save,
Twelve val - iant saints, their hope they knew, And mocked the cross and flame;
A - round the Sav - ior's throne re - joice, In robes of light ar - rayed;
Who best can drink his cup of woe, Tri - um - phant o - ver pain,
Like him, with par - don on his tongue, In midst of mor - tal pain,
They met the ty - rant's brandished steel, The li - on's gor - y mane;
They climbed the steep as - cent of heaven Through per - il, toil, and pain:
Who pa - tient bears his cross be - low, He fol - lows in his train.
He prayed for them that did the wrong: Who fol - lows in his train?
They bowed their necks the death to feel: Who fol - lows in their train?
O God, to us may grace be given To fol - low in their train. A - men.

We Are Living, We Are Dwelling

Arthur C. Coxe, 1818-1896, alt.

BLAENHAFREN 8.7.8.7.D.
Welsh Melody

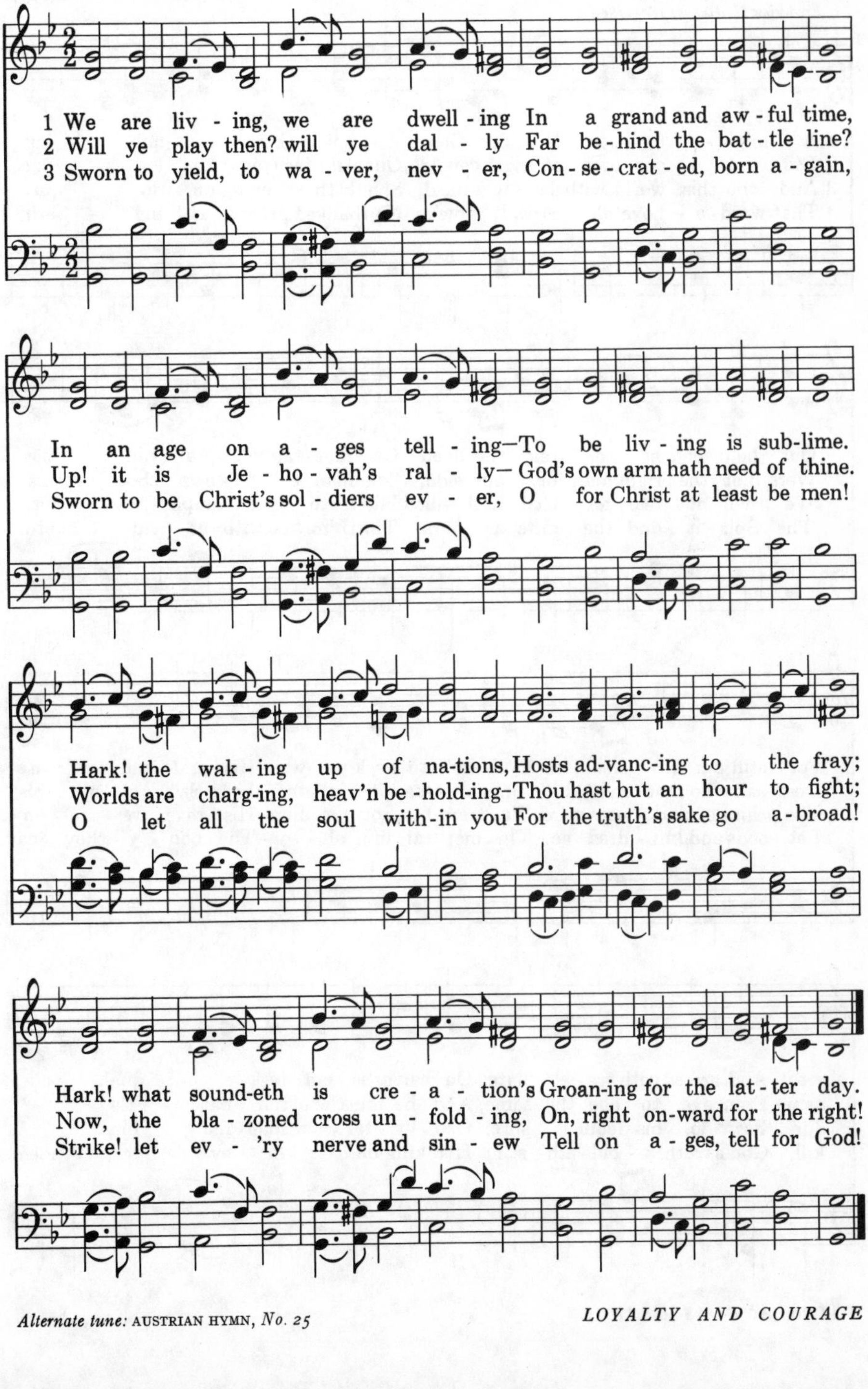

1 We are liv - ing, we are dwell - ing In a grand and aw - ful time,
2 Will ye play then? will ye dal - ly Far be - hind the bat - tle line?
3 Sworn to yield, to wa - ver, nev - er, Con - se - crat - ed, born a - gain,

In an age on a - ges tell - ing—To be liv - ing is sub - lime.
Up! it is Je - ho - vah's ral - ly— God's own arm hath need of thine.
Sworn to be Christ's sol - diers ev - er, O for Christ at least be men!

Hark! the wak - ing up of na - tions, Hosts ad - vanc - ing to the fray;
Worlds are charg - ing, heav'n be - hold - ing—Thou hast but an hour to fight;
O let all the soul with - in you For the truth's sake go a - broad!

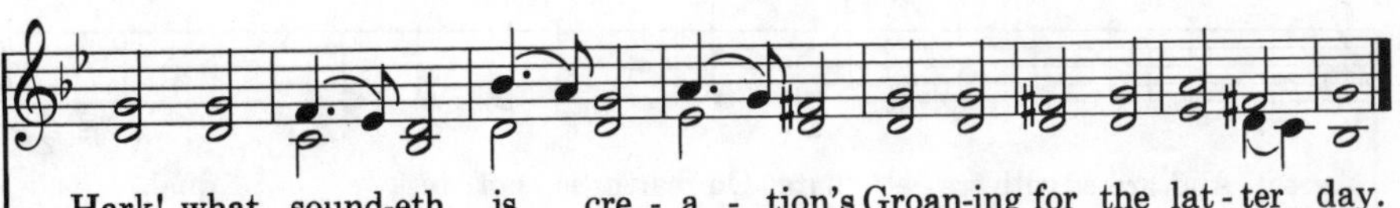

Hark! what sound - eth is cre - a - tion's Groan - ing for the lat - ter day.
Now, the bla - zoned cross un - fold - ing, On, right on - ward for the right!
Strike! let ev - 'ry nerve and sin - ew Tell on a - ges, tell for God!

Alternate tune: AUSTRIAN HYMN, *No. 25*

377 A Mighty Fortress Is Our God

Based on Psalm 46
Martin Luther, 1483-1546
Tr. Frederick H. Hedge, 1805-1890
EIN' FESTE BURG 8.7.8.7.6.6.6.6.7.
Martin Luther, 1483-1546
1 A mighty fortress is our God, A bulwark never failing;
2 Did we in our own strength confide, Our striving would be losing,
3 And tho this world, with devils filled, Should threaten to undo us,
4 That word above all earthly pow'rs, No thanks to them, abideth;
Our helper he amid the flood Of mortal ills prevailing.
Were not the right man on our side, The man of God's own choosing.
We will not fear, for God hath willed His truth to triumph thru us.
The Spirit and the gifts are ours Thru him who with us sideth.
For still our ancient foe Doth seek to work us woe—His craft and pow'r are
Dost ask who that may be? Christ Jesus, it is he—Lord Sabaoth his
The prince of darkness grim, We tremble not for him—His rage we can en-
Let goods and kindred go, This mortal life also—The body they may
great, And, armed with cruel hate, On earth is not his equal.
name, From age to age the same, And he must win the battle.
dure, For lo, his doom is sure: One little word shall fell him.
kill; God's truth abideth still: His kingdom is forever. Amen.

Blessed Assurance, Jesus Is Mine! 378

Fanny J. Crosby, 1820-1915

ASSURANCE 9.10.9.9. *with Refrain*
Phoebe P. Knapp, 1839-1908

1 Bless-ed as-sur-ance, Je-sus is mine! O what a fore-taste of
2 Per-fect sub-mis-sion, per-fect de-light, Vi-sions of rap-ture now
3 Per-fect sub-mis-sion, all is at rest, I in my Sav-ior am

glo-ry di-vine! Heir of sal-va-tion, pur-chase of God,
burst on my sight; An-gels de-scend-ing bring from a-bove
hap-py and blest; Watching and wait-ing, look-ing a-bove,

Born of his Spir-it, washed in his blood.
Ech-oes of mer-cy, whis-pers of love.
Filled with his goodness, lost in his love.

REFRAIN

This is my sto-ry, this is my song, Prais-ing my Sav-ior all the day long; This is my sto-ry, this is my song, Prais-ing my Sav-ior all the day long.

379 A Wonderful Savior Is Jesus My Lord

Fanny J. Crosby, 1820-1915

HE HIDETH MY SOUL 11.8.11.8. *with Refrain*
William J. Kirkpatrick, 1838-1921

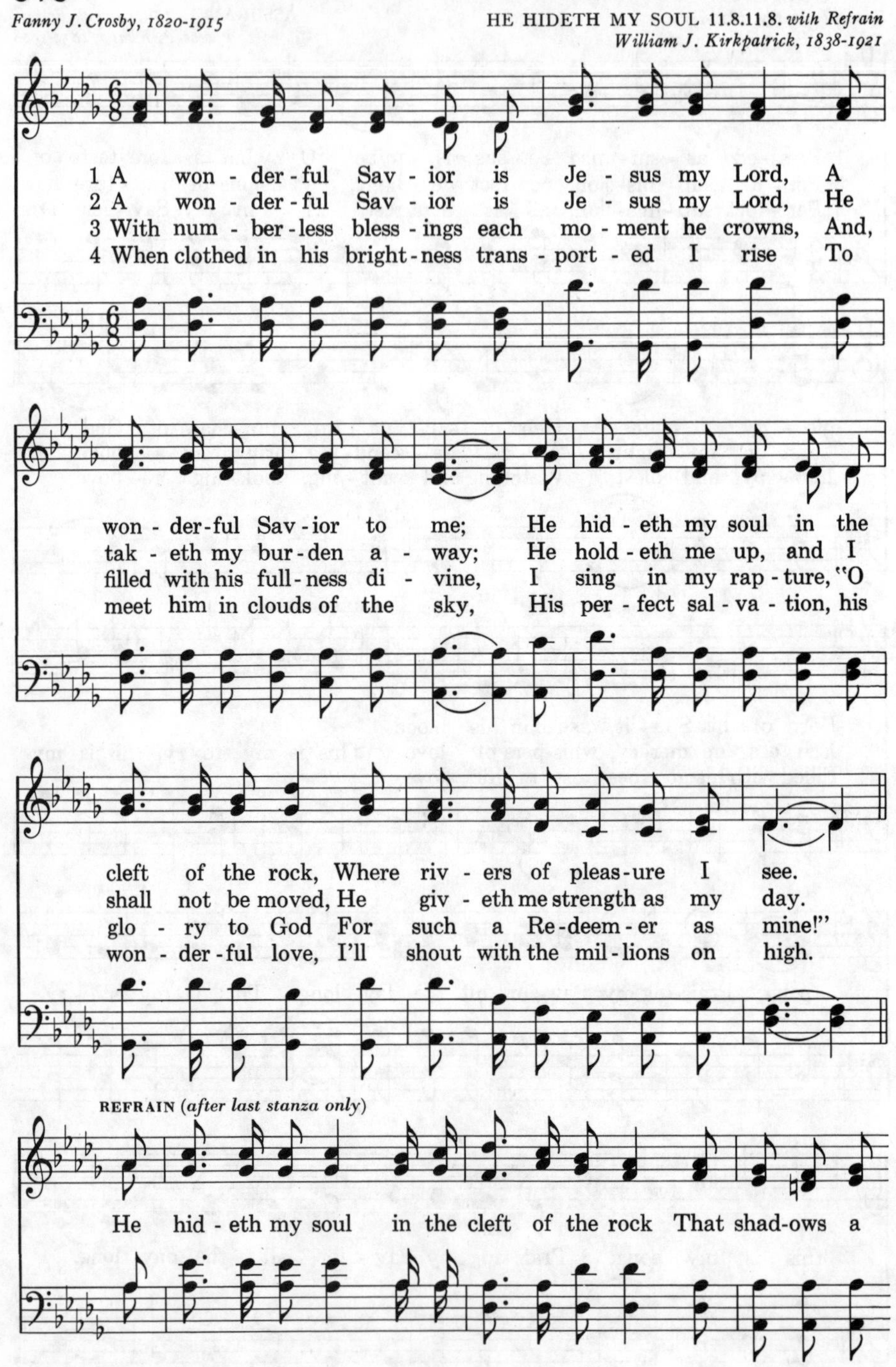
1 A won - der - ful Sav - ior is Je - sus my Lord, A
2 A won - der - ful Sav - ior is Je - sus my Lord, He
3 With num - ber - less bless - ings each mo - ment he crowns, And,
4 When clothed in his bright - ness trans - port - ed I rise To
won - der - ful Sav - ior to me; He hid - eth my soul in the
tak - eth my bur - den a - way; He hold - eth me up, and I
filled with his full - ness di - vine, I sing in my rap - ture, "O
meet him in clouds of the sky, His per - fect sal - va - tion, his
cleft of the rock, Where riv - ers of pleas - ure I see.
shall not be moved, He giv - eth me strength as my day.
glo - ry to God For such a Re - deem - er as mine!"
won - der - ful love, I'll shout with the mil - lions on high.
REFRAIN (after last stanza only)
He hid - eth my soul in the cleft of the rock That shad - ows a

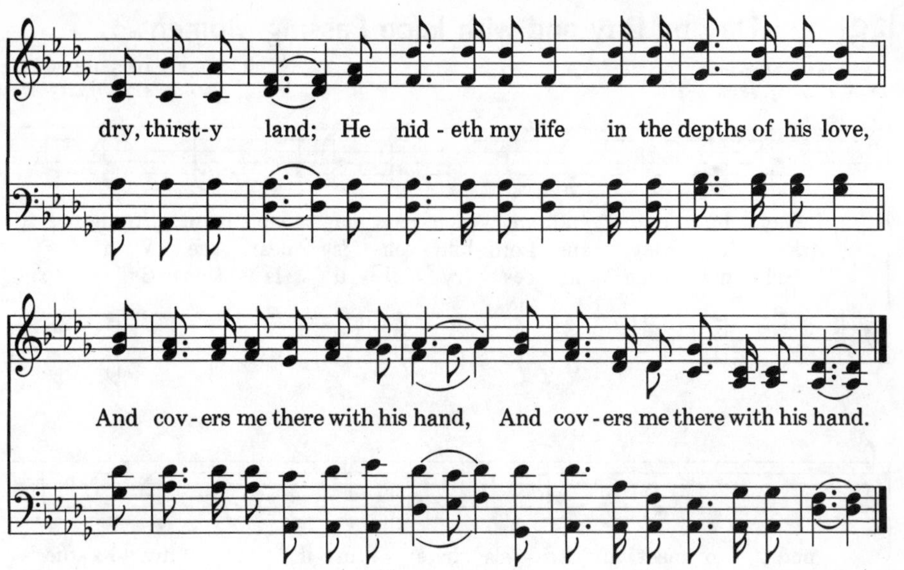
dry, thirst-y land; He hid - eth my life in the depths of his love,
And cov-ers me there with his hand, And cov-ers me there with his hand.

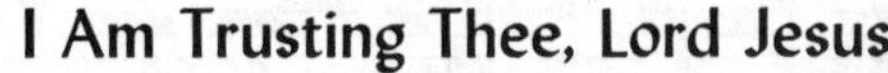

I Am Trusting Thee, Lord Jesus 380

Frances Ridley Havergal, 1836-1879

BULLINGER 8.5.8.3.
Ethelbert W. Bullinger, 1837-1913

1 I am trust-ing thee, Lord Je - sus—Trust-ing on - ly thee;
Trust - ing thee for full sal - va - tion, Great and free.

2 I am trust-ing thee to guide me—Thou a - lone shalt lead,
Ev - 'ry day and hour sup - ply - ing All my need.

3 I am trust-ing thee for pow - er—Thine can nev - er fail;
Words which thou thy - self shalt give me Must pre - vail.

4 I am trust-ing thee, Lord Je - sus—Nev er let me fall;
I am trust-ing thee for - ev - er, And for all. A-men.

A lower setting may be found at No. 610

381 Day by Day and with Each Passing Moment

Lina Sandell, 1832-1903
Tr. A. L. Skoog, 1856-1934

BLOTT EN DAG 10.9.10.9.D.
Oscar Ahnfelt, 1813-1882

1 Day by day and with each pass - ing mo - ment, Strength I
2 Ev - 'ry day the Lord him - self is near me With a
3 Help me then in ev - 'ry trib - u - la - tion So to
find to meet my tri - als here; Trust - ing in my Fa - ther's
spe - cial mer - cy for each hour; All my cares he fain would
trust thy prom - is - es, O Lord, That I lose not faith's sweet
wise be - stow - ment, I've no cause for wor - ry or for fear.
bear, and cheer me, He whose name is Coun - sel - lor and Pow'r.
con - so - la - tion Of - fered me with - in thy ho - ly word.
He whose heart is kind be - yond all meas - ure Gives un -
The pro - tec - tion of his child and treas - ure Is a
Help me, Lord, when toil and trou - ble meet - ing, E'er to

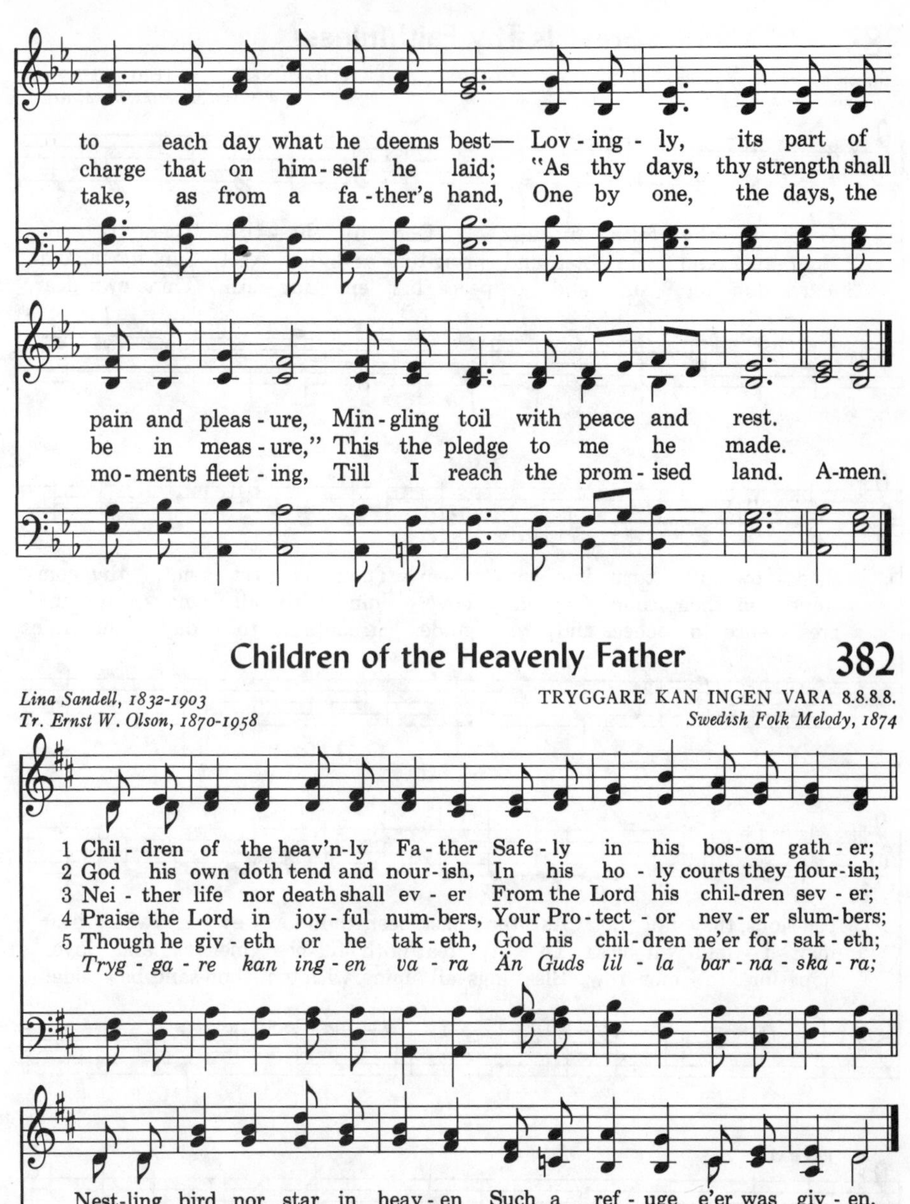
to each day what he deems best— Lov-ing-ly, its part of
charge that on him-self he laid; "As thy days, thy strength shall
take, as from a fa-ther's hand, One by one, the days, the
pain and pleas-ure, Min-gling toil with peace and rest.
be in meas-ure," This the pledge to me he made.
mo-ments fleet-ing, Till I reach the prom-ised land. A-men.

Children of the Heavenly Father 382

Lina Sandell, 1832-1903
Tr. Ernst W. Olson, 1870-1958

TRYGGARE KAN INGEN VARA 8.8.8.8.
Swedish Folk Melody, 1874

1 Chil-dren of the heav'n-ly Fa-ther Safe-ly in his bos-om gath-er;
2 God his own doth tend and nour-ish, In his ho-ly courts they flour-ish;
3 Nei-ther life nor death shall ev-er From the Lord his chil-dren sev-er;
4 Praise the Lord in joy-ful num-bers, Your Pro-tect-or nev-er slum-bers;
5 Though he giv-eth or he tak-eth, God his chil-dren ne'er for-sak-eth;
Tryg-ga-re kan ing-en va-ra Än Guds lil-la bar-na-ska-ra;

Nest-ling bird nor star in heav-en Such a ref-uge e'er was giv-en.
From all e-vil things he spares them, In his might-y arms he bears them.
Un-to them his grace he show-eth, And their sor-rows all he know-eth.
At the will of your De-fend-er Ev-'ry foe-man must sur-ren-der.
His the lov-ing pur-pose sole-ly To pre-serve them pure and ho-ly.
Stjär-nan ej på him-la-fäs-tet, Få-geln ej i kän-da näs-tet.

383 Great Is Thy Faithfulness

Based on Lamentations 3:22,23
Thomas O. Chisholm, 1866-1960

FAITHFULNESS 11.10.11.10. *with Refrain*
William M. Runyan, 1870-1957

1 Great is thy faith - ful-ness, O God my Fa - ther! There is no
2 Sum - mer and win - ter, and spring-time and har - vest, Sun, moon, and
3 Par - don for sin and a peace that en - dur - eth, Thine own dear
shad - ow of turn-ing with thee; Thou chang-est not, thy com-
stars in their cours-es a - bove, Join with all na - ture in
pres - ence to cheer and to guide, Strength for to - day and bright
pas-sions, they fail not: As thou hast been thou for - ev - er wilt be.
man - i - fold wit - ness To thy great faith - ful-ness, mer - cy, and love.
hope for to - mor - row—Bless-ings all mine, with ten thou-sand be - side!
REFRAIN
Great is thy faith-ful-ness, Great is thy faith - ful-ness, Morn-ing by

morn-ing new mer-cies I see; All I have need-ed thy
hand hath pro-vid-ed— Great is thy faith-ful-ness, Lord, un-to me! A-men.

My Times Are in Thy Hand

384

William F. Lloyd, 1791-1853

FRANCONIA S.M.
Johann B. König, 1691-1758
Adapted by William H. Havergal, 1793-1870

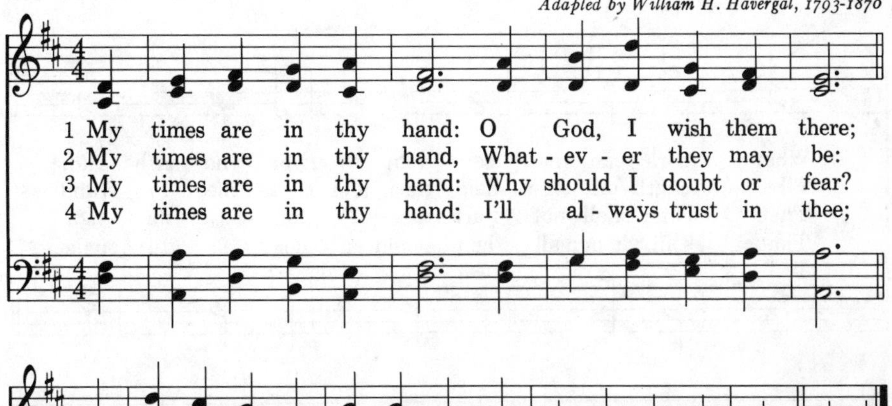
1 My times are in thy hand: O God, I wish them there;
2 My times are in thy hand, What-ev-er they may be:
3 My times are in thy hand: Why should I doubt or fear?
4 My times are in thy hand: I'll al-ways trust in thee;

My life, my friends, my soul, I leave En-tire-ly to thy care.
Pleas-ing or pain-ful, dark or bright, As best may seem to thee.
My Fa-ther's hand will nev-er cause His child a need-less tear.
And, aft-er death, at thy right hand I shall for-ev-er be. A-men.

385 How Firm a Foundation

"K" in John Rippon's "Selection of Hymns," 1787, alt.

FOUNDATION 11.11.11.11.
American Melody
Harm. by A. Royce Eckhardt, 1937-

In unison

1 How firm a foun - da - tion, ye saints of the Lord,
2 "Fear not, I am with thee, O be not dis - mayed,
3 "When through fier - y tri - als thy path - way shall lie,
4 "The soul that on Je - sus hath leaned for re - pose

Is laid for your faith in his ex - cel - lent word!
For I am thy God, I will still give thee aid;
My grace, all - suf - fi - cient, shall be thy sup - ply;
I will not, I will not de - sert to his foes:

What more can he say than to you he hath said,
I'll strength - en thee, help thee, and cause thee to stand,
The flame shall not hurt thee— I on - ly de - sign
That soul, though all hell should en - deav - or to shake,

To you, who for ref - uge to Je - sus have fled?
Up - held by my gra - cious, om - ni - po - tent hand.
Thy dross to con - sume and thy gold to re - fine.
I'll nev - er, no, nev - er, no, nev - er for - sake!"

Alternate tune: ST. DENIO (JOANNA), *No. 346*

I Know Not Why God's Wondrous Grace

Based on 2 Timothy 1:12b
Daniel W. Whittle, 1840-1901

EL NATHAN C.M. *with Refrain*
James McGranahan, 1840-1907

1 I know not why God's won-drous grace To me he hath made known,
2 I know not how this sav - ing faith To me he did im - part,
3 I know not how the Spir - it moves, Con - vinc - ing men of sin,
4 I know not when my Lord may come, At night or noon-day fair,
Nor why, un - wor - thy, Christ in love Re - deemed me for his own.
Nor how be - liev - ing in his word Wrought peace with-in my heart.
Re - veal - ing Je - sus thru the word, Cre - at - ing faith in him.
Nor if I walk the vale with him, Or meet him in the air.
REFRAIN
But "I know whom I have be - liev - ed, and am per-suad - ed that he is
a - ble To keep that which I've com-mit-ted Un-to him a-gainst that day."

387 I Sought the Lord

Unknown
"The Pilgrim Hymnal," 1904
WACHUSETT 10.10.10.6.
Katherine K. Davis, 1892-
In unison
1 I sought the Lord, and aft - er - ward I knew
He moved my soul to seek him, seek - ing me;
It was not I that found, O Sav - ior true:
No, I was found of thee.
2 Thou didst reach forth thy hand and mine en - fold,
I walked and sank not on the storm - vexed sea;
'Twas not so much that I on thee took hold
As thou, dear Lord, on me.
3 I find, I walk, I love, but O the whole
Of love is but my an - swer, Lord, to thee;
For thou wert long be - fore - hand with my soul:
Al - ways thou lov - edst me. A - men.

If Asked Whereon I Rest My Claim

"Brödraförsamlingen," Copenhagen, 1748
Tr. A. Samuel Wallgren, 1885-1940

SALIGHETSGRUND 8.6.8.6.8.8.8.6.
Swedish Folk Melody
"Sions Nya Sånger," 1874

1 If asked where-on I rest my claim To full sal-va-tion's joy,
2 This is my hope's foun-da-tion firm, Which ev-er shall en-dure;
If noth-ing more I need to name Or oth-er words em-ploy
And, at the end of life's brief term, I'll rest there-on se-cure:
Be-sides our Sav-ior's blood and wounds, To me all-sat-is-fy-ing grounds,
Then dread-ed death shall lose its sting As of my Sav-ior's wounds I sing;
I an-swer then, "My claim is good! 'Tis based on Je-sus' blood."
His pre-cious blood shall be the key That o-pens heav'n for me.

389 In Heavenly Love Abiding

Anna L. Waring, 1820-1910
DEDEKAM 7.6.7.6.D.
Sophie H. Dedekam, 1820-1894
1 In heav'n-ly love a - bid - ing, No change my heart shall fear;
2 Wher - ev - er he may guide me, No want shall turn me back;
3 Green pas - tures are be - fore me, Which yet I have not seen;
And safe is such con - fid - ing, For noth - ing chang - es here.
My Shep-herd is be - side me, And noth - ing can I lack.
Bright skies will soon be o'er me, Where dark-est clouds have been.
The storm may roar with - out me, My heart may low be laid;
His wis - dom ev - er wak - eth, His sight is nev - er dim;
My hope I can - not meas - ure, My path to life is free;
But God is round a - bout me, And can I be dis - mayed?
He knows the way he tak - eth, And I will walk with him.
My Sav - ior has my treas - ure, And he will walk with me.

Lord, I Want to Be a Christian

American Folk Hymn

I WANT TO BE A CHRISTIAN *Irregular*
American Folk Melody

In unison
1 Lord, I want to be a Chris-tian in my heart, in my heart; Lord, I want to be a Chris-tian in my heart. In my heart, in my heart, Lord, I want to be a Chris-tian in my heart.
2 Lord, I want to be more lov-ing in my heart, in my heart; Lord, I want to be more lov-ing in my heart. In my heart, in my heart, Lord, I want to be more lov-ing in my heart.
3 Lord, I want to be more ho-ly in my heart, in my heart; Lord, I want to be more ho-ly in my heart. In my heart, in my heart, Lord, I want to be more ho-ly in my heart.
4 Lord, I want to be like Je-sus in my heart, in my heart; Lord, I want to be like Je-sus in my heart. In my heart, in my heart, Lord, I want to be like Je-sus in my heart.

391 My Faith Has Found a Resting Place

Lidie H. Edmunds, 19th century, alt.

NO OTHER PLEA C.M. *with Refrain*
Norwegian Melody

1 My faith has found a rest-ing place, Not in a man-made creed;
2 E - nough for me that Je - sus saves, This ends my fear and doubt;
3 My soul is rest - ing on the Word, The liv - ing Word of God:
4 The great Phy - si - cian heals the sick, The lost he came to save;
I trust the ev - er - liv - ing One, That he for me will plead.
A sin - ful soul I come to him, He will not cast me out.
Sal - va - tion in my Sav-ior's name, Sal - va-tion through his blood.
For me his pre - cious blood he shed, For me his life he gave.
REFRAIN
I need no oth - er ev - i - dence, I need no oth - er plea;
It is e - nough that Je - sus died And rose a - gain for me.

My Hope Is Built on Nothing Less

Edward Mote, 1797-1874

MELITA 8.8.8.8.8.8.
John B. Dykes, 1823-1876

1 My hope is built on noth - ing less Than Je - sus' blood and right - eous - ness; I dare not trust the sweet - est frame, But whol - ly lean on Je - sus' name. On Christ, the sol - id Rock, I stand: All oth - er ground is sink - ing sand.
2 When dark - ness veils his love - ly face, I rest on his un - chang - ing grace; In ev - 'ry high and storm - y gale, My an - chor holds with - in the veil. On Christ, the sol - id Rock, I stand: All oth - er ground is sink - ing sand.
3 His oath, his cov - e - nant, his blood, Sup - port me in the whelm - ing flood; When all a - round my soul gives way, He then is all my hope and stay. On Christ, the sol - id Rock, I stand: All oth - er ground is sink - ing sand.
4 When he shall come with trum - pet sound, O may I then in him be found: Dressed in his right - eous - ness a - lone, Fault - less to stand be - fore the throne. On Christ, the sol - id Rock, I stand: All oth - er ground is sink - ing sand.

A higher setting may be found at No. 584

393
I Am Not Skilled to Understand
Dora Greenwell, 1821-1882
EWHURST 8.8.8.7.
Cecil J. Allen, 1886-
1 I am not skilled to un - der - stand What
2 I take him at his word and deed: "Christ
3 That he should leave his place on high And
4 And O that he ful - filled may see The
5 Yea, liv - ing, dy - ing, let me bring My
God hath willed, what God hath planned; I on - ly know at
died to save me," this I read; And in my heart I
come for sin - ful man to die, You count it strange? so
trav - ail of his soul in me, And with his work con -
strength, my sol - ace, from this spring, That he who lives to
his right hand Stands one who is my Sav - ior.
find a need Of him to be my Sav - ior.
once did I Be - fore I knew my Sav - ior.
tent - ed be, As I with my dear Sav - ior!
be my King Once died to be my Sav - ior!
Music used by permission of Cecil J. Allen.
394
O for a Heart to Praise My God
Charles Wesley, 1707-1788
O JESU CHRIST C.M.
Leipzig, 1625
Adapted by A. Royce Eckhardt, 1937-
1 O for a heart to praise my God, A heart from sin set free,
2 A heart re - signed, sub - mis - sive, meek, My great Re - deem - er's throne,
3 A heart in ev - 'ry thought re - newed, And full of love di - vine,
4 Thy na - ture, gra - cious Lord, im - part—Come quick - ly from a - bove:

Alternate tune: RICHMOND, No. 348

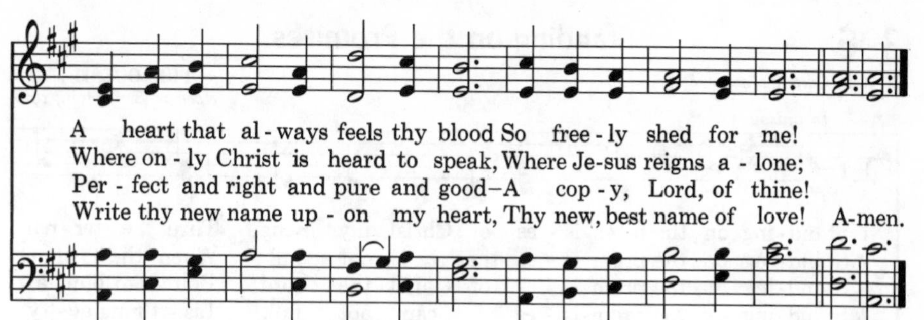
A heart that al - ways feels thy blood So free - ly shed for me!
Where on - ly Christ is heard to speak, Where Je - sus reigns a - lone;
Per - fect and right and pure and good—A cop - y, Lord, of thine!
Write thy new name up - on my heart, Thy new, best name of love! A-men.

Jesus, Thy Blood and Righteousness 395

Nicolaus L. von Zinzendorf, 1700-1760
Tr. John Wesley, 1703-1791

GERMANY L.M.
William Gardiner's "Sacred Melodies," 1815

1 Je - sus, thy blood and right - eous - ness My beau - ty
2 Bold shall I stand in thy great day, For who aught
3 Lord, I be - lieve thy pre - cious blood, Which, at the
4 Lord, I be - lieve were sin - ners more Than sands up -

are, my glo - rious dress; 'Midst flam - ing worlds, in these ar -
to my charge shall lay? Ful - ly ab - solved thru these I
mer - cy seat of God, For - ev - er doth for sin - ners
on the o - cean shore, Thou hast for all a ran - som

rayed, With joy shall I lift up my head.
am, From sin and fear, from guilt and shame.
plead, For me, e'en for my soul was shed.
paid, For all a full a - tone - ment made. A - men.

A higher setting may be found at No. 623

396 Standing on the Promises

R. Kelso Carter, 1849-1928
TURLOCK 11.11.11.9.
Norman E. Johnson, 1928-
In unison
1 Stand-ing on the prom-is-es of Christ my King, Thru e-ter-nal a-ges let his prais-es ring! Glo-ry in the high-est I will shout and sing— Stand-ing on the prom-is-es of God, Stand-ing on the prom-is-es of God!
2 Stand-ing on the prom-is-es that can-not fail When the howl-ing storms of doubt and fear as-sail; By the liv-ing word of God I shall pre-vail— Stand-ing on the prom-is-es of God,
3 Stand-ing on the prom-is-es of Christ the Lord, Bound to him e-ter-nal-ly by love's strong cord, O-ver-com-ing dai-ly with the Spir-it's sword— Stand-ing on the prom-is-es of God,
4 Stand-ing on the prom-is-es I can-not fall, Lis-t'ning ev-'ry mo-ment to the Spir-it's call, Rest-ing in my Sav-ior as my all in all— Stand-ing on the prom-is-es of God,
1-3
4
God!

Through the Love of God, Our Savior

Mary Peters, 1813-1856

AR HYD Y NOS 8.4.8.4.8.8.8.4.
Welsh Melody

1 Through the love of God, our Sav - ior, All will be well;
2 Though we pass through trib - u - la - tion, All will be well;
3 We ex - pect a bright to - mor - row, All will be well;
Free and change-less is his fa - vor— All, all is well.
Ours is such a full sal - va - tion— All, all is well.
Faith can sing through days of sor - row, All, all is well.
Pre-cious is the blood that healed us, Per - fect is the grace that sealed us,
Hap - py when in God con - fid - ing, Fruit-ful if in Christ a - bid - ing,
On our Fa-ther's love re - ly - ing, Je - sus ev - 'ry need sup-ply - ing,
Strong the hand stretched out to shield us— All must be well.
Ho - ly through the Spir - it's guid - ing— All must be well.
Or in liv - ing or in dy - ing, All must be well.

398 Wheresoe'er I Roam

Carl Olof Rosenius, 1816-1868
Tr. Victor O. Peterson, 1864-1929
VAR JAG GÅR 10.9.10.9.10.9.10.7.
Ahnfelt's "Sånger," 1868
1 Where - so - e'er I roam, thru val - leys drear - y, O - ver
2 All my needs e - ter - nal - ly sup - ply - ing, All in
3 Pierc - ed heart, with love o'er - flow - ing, guide me, Help me
moun - tains, or in path - less wood, Ev - er with me is a
all to me that Friend shall be; Ev - 'ry - thing for which my
through life's des - ert find my way; Let my faith, no mat - ter
Friend to cheer me, Warn - ing, com - fort - ing as none else could.
heart is sigh - ing He per - ceives, and helps me lov - ing - ly.
what be - tide me, Find as - sur - ance in thy wounds for aye.
'Tis the Shep - herd, who once dy - ing, bleed - ing, Still through
Though I oft - en feel for - sak - en, lone - ly, He is
To thy bos - om— for this life is fleet - ing— Take me,

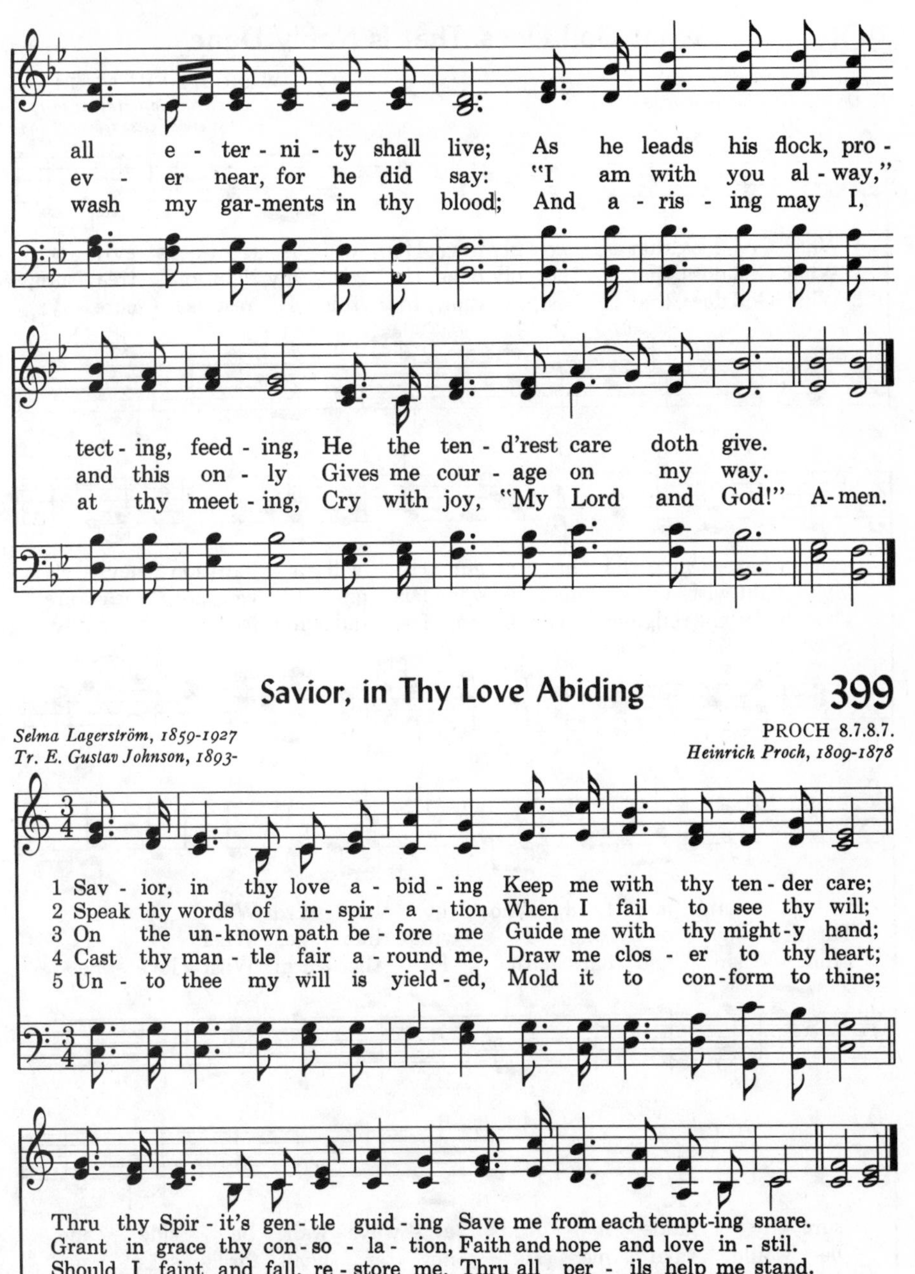
all e - ter - ni - ty shall live; As he leads his flock, pro - tect - ing, feed - ing, He the ten - d'rest care doth give.
ev - er near, for he did say: "I am with you al - way," and this on - ly Gives me cour - age on my way.
wash my gar - ments in thy blood; And a - ris - ing may I, at thy meet - ing, Cry with joy, "My Lord and God!" A - men.
1 Sav - ior, in thy love a - bid - ing Keep me with thy ten - der care; Thru thy Spir - it's gen - tle guid - ing Save me from each tempt - ing snare.
2 Speak thy words of in - spir - a - tion When I fail to see thy will; Grant in grace thy con - so - la - tion, Faith and hope and love in - stil.
3 On the un - known path be - fore me Guide me with thy might - y hand; Should I faint and fall, re - store me, Thru all per - ils help me stand.
4 Cast thy man - tle fair a - round me, Draw me clos - er to thy heart; When thy peace and joy sur - round me Pains and sor - rows all de - part.
5 Un - to thee my will is yield - ed, Mold it to con - form to thine; By thy grace and mer - cy shield - ed, Help me live a life di - vine. A - men.

Savior, in Thy Love Abiding

399

Selma Lagerström, 1859-1927
Tr. E. Gustav Johnson, 1893-

PROCH 8.7.8.7.
Heinrich Proch, 1809-1878

400 What God Does, That Is Nobly Done

Benjamin Schmolck, 1672-1737
Tr. Obed L. Grender, 1900-1970
WAS GOTT TUT 8.7.8.7.4.4.7.7.
Severus Gastorius, 1649-1708
"Weimar Gesangbuch," 1681
1 What God does, that is no - bly done, His will is right-eous ev - er;
2 What God does, that is no - bly done, He is my light and trea - sure;
3 What God does, that is best, I know, In this I rest se - cure - ly;
And what with me he has be - gun He will a - ban - don nev - er.
My fight with e - vil shall be won, His gifts I can - not meas - ure.
Though o'er the rough-est road I go, He guides my feet so sure - ly.
He is my Lord, Who by his word Will ev - er
Through joy or woe I with him go, Wher - ev - er
From sin and harm, In Fa - ther - arm With love he
sure - ly guide me, And al - ways walk be - side me.
he would take me: He nev - er shall for - sake me.
shall en - fold me, And safe - ly he shall hold me.

Who Trusts in God, a Strong Abode

Joachim Magdeburg, c.1525-?
Tr. Benjamin H. Kennedy, 1804-1889
Alt. by William W. How, 1823-1897

BISHOPGARTH 8.7.8.7.D.
Arthur S. Sullivan, 1842-1900
Harm. by Norman E. Johnson, 1928-

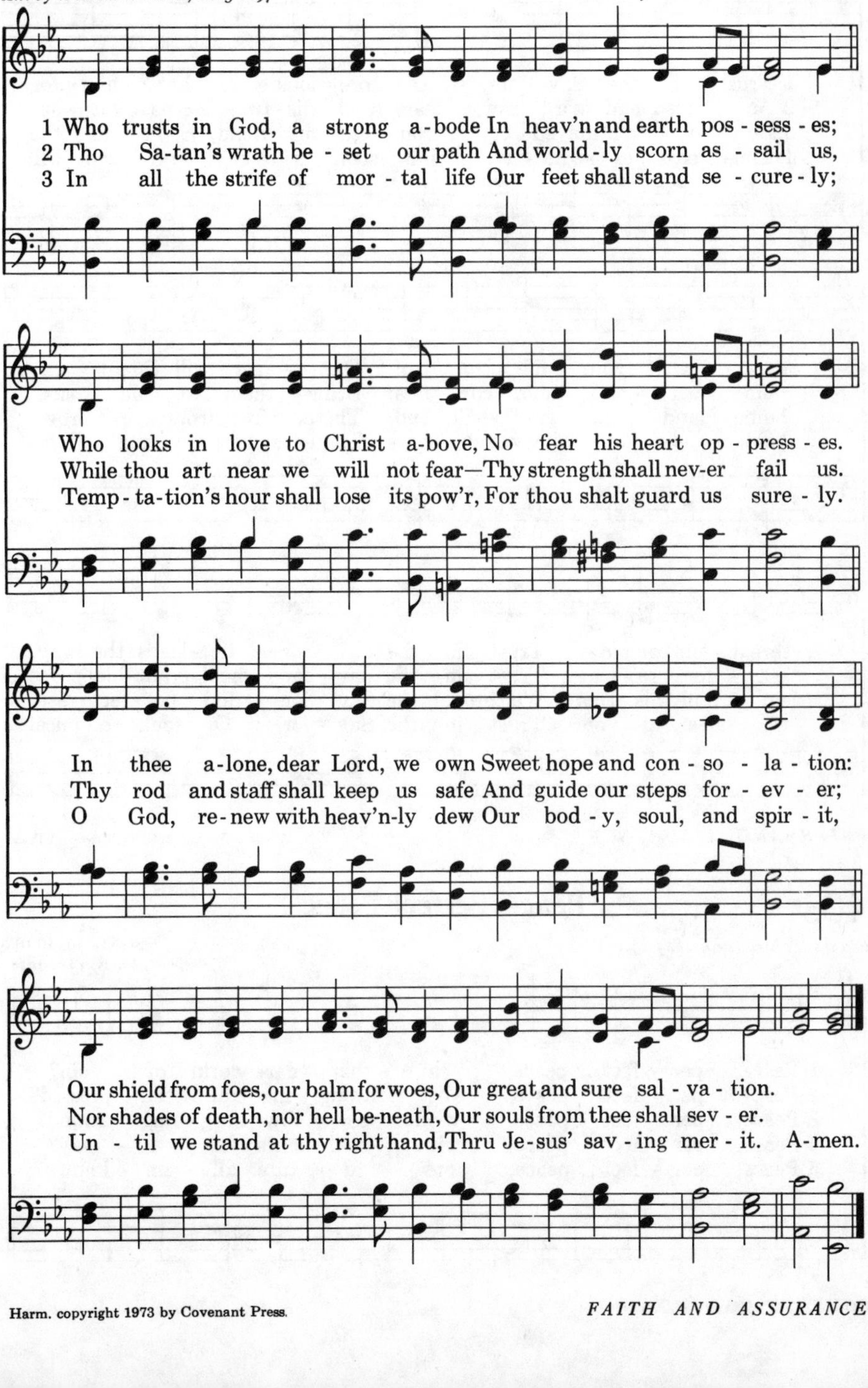

1 Who trusts in God, a strong a-bode In heav'n and earth pos-sess-es;
Who looks in love to Christ a-bove, No fear his heart op-press-es.
In thee a-lone, dear Lord, we own Sweet hope and con-so-la-tion:
Our shield from foes, our balm for woes, Our great and sure sal-va-tion.

2 Tho Sa-tan's wrath be-set our path And world-ly scorn as-sail us,
While thou art near we will not fear—Thy strength shall nev-er fail us.
Thy rod and staff shall keep us safe And guide our steps for-ev-er;
Nor shades of death, nor hell be-neath, Our souls from thee shall sev-er.

3 In all the strife of mor-tal life Our feet shall stand se-cure-ly;
Temp-ta-tion's hour shall lose its pow'r, For thou shalt guard us sure-ly.
O God, re-new with heav'n-ly dew Our bod-y, soul, and spir-it,
Un-til we stand at thy right hand, Thru Je-sus' sav-ing mer-it. A-men.

402 Trust in the Savior, O Precious Soul

Otto A. Ottander, 1842-1926 EKSTRÖM 9.9.9.9.
Tr. A. Eldon Palmquist, 1912- *Fredrik A. Ekström, 1819-1901*

1 Trust in the Sav - ior, O pre-cious soul, Let him for -
2 An - guish and sor - row, fears and dis-tress, Sins with-out
3 Be not dis-mayed or trou-bled, my friend, Soon in the
4 Time pass - es swift - ly, life soon is o'er, Je - sus will

ev - er your life con - trol; Dan - ger will threat - en,
num - ber all must con - fess; Bring them to Je - sus,
home - land all grief shall end; There, free from sor - row,
guide us to heav-en's shore; Though storms are rag - ing,

threat - en each day: Trust in the Sav - ior— he leads the way.
ask for re - lease: Trust in the Sav - ior— he'll grant his peace.
sin, and dis - tress, We through the Sav - ior find per-fect rest.
we hear his voice: Trust in the Sav - ior— O soul, re - joice!

FAITH AND ASSURANCE

403 Peace, Perfect Peace

Edward H. Bickersteth, 1825-1906 SONG 46 10.10.
Orlando Gibbons, 1583-1625

1 Peace, per - fect peace, in this dark world of sin?
2 Peace, per - fect peace, by throng - ing du - ties pressed?
3 Peace, per - fect peace, with sor - rows surg - ing round?
4 Peace, per - fect peace, with loved ones far a - way?
5 Peace, per - fect peace, our fu - ture all un - known?

COMFORT AND PEACE

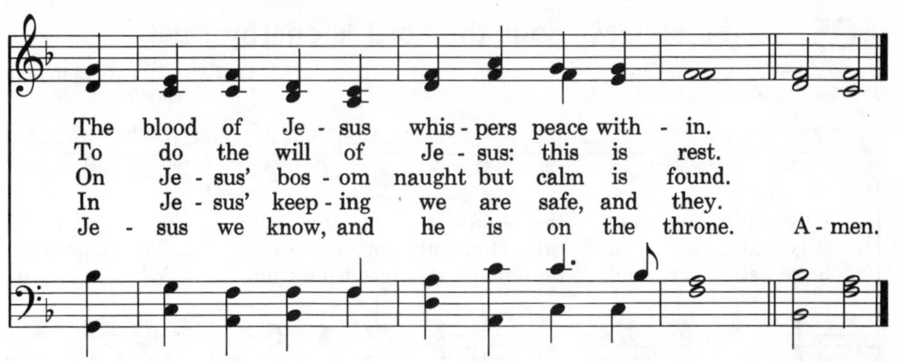
The blood of Je - sus whis - pers peace with - in.
To do the will of Je - sus: this is rest.
On Je - sus' bos - om naught but calm is found.
In Je - sus' keep - ing we are safe, and they.
Je - sus we know, and he is on the throne. A - men.

Come, Ye Disconsolate

404

Thomas Moore, 1779-1852, Sts. 1, 2
Thomas Hastings, 1784-1872, St. 3

CONSOLATOR 11.10.11.10.
Samuel Webbe, 1740-1816

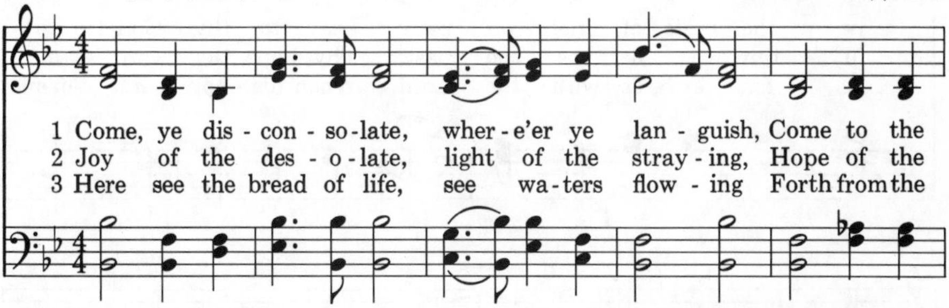

1 Come, ye dis - con - so - late, wher - e'er ye lan - guish, Come to the
2 Joy of the des - o - late, light of the stray - ing, Hope of the
3 Here see the bread of life, see wa - ters flow - ing Forth from the

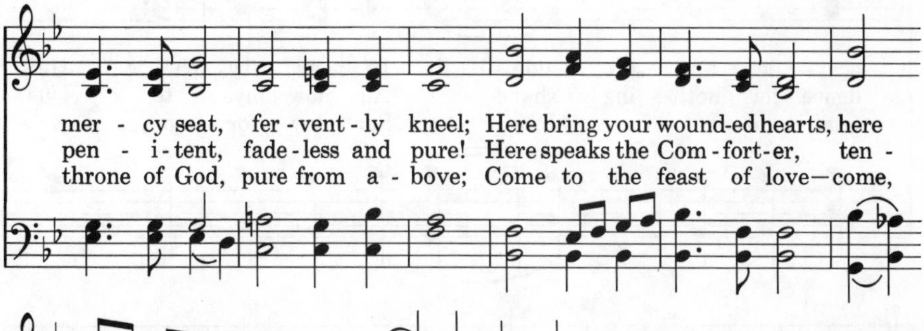

mer - cy seat, fer - vent - ly kneel; Here bring your wound - ed hearts, here
pen - i - tent, fade - less and pure! Here speaks the Com - fort - er, ten -
throne of God, pure from a - bove; Come to the feast of love—come,

tell your an - guish; Earth has no sor - row that heav'n can - not heal.
der - ly say - ing, "Earth has no sor - row that heav'n can - not cure."
ev - er know - ing Earth has no sor - row but heav'n can re - move.

405 Be Still, My Soul: the Lord Is on Thy Side!

Katharina von Schlegel, 1697-?
Tr. Jane L. Borthwick, 1813-1897
FINLANDIA 10.10.10.10.10.10.
Jean Sibelius, 1865-1957
1 Be still, my soul: the Lord is on thy side! Bear pa-tient-ly the cross of grief or pain; Leave to thy God to or-der and pro-vide— In ev-'ry change He faith-ful will re-main. Be still, my soul: thy best, thy heav'n-ly
2 Be still, my soul: thy God doth un-der-take To guide the fu-ture as he has the past; Thy hope, thy con-fi-dence let noth-ing shake— All now mys-te-rious shall be bright at last. Be still, my soul: the waves and winds still
3 Be still, my soul: the hour is has-t'ning on When we shall be for-ev-er with the Lord, When dis-ap-point-ment, grief, and fear are gone, Sor-row for-got, love's pur-est joys re-stored. Be still, my soul: when change and tears are

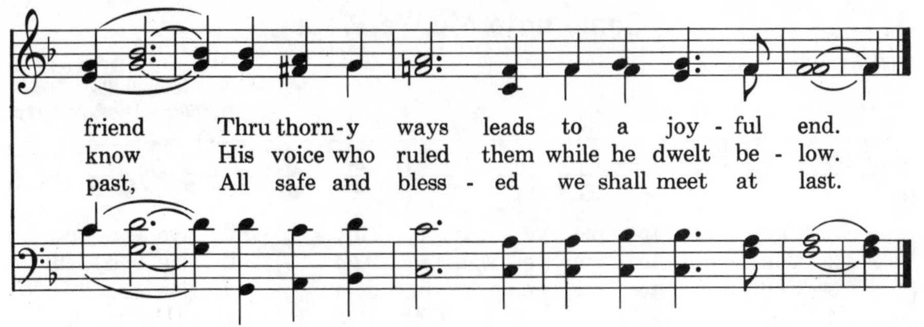

friend Thru thorn-y ways leads to a joy - ful end.
know His voice who ruled them while he dwelt be - low.
past, All safe and bless - ed we shall meet at last.

They Cast Their Nets in Galilee

406

William A. Percy, 1885-1942, alt.

GEORGETOWN C.M.
David McK. Williams, 1887-

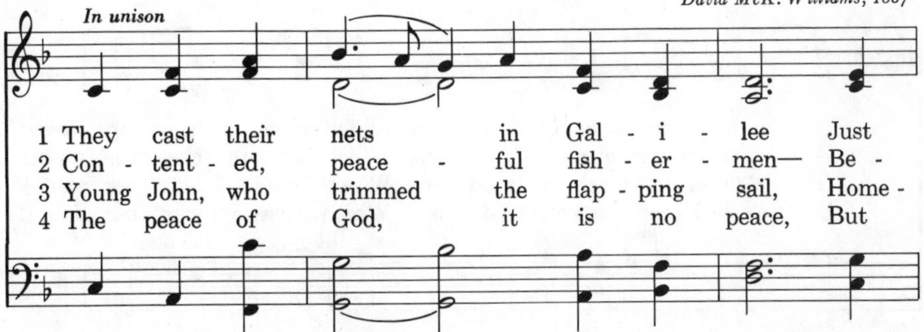

In unison

1 They cast their nets in Gal - i - lee Just
2 Con - tent - ed, peace - ful fish - er - men— Be -
3 Young John, who trimmed the flap - ping sail, Home -
4 The peace of God, it is no peace, But

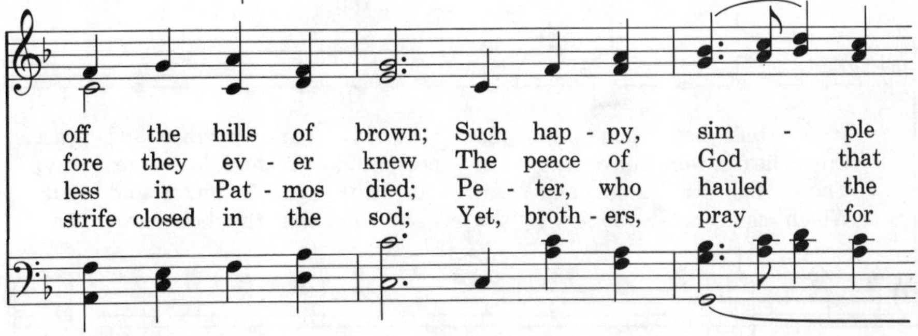

off the hills of brown; Such hap - py, sim - ple
fore they ev - er knew The peace of God that
less in Pat - mos died; Pe - ter, who hauled the
strife closed in the sod; Yet, broth - ers, pray for

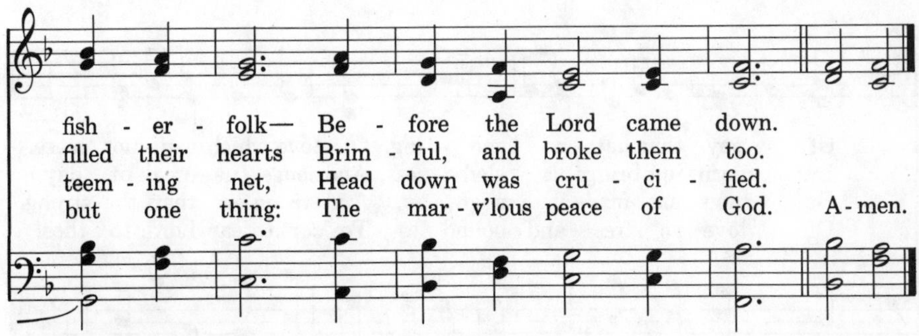

fish - er - folk— Be - fore the Lord came down.
filled their hearts Brim - ful, and broke them too.
teem - ing net, Head down was cru - ci - fied.
but one thing: The mar - v'lous peace of God. A - men.

407 Come unto Me, Ye Weary

William C. Dix, 1837-1898

MEIRIONYDD 7.6.7.6.D.
Welsh Melody
Attr. to William Lloyd, 1786-1852

1 "Come un - to me, ye wea - ry, And I will give you rest."
O bless - ed voice of Je - sus, Which comes to hearts op - pressed!
It tells of ben - e - dic - tion, Of par - don, grace and peace,
Of joy that hath no end - ing, Of love which can - not cease.

2 "Come un - to me, ye wan-d'rers, And I will give you light."
O lov - ing voice of Je - sus, Which comes to cheer the night!
Our hearts were filled with sad - ness, And we had lost our way;
But morn - ing brings us glad - ness, And songs the break of day.

3 "Come un - to me, ye faint - ing, And I will give you life."
O cheer - ing voice of Je - sus, Which comes to aid our strife!
The foe is stern and ea - ger, The fight is fierce and long;
But thou hast made us might - y, And strong-er than the strong.

4 "And who - so - ev - er com - eth, I will not cast him out."
O wel - come voice of Je - sus, Which drives a - way our doubt!
Which calls us, ver - y sin - ners, Un - wor - thy though we be
Of love so free and bound - less, To come. dear Lord, to thee!

Another harmonization in a lower setting may be found at No. 196

Give, O Lord, unto Thy Servant

408

Lina Sandell, 1832-1903
Tr. E. Gustav Johnson, 1893-

TILLFLYKT 8.7.8.7.8.7.
Swedish Folk Melody
"Sionstoner," 1889
Harm. by A. Royce Eckhardt, 1937-

1 Give, O Lord, un - to thy serv - ant Rest and
2 May thy ten - der Spir - it guide me And di -
3 May not sin nor world - ly pleas - ure Lure me
4 Make me calm and still be - fore thee, Hide me
qui - et peace in thee, For the world's wild rush - ing
rect my ev - 'ry deed, Walk in love and grace be -
from thy path a - stray; Help me on - ly thee to
in thy shel - ter mild; There no e - vil can come
cur - rent Has no rest - ing place for me. I am
side me, In thy pas - tures let me feed. Come, O
treas - ure And thy pres - ence seek each day. Lead me,
o'er me, There I'm safe from tem - pests wild. In that
long - ing, I am long - ing, Safe with - in thy gates to be!
Sav - ior! come, O Sav - ior, Give the strength I dai - ly need!
Sav - ior! lead me, Sav - ior, On the right - eous road, I pray!
shel - ter, in that shel - ter, Is the ref - uge for thy child! A-men.

409 In Loving-Kindness Jesus Came

Charles H. Gabriel, 1856-1932

HE LIFTED ME 8.8.8.6. *with Refrain*
Charles H. Gabriel, 1856-1932

1 In lov-ing-kind-ness Je-sus came My soul in mer-cy to re-claim,
2 He called me long be-fore I heard, Be-fore my sin-ful heart was stirred,
3 His brow was pierced with man-y a thorn, His hands by cru-el nails were torn,
4 Now on a high-er plane I dwell, And with my soul I know 'tis well;
And from the depths of sin and shame Thru grace he lift-ed me.
But when I took him at his word, For-giv'n, he lift-ed me.
When from my guilt and grief, for-lorn, In love he lift-ed me.
Yet how or why, I can-not tell, He should have lift-ed me.
He lift-ed me.
REFRAIN
From sink-ing sand he lift-ed me, With ten-der hand he lift-ed me;
From shades of night to plains of light, O praise his name, he lift-ed me!

Jesus, Priceless Treasure

410

Johann Franck, 1618-1677
Tr. Catherine Winkworth, 1827-1878

JESU, MEINE FREUDE 6.6.5.6.6.5.7.8.6.
German Melody
Adapted by Johann Crüger, 1598-1662

1 Je - sus, price - less treas - ure, Source of pur - est pleas-ure,
2 In thine arm I rest me; Foes who would mo - lest me
3 Hence, all thoughts of sad - ness! For the Lord of glad - ness,
Tru - est friend to me: Long my heart hath pant - ed, Till it well-nigh
Can - not reach me here. Though the earth be shak - ing, Ev - ery heart be
Je - sus, en - ters in: Those who love the Fa - ther, Though the storms may
faint - ed, Thirst-ing aft - er thee. Thine I am, O spot - less Lamb,
quak-ing, God dis-pels our fear. Sin and hell in con - flict fell
gath - er, Still have peace with - in. Yea, what-e'er we here must bear,
I will suf-fer nought to hide thee, Ask for nought be-side thee.
With their heav-iest storms as-sail us: Je - sus will not fail us.
Still in thee lies pur - est pleas - ure, Je - sus, price-less treas - ure! A-men.

411 Like a River Glorious

Frances Ridley Havergal, 1836-1879

WYE VALLEY 6.5.6.5.D. *with Refrain*
James Mountain, 1844-1933

1 Like a riv - er glo - rious Is God's per - fect peace, O - ver all vic -
2 Hid - den in the hol - low Of his bless - ed hand, Nev - er foe can
3 Ev - 'ry joy or tri - al Fall - eth from a - bove, Traced up - on our
to - rious In its bright in - crease; Per - fect, yet it flow - eth Full - er
fol - low, Nev - er trai - tor stand; Not a surge of wor - ry, Not a
di - al By the sun of love; We may trust him ful - ly All for
ev - 'ry day, Per - fect, yet it grow - eth Deep - er all the way.
shade of care, Not a blast of hur - ry Touch the spir - it there.
us to do— They who trust him whol - ly Find him whol - ly true.
REFRAIN
Stayed up - on Je - ho - vah, Hearts are ful - ly blest—
Find - ing, as he prom - ised, Per - fect peace and rest.

Sitting at the Feet of Jesus

412

Source unknown

ELLESDIE 8.7.8.7.D.
"The Christian Lyre," 1831
Attr. to Wolfgang A. Mozart, 1756-1791

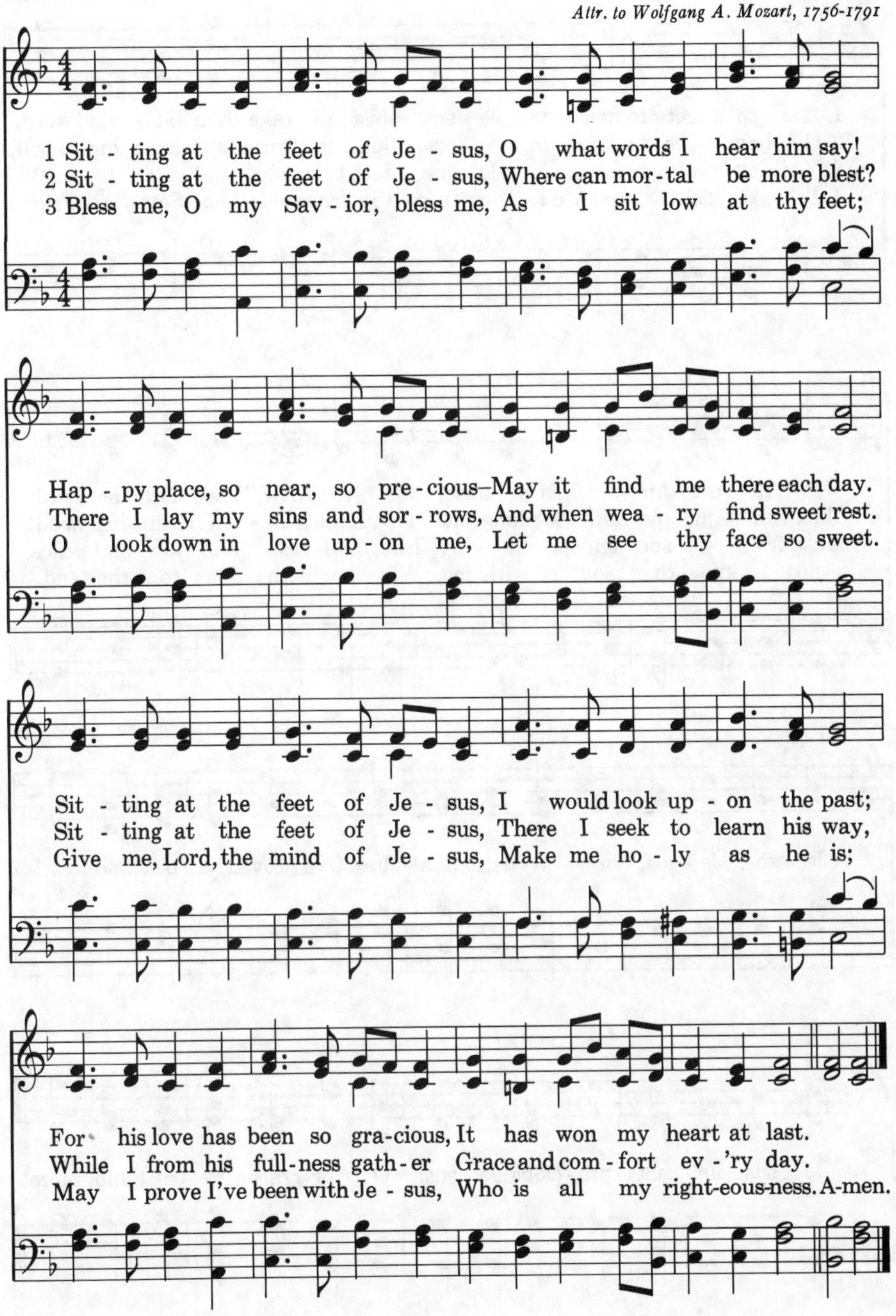

1 Sit - ting at the feet of Je - sus, O what words I hear him say!
2 Sit - ting at the feet of Je - sus, Where can mor - tal be more blest?
3 Bless me, O my Sav - ior, bless me, As I sit low at thy feet;

Hap - py place, so near, so pre - cious–May it find me there each day.
There I lay my sins and sor - rows, And when wea - ry find sweet rest.
O look down in love up - on me, Let me see thy face so sweet.

Sit - ting at the feet of Je - sus, I would look up - on the past;
Sit - ting at the feet of Je - sus, There I seek to learn his way,
Give me, Lord, the mind of Je - sus, Make me ho - ly as he is;

For his love has been so gra - cious, It has won my heart at last.
While I from his full - ness gath - er Grace and com - fort ev - 'ry day.
May I prove I've been with Je - sus, Who is all my right - eous - ness. A - men.

413 'Tis So Sweet to Trust in Jesus

Louisa M. R. Stead, c.1850-1917

TRUST IN JESUS 8.7.8.7. *with Refrain*
William J. Kirkpatrick, 1838-1921

1 'Tis so sweet to trust in Je - sus, Just to take him at his word,
2 O how sweet to trust in Je - sus, Just to trust his cleans-ing blood,
3 Yes, 'tis sweet to trust in Je - sus, Just from sin and self to cease,
4 I'm so glad I learned to trust thee, Pre-cious Je - sus, Sav - ior, Friend;
Just to rest up - on his prom-ise, Just to know, "Thus saith the Lord."
Just in sim - ple faith to plunge me 'Neath the heal - ing, cleans-ing flood!
Just from Je - sus sim - ply tak - ing Life and rest and joy and peace.
And I know that thou art with me, Wilt be with me to the end.
REFRAIN
Je - sus, Je - sus, how I trust him! How I've proved him o'er and o'er!
Je - sus, Je - sus, pre - cious Je - sus! O for grace to trust him more!

What a Friend We Have in Jesus

414

Joseph Scriven, 1820-1886

ERIE 8.7.8.7.D.
Charles C. Converse, 1832-1918

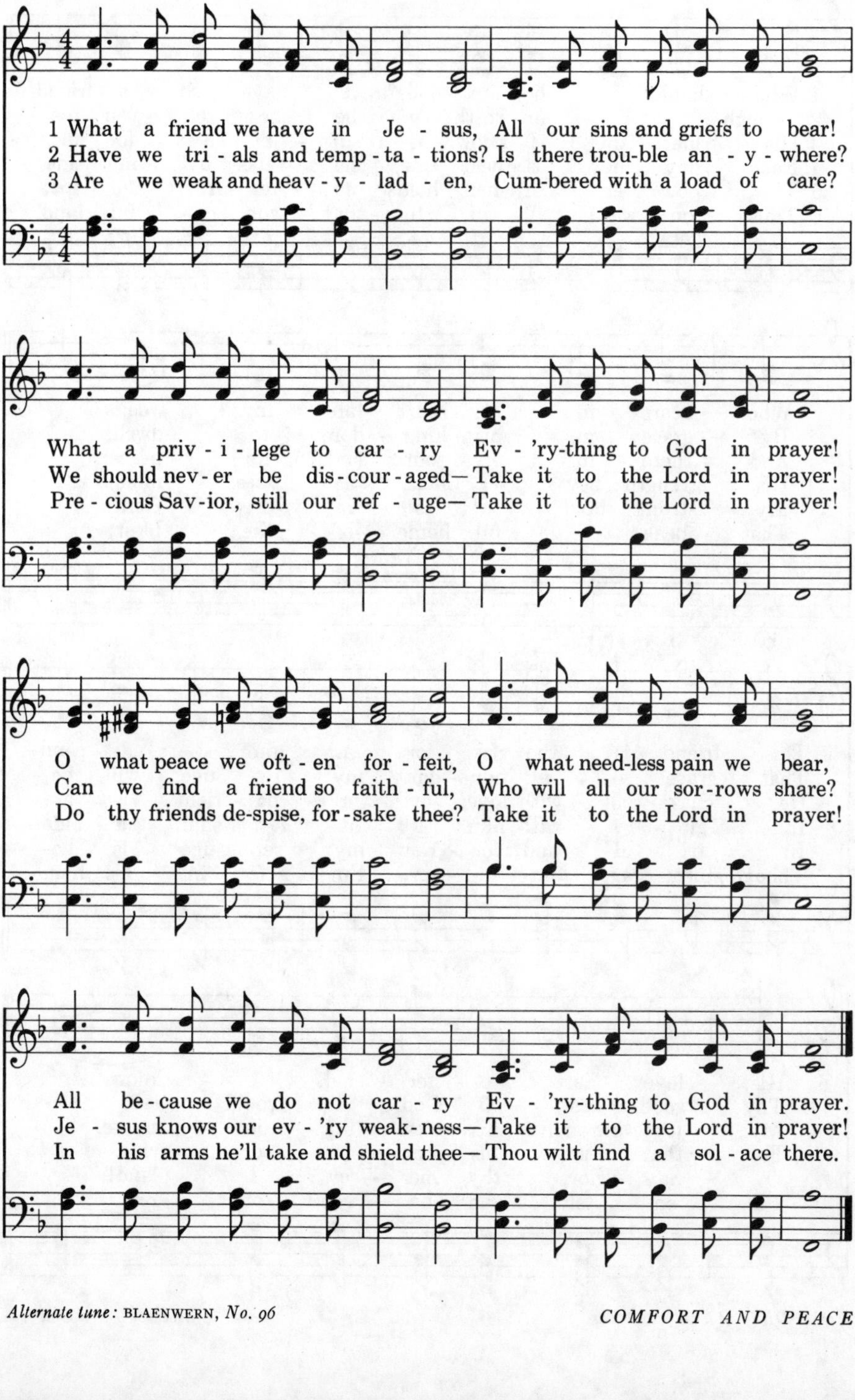

1 What a friend we have in Je - sus, All our sins and griefs to bear!
2 Have we tri - als and temp - ta - tions? Is there trou-ble an - y - where?
3 Are we weak and heav - y - lad - en, Cum-bered with a load of care?

What a priv - i - lege to car - ry Ev - 'ry-thing to God in prayer!
We should nev - er be dis - cour - aged— Take it to the Lord in prayer!
Pre - cious Sav - ior, still our ref - uge— Take it to the Lord in prayer!

O what peace we oft - en for - feit, O what need-less pain we bear,
Can we find a friend so faith - ful, Who will all our sor - rows share?
Do thy friends de - spise, for - sake thee? Take it to the Lord in prayer!

All be - cause we do not car - ry Ev - 'ry-thing to God in prayer.
Je - sus knows our ev - 'ry weak - ness— Take it to the Lord in prayer!
In his arms he'll take and shield thee— Thou wilt find a sol - ace there.

Alternate tune: BLAENWERN, *No. 96*

415 Why Should I Be Anxious?

Nils Frykman, 1842-1911
Tr. Aaron Markuson, 1910-

SUNNE 11.8.11.8.
Source unknown

1 Why should I be anx - ious? I have such a friend,
2 Though I am un-worth - y he chose e - ven me,
3 His mer - cy, I know, is suf - fi - cient for me,
4 Each day he is near me, he walks by my side,
5 The pow - er of hell holds no ter - ror for me,
6 Thus on - ward I go to that won - der - ful land,

Who bears in his heart all my woe;
By grace in his king - dom to dwell;
And there - in my soul finds its peace;
His strength nev - er fails, as does mine;
My strong - hold is Is - ra - el's God;
That beau - ti - ful home of the blest;

This friend is the Sav - ior, on him I de - pend—
That grace so a - bun - dant my ref - uge will be—
He chas - tens with love, ev - er pa - tient is he—
In glo - ry with him I at last shall a - bide—
In tri - al and sor - row my ref - uge is he—
Though storms rage in fu - ry, I'm safe in his hand—

His love is e - ter - nal, I know.
Thy good - ness, O God, I would tell.
My joys through his bless - ing in - crease.
For that is his prom - ise di - vine.
O Sav - ior, thy mer - cy I laud!
I'll en - ter the ha - ven of rest.

I Have a Friend Who Loveth Me

Nils Frykman, 1842-1911

FRYKMAN L.M. *with Refrain*
Nils Frykman, 1842-1911
Harm. by A. Royce Eckhardt, 1937-

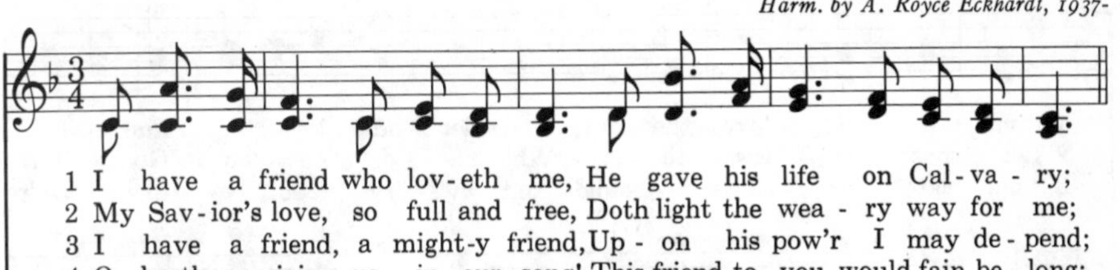

1 I have a friend who lov-eth me, He gave his life on Cal-va-ry;
2 My Sav-ior's love, so full and free, Doth light the wea-ry way for me;
3 I have a friend, a might-y friend, Up-on his pow'r I may de-pend;
4 O broth-er, join us in our song! This friend to you would fain be-long;

Up-on the cross my sins he bore, And I am saved for-ev-er-more.
It fills with joy each pass-ing day And drives my sor-rows all a-way.
He reign-eth o-ver ev-'ry land, O'er val-ley, hill, o'er sea and strand.
Tho far from what you'd like to be, His grace suf-fi-cient is for thee.

REFRAIN

O hal-le-lu-jah, he's my friend! He guides me to the jour-ney's end;

He walks be-side me all the way And will be-stow a crown some day.

417 Come, We That Love the Lord

Isaac Watts, 1674-1748
Robert Lowry, 1826-1899, Refrain
MARCHING TO ZION S.M. with Refrain
Robert Lowry, 1826-1899
1 Come, we that love the Lord, And let our joys be known; Join
2 Let those re - fuse to sing Who nev - er knew our God; But
3 Then let our songs a-bound And ev - 'ry tear be dry; We're
in a song with sweet ac-cord, Join in a song with sweet ac-cord
chil - dren of the heav'n-ly King, But chil-dren of the heav'n-ly King
march-ing thru Em-man-uel's ground, We're march-ing thru Em - man-uel's ground
And thus sur - round the throne, And thus sur-round the throne.
May speak their joys a - broad, May speak their joys a - broad.
To fair - er worlds on high, To fair - er worlds on high.
REFRAIN
We're march-ing to Zi - on, Beau - ti-ful, beau - ti - ful Zi - on; We're
march-ing up-ward to Zi - on, The beau - ti - ful cit - y of God.

I Sing with Joy and Gladness

Nils Frykman, 1842-1911
Tr. E. Gustav Johnson, 1893-

JOYFUL PILGRIM 13.13.13.8.
Nils Frykman, 1842-1911

1 I sing with joy and glad - ness, my soul has found re - lease;
2 My for - mer res - o - lu - tions to lead a bet - ter life
3 When thoughts of guilt op - press me and I thru weak - ness fail,
4 The e - vil ad - ver - sar - y may in his fu - ry smite;
5 Thus march - ing on cou - ra - geous, with joy I see my goal—
Now free from sin and sad - ness, with God I live in peace:
Were on - ly vain il - lu - sions—my soul was still at strife:
The Sav - ior yet will bless me, his mer - cy does pre - vail:
I fear not, for I car - ry God's ar - mor in the fight:
The bless - ing of the a - ges, the ha - ven of my soul:
His ev - er - last - ing mer - cy to me has been re -
Now on the love of Je - sus com - plete - ly I re -
For - give - ness for the sin - ner his lov - ing heart pro -
The word, di - vine and might - y, shall vic - to - ry ob -
And on the pil - grim jour - ney my voice in song I
vealed, His truth in my heart has been sealed.
ly— For me he was will - ing to die.
vides, His faith - ful - ness ev - er a - bides.
tain, Its strength shall for - ev - er re - main.
raise, My God and my Sav - ior to praise.

419 I Stand Amazed in the Presence

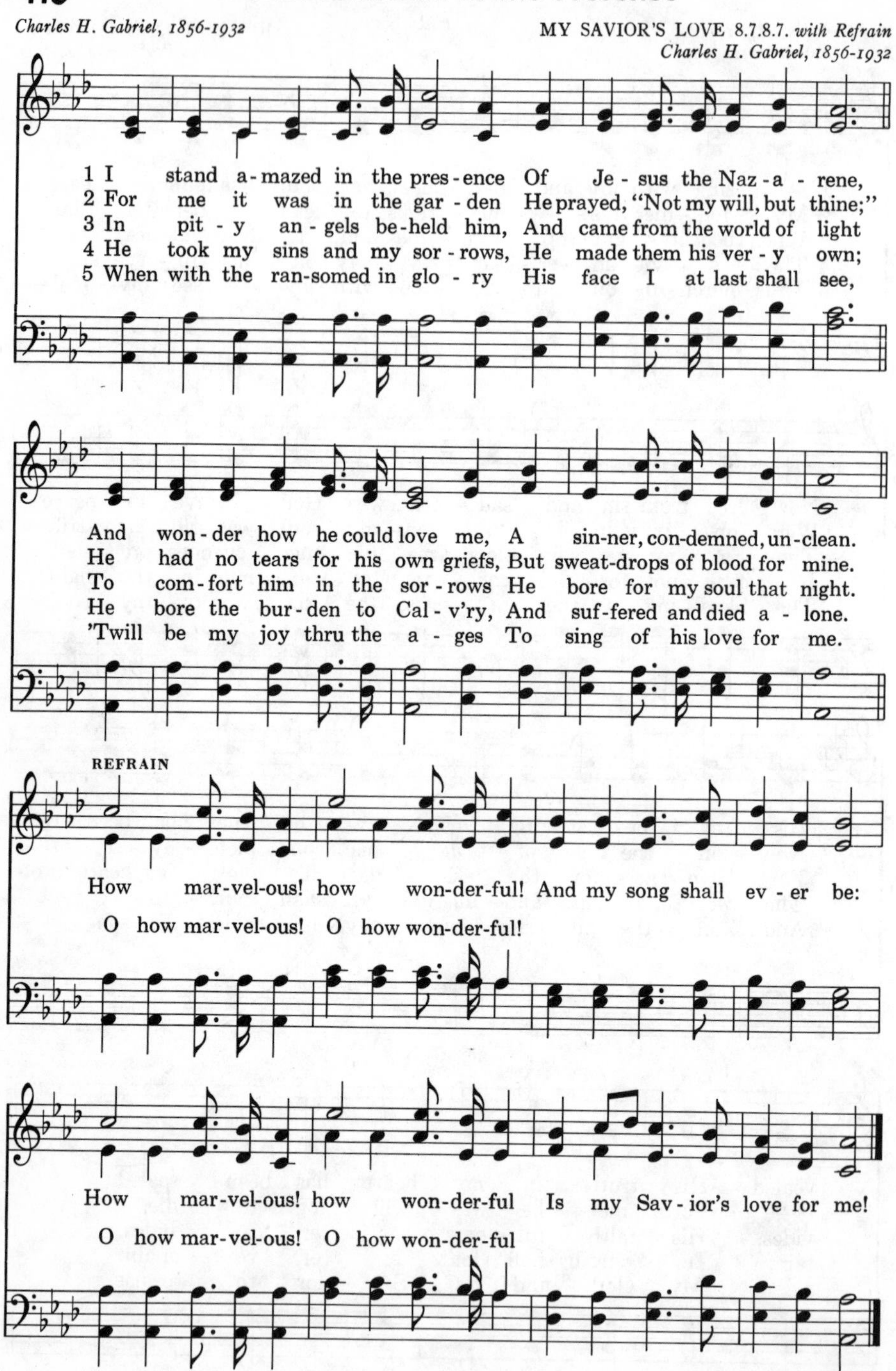
Charles H. Gabriel, 1856-1932
MY SAVIOR'S LOVE 8.7.8.7. with Refrain
Charles H. Gabriel, 1856-1932
1 I stand a-mazed in the pres-ence Of Je-sus the Naz-a-rene,
2 For me it was in the gar-den He prayed, "Not my will, but thine;"
3 In pit-y an-gels be-held him, And came from the world of light
4 He took my sins and my sor-rows, He made them his ver-y own;
5 When with the ran-somed in glo-ry His face I at last shall see,
And won-der how he could love me, A sin-ner, con-demned, un-clean.
He had no tears for his own griefs, But sweat-drops of blood for mine.
To com-fort him in the sor-rows He bore for my soul that night.
He bore the bur-den to Cal-v'ry, And suf-fered and died a-lone.
'Twill be my joy thru the a-ges To sing of his love for me.
REFRAIN
How mar-vel-ous! how won-der-ful! And my song shall ev-er be:
O how mar-vel-ous! O how won-der-ful!
How mar-vel-ous! how won-der-ful Is my Sav-ior's love for me!
O how mar-vel-ous! O how won-der-ful

What a Fellowship, What a Joy Divine

Elisha A. Hoffman, 1839-1929
LEANING ON JESUS 10.9.10.9. with Refrain
Anthony J. Showalter, 1858-1924
Harm. by James P. Davies, 1913-
1 What a fel - low-ship, what a joy di - vine, Lean - ing on the ev - er - last - ing arms; What a bless - ed - ness, what a peace is mine, Lean - ing on the ev - er - last - ing arms.
2 O how sweet to walk in this pil - grim way, Lean - ing on the ev - er - last - ing arms; O how bright the path grows from day to day, Lean - ing on the ev - er - last - ing arms.
3 What have I to dread, what have I to fear, Lean - ing on the ev - er - last - ing arms? I have bless - ed peace with my Lord so near, Lean - ing on the ev - er - last - ing arms.
REFRAIN
Lean - ing, lean - ing, Safe and se-cure from all a - larms;
Lean - ing, lean - ing, Lean - ing on the ev - er - last - ing arms.

421 My Soul Now Magnifies the Lord

Based on Luke 1:46-55
Carl Boberg, 1859-1940
Tr. Obed Johnson, 1881-1970

MARIAS LOVSÅNG C.M.D.
Swedish Folk Melody

1 My soul now mag - ni - fies the Lord, With joy his
2 The pow - er of his right - eous arm A - maz - ing
3 His mer - cy is in - deed so great Its length can -
4 His wis - dom can - not be dis - cerned By car - nal -
5 My soul now mag - ni - fies the Lord, With joy his
praise I sing; For God my Sav - ior un - to me
things has wrought; Earth's might - y men he has sub - dued,
not be spanned; For those who trust his prom - is - es
mind - ed man; But he who tru - ly loves the Lord
praise I sing; For God my Sav - ior un - to me
Has done a won - drous thing: This child of dust he
Like dust they've come to naught: The proud of spir - it
His help is near at hand: The cov - e - nant that
Shall know his sa - cred plan: The man whose heart is
Has done a won - drous thing: This child of dust he
rich - ly blessed, His mer - cy fills my soul; For
he has sent With emp - ty souls a - way; To
he has made, As in our fa - thers' day, For -
filled with pride Will God, the Lord, bring low; To
set a - part For bless - ed - ness sub - lime; His

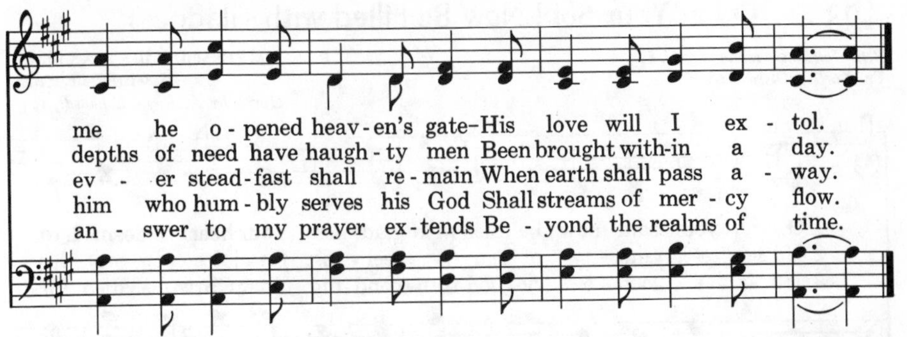
me he o - pened heav - en's gate– His love will I ex - tol.
depths of need have haugh - ty men Been brought with-in a day.
ev - er stead-fast shall re - main When earth shall pass a - way.
him who hum - bly serves his God Shall streams of mer - cy flow.
an - swer to my prayer ex - tends Be - yond the realms of time.

Rejoice, Ye Pure in Heart 422

Edward H. Plumptre, 1821-1891

MARION S.M. *with Refrain*
Arthur H. Messiter, 1834-1916

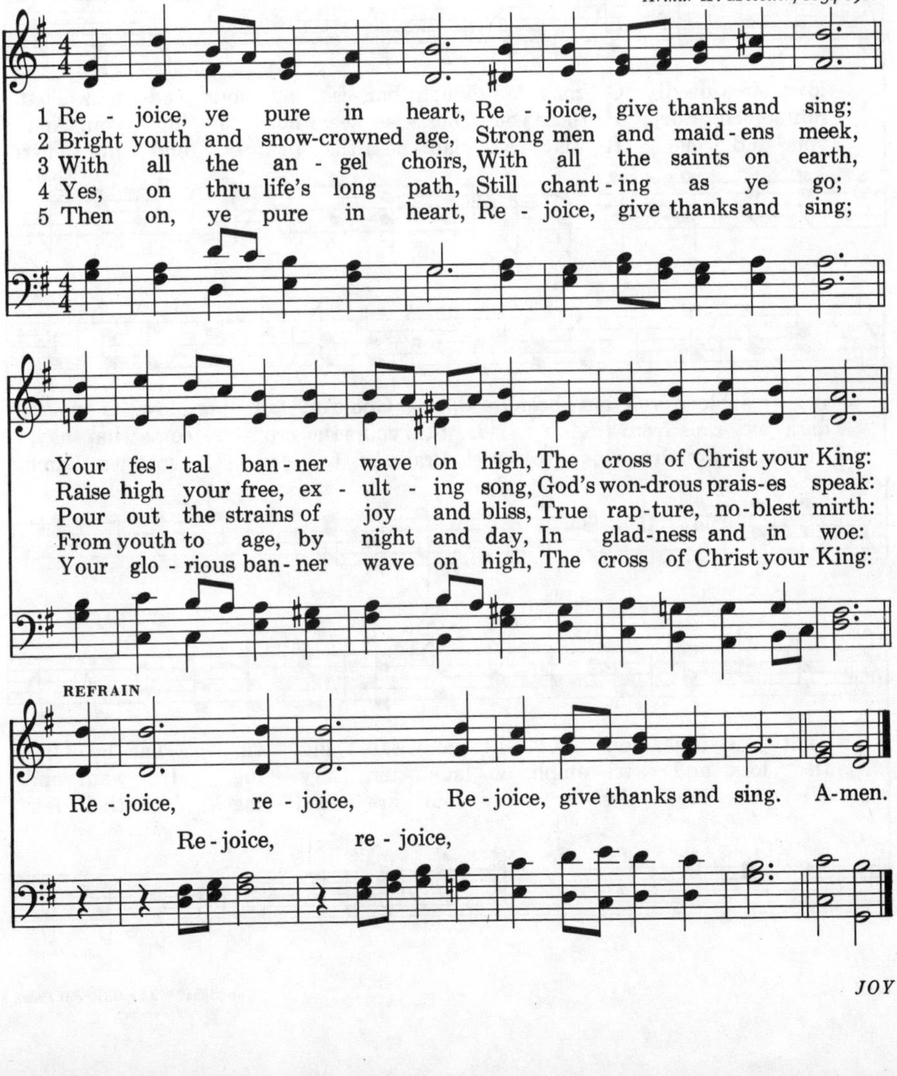

1 Re - joice, ye pure in heart, Re - joice, give thanks and sing;
2 Bright youth and snow-crowned age, Strong men and maid - ens meek,
3 With all the an - gel choirs, With all the saints on earth,
4 Yes, on thru life's long path, Still chant - ing as ye go;
5 Then on, ye pure in heart, Re - joice, give thanks and sing;

Your fes - tal ban - ner wave on high, The cross of Christ your King:
Raise high your free, ex - ult - ing song, God's won-drous prais - es speak:
Pour out the strains of joy and bliss, True rap - ture, no - blest mirth:
From youth to age, by night and day, In glad - ness and in woe:
Your glo - rious ban - ner wave on high, The cross of Christ your King:

REFRAIN

Re - joice, re - joice, Re - joice, give thanks and sing. A - men.

Re - joice, re - joice,

423 O Let Your Soul Now Be Filled with Gladness

Peter Jönsson Aschan, 1726-1813
Tr. Karl A. Olsson, 1913-

RANSOMED SOUL 10.8.10.8.8.10.10.8.
Swedish Folk Melody
Harm. by A. Royce Eckhardt, 1937-

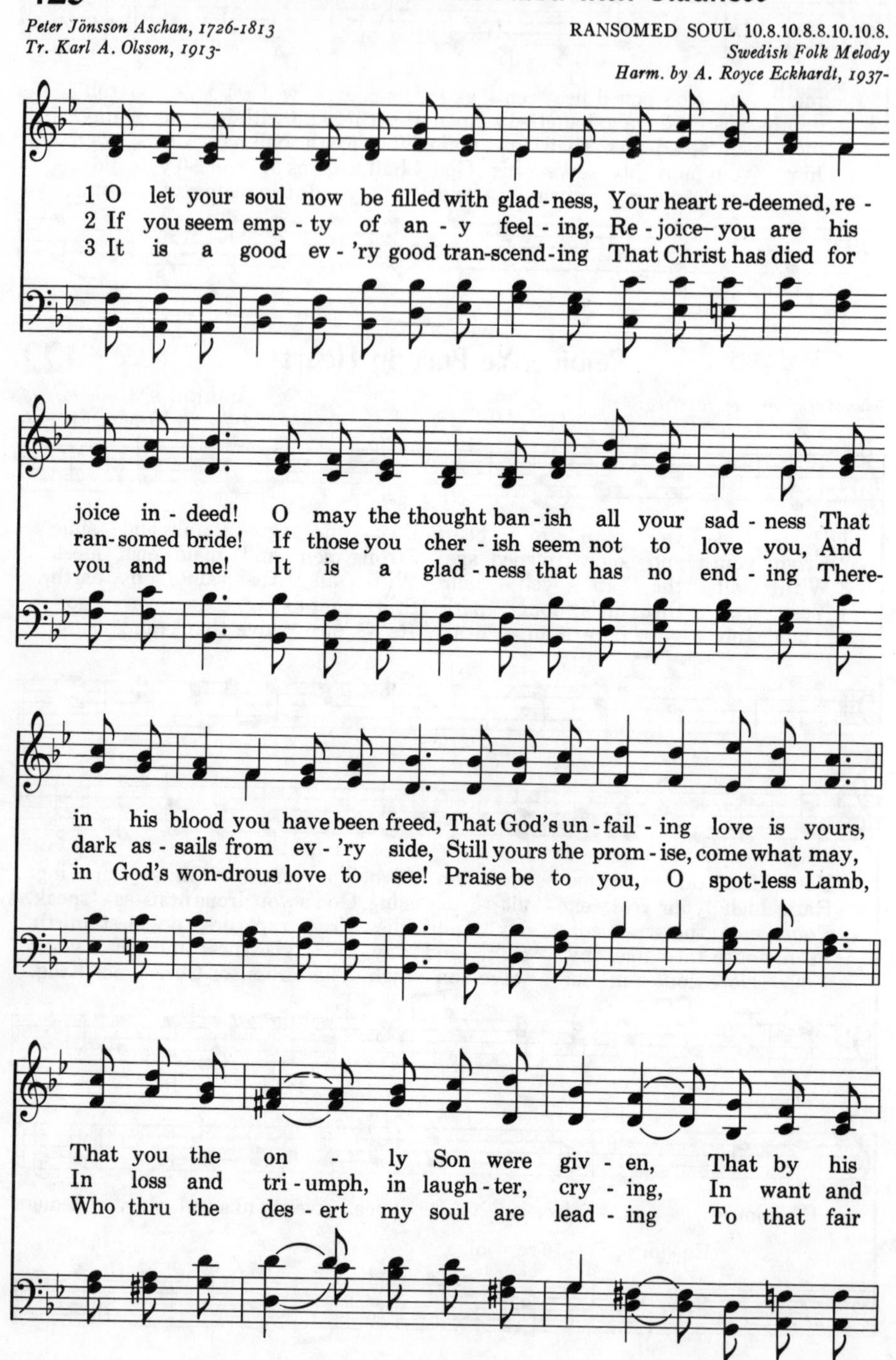
1 O let your soul now be filled with glad-ness, Your heart re-deemed, re - joice in - deed! O may the thought ban - ish all your sad - ness That in his blood you have been freed, That God's un - fail - ing love is yours, That you the on - ly Son were giv - en, That by his
2 If you seem emp - ty of an - y feel - ing, Re - joice– you are his ran-somed bride! If those you cher - ish seem not to love you, And dark as - sails from ev - 'ry side, Still yours the prom - ise, come what may, In loss and tri - umph, in laugh - ter, cry - ing, In want and
3 It is a good ev - 'ry good tran-scend-ing That Christ has died for you and me! It is a glad - ness that has no end - ing There - in God's won-drous love to see! Praise be to you, O spot-less Lamb, Who thru the des - ert my soul are lead - ing To that fair

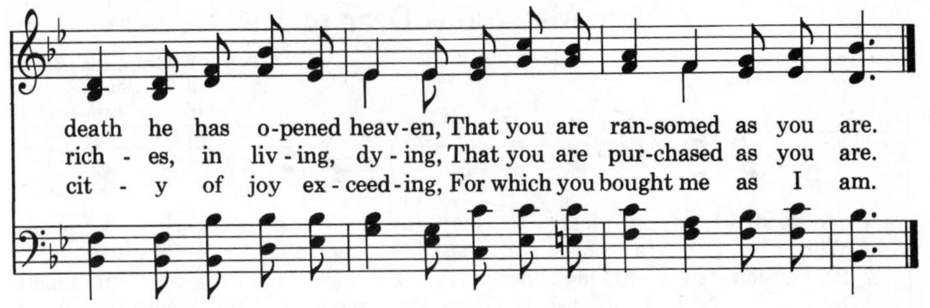
death he has o-pened heav-en, That you are ran-somed as you are.
rich - es, in liv - ing, dy - ing, That you are pur-chased as you are.
cit - y of joy ex - ceed - ing, For which you bought me as I am.

Ask Ye What Great Thing I Know 424

Based on 1 Corinthians 2:2
Johann C. Schwedler, 1672-1730
Tr. Benjamin H. Kennedy, 1804-1889

HENDON 7.7.7.7.7.
H. A. César Malan, 1787-1864

1 Ask ye what great thing I know That de - lights and stirs me so? What the high re - ward I win? Whose the name I glo - ry in? Je - sus Christ, the cru - ci - fied.

2 Who de - feats my fierc - est foes? Who con - soles my sad - dest woes? Who re - vives my faint - ing heart, Heal - ing all its hid - den smart? Je - sus Christ, the cru - ci - fied.

3 Who is life in life to me? Who the death of death will be? Who will place me on his right With the count - less hosts of light? Je - sus Christ, the cru - ci - fied.

4 This is that great thing I know, This de - lights and stirs me so: Faith in him who died to save, Him who tri - umphed o'er the grave— Je - sus Christ, the cru - ci - fied.

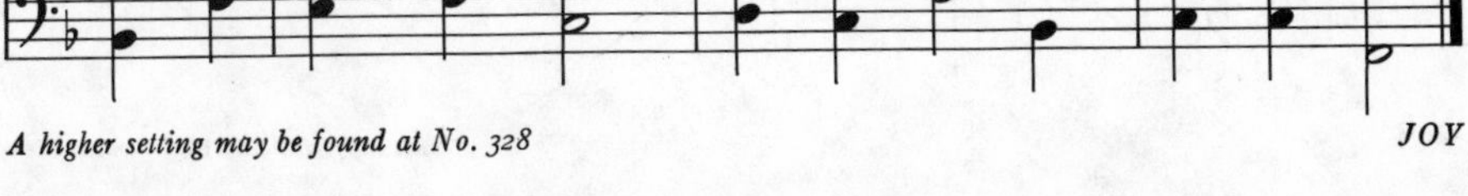

A higher setting may be found at No. 328

425 When My Lord Is Dear to Me

Nils Frykman, 1842-1911
Tr. Lennart E. Anderson, 1911-

PENNOCK 7.7.7.7. *with Refrain*
Nils Frykman, 1842-1911

1 When my Lord is dear to me, Joy is mine, wher-e'er I be,
2 When his peace a-bides with me, Joy is mine e-ter-nal-ly,
3 Peace, con-tent-ment, joy are mine, What a her-it-age di-vine!
4 Kept thru faith in Christ a-bove, Shel-tered in his arms of love,
Wheth-er dark and drear the way, Or, like E-den, fair as day.
When the sun shines fair and bright, When it shad-ows in-to night.
With that pearl su-preme-ly rare, Earth-ly gold can-not com-pare.
In what-ev-er may be-fall, He is now my all in all!
REFRAIN
Hal-le-lu-jah! Hal-le-lu-jah! Je-sus is my friend!
He is faith-ful to de-fend His re-deemed un-to the end.

JOY

I've Found a Friend, O Such a Friend! 426

James G. Small, 1817-1888

CONSTANCE 8.7.8.7.D.
Arthur S. Sullivan, 1842-1900

1 I've found a friend, O such a friend! He loved me ere I knew him;
2 I've found a friend, O such a friend! He bled, he died to save me;
3 I've found a friend, O such a friend! So kind and true and ten - der,
He drew me with the cords of love, And thus he bound me to him!
And not a - lone the gift of life, But his own self he gave me!
So wise a coun-sel - or and guide, So might - y a de- fend - er!
And round my heart still close - ly twine Those ties which naught can sev - er,
Naught that I have my own I call, I hold it for the giv - er:
From him who loves me now so well What pow'r my soul can sev - er?
For I am his, and he is mine, For - ev - er and for - ev - er.
My heart, my strength, my life, my all Are his, and his for - ev - er.
Shall life or death, shall earth or hell? No! I am his for - ev - er.

427 From Every Stormy Wind That Blows

Hugh Stowell, 1799-1865

RETREAT L.M.
Thomas Hastings, 1784-1872

1 From ev - 'ry storm - y wind that blows, From
2 There is a place where Je - sus sheds The
3 There is a place where spir - its blend, Where
4 Ah! there on ea - gle - wings we soar, Where

ev - 'ry swell - ing tide of woes, There is a calm, a
oil of glad - ness on our heads, A place than all be -
friend holds fel - low - ship with friend; Though sun - dered far, by
sin and sense mo - lest no more; For heav'n comes down our

sure re - treat: 'Tis found be - neath the mer - cy seat.
side more sweet: It is the blood-bought mer - cy seat.
faith they meet A - round one com - mon mer - cy seat.
souls to greet, And glo - ry crowns the mer - cy seat.

428 How Sweet the Name of Jesus Sounds

John Newton, 1725-1807, alt.

ST. PETER C.M.
Alexander R. Reinagle, 1799-1877

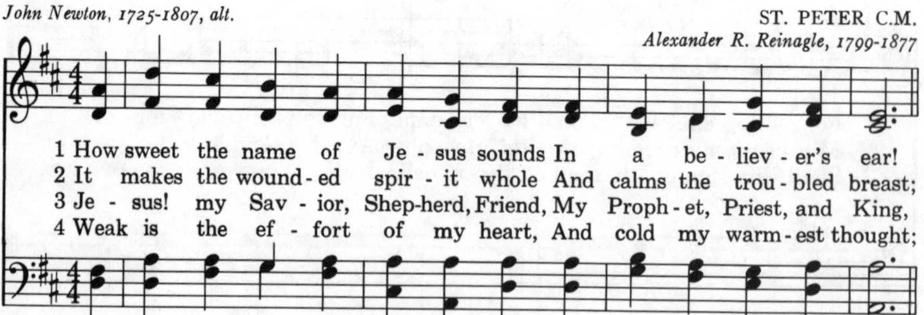
1 How sweet the name of Je - sus sounds In a be - liev - er's ear!
2 It makes the wound - ed spir - it whole And calms the trou - bled breast;
3 Je - sus! my Sav - ior, Shep-herd, Friend, My Proph - et, Priest, and King,
4 Weak is the ef - fort of my heart, And cold my warm - est thought;

A higher setting may be found at No. 485

It soothes his sor-rows, heals his wounds, And drives a-way his fear.
'Tis man-na to the hun-gry soul, And to the wea-ry rest.
My Lord, my Life, my Way, my End, Ac-cept the praise I bring.
But when I see thee as thou art, I'll praise thee as I ought. A-men.
Jesus, Keep Me Near the Cross
429
Fanny J. Crosby, 1820-1915
NEAR THE CROSS 7.6.7.6. with Refrain
William H. Doane, 1832-1915
1 Je-sus, keep me near the cross— There a pre-cious foun-tain,
2 Near the cross, a trem-bling soul, Love and mer-cy found me;
3 Near the cross! O Lamb of God, Bring its scenes be-fore me;
4 Near the cross I'll watch and wait, Hop-ing, trust-ing ev-er,
Free to all, a heal-ing stream, Flows from Cal-v'ry's moun-tain.
There the bright and morn-ing star Shed its beams a-round me.
Help me walk from day to day With its shad-ow o'er me.
Till I reach the gold-en strand Just be-yond the riv-er.
REFRAIN
In the cross, in the cross, Be my glo-ry ev-er,
Till my rap-tured soul shall find Rest be-yond the riv-er. A-men.

430 Jesus, I Am Resting, Resting

Jean Sophia Pigott, 1845-1882

TRANQUILLITY 8.7.8.5.D.
James Mountain, 1844-1933

1 Je - sus, I am rest - ing, rest - ing In the joy of what thou art;
I am find - ing out the great - ness Of thy lov - ing heart.
Thou hast bid me gaze up - on thee, And thy beau - ty fills my soul,
For by thy trans - form - ing pow - er Thou hast made me whole.

2 Sim - ply trust - ing thee, Lord Je - sus, I be - hold thee as thou art,
And thy love, so pure, so change - less, Sat - is - fies my heart—
Sat - is - fies its deep - est long - ings, Meets, sup - plies its ev - 'ry need,
Com - pass - es me round with bless - ings: Thine is love in - deed!

3 Ev - er lift thy face up - on me As I work and wait for thee;
Rest - ing 'neath thy smile, Lord Je - sus, Earth's dark shad - ows flee.
Bright - ness of my Fa - ther's glo - ry, Sun - shine of my Fa - ther's face,
Keep me ev - er trust - ing, rest - ing, Fill me with thy grace. A - men.

Love Divine, All Loves Excelling 431

Charles Wesley, 1707-1788, alt.

BEECHER 8.7.8.7.D.
John Zundel, 1815-1882

1 Love di - vine, all loves ex - cel - ling, Joy of heav'n to earth come down,
2 Breathe, O breathe thy lov - ing Spir - it In - to ev - 'ry trou - bled breast;
3 Come, Al - might - y to de - liv - er, Let us all thy life re - ceive;
4 Fin - ish then thy new cre - a - tion, Pure and spot - less let us be;
Fix in us thy hum - ble dwell - ing, All thy faith - ful mer - cies crown.
Let us all in thee in - her - it, Let us find thy prom - ised rest.
Sud - den - ly re - turn, and nev - er, Nev - er - more thy tem - ples leave.
Let us see thy great sal - va - tion Per - fect - ly re - stored in thee.
Je - sus, thou art all com - pas - sion, Pure, un - bound - ed love thou art;
Take a - way our bent to sin - ning, Al - pha and O - me - ga be;
Thee we would be al - ways bless - ing, Serve thee as thy hosts a - bove,
Changed from glo - ry in - to glo - ry, Till in heav'n we take our place,
Vis - it us with thy sal - va - tion, En - ter ev - 'ry trem - bling heart.
End of faith, as its be - gin - ning, Set our hearts at lib - er - ty.
Pray, and praise thee with - out ceas - ing, Glo - ry in thy per - fect love.
Till we cast our crowns be - fore thee, Lost in won - der, love, and praise. A - men.

Alternate tunes: HYFRYDOL, *No. 335;* BLAENWERN, *No. 96*

432 O the Deep, Deep Love of Jesus

Samuel Trevor Francis, 1834-1925
EBENEZER 8.7.8.7.D.
Thomas J. Williams, 1869-1944
1 O the deep, deep love of Je - sus, Vast, un - mea-sured,
2 O the deep, deep love of Je - sus— Spread his praise from
3 O the deep, deep love of Je - sus, Love of ev - 'ry
bound-less, free! Roll - ing as a might - y o - cean In its
shore to shore! How he lov - eth, ev - er lov - eth, Chang-eth
love the best! 'Tis an o - cean vast of bless-ing, 'Tis a
full - ness o - ver me! Un - der - neath me, all a - round me,
nev - er, nev - er - more! How he watch - es o'er his loved ones,
ha - ven sweet of rest! O the deep, deep love of Je - sus—
Is the cur - rent of thy love— Lead - ing on - ward,
Died to call them all his own; How for them he
'Tis a heav'n of heav'ns to me; And it lifts me

 A higher setting may be found at No. 367

3
3
lead - ing home-ward, To thy glo - rious rest a - bove!
in - ter - ced - eth, Watch-eth o'er them from the throne!
up to glo - ry, For it lifts me up to thee! A-men.
3

Jesus, Lord and Precious Savior **433**

Jakob Arrhenius, 1642-1725
Tr. Augustus Nelson, 1863-1949

KALMAR 8.7.8.7.7.7.
Swedish Melody, 1676

4/4

1 Je - sus, Lord and pre-cious Sav-ior, All my com-fort and my joy,
2 All I do, O let me ev - er, Je - sus, in thy name be - gin;
3 Let my words and thoughts, O Sav-ior, To thy praise and glo - ry tend;
4 When my days on earth are o - ver, Let me en - ter in - to rest;

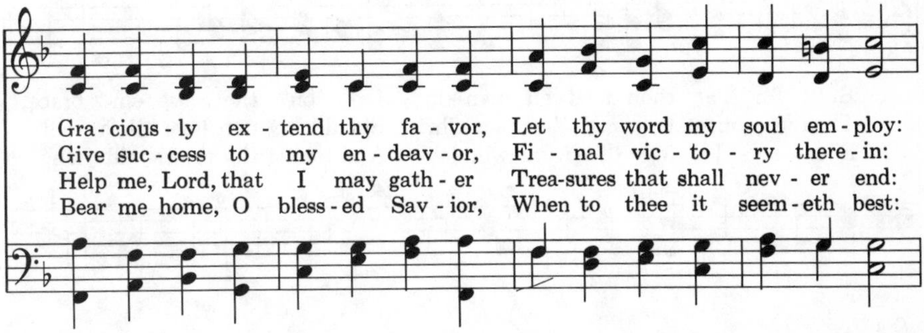

Gra-cious-ly ex - tend thy fa - vor, Let thy word my soul em - ploy:
Give suc-cess to my en-deav-or, Fi - nal vic - to - ry there - in:
Help me, Lord, that I may gath - er Trea-sures that shall nev - er end:
Bear me home, O bless-ed Sav-ior, When to thee it seem-eth best:

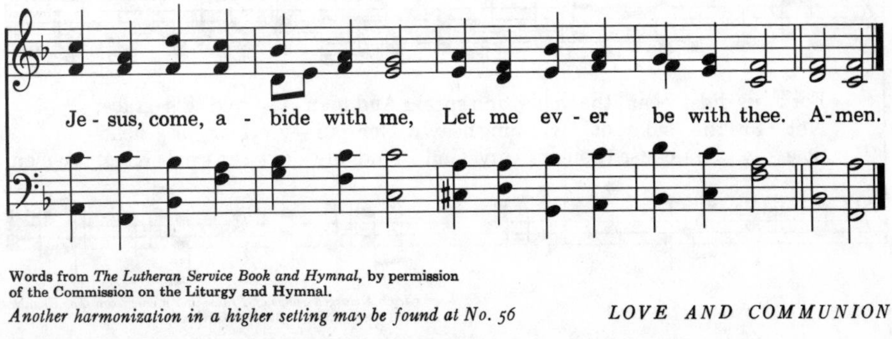

Je - sus, come, a - bide with me, Let me ev - er be with thee. A-men.

Words from *The Lutheran Service Book and Hymnal*, by permission of the Commission on the Liturgy and Hymnal.

Another harmonization in a higher setting may be found at No. 56

434 My God, I Love Thee

Attr. to Francis Xavier, 1506-1552
Tr. Edward Caswall, 1814-1878, alt.

KINGSFOLD C.M.D.
English Melody
Harm. by Ralph Vaughan Williams, 1872-1958

1 My God, I love thee—not because I hope for heav'n thereby,
Nor yet for fear that loving not I might forever die;
But for that thou didst all mankind Upon the cross embrace;
For us didst bear the nails and spear, And manifold disgrace;

2 And griefs and torments numberless, And sweat of agony;
E'en death itself—and all for man, Who was thine enemy.
Then why, most loving Jesus Christ, Should I not love thee well?
Not for the sake of winning heav'n, Nor any fear of hell;

3 Not with the hope of gaining aught, Not seeking a reward—
But as thyself hast loved me, O everloving Lord!
E'en so I love thee, and will love, And in thy praise will sing,
Solely because thou art my God And my eternal King! Amen.

O Jesus, Thy Boundless Love to Me

Paul Gerhardt, 1607-1676
Tr. John Wesley, 1703-1791

STELLA *Irregular*
English Melody
Hemy's "Easy Hymn Tunes," 1851
Harm. by A. Royce Eckhardt, 1937-

1 O Je-sus, thy bound-less love to me No thought can reach, no
2 O grant that noth - ing in my soul May dwell, but thy pure
3 O Love, how gra - cious is thy way! All fear be - fore thy
tongue de - clare; O knit my thank - ful heart to thee,
love a - lone; O may thy love pos - sess me whole,
pres - ence flies; Care, an - guish, sor - row, melt a - way,
And reign with - out a ri - val there! Thine whol - ly, thine a -
My joy, my treas - ure and my crown! All cold - ness from my
Wher - e'er thy heal - ing beams a - rise! O Je - sus, noth - ing
lone, I'd live, My - self to thee en - tire - ly give.
heart re - move: May ev - 'ry act, word, thought, be love.
may I see, And naught de - sire, or seek, but thee. A-men.

436 O Love That Wilt Not Let Me Go

George Matheson, 1842-1906
ST. MARGARET 8.8.8.8.6.
Albert L. Peace, 1844-1912
1 O Love that wilt not let me go, I rest my wea-ry
2 O Light that fol-l'west all my way, I yield my flick-'ring
3 O Joy that seek-est me thru pain, I can-not close my
4 O Cross that lift-est up my head, I dare not ask to
soul in thee; I give thee back the life I owe, That
torch to thee; My heart re-stores its bor-rowed ray, That
heart to thee; I trace the rain-bow thru the rain, And
fly from thee; I lay in dust life's glo-ry dead, And
in thine o-cean depths its flow May rich-er, full-er be.
in thy sun-shine's blaze its day May bright-er, fair-er be.
feel the prom-ise is not vain That morn shall tear-less be.
from the ground there blos-soms red Life that shall end-less be. A-men.
437 Jesus, the Very Thought of Thee
Latin: 12th century
Tr. Edward Caswall, 1814-1878, alt.
ST. AGNES C.M.
John B. Dykes, 1823-1876
1 Je-sus, the ver-y thought of thee With sweet-ness fills my breast;
2 No voice can sing, no heart can frame, Nor can the mem-'ry find
3 O hope of ev-'ry con-trite heart, O joy of all the meek,
4 But what to those who find? Ah, this Nor tongue nor pen can show;
5 Je-sus, our on-ly joy be thou, As thou our prize wilt be;

But sweet-er far thy face to see And in thy pres-ence rest.
A sweet-er sound than thy blest name, O Sav-ior of man-kind.
To those who fall, how kind thou art! How good to those who seek!
The love of Je-sus, what it is None but his loved ones know.
Je-sus, be thou our glo-ry now And thru e-ter-ni-ty. A-men.
LOVE AND COMMUNION
Jesus, Thou Joy of Loving Hearts
438
Attr. to Bernard of Clairvaux, 1091-1153
Tr. Ray Palmer, 1808-1887
QUEBEC L.M.
Henry Baker, 1835-1910
1 Je-sus, thou joy of lov-ing hearts, Thou fount of life, thou light of men, From the best bliss that earth im-parts We turn un-filled to thee a-gain.
2 Thy truth un-changed hath ev-er stood, Thou sav-est those that on thee call; To them that seek thee thou art good, To them that find thee, all in all.
3 We taste thee, O thou liv-ing bread, And long to feast up-on thee still; We drink of thee, the foun-tain-head, And thirst our souls from thee to fill.
4 Our rest-less spir-its yearn for thee, Wher-e'er our change-ful lot is cast: Glad when thy gra-cious smile we see, Blest when our faith can hold thee fast.
5 O Je-sus, ev-er with us stay, Make all our mo-ments calm and bright; Chase the dark night of sin a-way, Shed o'er the world thy ho-ly light. A-men.

A lower setting may be found at No. 600

439 I Need Thee Every Hour

Annie S. Hawks, 1835-1918
Robert Lowry, 1826-1899, Refrain

NEED 6.4.6.4. *with Refrain*
Robert Lowry, 1826-1899

1 I need thee ev - 'ry hour, Most gra - cious Lord;
2 I need thee ev - 'ry hour— Stay thou near by;
3 I need thee ev - 'ry hour, In joy or pain;
4 I need thee ev - 'ry hour— Teach me thy will,
No ten - der voice like thine Can peace af - ford.
Temp - ta - tions lose their pow'r When thou art nigh.
Come quick - ly, and a - bide, Or life is vain.
And thy rich prom - is - es In me ful - fill.
REFRAIN
I need thee, O I need thee; Ev - 'ry hour I need thee!
O bless me now, my Sav - ior— I come to thee. A - men.

Open My Eyes, That I May See

Clara H. Scott, 1841-1897

OPEN MY EYES 8.8.9.8.8.8.8.4.
Clara H. Scott, 1841-1897

1 O-pen my eyes, that I may see Glimp-ses of truth thou hast for me;
2 O-pen my ears, that I may hear Voic-es of truth thou send-est clear;
3 O-pen my mouth, and let me bear Glad-ly the warm truth ev-'ry-where;

Place in my hands the won-der-ful key That shall un-clasp and set me free.
And while the wave-notes fall on my ear, Ev-'ry-thing false will dis-ap-pear.
O-pen my heart, and let me pre-pare Love with thy chil-dren thus to share.

Si-lent-ly now I wait for thee, Read-y, my God, thy will to see;

O-pen my eyes, il-lu-mine me, Spir-it di-vine!
O-pen my ears, il-lu-mine me, Spir-it di-vine!
O-pen my heart, il-lu-mine me, Spir-it di-vine! A-men.

441 If I Gained the World

Anna Ölander, 1861-1939
Tr. composite

TRUE RICHES 10.9.10.9.D.
Swedish Melody

1 If I gained the world but lost the Sav - ior, Were my life worth
2 Had I wealth and love in full - est meas - ure, And a name re -
3 O what emp - ti - ness with - out the Sav - ior Mid the sins and
4 O the joy of hav - ing all in Je - sus! What a balm the
liv - ing for a day? Could my yearn - ing heart find rest and
vered both far and near, Yet no hope be - yond, no har - bor
sor - rows here be - low! And e - ter - ni - ty, how dark with -
bro - ken heart to heal! Ne'er a sin so great but he'll for -
com - fort In the things that soon must pass a - way?
wait - ing Where my storm - tossed ves - sel I could steer—
out him— On - ly night and tears and end - less woe!
give it, Nor a sor - row that he does not feel!
If I gained the world, but lost the Sav - ior, Would my gain be
If I gained the world, but lost the Sav - ior, Who en - dured the
What tho I might live with - out the Sav - ior, When I come to
If I have but Je - sus, on - ly Je - sus, Noth - ing else in

worth the life-long strife? Are all earth-ly pleas-ures worth com-
cross and died for me, Could then all the world af-ford a
die, how would it be? O to face the val-ley's gloom with-
all the world be - side, O then ev - 'ry - thing is mine in

par - ing For a mo-ment with a Christ-filled life?
ref - uge, Whith - er in my an - guish I might flee?
out him! And with-out him all e - ter - ni - ty!
Je - sus— For my needs and more he will pro - vide.

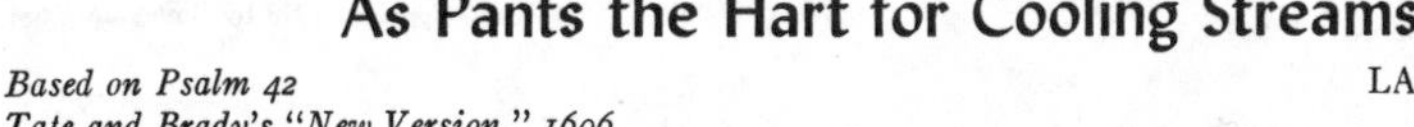

As Pants the Hart for Cooling Streams 442

Based on Psalm 42
Tate and Brady's "New Version," 1696

LAND OF REST C.M.
American Melody
Harm. by Norman E. Johnson, 1928-

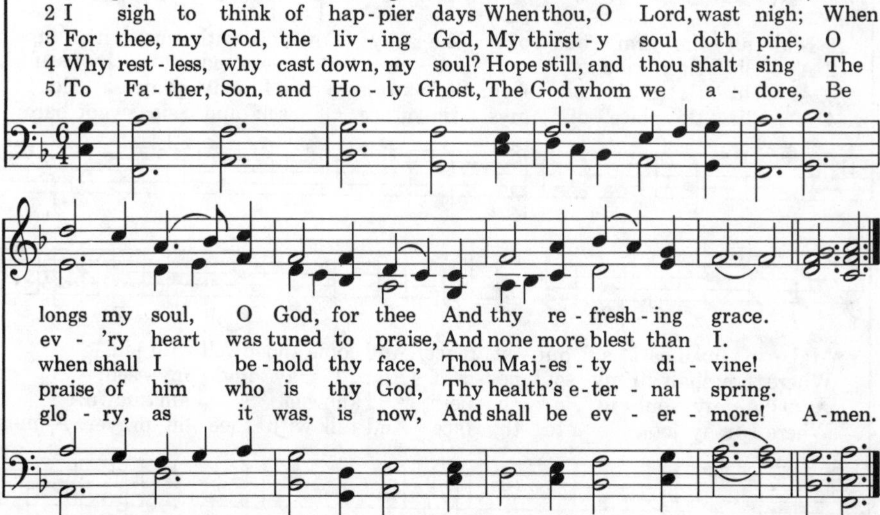

In unison 
1 As pants the hart for cool-ing streams When heat-ed in the chase, So
2 I sigh to think of hap-pier days When thou, O Lord, wast nigh; When
3 For thee, my God, the liv - ing God, My thirst - y soul doth pine; O
4 Why rest - less, why cast down, my soul? Hope still, and thou shalt sing The
5 To Fa - ther, Son, and Ho - ly Ghost, The God whom we a - dore, Be
longs my soul, O God, for thee And thy re - fresh - ing grace.
ev - 'ry heart was tuned to praise, And none more blest than I.
when shall I be - hold thy face, Thou Maj - es - ty di - vine!
praise of him who is thy God, Thy health's e - ter - nal spring.
glo - ry, as it was, is now, And shall be ev - er - more! A-men.

Alternate tune: MARTYRDOM, *No. 186*

443 Father of Love, Our Guide and Friend

William J. Irons, 1812-1883 GROVELAND C.M.
James P. Davies, 1913-

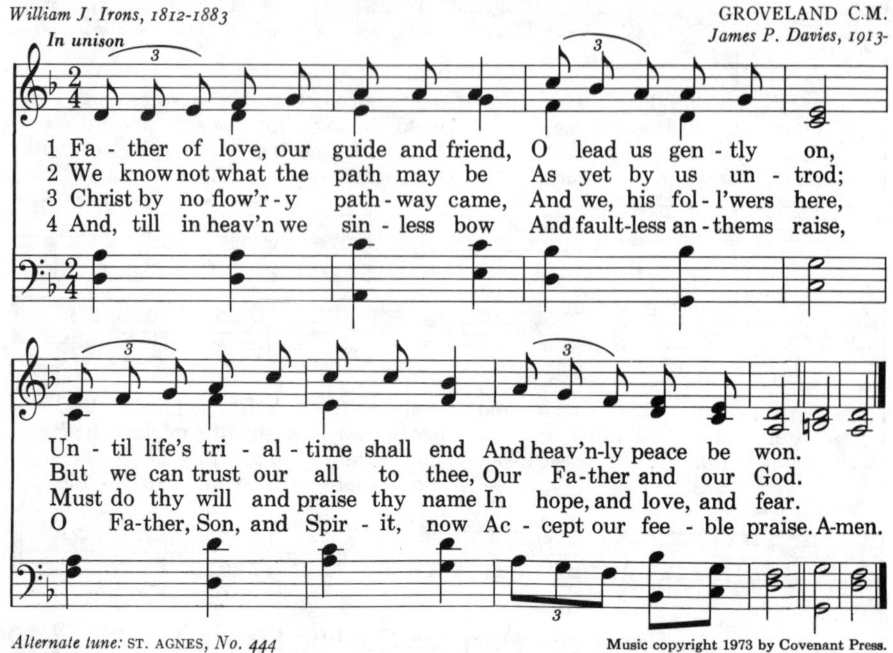
In unison
1 Fa - ther of love, our guide and friend, O lead us gen - tly on,
2 We know not what the path may be As yet by us un - trod;
3 Christ by no flow'r - y path - way came, And we, his fol - l'wers here,
4 And, till in heav'n we sin - less bow And fault-less an - thems raise,
Un - til life's tri - al - time shall end And heav'n-ly peace be won.
But we can trust our all to thee, Our Fa-ther and our God.
Must do thy will and praise thy name In hope, and love, and fear.
O Fa-ther, Son, and Spir - it, now Ac - cept our fee - ble praise. A-men.

Alternate tune: ST. AGNES, *No. 444*

444 Mid All the Traffic of the Ways

John Oxenham, 1852-1941 ST. AGNES C.M.
John B. Dykes, 1823-1876

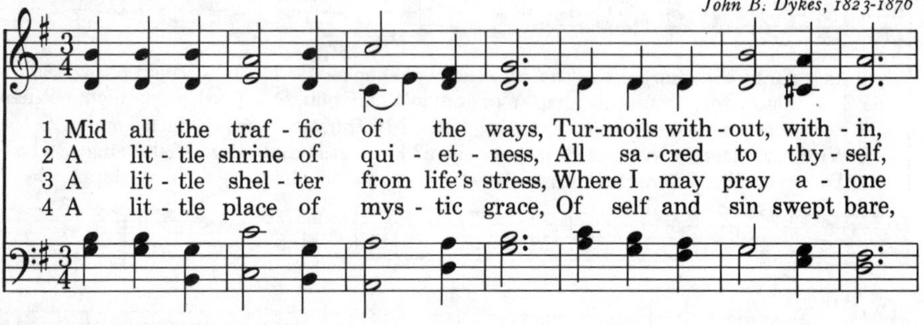

1 Mid all the traf - fic of the ways, Tur-moils with - out, with - in,
2 A lit - tle shrine of qui - et - ness, All sa - cred to thy - self,
3 A lit - tle shel - ter from life's stress, Where I may pray a - lone
4 A lit - tle place of mys - tic grace, Of self and sin swept bare,

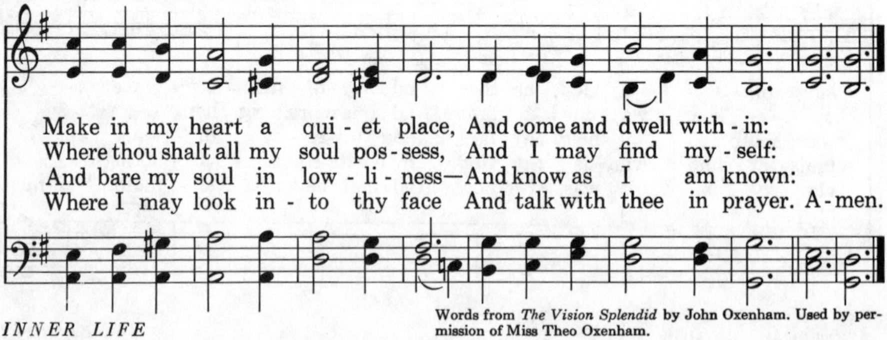

Make in my heart a qui - et place, And come and dwell with - in:
Where thou shalt all my soul pos - sess, And I may find my - self:
And bare my soul in low - li - ness—And know as I am known:
Where I may look in - to thy face And talk with thee in prayer. A - men.

Watch, My Soul, and Pray

Johann Olof Wallin, 1779-1839
Tr. Carl Doving, 1867-1937

SEELENBRÄUTIGAM 5.5.8.8.5.5.
Adam Drese, 1620-1701

1 Watch, my soul, and pray, Arm for life's af - fray!
2 Watch and pray, my soul, Flesh and blood con - trol!
3 See the good - ly land On the heav'n - ly strand!
4 Through thy pil - grim - age Guard thy her - i - tage!
5 Watch and fight and pray Through this mor - tal day!
When the dan - ger least thou fear - est,
When the world, in tempt - ing sto - ry,
See God's peo - ple, thith - er tend - ing,
Pray and fight, on Christ re - ly - ing,
Soon thy Ca - naan thou at - tain - est,
Watch, the tempt - er's snares are near - est;
Tells of pleas - ure, wealth, and glo - ry,
Through the sea and des - ert wend - ing,
Live to him, thy - self de - ny - ing;
Soon the crown and palm thou gain - est,
Such is e'er his way: Watch, my soul, and pray.
Be not led a - stray: Watch, my soul, and pray.
Led by Josh - ua's hand: Seek the good - ly land.
On - ward to the goal: Win the crown, my soul.
Peace is won for aye: Watch, my soul, and pray.

Words used by permission of Fortress Press.

Once Far from God and Dead in Sin

Daniel W. Whittle, 1840-1901

CHRIST LIVETH IN ME C.M. *with Refrain*
James McGranahan, 1840-1907

1 Once far from God and dead in sin, No light my heart could see;
But in God's word the light I found, Now Christ liv-eth in me.

2 As rays of light from yon-der sun The flow'rs of earth set free,
So life and light and love came forth From Christ liv-ing in me.

3 As lives the flow'r with-in the seed, As in the cone the tree,
So, praise the God of truth and grace, His Spir-it dwell-eth in me.

4 With long-ing all my heart is filled That like him I may be,
As on the won-drous thought I dwell, That Christ liv-eth in me.

REFRAIN

Christ liv-eth in me, Christ liv-eth in me;
O what a sal-va-tion this, That Christ liv-eth in me!

There Is a Place of Quiet Rest

Cleland B. McAfee, 1866-1944

McAFEE C.M. *with Refrain*
Cleland B. McAfee, 1866-1944

1 There is a place of qui - et rest, Near to the heart of God,
A place where sin can - not mo - lest, Near to the heart of God.

2 There is a place of com - fort sweet, Near to the heart of God,
A place where we our Sav - ior meet, Near to the heart of God.

3 There is a place of full re - lease, Near to the heart of God,
A place where all is joy and peace, Near to the heart of God.

REFRAIN

O Je - sus, blest Re - deem - er, Sent from the heart of God,
Hold us, who wait be - fore thee, Near to the heart of God. A-men.

448 Make Room Within My Heart, O God

Bryan Jeffery Leech, 1931-

MASSACHUSETTS C.M.D.
Katherine K. Davis, 1892-

In unison
1 Make room with-in my heart, O God, That you may form in me
2 Di - rect my will, O King of kings, Sub - ject it to your own,
The im - age you have shown in Christ, My ver - y life to be.
That ev - 'ry im - pulse, ac - tion, word, May make your king - dom known.
In - spire my thought, O loft - y One, To reach the high - est plane,
Ef - fect my prayer, great Trin - i - ty, E - ter - nal Three-in - One;
That I may know the mind of Christ, And him as great - est gain.
Com - bine each part of me to praise The Fa - ther, Spir - it, Son. A - men.

Thou True Vine That Heals the Nations

Based on John 15:1-8
Percy Dearmer, 1867-1936

PLEADING SAVIOR 8.7.8.7.D.
"The Christian Lyre," 1831
Harm. by Norman E. Johnson, 1928-

In unison
1 Thou true Vine that heals the na-tions, Tree of life, thy branch-es we;
2 Noth-ing can we do with-out thee—On thy life de-pends each one;
They who leave thee fade and with-er, None bear fruit ex-cept in thee.
If we keep thy words and love thee, All we ask for shall be done.
Cleanse us, make us sane and sim-ple, Till we merge our lives in thine,
May we, lov-ing one an-oth-er, Ra-diant in thy light a-bide;
Gain our-selves in thee, the Vin-tage, Give our-selves thru thee, the Vine.
So thru us, made fruit-ful by thee, Shall our God be glo-ri-fied. A-men.

450 When We Walk with the Lord

James H. Sammis, 1846-1919 TRUST AND OBEY 6.6.9.D. *with Refrain*
Daniel B. Towner, 1850-1919

1 When we walk with the Lord In the light of his word, What a
2 Not a shad - ow can rise, Not a cloud in the skies, But his
3 Not a bur - den we bear, Not a sor - row we share, But our
4 Then in fel - low - ship sweet We will sit at his feet, Or we'll
glo - ry he sheds on our way! While we do his good will, He a -
smile quick - ly drives it a - way; Not a doubt nor a fear, Not a
toil he doth rich - ly re - pay; Not a grief nor a loss, Not a
walk by his side in the way; What he says we will do, Where he
bides with us still, And with all who will trust and o - bey.
sigh nor a tear, Can a - bide while we trust and o - bey.
frown nor a cross, But is blest if we trust and o - bey.
sends we will go— Nev - er fear, on - ly trust and o - bey.
REFRAIN
Trust and o - bey, for there's no oth - er way To be
hap - py in Je - sus, But to trust and o - bey.

 Alternate tune: ELFÅKER, *No. 307* *(omitting the refrain)*

451 O for a Closer Walk with God

William Cowper, 1731-1800
BEATITUDO C.M.
John B. Dykes, 1823-1876
1 O for a clos-er walk with God, A calm and heav'n-ly frame,
A light to shine up-on the road That leads me to the Lamb!
2 Where is the bless-ed-ness I knew When first I saw the Lord?
Where is the soul-re-fresh-ing view Of Je-sus and his word?
3 Re-turn, O ho-ly Dove, re-turn, Sweet mes-sen-ger of rest;
I hate the sins that made thee mourn And drove thee from my breast.
4 The dear-est i-dol I have known, What-e'er that i-dol be,
Help me to tear it from thy throne And wor-ship on-ly thee.
5 So shall my walk be close with God, Calm and se-rene my frame;
So pur-er light shall mark the road That leads me to the Lamb. A-men.
We Walk by Faith and Not by Sight
452
Based on John 20:27-29
Henry Alford, 1810-1871
WINCHESTER OLD C.M.
Thomas Este's "The Whole Book of Psalms," 1592
1 We walk by faith and not by sight: No gra-cious words we hear
From him who spake as man ne'er spake–But we be-lieve him near.
2 We may not touch his hands and side, Nor fol-low where he trod;
But in his prom-ise we re-joice, And cry, "My Lord and God!"
3 Help then, O Lord, our un-be-lief! And may our faith a-bound
To call on thee when thou art near And seek where thou art found:
4 That, when our life of faith is done, In realms of clear-er light
We may be-hold thee as thou art, With full and end-less sight. A-men.

Alternate tune: ARLINGTON, No. 321

453 All the Way My Savior Leads Me

Fanny J. Crosby, 1820-1915

ALL THE WAY 8.7.8.7.D.
Robert Lowry, 1826-1899
Harm. by James P. Davies, 1913-

In unison
1 All the way my Sav-ior leads me—What have I to ask be-side?
2 All the way my Sav-ior leads me—Cheers each wind-ing path I tread,
3 All the way my Sav-ior leads me—O the full-ness of his love!
Can I doubt his ten-der mer-cy, Who thru life has been my guide?
Gives me grace for ev-'ry tri-al, Feeds me with the liv-ing bread.
Per-fect rest to me is prom-ised In my Fa-ther's house a-bove.
Heav'n-ly peace, di-vin-est com-fort, Here by faith in him to dwell!
Though my wea-ry steps may fal-ter And my soul a-thirst may be,
When my spir-it, clothed im-mor-tal, Wings its flight to realms of day,
For I know, what-e'er be-fall me, Je-sus do-eth all things well;
Gush-ing from the Rock be-fore me, Lo! a spring of joy I see;
This my song thru end-less a-ges: Je-sus led me all the way;

For I know, what-e'er be - fall me, Je - sus do - eth all things well.
Gush-ing from the Rock be - fore me, Lo! a spring of joy I see.
This my song thru end - less a - ges: Je - sus led me all the way.

God Gives His People Strength! 454

Miriam Therese Winter, 1938-

VANGUARD *Irregular*
Miriam Therese Winter, 1938-

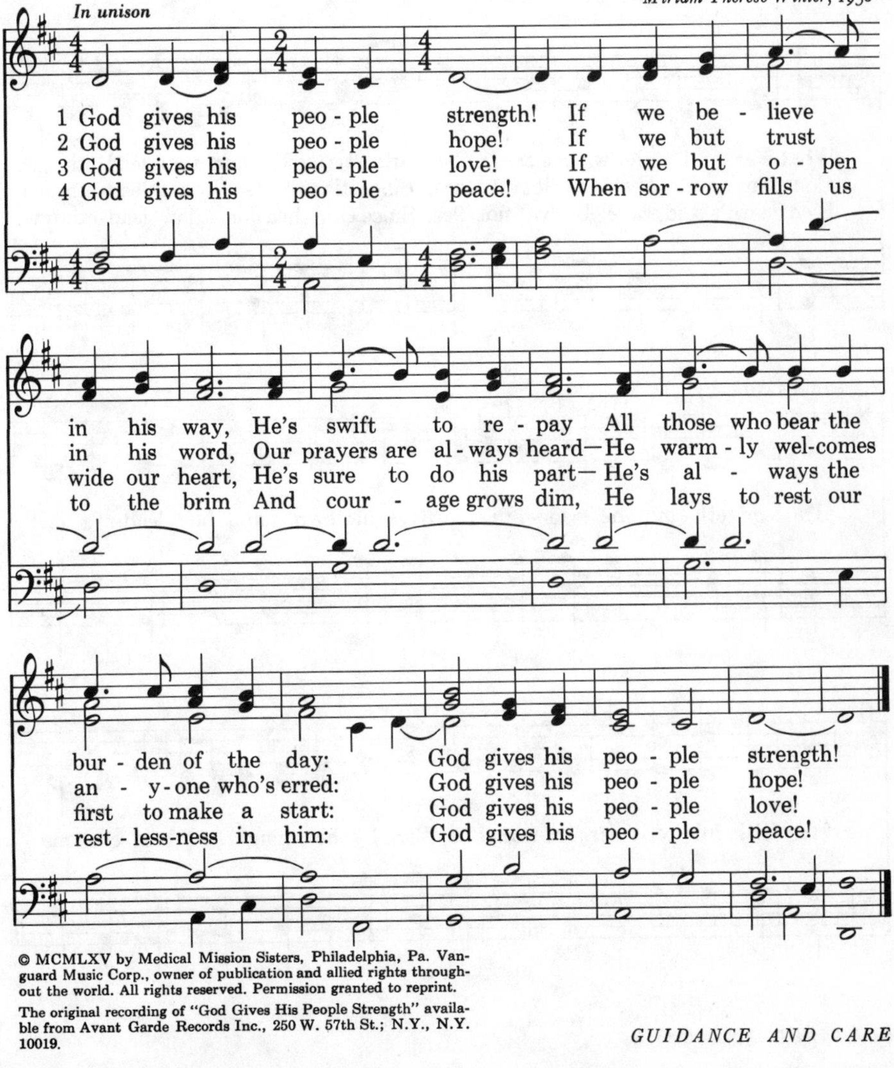

In unison

1 God gives his peo - ple strength! If we be - lieve
2 God gives his peo - ple hope! If we but trust
3 God gives his peo - ple love! If we but o - pen
4 God gives his peo - ple peace! When sor - row fills us

in his way, He's swift to re - pay All those who bear the
in his word, Our prayers are al - ways heard—He warm - ly wel-comes
wide our heart, He's sure to do his part—He's al - ways the
to the brim And cour - age grows dim, He lays to rest our

bur - den of the day: God gives his peo - ple strength!
an - y - one who's erred: God gives his peo - ple hope!
first to make a start: God gives his peo - ple love!
rest - less-ness in him: God gives his peo - ple peace!

The original recording of "God Gives His People Strength" available from Avant Garde Records Inc., 250 W. 57th St.; N.Y., N.Y. 10019.

455 He Leadeth Me, O Blessed Thought!

Joseph H. Gilmore, 1834-1918
HE LEADETH ME L.M. with Refrain
William B. Bradbury, 1816-1868
1 He lead-eth me, O bless-ed thought! O words with heav'n-ly com-fort fraught!
2 Lord, I would clasp thy hand in mine, Nor ev - er mur - mur nor re-pine;
3 And when my task on earth is done, When by thy grace the vic-t'ry's won,
What-e'er I do, wher-e'er I be, Still 'tis God's hand that lead-eth me.
Con-tent, what-ev - er lot I see, Since 'tis my God that lead-eth me.
E'en death's cold wave I will not flee, Since God thru Jor - dan lead-eth me.
REFRAIN
He lead-eth me, he lead - eth me, By his own hand he lead-eth me;
His faith-ful fol-l'wer I would be, For by his hand he lead-eth me.

If Thou But Suffer God to Guide Thee 456

Georg Neumark, 1621-1681
Tr. Catherine Winkworth, 1827-1878

NEUMARK 9.8.9.8.8.8.
Georg Neumark, 1621-1681

1 If thou but suf - fer God to guide thee, And hope in
2 On - ly be still and wait his lei - sure In cheer - ful
3 Sing, pray, and keep his ways un - swerv - ing— So do thine
him through all thy ways, He'll give thee strength, what-e'er be - tide thee,
hope, with heart con - tent To take what-e'er thy Fa - ther's pleas-ure
own part faith - ful - ly; And trust his word, though un - de - serv - ing—
And bear thee through the e - vil days; Who trusts in God's un-
And all - de - serv - ing love have sent; Nor doubt our in - most
Thou yet shalt find it true for thee; God nev - er yet for-
chang - ing love Builds on the rock that nought can move.
wants are known To him who chose us for his own.
sook at need The soul that trust - ed him in - deed. A-men.

457 Jesus Lives and Jesus Leads

Edwin Paxton Hood, 1820-1885

VARNDEAN 7.6.7.6.7.7.
Erik R. Routley, 1917-

1 Je - sus lives and Je - sus leads, Though the way be drear - y;
2 All the words he ev - er spoke Still to us he speak - eth;
3 Je - sus lives, but Je - sus died—Love to death con - signed him;
4 Je - sus lives, and ev - 'ry grace Comes be-cause he giv - eth;
Morn to dark-est night suc - ceeds—Cour-age, then, ye wea - ry:
All the bread he ev - er broke Still for us he break - eth:
Death the might-y love re - signed, Could not hold or bind him:
Life and love in ev - 'ry place Live, for Je - sus liv - eth:
Still the faith-ful shep-herd feeds— Je - sus lives and Je - sus leads.
Still the faith-ful shep-herd feeds— Je - sus lives and Je - sus leads.
There-fore still he meets our needs— Je - sus lives and Je - sus leads.
All our thoughts his love ex - ceeds— Je - sus lives and Je - sus leads.
Music used by permission of Erik R. Routley.
458 We Search the Starlit Milky Way
William W. Reid, 1890-
EWHURST 8.8.8.7.
Cecil J. Allen, 1886-
1 We search the star-lit Milk - y Way, A mil-lion worlds in rhyth-mic sway,
2 But as I grope from sphere to sphere, New won-ders crowd the eye, the ear,
3 We probe the at - oms for their cause, Ex - plore the earth for na-ture's laws,
4 Each flash of fact from out the night, Each burst of truth up - on my sight

Yet in our blind-ness some will say, "There is no God con - trol - ling!"
And faith grows firm-er ev - 'ry year: "My God is there, con - trol - ling!"
Yet sel - dom in our search-ing pause To think of God con - trol - ling.
That quick-ens awe or adds de - light, Re - veals my God con - trol - ling.
Jesus, Still Lead On
459
Nicolaus L. von Zinzendorf, 1700-1760
Tr. Jane L. Borthwick, 1813-1897
SEELENBRÄUTIGAM 5.5.8.8.5.5.
Adam Drese, 1620-1701
1 Je - sus, still lead on, Till our rest be won; And, al -
2 If the way be drear, If the foe be near, Let not
3 When we seek re - lief From a long - felt grief, When temp -
4 Je - sus, still lead on, Till our rest be won; Heav'n-ly
though the way be cheer - less, We will fol - low, calm and fear - less:
faith - less fears o'er-take us, Let not faith and hope for - sake us:
ta - tions come al - lur - ing, Make us pa - tient and en - dur - ing:
Lead - er, still di - rect us, Still sup - port, con - sole, pro - tect us,
Guide us by thy hand To our fa - ther - land.
For through man - y a foe To our home we go.
Show us that bright shore Where we weep no more.
Till we safe - ly stand In our fa - ther - land! A - men.

460 Lead Us, Heavenly Father, Lead Us

James Edmeston, 1791-1867
DULCE CARMEN 8.7.8.7.8.7.
"An Essay on the Church Plain Chant," 1782
1 Lead us, heav'n - ly Fa - ther, lead us O'er the world's tem -
2 Sav - ior, breathe for - give - ness o'er us— All our weak - ness
3 Spir - it of our God, de - scend - ing, Fill our hearts with
pes - tuous sea; Guard us, guide us, keep us, feed us,
thou dost know; Thou didst tread this earth be - fore us,
heav'n - ly joy, Love, all oth - er love trans - cend - ing,
For we have no help but thee: Yet pos - sess - ing
Thou didst feel its keen - est woe: Lone and drear - y,
Plea - sure that can nev - er cloy: Thus pro - vid - ed,
ev - 'ry bless - ing, If our God our Fa - ther be.
faint and wea - ry, Thru the des - ert thou didst go.
par - doned, guid - ed, Noth - ing can our peace de - stroy. A - men.

O Savior, Thou Who for Us Died

461

Anders Carl Rutström, 1721-1772
Tr. E. Gustav Johnson, 1893-

NUN FREUT EUCH 8.7.8.7.8.8.7.
Joseph Klug's "Geistliche Lieder," Wittenberg, 1535

1 O Sav-ior, thou who for us died, Come be our shep-herd ten-der;
Thy flock to liv-ing wa-ters guide, Be thou our true de-fend-er.
To Zi-on's ver-dant slopes now lead, Where all thy sheep may
safe-ly feed—Thus in thy keep-ing hold us.
2 O love un-bound-ed, pour thy balm Up-on our hu-man an-guish;
With strength of peace our fears be-calm, Our dark fore-bod-ings van-quish.
O thou whose mer-cy is com-plete, Trans-form our cold to
fer-vent heat, That we may serve thee whol-ly. A-men.

462 Lord, As a Pilgrim

Wilhelmi Malmivaara, 1854-1922
Paraphrase, Ernest Edwin Ryden, 1886-
Based on tr. by Aino Lilja Kantonen-Halkola, 1901-

PILGRIM SONG 9.9.5.5.4.
Ernest August Hagfors, 1827-1913
Harm. by Norman E. Johnson, 1928-

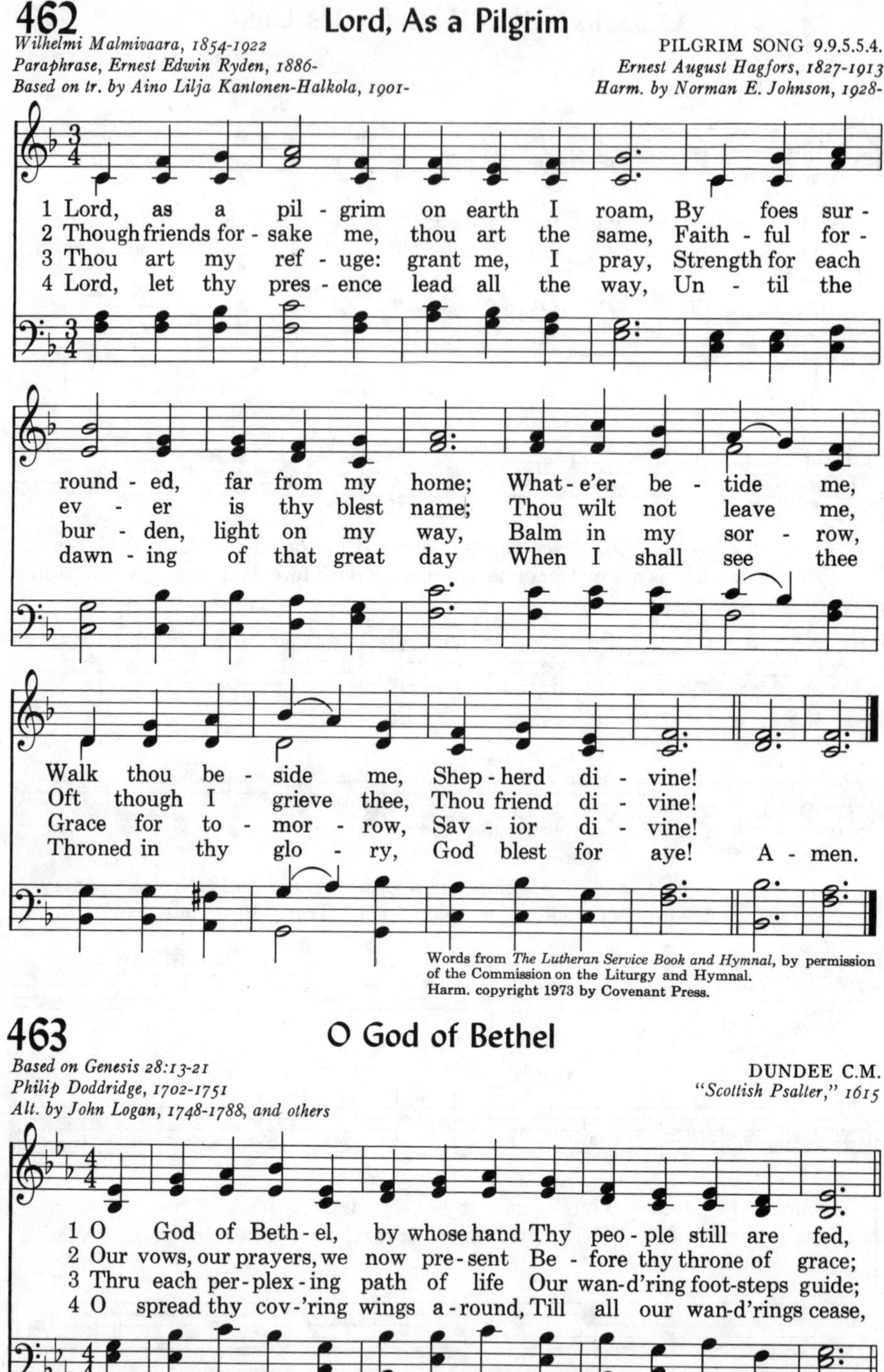
1 Lord, as a pil - grim on earth I roam, By foes sur - round - ed, far from my home; What - e'er be - tide me, Walk thou be - side me, Shep - herd di - vine!
2 Though friends for - sake me, thou art the same, Faith - ful for - ev - er is thy blest name; Thou wilt not leave me, Oft though I grieve thee, Thou friend di - vine!
3 Thou art my ref - uge: grant me, I pray, Strength for each bur - den, light on my way, Balm in my sor - row, Grace for to - mor - row, Sav - ior di - vine!
4 Lord, let thy pres - ence lead all the way, Un - til the dawn - ing of that great day When I shall see thee Throned in thy glo - ry, God blest for aye! A - men.

Words from *The Lutheran Service Book and Hymnal*, by permission of the Commission on the Liturgy and Hymnal.
Harm. copyright 1973 by Covenant Press.

463 O God of Bethel

Based on Genesis 28:13-21
Philip Doddridge, 1702-1751
Alt. by John Logan, 1748-1788, and others

DUNDEE C.M.
"Scottish Psalter," 1615

1 O God of Beth - el, by whose hand Thy peo - ple still are fed,
2 Our vows, our prayers, we now pre - sent Be - fore thy throne of grace;
3 Thru each per - plex - ing path of life Our wan - d'ring foot - steps guide;
4 O spread thy cov - 'ring wings a - round, Till all our wan - d'rings cease,

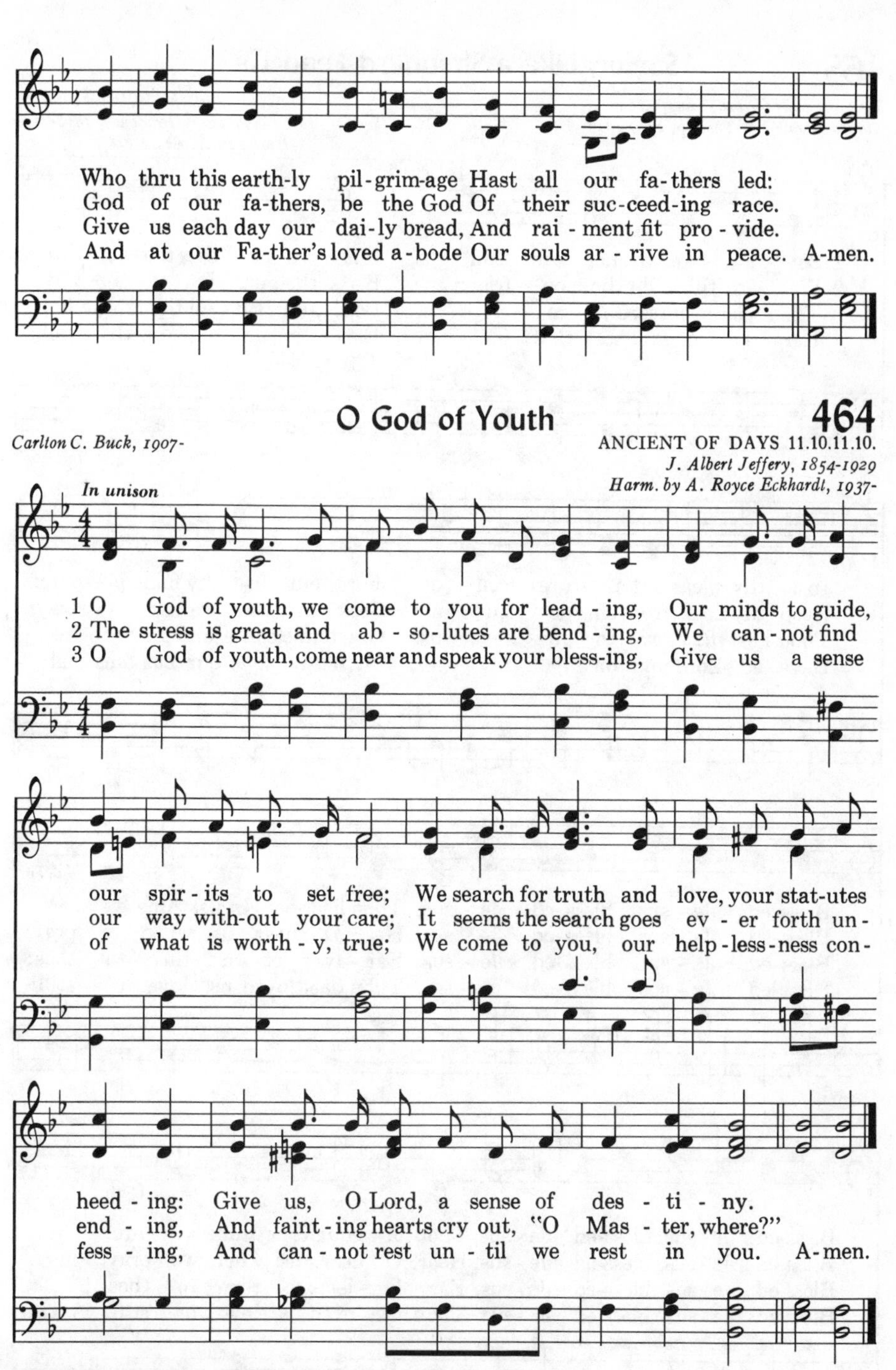
Who thru this earth-ly pil-grim-age Hast all our fa-thers led:
God of our fa-thers, be the God Of their suc-ceed-ing race.
Give us each day our dai-ly bread, And rai - ment fit pro - vide.
And at our Fa-ther's loved a-bode Our souls ar - rive in peace. A-men.
O God of Youth
464
Carlton C. Buck, 1907-
ANCIENT OF DAYS 11.10.11.10.
J. Albert Jeffery, 1854-1929
Harm. by A. Royce Eckhardt, 1937-
In unison
1 O God of youth, we come to you for lead - ing, Our minds to guide,
2 The stress is great and ab - so-lutes are bend - ing, We can-not find
3 O God of youth, come near and speak your bless-ing, Give us a sense
our spir-its to set free; We search for truth and love, your stat-utes
our way with-out your care; It seems the search goes ev - er forth un-
of what is worth - y, true; We come to you, our help-less-ness con-
heed - ing: Give us, O Lord, a sense of des - ti - ny.
end - ing, And faint-ing hearts cry out, "O Mas - ter, where?"
fess - ing, And can-not rest un - til we rest in you. A-men.

A higher setting may be found at No. 272
Alternate tune: CHARTERHOUSE, *No. 280*

465 Savior, Like a Shepherd Lead Us

From "Hymns for the Young," 1836
Attr. to Dorothy A. Thrupp, 1779-1847
BRADBURY 8.7.8.7.D.
William B. Bradbury, 1816-1868
Harm. by A. Royce Eckhardt, 1937-
1 Sav - ior, like a shep-herd lead us, Much we need thy ten-der care;
2 We are thine, do thou be - friend us, Be the guard-ian of our way;
3 Thou hast prom-ised to re - ceive us, Poor and sin - ful though we be;
4 Ear - ly let us seek thy fa - vor, Ear - ly let us do thy will;
In thy pleas-ant pas-tures feed us, For our use thy folds pre-pare:
Keep thy flock, from sin de - fend us, Seek us when we go a - stray:
Thou hast mer - cy to re - lieve us, Grace to cleanse and pow'r to free:
Bless - ed Lord and on - ly Sav - ior, With thy love our bos-oms fill:
Bless-ed Je - sus, bless-ed Je - sus, Thou hast bought us, thine we are;
Bless-ed Je - sus, bless-ed Je - sus, Hear, O hear us, when we pray;
Bless-ed Je - sus, bless-ed Je - sus, Ear - ly let us turn to thee;
Bless-ed Je - sus, bless-ed Je - sus, Thou hast loved us, love us still;
Bless-ed Je - sus, bless-ed Je - sus, Thou hast bought us, thine we are.
Bless-ed Je - sus, bless-ed Je - sus, Hear, O hear us, when we pray.
Bless-ed Je - sus, bless-ed Je - sus, Ear - ly let us turn to thee.
Bless-ed Je - sus, bless-ed Je - sus, Thou hast loved us, love us still. A-men.

Alternate tune: SICILIAN MARINERS, *No. 60*

Take Thou My Hand, O Father

Julie Katharina Hausmann, 1825-1901
Tr. Herman Brückner, 1866-1942, alt.
SO NIMM DENN MEINE HÄNDE 7.4.7.4.D.
Friedrich Silcher, 1789-1860
1 Take thou my hand, O Fa - ther, And lead thou me,
2 O cov - er with thy mer - cy My poor, weak heart!
3 Though oft thy pow'r but faint - ly May stir my soul,
Un - til my jour - ney end - eth E - ter - nal - ly.
Let ev - 'ry thought re - bel - lious From me de - part.
With thee, thru night and dark - ness, I reach the goal.
A - lone I would not wan - der One sin - gle day;
Per - mit thy child to lin - ger Here at thy feet,
Take, then, my hand, O Fa - ther, And lead thou me
Be thou my true com - pan - ion And with me stay.
And blind - ly trust thy good - ness With faith com - plete.
Un - til my jour - ney end - eth E - ter - nal - ly. A-men.

467 Jesus, Where'er Thy People Meet

William Cowper, 1731-1800

STUART L.M.
Bonnevieve M. Opel, 1915-

1 Je - sus, wher - e'er thy peo - ple meet, There they be - hold thy mer - cy seat; Wher - e'er they seek thee, thou art found, And ev - 'ry place is hal - lowed ground.
2 And since, with - in no walls con - fined, Thou dwell - est in the hum - ble mind; Let all with - in thy house who come, De - part - ing take thee to their home.
3 Great Shep-herd of thy cho - sen few, Thy for - mer mer - cies here re - new; Here to our wait - ing hearts pro - claim The sweet - ness of thy sav - ing name.
4 Here may we prove the pow'r of prayer To strength-en faith and sweet - en care, To teach our faint de - sires to rise, And bring all heav'n be - fore our eyes. A - men.

Alternate tune: FEDERAL STREET, No. 506

468 Great Shepherd of Thy People, Hear

John Newton, 1725-1807

SHELL LAKE C.M.
Harry P. Opel, 1921-

1 Great Shep-herd of thy peo - ple, hear—Thy pres-ence now dis - play; As
2 With - in these walls let ho - ly peace And love and con-cord dwell; Here
3 May we in faith re - ceive thy word, In faith pre-sent our prayers, And
4 The hear-ing ear, the see - ing eye, The con-trite heart be - stow; And

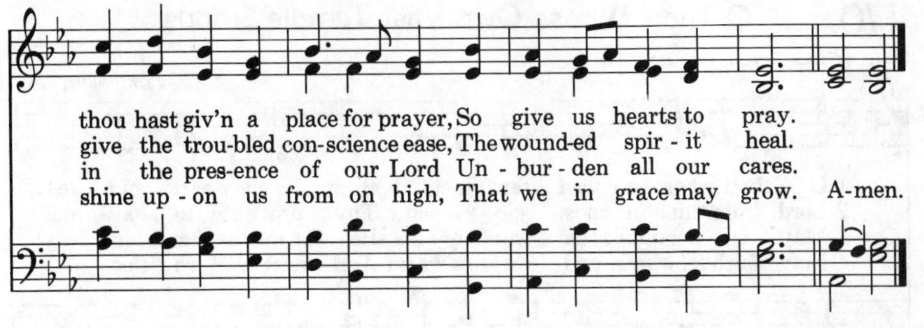
thou hast giv'n a place for prayer, So give us hearts to pray.
give the trou-bled con-science ease, The wound-ed spir - it heal.
in the pres-ence of our Lord Un - bur - den all our cares.
shine up - on us from on high, That we in grace may grow. A-men.

How Blessed Is This Place, O Lord 469

Ernest Edwin Ryden, 1886-

TALLIS' CANON L.M.
Thomas Tallis, c.1505-1585

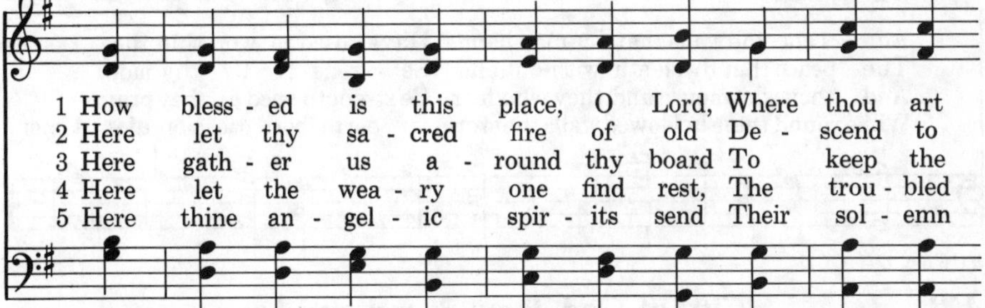

1 How bless - ed is this place, O Lord, Where thou art
2 Here let thy sa - cred fire of old De - scend to
3 Here gath - er us a - round thy board To keep the
4 Here let the wea - ry one find rest, The trou - bled
5 Here thine an - gel - ic spir - its send Their sol - emn

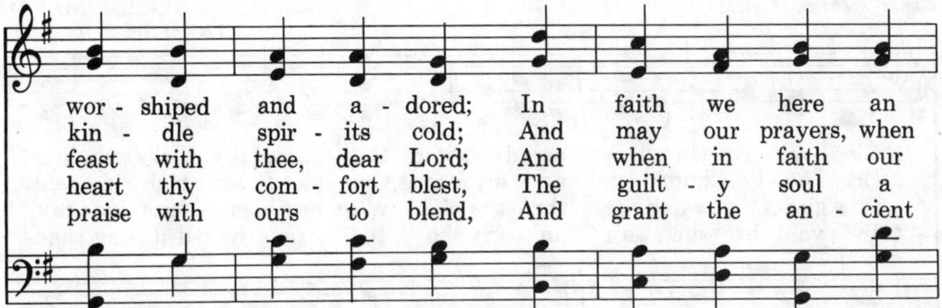

wor - shiped and a - dored; In faith we here an
kin - dle spir - its cold; And may our prayers, when
feast with thee, dear Lord; And when in faith our
heart thy com - fort blest, The guilt - y soul a
praise with ours to blend, And grant the an - cient

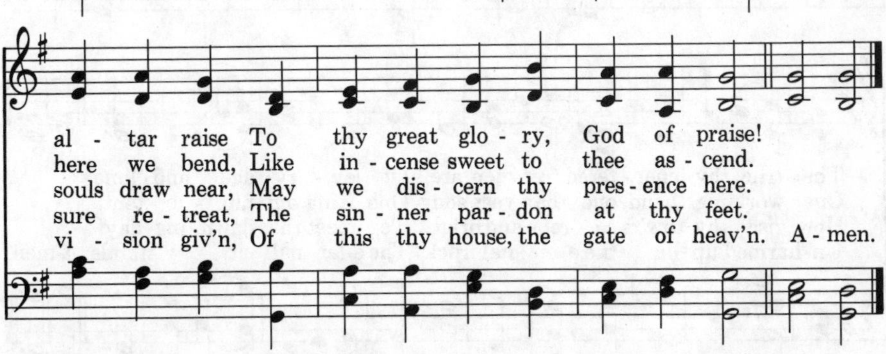

al - tar raise To thy great glo - ry, God of praise!
here we bend, Like in - cense sweet to thee as - cend.
souls draw near, May we dis - cern thy pres - ence here.
sure re - treat, The sin - ner par - don at thy feet.
vi - sion giv'n, Of this thy house, the gate of heav'n. A - men.

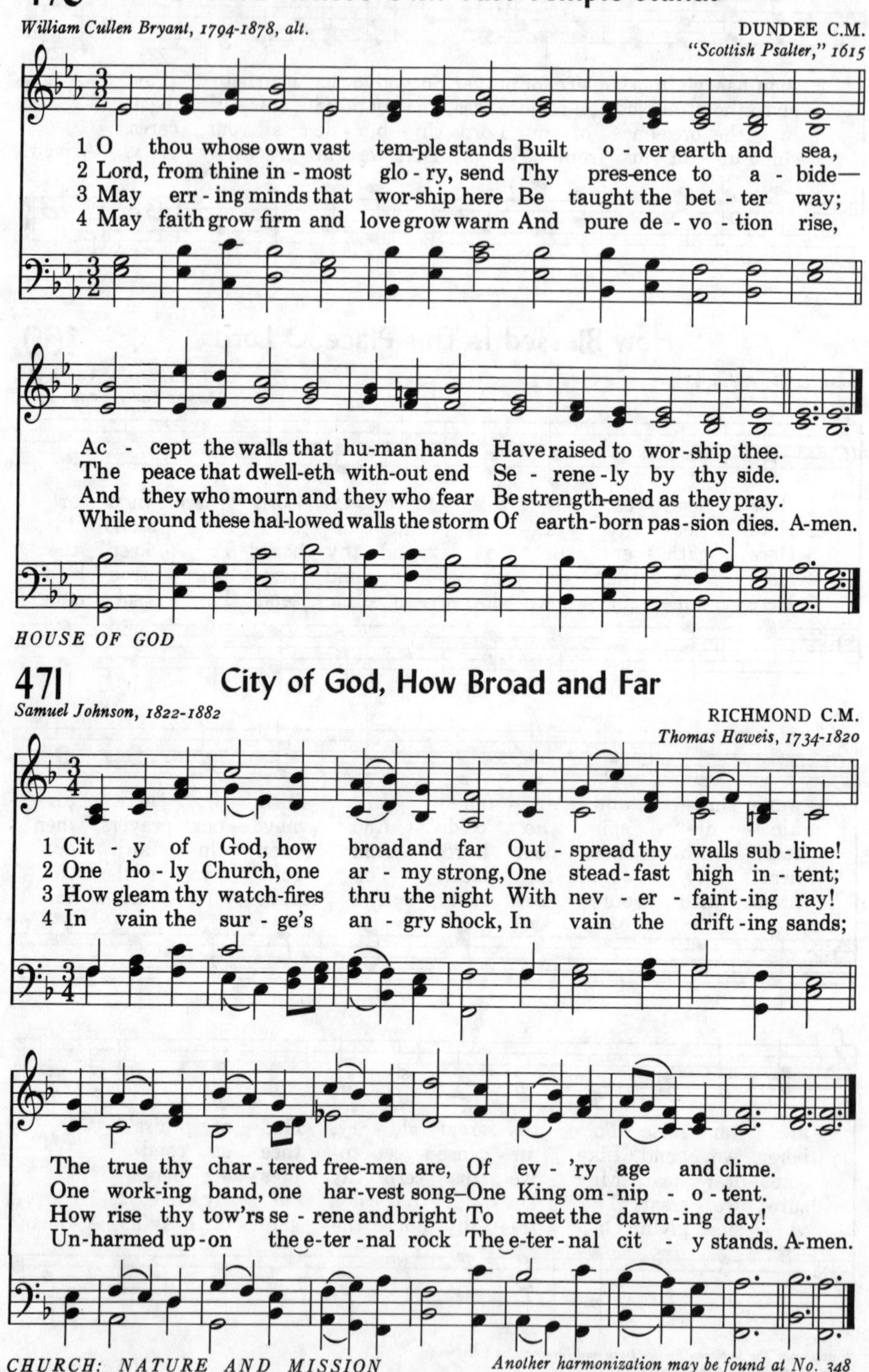
470 O Thou Whose Own Vast Temple Stands
William Cullen Bryant, 1794-1878, alt.
DUNDEE C.M.
"Scottish Psalter," 1615
1 O thou whose own vast temple stands Built o-ver earth and sea,
2 Lord, from thine in-most glo-ry, send Thy pres-ence to a-bide—
3 May err-ing minds that wor-ship here Be taught the bet-ter way;
4 May faith grow firm and love grow warm And pure de-vo-tion rise,
Ac-cept the walls that hu-man hands Have raised to wor-ship thee.
The peace that dwell-eth with-out end Se-rene-ly by thy side.
And they who mourn and they who fear Be strength-ened as they pray.
While round these hal-lowed walls the storm Of earth-born pas-sion dies. A-men.
HOUSE OF GOD
471 City of God, How Broad and Far
Samuel Johnson, 1822-1882
RICHMOND C.M.
Thomas Haweis, 1734-1820
1 Cit-y of God, how broad and far Out-spread thy walls sub-lime!
2 One ho-ly Church, one ar-my strong, One stead-fast high in-tent;
3 How gleam thy watch-fires thru the night With nev-er-faint-ing ray!
4 In vain the sur-ge's an-gry shock, In vain the drift-ing sands;
The true thy char-tered free-men are, Of ev-'ry age and clime.
One work-ing band, one har-vest song—One King om-nip-o-tent.
How rise thy tow'rs se-rene and bright To meet the dawn-ing day!
Un-harmed up-on the e-ter-nal rock The e-ter-nal cit-y stands. A-men.

Another harmonization may be found at No. 348

Built on the Rock

472

Nicolai F. S. Grundtvig, 1783-1872
Tr. Carl Doving, 1867-1937, alt.
Revised, Fred C. M. Hansen, 1888-

KIRKEN 8.8.8.8.8.8.8.8.
Ludvig M. Lindeman, 1812-1887

1 Built on the rock the Church doth stand, E - ven when stee - ples are
2 Sure - ly in tem - ples made with hands God, the most high, is not
3 We are God's house of liv - ing stones, Built for his own hab - i -
4 Yet in this house, an earth - ly frame, Je - sus his chil - dren is
5 Here stands the font be - fore our eyes Tell - ing how God did re -
fall - ing; Crum - bled have spires in ev - 'ry land— Bells still are
dwell - ing; High in the heav'ns his tem - ple stands, All earth - ly
ta - tion; He fills our hearts, his hum - ble thrones, Grant - ing us
bless - ing; Hith - er we come to praise his name, Faith in our
ceive us; Th'al - tar re - calls Christ's sac - ri - fice And what his
chim - ing and call - ing, Call - ing the young and old to rest, Call - ing the
tem - ples ex - cell - ing; Yet he who dwells in heav'n a - bove Deigns to a -
life and sal - va - tion; Were two or three to seek his face, He in their
Sav - ior con - fess - ing; Je - sus to us his Spir - it sent, Mak - ing with
ta - ble doth give us; Here sounds the word that doth pro - claim Christ yes - ter -
souls of men dis - tressed, Long - ing for life ev - er - last - ing.
bide with us in love, Mak - ing our bod - ies his tem - ple.
midst would show his grace, Bless - ings up - on them be - stow - ing.
us his cov - e - nant, Grant - ing his chil - dren the king - dom.
day, to - day, the same, Yea, and for aye our Re - deem - er.

Words from *The Lutheran Service Book and Hymnal*, by permission of the Commission on the Liturgy and Hymnal.

473 Chosen Seed and Zion's Children

Anders Carl Rutström, 1721-1772
Tr. Claude W. Foss, 1855-1935

LAMMETS FOLK 8.7.8.7.D.
Attr. to Anders Carl Rutström, 1721-1772
"Sions Nya Sånger," 1854

1 Cho - sen seed and Zi - on's chil - dren, Ran - somed from e -
2 Still re - joice a - mid thy tri - als, Nor re - gard thy
3 Pleas - ant - ly thy lines have fall - en Un - der - neath the
4 Faith and love are the con - di - tions—All on faith and
5 And up - on this blest foun - da - tion, Lord, our Lord and
ter - nal wrath, Trav - 'ling to the heav'n - ly Ca - naan
lot a - miss, For the kind and lov - ing Sav - ior
tree of life, For the Lord is thy sal - va - tion
love de - pends; Love of law is the ful - fill - ment,
Sav - ior - King, May thy Spir - it e'er u - nite us,
On a rough and thorn - y path: Church of God, in
Is the source of all thy bliss. May he ev - er
And thy shield in all thy strife. Here the tim - id
Faith God's mer - cy ap - pre - hends: Who hath faith shall
To it may we ev - er cling. May we, mem - bers
Christ e - lect - ed, Thou to God art rec - on - ciled; But on earth thou
be thy por - tion, He who gave thee life and breath; In his keep - ing
bird finds shel - ter, Here the swal - low finds a nest, Trem-bling fu - gi -
see sal - va - tion, Who hath love shall life ob - tain; May, O Lord, thy
of one bod - y, Grow in - to a per - fect whole; Grant, O Lord, that

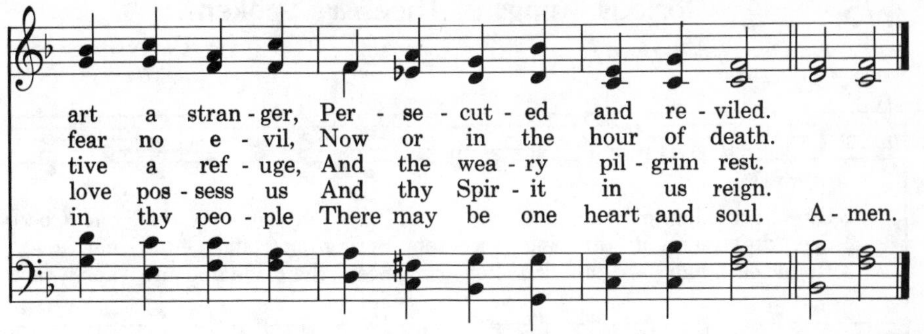

art a stran-ger, Per-se-cut-ed and re-viled.
fear no e-vil, Now or in the hour of death.
tive a ref-uge, And the wea-ry pil-grim rest.
love pos-sess us And thy Spir-it in us reign.
in thy peo-ple There may be one heart and soul. A-men.

Christ Is Made the Sure Foundation 474

Latin: 7th century
Tr. John M. Neale, 1818-1866, alt.

REGENT SQUARE 8.7.8.7.8.7.
Henry T. Smart, 1813-1879

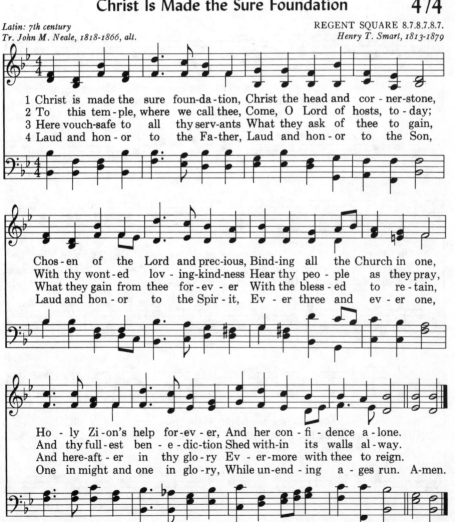

1 Christ is made the sure foun-da-tion, Christ the head and cor-ner-stone,
2 To this tem-ple, where we call thee, Come, O Lord of hosts, to-day;
3 Here vouch-safe to all thy serv-ants What they ask of thee to gain,
4 Laud and hon-or to the Fa-ther, Laud and hon-or to the Son,

Chos-en of the Lord and prec-ious, Bind-ing all the Church in one,
With thy wont-ed lov-ing-kind-ness Hear thy peo-ple as they pray,
What they gain from thee for-ev-er With the bless-ed to re-tain,
Laud and hon-or to the Spir-it, Ev-er three and ev-er one,

Ho-ly Zi-on's help for-ev-er, And her con-fi-dence a-lone.
And thy full-est ben-e-dic-tion Shed with-in its walls al-way.
And here-aft-er in thy glo-ry Ev-er-more with thee to reign.
One in might and one in glo-ry, While un-end-ing a-ges run. A-men.

475 Glorious Things of Thee Are Spoken

Based on Psalm 87:3; Isaiah 33:20-21 AUSTRIAN HYMN 8.7.8.7.D.
John Newton, 1725-1807 *Franz Joseph Haydn, 1732-1809*

1 Glo-rious things of thee are spo-ken, Zi-on, cit-y of our God;
2 See, the streams of liv-ing wa-ters, Spring-ing from e-ter-nal love,
3 Round each hab-i-ta-tion hov-'ring, See the cloud and fire ap-pear
He whose word can-not be bro-ken Formed thee for his own a-bode.
Well sup-ply thy sons and daugh-ters And all fear of want re-move.
For a glo-ry and a cov-'ring, Show-ing that the Lord is near!
On the Rock of A-ges found-ed, What can shake thy sure re-pose?
Who can faint while such a riv-er Ev-er flows their thirst to as-suage?
Glo-rious things of thee are spo-ken, Zi-on, cit-y of our God;
With sal-va-tion's walls sur-round-ed, Thou mayst smile at all thy foes.
Grace, which like the Lord, the Giv-er, Nev-er fails from age to age.
He whose word can-not be bro-ken Formed thee for his own a-bode.

Lord, We Thank Thee for Our Brothers 476

Roger K. Powell, 1914-

AUSTRIAN HYMN 8.7.8.7.D.
Franz Joseph Haydn, 1732-1809

1 Lord, we thank thee for our brothers
Keeping faith with us and thee,
Joining heart to heart with others,
Making strong our company.
With the cross our only standard
Let us sing with one great voice:
"Glory, glory, thine the kingdom!"
Churches in thy Church rejoice.

2 God be praised for congregations
Coming side by side to thee;
Many tongues of many nations
Sing the greater unity.
Sweet the psalm and sweet the carol
When our song is raised as one:
"Glory, glory, thine the power—
As in heav'n thy will be done!"

3 Hallowed be thy name forever!
Heal our diff'rences of old;
Bless thy Church's new endeavor,
For thy kingdom make us bold.
One our Christ and one our gospel—
Make us one we now implore:
"Glory, glory, thine the glory
Through the ages evermore!" Amen.

I Love Thy Kingdom, Lord 477

Based on Psalm 26:8
Timothy Dwight, 1752-1817

ST. THOMAS S.M.
Williams' "New Universal Psalmodist," 1770

1 I love thy king - dom, Lord, The house of thine a - bode,
2 I love thy Church, O God— Her walls be - fore thee stand,
3 For her my tears shall fall, For her my prayers as - cend,
4 Be - yond my high - est joy I prize her heav'n-ly ways,
5 Sure as thy truth shall last, To Zi - on shall be giv'n
The Church our blest Re - deem - er saved With his own pre - cious blood.
Dear as the ap - ple of thine eye, And grav - en on thy hand.
To her my cares and toils be giv'n Till toils and cares shall end.
Her sweet com - mun - ion, sol - emn vows, Her hymns of love and praise.
The bright - est glo - ries earth can yield, And bright - er bliss of heav'n. A - men.

A higher setting may be found at No. 23

478 Jesus, with Thy Church Abide

Thomas B. Pollock, 1836-1896

SONG 13 7.7.7.6.
Orlando Gibbons, 1583-1625
Harm. by C. H. Kitson, 1874-1944

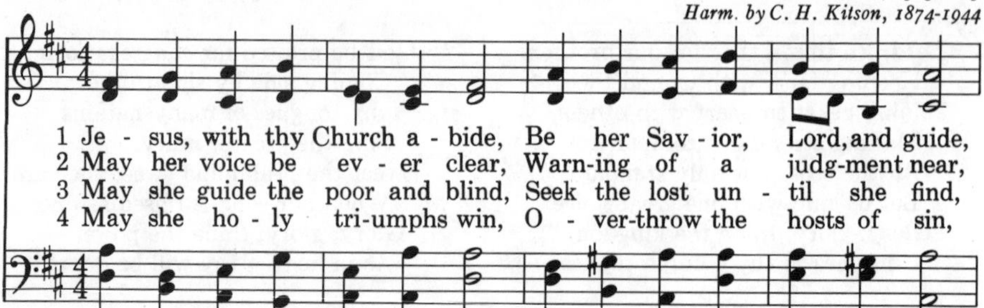

1 Je - sus, with thy Church a - bide, Be her Sav - ior, Lord, and guide,
While on earth her faith is tried: We be - seech thee, hear us.

2 May her voice be ev - er clear, Warn-ing of a judg-ment near,
Tell - ing of a Sav - ior dear: We be - seech thee, hear us.

3 May she guide the poor and blind, Seek the lost un - til she find,
And the bro - ken-heart - ed bind: We be - seech thee, hear us.

4 May she ho - ly tri - umphs win, O - ver-throw the hosts of sin,
Gath - er all the na - tions in: We be - seech thee, hear us. A-men.

479 Lord God, Our Thanks to Thee We Raise

Frederick K. Brewster, 1884-1966

BREWSTER L.M.
Norman E. Johnson, 1928-

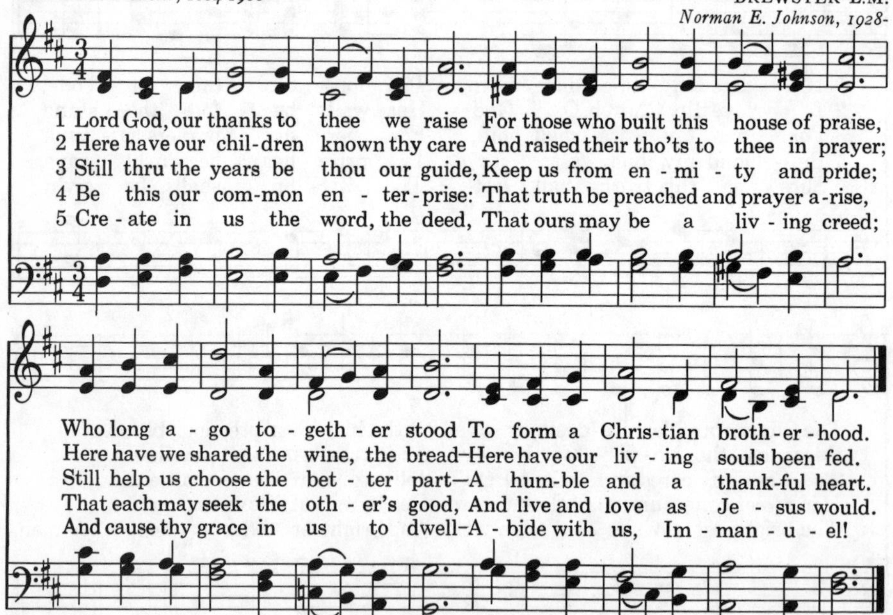
1 Lord God, our thanks to thee we raise For those who built this house of praise,
2 Here have our chil-dren known thy care And raised their tho'ts to thee in prayer;
3 Still thru the years be thou our guide, Keep us from en - mi - ty and pride;
4 Be this our com-mon en - ter-prise: That truth be preached and prayer a-rise,
5 Cre - ate in us the word, the deed, That ours may be a liv - ing creed;
Who long a - go to - geth - er stood To form a Chris-tian broth - er - hood.
Here have we shared the wine, the bread–Here have our liv - ing souls been fed.
Still help us choose the bet - ter part–A hum-ble and a thank-ful heart.
That each may seek the oth - er's good, And live and love as Je - sus would.
And cause thy grace in us to dwell–A - bide with us, Im - man - u - el!

Alternate tune: DUKE STREET, *No. 362*

O Church of Christ, Be Watchful and Awake! 480

Paul P. Fryhling, 1912-1973
CENTENNIAL 10.8.10.8.
In unison
James P. Davies, 1913-
1 O Church of Christ, be watch - ful and a - wake!
2 O Church of Christ, with ra - diant life a - rise!
3 O Church of Christ, in vi - brant strength go forth!
4 O Church of Christ, in bless - ed hope look up!
5 O Church of Christ, in acts of love be near,
A long - a - wait - ed day dawns clear;
Look out up - on the world's vast scene;
The liv - ing Spir - it through you move,
Our God and Sav - ior shall ap - pear,
Wher - ev - er need - y peo - ple be,
In word and life your Christ - ly wit - ness make
Pre - sent your - self a liv - ing sac - ri - fice,
That sin - bound men, to God of price - less worth,
On e - vil pow'rs to pour wrath's awe - some cup
To lift their loads and to dis - pel their fear
To all man - kind that God is near.
That men may see what you have seen.
A - mazed, shall learn that God is love.
And ran - som cap - tives far and near.
With peace in God e - ter - nal - ly!

481 O Church of God, Triumphant

S. Ralph Harlow, 1885-1972
LANCASHIRE 7.6.7.6.D.
Henry T. Smart, 1813-1879
1 O Church of God, tri - um - phant A - bove the world's dark fears,
2 On Christ-mas Eve her car - ols Have set our hearts a - glow,
3 Her task on earth un - fin - ished Till threats of war shall cease,
4 O Church of God, tri - um - phant, We of - fer now in prayer
Where - in our souls find re - fuge Through all these earth - ly years!
Her bells on Eas - ter morn - ing With faith still o - ver - flow;
Her voice must raise a pro - test Where greed still robs men's peace;
Our youth, our full - er man - hood, For Christ's great cause to dare,
Christ's stead-fast ho - ly pur - pose, Il - lum - ined by the cross,
Be - fore her hal - lowed al - tars We pledge our love in youth,
One broth - er - hood Christ called for, Of ev - 'ry class and race:
That his re - deem - ing pur - pose May prove be - yond de - feat,
Guards her from e - vil's pow - er, Re - veal - ing it but dross.
While in her sa - cred por - tals Our minds have found God's truth.
The church must live the vi - sion That shone in Je - sus' face.
Till in the life im - mor - tal With joy his chil - dren meet.

Alternate tune: FAR-OFF LANDS, *No. 97*

A lower setting may be found at No. 532

The Church's One Foundation

Samuel J. Stone, 1839-1900
AURELIA 7.6.7.6.D.
Samuel S. Wesley, 1810-1876
1 The Church-'s one foun - da - tion Is Je - sus Christ her Lord;
2 E - lect from ev - ery na - tion, Yet one o'er all the earth,
3 'Mid toil and trib - u - la - tion, And tu - mult of her war,
4 Yet she on earth hath un - ion With God, the Three in One,
She is his new cre - a - tion By wa - ter and the word.
Her char - ter of sal - va - tion, One Lord, one faith, one birth;
She waits the con - sum - ma - tion Of peace for ev - er - more;
And mys - tic sweet com - mun - ion With those whose rest is won.
From heav'n he came and sought her To be his ho - ly bride;
One ho - ly name she bless - es, Par - takes one ho - ly food,
Till with the vi - sion glo - rious, Her long - ing eyes are blest,
O hap - py ones and ho - ly! Lord, give us grace that we
With his own blood he bought her, And for her life he died.
And to one hope she press - es, With ev - ery grace en - dued.
And the great Church vic - to - rious Shall be the Church at rest.
Like them, the meek and low - ly, On high may dwell with thee. A-men.

483 Within the Church's Hallowed Walls

Miriam Drury, 1900-

NUN FREUT EUCH 8.7.8.7.8.8.7.
Joseph Klug's "Geistliche Lieder," Wittenberg, 1535

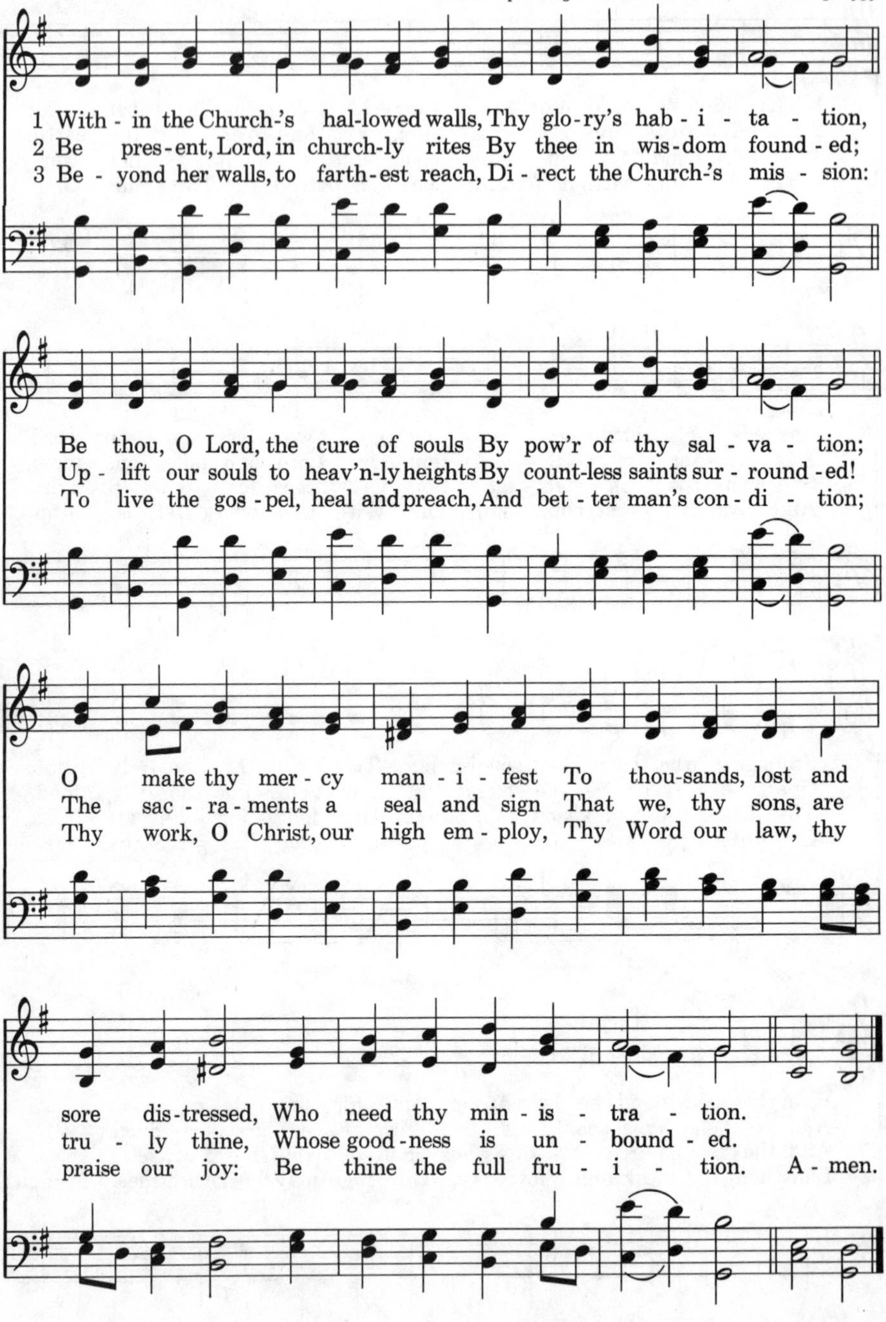

1 With - in the Church-'s hal-lowed walls, Thy glo-ry's hab - i - ta - tion,
2 Be pres-ent, Lord, in church-ly rites By thee in wis-dom found - ed;
3 Be - yond her walls, to farth-est reach, Di - rect the Church-'s mis - sion:

Be thou, O Lord, the cure of souls By pow'r of thy sal - va - tion;
Up - lift our souls to heav'n-ly heights By count-less saints sur - round - ed!
To live the gos - pel, heal and preach, And bet - ter man's con - di - tion;

O make thy mer - cy man - i - fest To thou-sands, lost and
The sac - ra - ments a seal and sign That we, thy sons, are
Thy work, O Christ, our high em - ploy, Thy Word our law, thy

sore dis-tressed, Who need thy min - is - tra - tion.
tru - ly thine, Whose good - ness is un - bound - ed.
praise our joy: Be thine the full fru - i - tion. A - men.

Jesus, Lord, We Look to Thee

Charles Wesley, 1707-1788

ABERYSTWYTH 7.7.7.7.D.
Joseph Parry, 1841-1903

1 Je - sus, Lord, we look to thee, Let us in thy name a - gree;
2 Let us for each oth - er care, Each the oth - er's bur - den bear,
3 Clos - er knit to thee, our Head, Nour-ish us, O Christ, and feed;
Show thy - self the Prince of peace, Bid our strife for - ev - er cease.
To thy Church the pat - tern give, Show how true be - liev - ers live.
Let us dai - ly grace re - ceive, More and more in Je - sus live.
Make us of one heart and mind, Gra - cious, full of pit - y, kind,
Free from an - ger and from pride, Let us thus in God a - bide,
Fill us with the Fa - ther's love, Nev - er from our souls re - move;
Low - ly, meek, in thought and word, Al - to - geth - er like our Lord.
All the depths of love ex - press, All the heights of ho - li - ness.
Dwell in us, and we shall be Thine thru all e - ter - ni - ty. A-men.

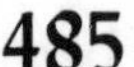

In Christ There Is No East or West

First Tune

John Oxenham, 1852-1941

ST. PETER C.M.
Alexander R. Reinagle, 1799-1877

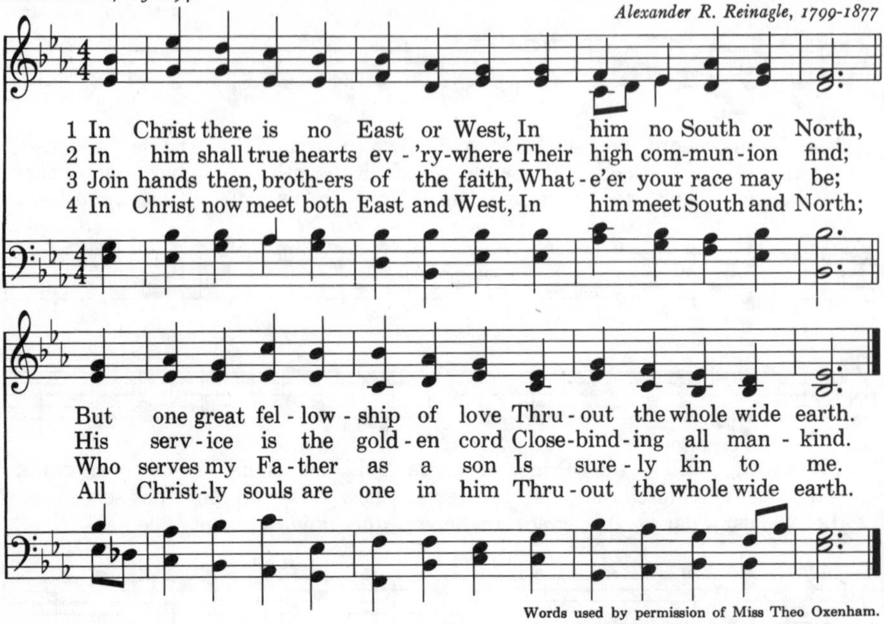

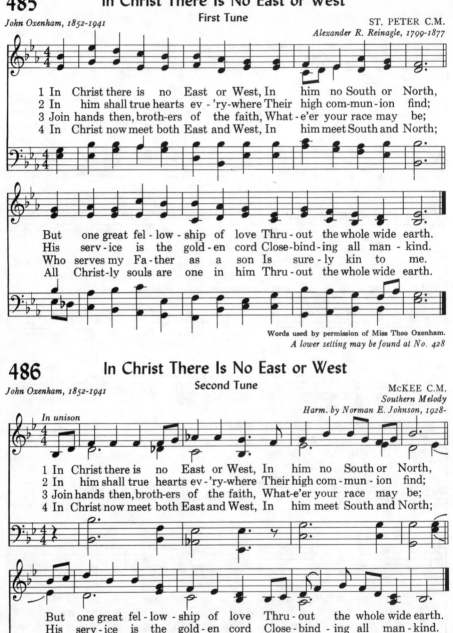

1 In Christ there is no East or West, In him no South or North,
But one great fel-low-ship of love Thru-out the whole wide earth.

2 In him shall true hearts ev-'ry-where Their high com-mun-ion find;
His serv-ice is the gold-en cord Close-bind-ing all man-kind.

3 Join hands then, broth-ers of the faith, What-e'er your race may be;
Who serves my Fa-ther as a son Is sure-ly kin to me.

4 In Christ now meet both East and West, In him meet South and North;
All Christ-ly souls are one in him Thru-out the whole wide earth.

Words used by permission of Miss Theo Oxenham.

A lower setting may be found at No. 428

486 In Christ There Is No East or West

Second Tune

John Oxenham, 1852-1941

McKEE C.M.
Southern Melody
Harm. by Norman E. Johnson, 1928-

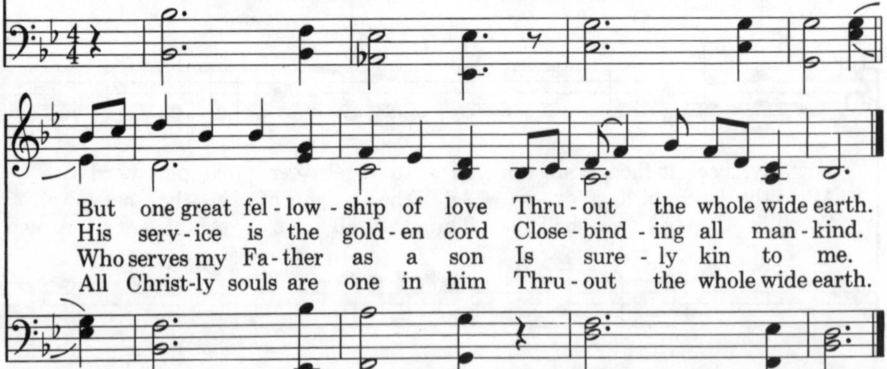

In unison

1 In Christ there is no East or West, In him no South or North,
But one great fel-low-ship of love Thru-out the whole wide earth.

2 In him shall true hearts ev-'ry-where Their high com-mun-ion find;
His serv-ice is the gold-en cord Close-bind-ing all man-kind.

3 Join hands then, broth-ers of the faith, What-e'er your race may be;
Who serves my Fa-ther as a son Is sure-ly kin to me.

4 In Christ now meet both East and West, In him meet South and North;
All Christ-ly souls are one in him Thru-out the whole wide earth.

Words used by permission of Miss Theo Oxenham.

We Are One in the Spirit

Based on John 13:35
Peter Scholtes, 1938-

ST. BRENDAN'S *Irregular*
Peter Scholtes, 1938-

In unison
1 We are one in the Spir - it, we are one in the Lord,
2 We will walk with each oth - er, we will walk hand in hand,
3 We will work with each oth - er, we will work side by side,
4 All praise to the Fa - ther, from whom all things come,
We are one in the Spir - it, we are one in the Lord,
We will walk with each oth - er, we will walk hand in hand,
We will work with each oth - er, we will work side by side,
And all praise to Christ Je - sus, his on - ly Son,
And we pray that all u - ni - ty may one day be re - stored:
And to - geth - er we'll spread the news that God is in our land:
And we'll guard each man's dig - ni - ty and save each man's pride:
And all praise to the Spir - it, who makes us one:
REFRAIN
And they'll know we are Christ-ians by our love, by our love,
Yes, they'll know we are Christ-ians by our love.

From the recording *They'll Know We Are Christians* by Peter Scholtes.

488 With God and His Friendship

Carl Olof Rosenius, 1816-1868
Tr. C. R. Osbeck, 1877-1963, Sts. 1, 2
Tr. Ernst W. Olson, 1870-1958, Sts. 3, 4, 5

AHNFELT 11.11.11.6.6.11.
Oscar Ahnfelt, 1813-1882
Harm. by James P. Davies, 1913-

1 With God and his friend - ship, his Spir - it and Word,
2 In per - il - ous times, thru the gloom of the night,
3 The sign of the cross we tri - um - phant - ly bear,
4 The pil - lar that guides us through per - il and strife,
5 O Shep - herd, a - bide with us, care for us still,
With breth - ren par - tak - ing the bread of our Lord,
A host march - es on through the dark - ness to light;
Though none of our kin - dred that em - blem may wear;
The rock that is cleft, giv - ing wa - ters of life,
And feed us and lead us, and teach us thy will;
With cour - age and joy we will meet com - ing days:
These pil - grims, ob - scured, are dis - owned by the world:
We joy - ful - ly fol - low the cham - pions of right,
Is Christ and his cross: By his Spir - it and word
And when in thy heav - en - ly fold we shall be,
The Shep - herd is with us, The Shep - herd is with us,
But owned by the Mas - ter, But owned by the Mas - ter,
Who march on to glo - ry, Who march on to glo - ry,
The heart he re - fresh - es, The heart he re - fresh - es,
Our thanks and our prais - es, Our thanks and our prais - es,

To lead us, pro - tect us and teach us his ways.
They march on to glo - ry with ban - ners un - furled.
Who march on to glo - ry with weap - ons of might.
The heart he re - fresh - es— our Sav - ior and Lord.
Our thanks and our prais - es we'll ren - der to thee. A - men.

Blest Be the Tie That Binds

489

John Fawcett, 1740-1817, alt.

DENNIS S.M.
Johann G. Naegeli, c.1768-1836
Arr. by Lowell Mason, 1792-1872

1 Blest be the tie that binds Our hearts in Chris - tian love;
2 Be - fore our Fa - ther's throne We pour our ar - dent prayers;
3 We share each oth - er's woes, Each oth - er's bur - dens bear;
4 When we are called to part It gives us in - ward pain;

The fel - low-ship of kin-dred minds Is like to that a - bove.
Our fears, our hopes, our aims are one, Our com-forts and our cares.
And oft - en for each oth - er flows The sym-pa - thiz - ing tear.
But we shall still be joined in heart, And hope to meet a - gain. A-men.

5 This glorious hope revives
Our courage by the way,
While each in expectation lives
And longs to see the day.

6 From sorrow, toil, and pain,
And sin we shall be free;
And perfect love and joy shall reign
Through all eternity.

490 We Come unto Our Fathers' God

Thomas H. Gill, 1819-1906

MIT FREUDEN ZART 8.7.8.7.8.8.7.
Bohemian Brethren's "Kirchengesänge," 1566

1 We come un-to our fa-thers' God, Their Rock is our sal - va - tion;
2 The fire di-vine their steps that led Still go-eth bright be - fore us;
3 Their joy un-to their Lord we bring, Their song to us de - scend-eth;
4 Ye saints to come, take up the strain, The same sweet theme en - deav-or;
Th' e-ter-nal arms, their dear a-bode, We make our hab - i - ta - tion.
The heav'n-ly shield a-round them spread Is still high hold-en o'er us.
The Spir-it who in them did sing To us his mu - sic lend-eth:
Un - bro-ken be the gold-en chain! Keep on the song for - ev - er!
We bring thee, Lord, the praise they brought, We seek thee as thy
The grace those sin-ners that sub-dued, The strength those weak-lings
His song in them, in us, is one; We raise it high, we
Safe in the same dear dwell-ing place, Rich with the same e -
saints have sought In ev - 'ry gen - er - a - tion.
that re-newed, Doth van-quish, doth re - store us.
send it on— The song that nev - er end - eth.
ter - nal grace, Bless the same bound - less Giv - er. A-men.

A higher setting may be found at No. 1
Alternate tune: KIRKEN, *No. 194*

O Breath of Life

Bessie Porter Head, 1850-1936

BLOMQVIST 9.8.9.8.
Joel Blomqvist, 1840-1930

1 O Breath of Life, come sweep - ing through us,
2 O Wind of God, come bend us, break us,
3 O Breath of Love, come breathe with - in us,
4 O Heart of Christ, once bro - ken for us,
5 Re - vive us, Lord! Is zeal a - bat - ing
Re - vive thy Church with life and pow'r;
Till hum - bly we con - fess our need;
Re - new - ing thought and will and heart;
'Tis there we find our strength and rest;
While har - vest fields are vast and white?
O Breath of Life, come, cleanse, re - new us,
Then in thy ten - der - ness re - make us,
Come, love of Christ, a - fresh to win us,
Our bro - ken con - trite hearts now sol - ace,
Re - vive us, Lord— the world is wait - ing!
And fit thy Church to meet this hour.
Re - vive, re - store— for this we plead.
Re - vive thy Church in ev - 'ry part.
And let thy wait - ing Church be blest.
E - quip thy Church to spread the light. A - men.

492 Renew Thy Church, Her Ministries Restore

Kenneth Lorne Cober, 1902-
ALL IS WELL 10.6.10.6.8.8.8.6.
J. T. White's "Sacred Harp," 1844
1 Re - new thy church, her min - is - tries re-store: Both to serve and a-dore.
2 Teach us thy Word, re - veal its truth di-vine; On our path let it shine.
3 Teach us to pray, for thou art ev - er near; Thy still voice let us hear.
4 Teach us to love, with strength of heart and mind, Ev - 'ry-one, all man-kind.
Make her a-gain as salt through-out the land, And as light from a stand.
Tell of thy works, thy might - y acts of grace; From each page show thy face.
Our souls are rest - less till they rest in thee: This our glad des - ti - ny.
Break down old walls of pre - ju - dice and hate; Leave us not to our fate.
Mid som-ber shad - ows of the night Where greed and ha-tred spread their blight,
As thou hast loved us, sent thy Son, And our sal - va - tion now is won,
Be - fore thy pres - ence keep us still, That we may find for us thy will
As thou hast loved and giv'n thy life To end hos - til - i - ty and strife,
O send us forth with pow'r en-dued: Help us, Lord, be re-newed!
O let our hearts with love be stirred: Help us, Lord, know thy Word!
And seek thy guid - ance ev - 'ry day: Teach us, Lord, how to pray!
O share thy grace from heav'n a - bove: Teach us, Lord, how to love! A-men.

There Shall Be Showers of Blessing

Based on Ezekiel 34:26
Daniel W. Whittle, 1840-1901

SHOWERS OF BLESSING 8.7.8.7. *with Refrain*
James McGranahan, 1840-1907

1 "There shall be show-ers of bless-ing:" This is the prom-ise of love;
2 "There shall be show-ers of bless-ing:" Pre-cious re-viv-ing a-gain;
3 "There shall be show-ers of bless-ing:" Send them up-on us, O Lord;
4 "There shall be show-ers of bless-ing:" O that to-day they might fall,
There shall be sea-sons re-fresh-ing, Sent from the Sav-ior a-bove.
O-ver the hills and the val-leys, Sound of a-bun-dance of rain.
Grant to us now a re-fresh-ing, Come and now hon-or thy word.
Now as to God we're con-fess-ing, Now as on Je-sus we call!
REFRAIN
Show-ers of bless-ing, Show-ers of bless-ing we need:
Show-ers, show-ers of bless-ing,
Mer-cy-drops round us are fall-ing, But for the show-ers we plead.

494 Revive Thy Work, O Lord
Albert Midlane, 1825-1909
SWABIA S.M.
Johann Martin Spiess, 1715-c.1766
1 Re - vive thy work, O Lord, Thy might - y arm make bare;
2 Re - vive thy work, O Lord, Dis - turb this sleep of death;
3 Re - vive thy work, O Lord, Cre - ate soul-thirst for thee;
4 Re - vive thy work, O Lord, Ex - alt thy pre - cious name;
5 Re - vive thy work, O Lord, And give re - fresh - ing show'rs;
Speak with the voice that wakes the dead, And make thy peo - ple hear.
Quick - en the smol-d'ring em-bers now By thine al - might - y breath.
And hun-g'ring for the bread of life O may our spir - its be.
And, by the Ho - ly Ghost, our love For thee and thine in - flame.
The glo - ry shall be all thine own, The bless-ings, Lord, be ours. A-men.
RENEWAL
495 We Bid You Welcome
James Montgomery, 1771-1854
MISSIONARY CHANT L.M.
Heinrich C. Zeuner, 1795-1857
1 We bid you wel-come in the name Of Je - sus, our ex - alt - ed Head:
2 Come as a shep-herd—guard and keep This fold from harm of earth and sin;
3 Come as a teach - er sent from God, Charged his whole coun-sel to de - clare;
Come as a serv - ant—so he came, And we re - ceive you in his stead.
Nour - ish the lambs and feed the sheep, The wound-ed heal, the lost bring in.
Lift o'er our ranks the proph-et's rod, While we up - hold your hands with prayer.

A higher setting may be found at No. 559

Bless Thou Thy Chosen Sons

Miriam Drury, 1900-

TERRA BEATA S.M.D.
English Melody
Adapted by Franklin L. Sheppard, 1852-1930

1 Bless thou thy chos - en sons With gifts of Chris - tian grace,
2 Re - veal the light of truth And let its glo - ry shine,
3 En - due thy sons with pow'r To com - fort, teach and guide,

Thru change and stress do thou re - main Their con - stant dwell - ing place;
By hu - man words and deeds con - vey The sense of things di - vine;
To walk by faith, to per - se - vere What - ev - er may be - tide;

Thru them thy work is done, Thru them thy voice is heard,
In ev - 'ry speech and tongue Tran - scend im - per - fect creeds,
O mag - ni - fy thy law, Make thy sal - va - tion known,

Bear wit - ness to their sa - cred call, Thou true and liv - ing Word.
Pierce thru the veil of un - con - cern To meet our mod - ern needs.
And rec - on - cile the world to thee, Al - might - y, ho - ly One. A - men.

Alternate tune: DIADEMATA, *No. 523*

497 Go, Make of All Disciples

Based on Matthew 28:19, 20
Leon M. Adkins, 1896-

ANDREW 7.6.7.6.D.
Bonnevieve M. Opel, 1915-

In unison
1 "Go, make of all dis - ci - ples:" We hear the call, O Lord,
2 "Go, make of all dis - ci - ples:" Bap - tiz - ing in the name
3 "Go, make of all dis - ci - ples:" We at thy feet would stay
4 "Go, make of all dis - ci - ples:" We wel - come thy com - mand;
That comes from thee, our Fa - ther, In thy e - ter - nal Word.
Of Fa - ther, Son, and Spir - it— From age to age the same.
Un - til each life's vo - ca - tion Ac - cents thy ho - ly way.
"Lo, I am with you al - way:" We take thy guid - ing hand.
In - spire our ways of learn - ing Through earn - est, fer - vent prayer,
We call each new dis - ci - ple To fol - low thee, O Lord,
We cul - ti - vate the na - ture God plants in ev - 'ry heart,
The task looms large be - fore us— We fol - low with - out fear.

Alternate tune: GREENLAND, *No. 574*

And let our dai - ly liv - ing Re - veal thee ev - 'ry - where.
Re - deem - ing soul and bod - y By wa - ter and the Word.
Re - veal - ing in our wit - ness The Mas - ter Teach - er's art.
In heav'n and earth thy pow - er Shall bring God's king - dom here. A - men.
1 Lord of the Church, we hum - bly pray For those who guide us in thy way,
2 Help them to preach the truth of God, Re - demp - tion thru the Sav - ior's blood;
3 So may they live to thee a - lone, Then hear the wel - come word, "Well done!"
And speak thy ho - ly Word; With love di - vine their hearts in - spire, And
Nor let the Spir - it cease On all the Church his gifts to show'r: To
And take their crown a - bove; En - ter in - to their Mas - ter's joy, And
touch their lips with hal - lowed fire, And need - ful grace af - ford.
them, a mes - sen - ger of pow'r, To us, of life and peace.
all e - ter - ni - ty em - ploy In praise, and bliss, and love. A - men.

498 Lord of the Church, We Humbly Pray

Edward Osler, 1798-1863, Sts. 1, 2
Charles Wesley, 1707-1788, St. 3

INNSBRUCK NEW 8.8.6.D.
German Melody
Adapted by Heinrich Isaak, c.1450-1517
Harm. adapted from J. S. Bach, 1685-1750

499 God of the Prophets

Denis Wortman, 1835-1922, alt.

TOULON 10.10.10.10.

Abridged from "Genevan Psalter," 1551

1 God of the proph - ets, bless the proph - ets' sons!
2 A - noint them proph - ets! make their ears at - tent
3 A - noint them priests! strong in - ter - ces - sors they
4 Make them a - pos - tles! her - alds of the cross,
E - li - jah's man - tle o'er E - li - sha cast;
To thy di - vin - est speech; their hearts a - wake
For par - don and for char - i - ty and peace!
Forth may they go to tell all realms thy grace;
Each age its sol - emn task may claim but once—
To hu - man need; their lips make el - o - quent
Then they may lead the world, now gone a - stray,
In - spired by thee, may they count all but loss,
Make each one no - bler, strong - er than the last.
To strength - en right and ev - 'ry e - vil break.
In - to the dear Christ's life of sac - ri - fice!
And stand at last with joy be - fore thy face. A - men.

A lower setting may be found at No. 181

Lord, Who Didst Choose in Galilee 500

Based on Mark 3:14
William W. Reid, 1890-

MELITA 8.8.8.8.8.8.
John B. Dykes, 1823-1876

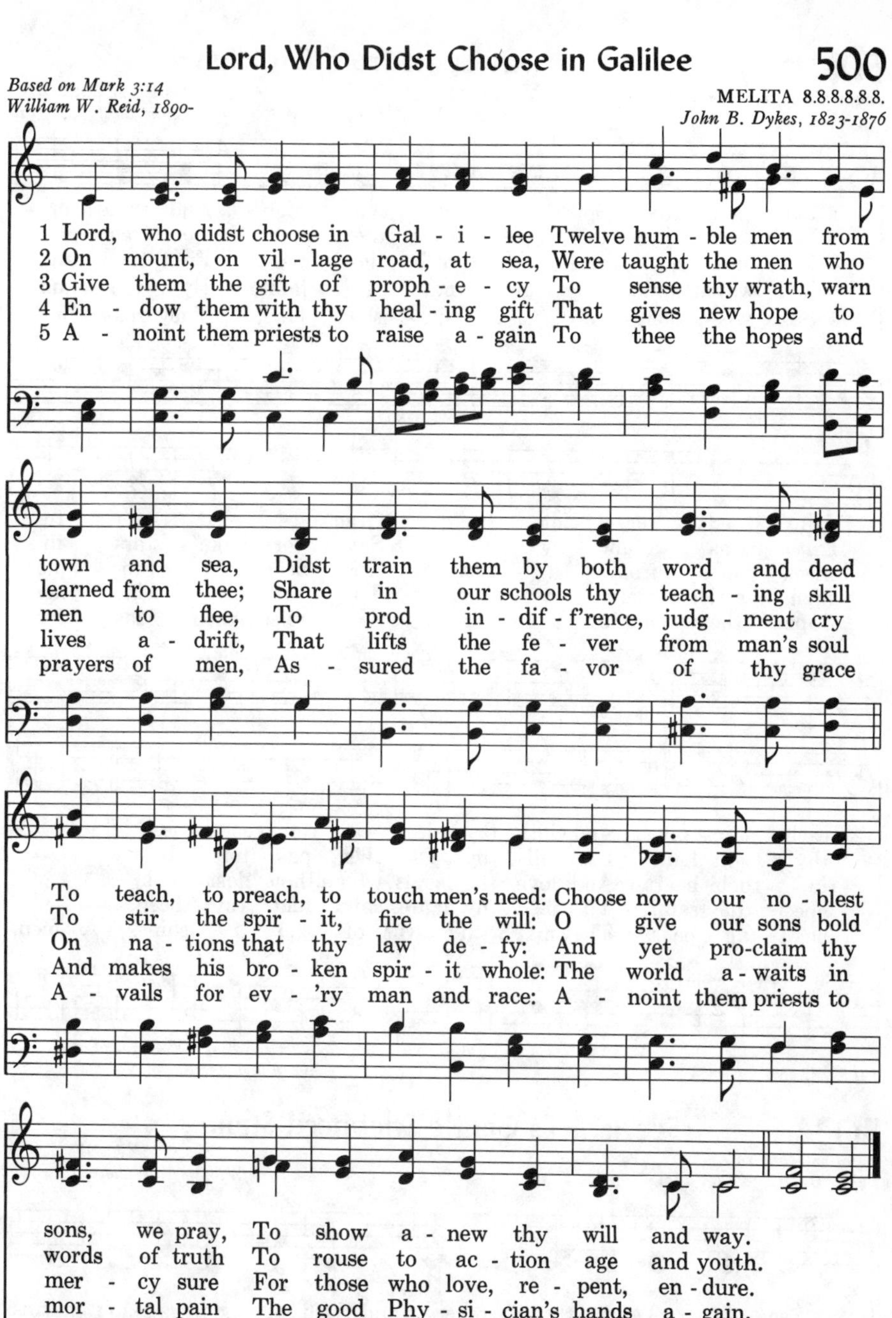
1 Lord, who didst choose in Gal - i - lee Twelve hum - ble men from
2 On mount, on vil - lage road, at sea, Were taught the men who
3 Give them the gift of proph - e - cy To sense thy wrath, warn
4 En - dow them with thy heal - ing gift That gives new hope to
5 A - noint them priests to raise a - gain To thee the hopes and
town and sea, Didst train them by both word and deed
learned from thee; Share in our schools thy teach - ing skill
men to flee, To prod in - dif - f'rence, judg - ment cry
lives a - drift, That lifts the fe - ver from man's soul
prayers of men, As - sured the fa - vor of thy grace
To teach, to preach, to touch men's need: Choose now our no - blest
To stir the spir - it, fire the will: O give our sons bold
On na - tions that thy law de - fy: And yet pro-claim thy
And makes his bro - ken spir - it whole: The world a - waits in
A - vails for ev - 'ry man and race: A - noint them priests to
sons, we pray, To show a - new thy will and way.
words of truth To rouse to ac - tion age and youth.
mer - cy sure For those who love, re - pent, en - dure.
mor - tal pain The good Phy - si - cian's hands a - gain.
know thee, Lord, And bring to earth thy love and word. A - men.

Another harmonization in a higher setting may be found at No. 584

501 Lord, Pour Thy Spirit from On High

James Montgomery, 1771-1854, alt.

PENTECOST L.M.
William Boyd, 1847-1928

1 Lord, pour thy Spir - it from on high, And thine or -
2 With - in thy tem - ple when they stand To teach the
3 Wis - dom and zeal and faith im - part, Firm - ness and
4 To watch and pray and nev - er faint, By day and
5 So, when their work is fin - ished here, They may in

dain - ed serv - ants bless; Grac - es and gifts to
truth as taught by thee, Sav - ior, like stars in
meek - ness from a - bove, To bear thy peo - ple
night strict guard to keep; To warn the sin - ner,
hope their charge re - sign; So, when their Mas - ter

each sup - ply, And clothe thy priests with right - eous - ness.
thy right hand Let all thy Church's pas - tors be.
in their heart, And love the souls whom thou dost love;
cheer the saint, To feed thy lambs and fold thy sheep.
shall ap - pear, They may with crowns of glo - ry shine. A - men.

A lower setting may be found at No. 336
and a higher setting at No. 372

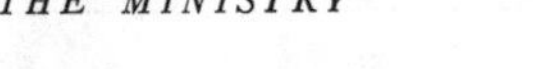

502 See Israel's Gentle Shepherd Stand

Based on Mark 10:14
Philip Doddridge, 1702-1751

SERENITY C.M.
William V. Wallace, 1814-1865

1 See Is - rael's gen - tle Shep - herd stand With all - en - gag - ing charms;
2 "Per - mit them to ap - proach," he cries, "Nor scorn their hum - ble name;
3 We bring them, Lord, in thank - ful hands, And yield them up to thee;

A higher setting may be found at No. 162

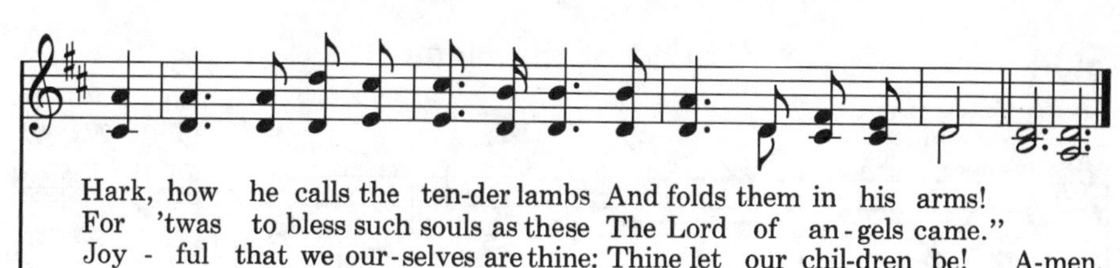
Hark, how he calls the ten-der lambs And folds them in his arms!
For 'twas to bless such souls as these The Lord of an-gels came."
Joy - ful that we our-selves are thine: Thine let our chil-dren be! A-men.

We Bless the Name of Christ, the Lord

503

Samuel F. Coffman, 1872-1954

RETREAT L.M.
Thomas Hastings, 1784-1872
Harm. by John W. Peterson, 1921-

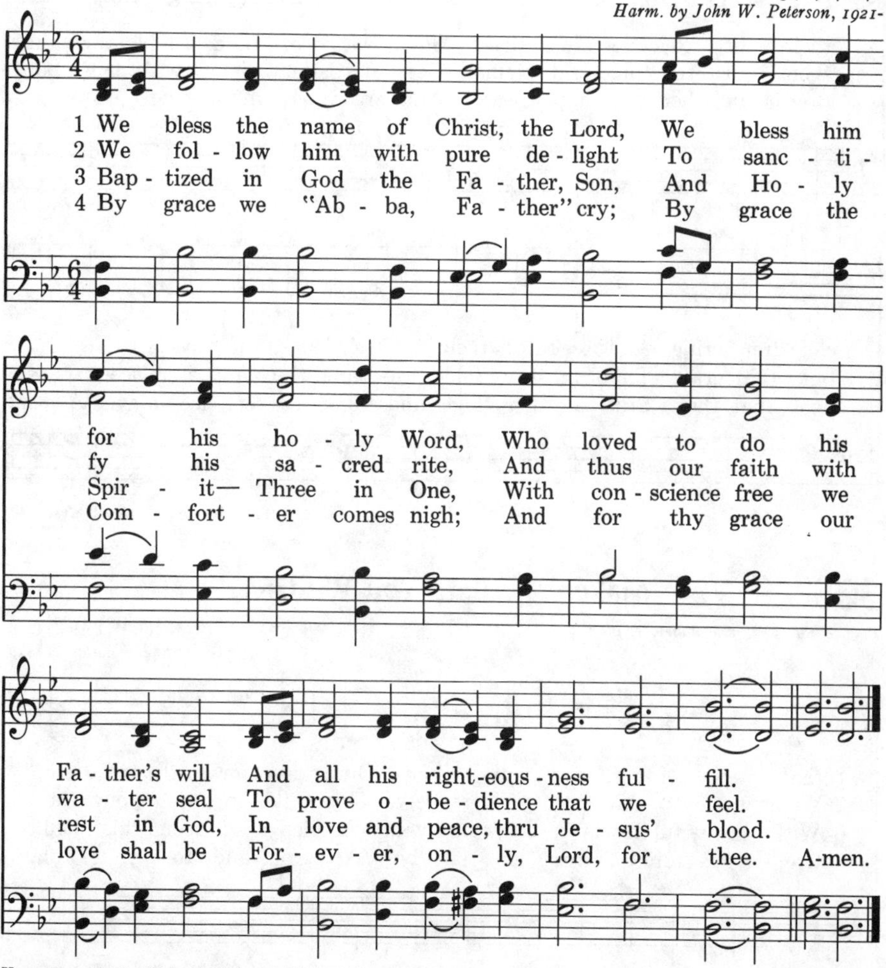

1 We bless the name of Christ, the Lord, We bless him
2 We fol - low him with pure de - light To sanc - ti -
3 Bap - tized in God the Fa - ther, Son, And Ho - ly
4 By grace we "Ab - ba, Fa - ther" cry; By grace the

for his ho - ly Word, Who loved to do his
fy his sa - cred rite, And thus our faith with
Spir - it— Three in One, With con - science free we
Com - fort - er comes nigh; And for thy grace our

Fa - ther's will And all his right-eous - ness ful - fill.
wa - ter seal To prove o - be - dience that we feel.
rest in God, In love and peace, thru Je - sus' blood.
love shall be For - ev - er, on - ly, Lord, for thee. A-men.

504 Friend of the Home

Based on Matthew 19:13
Howell Elvet Lewis, 1860-1953

ELLERS 10.10.10.10.
Edward J. Hopkins, 1818-1901

In unison

1 Friend of the home, as when in Gal - i - lee The moth-ers brought
2 Thine are they, by thy love's e - ter - nal claim, Thine we bap - tize
3 Lord, may thy Church, as with a moth-er's care, For thee the chil -

their lit - tle ones to thee, So we, dear Lord, would now the
them in the three-fold Name; Yet not the sign we trust, Lord,
dren in her bos - om bear; And grant, as morn - ing grows to

chil - dren bring, And seek for them the shel - ter of thy wing.
but the grace That in thy fold pre - pared the lambs a place.
noon, that they Still in her love and ho - ly serv - ice stay. A-men.

From the estate of Howell Elvet Lewis.

505 Maker of All, to You We Give

Pamela-Rae Yeager Maloney, 1945-

NORTH PARK C.M.
David L. Thorburn, 1936-

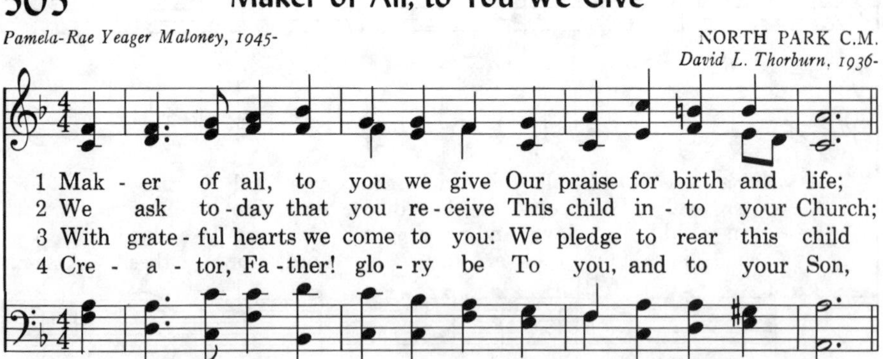
1 Mak - er of all, to you we give Our praise for birth and life;
2 We ask to - day that you re - ceive This child in - to your Church;
3 With grate - ful hearts we come to you: We pledge to rear this child
4 Cre - a - tor, Fa - ther! glo - ry be To you, and to your Son,

Words used by permission of Pamela-Rae Yeager Maloney.
Music used by permission of David L. Thorburn.

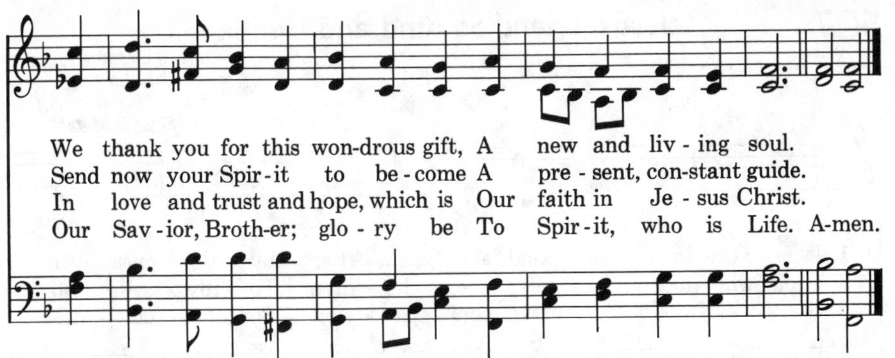
We thank you for this won-drous gift, A new and liv - ing soul.
Send now your Spir - it to be - come A pre - sent, con-stant guide.
In love and trust and hope, which is Our faith in Je - sus Christ.
Our Sav - ior, Broth-er; glo - ry be To Spir - it, who is Life. A-men.

This Child We Dedicate to Thee

506

From the German
Tr. Samuel Gilman, 1791-1858, alt.

FEDERAL STREET L.M.
Henry K. Oliver, 1800-1885

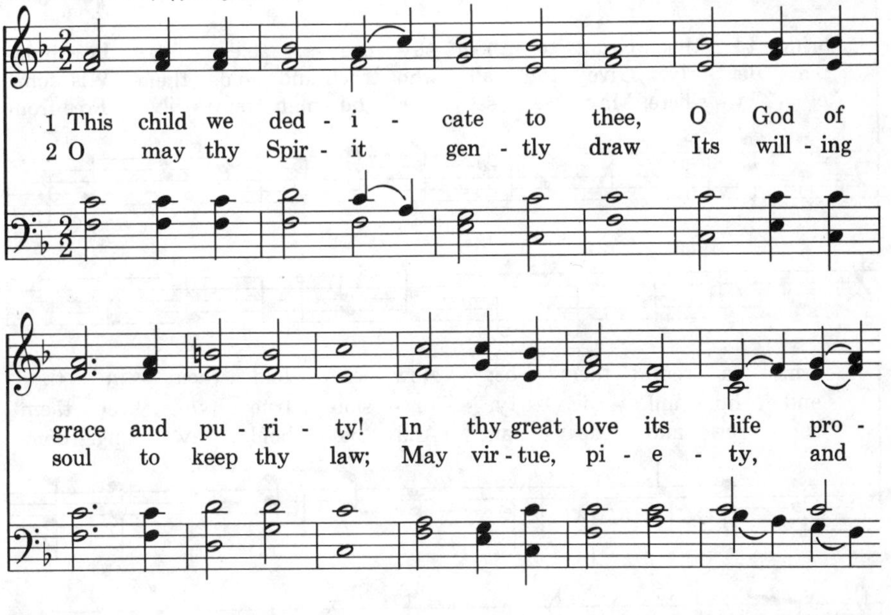

1 This child we ded - i - cate to thee, O God of
2 O may thy Spir - it gen - tly draw Its will - ing

grace and pu - ri - ty! In thy great love its life pro -
soul to keep thy law; May vir - tue, pi - e - ty, and

long, Shield it, we pray, from sin and wrong.
truth Dawn e - ven with its dawn - ing youth. A - men.

507 Jesus, Friend So Kind and Gentle

Philip E. Gregory, 1886-

TILLFLYKT 8.7.8.7.8.7.
Swedish Folk Melody
"Sionstoner," 1889
Harm. by A. Royce Eckhardt, 1937-

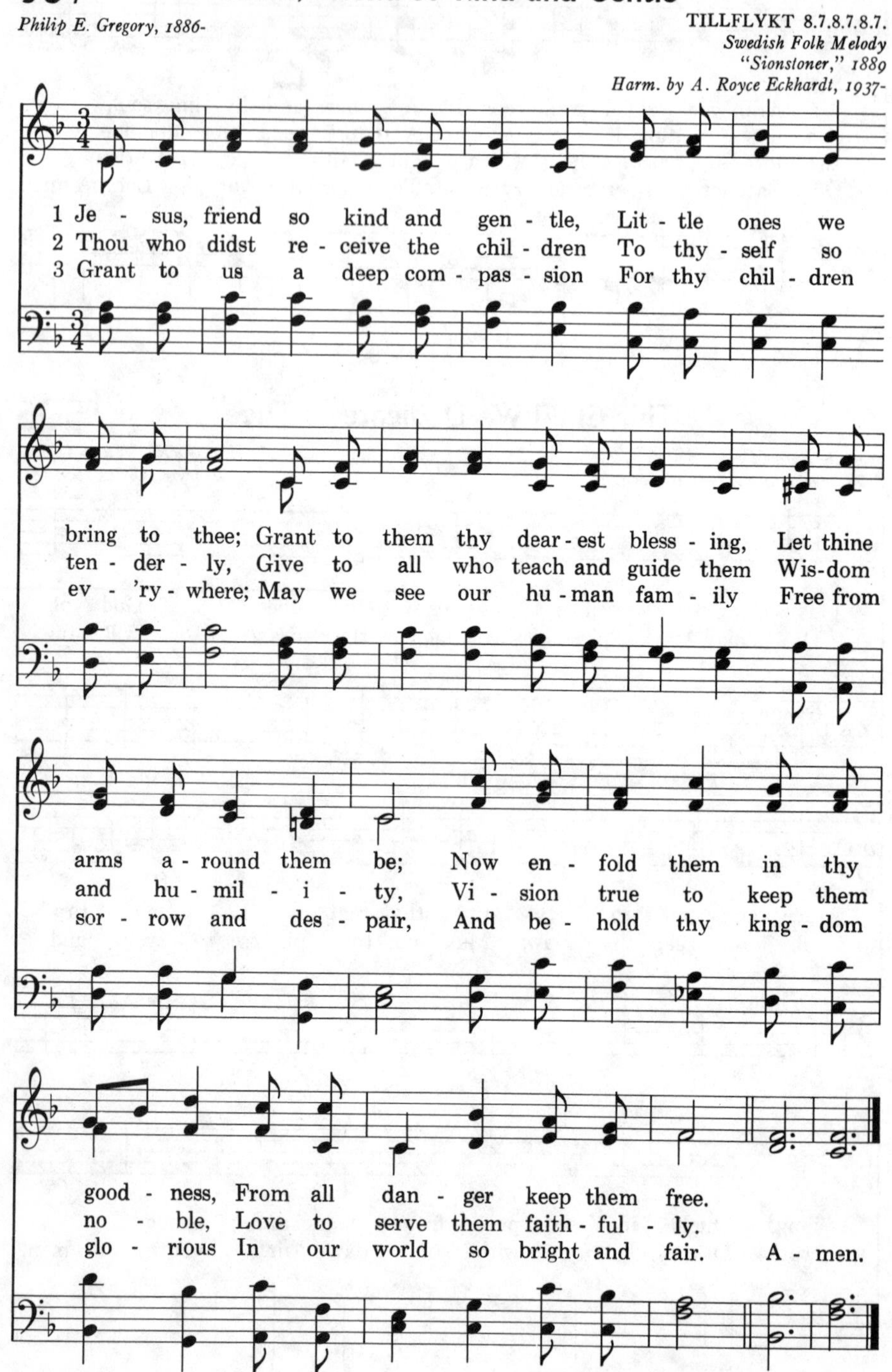

1 Je - sus, friend so kind and gen - tle, Lit - tle ones we bring to thee; Grant to them thy dear - est bless - ing, Let thine arms a - round them be; Now en - fold them in thy good - ness, From all dan - ger keep them free.
2 Thou who didst re - ceive the chil - dren To thy - self so ten - der - ly, Give to all who teach and guide them Wis - dom and hu - mil - i - ty, Vi - sion true to keep them no - ble, Love to serve them faith - ful - ly.
3 Grant to us a deep com - pas - sion For thy chil - dren ev - 'ry - where; May we see our hu - man fam - ily Free from sor - row and des - pair, And be - hold thy king - dom glo - rious In our world so bright and fair. A - men.

BAPTISM

Deck Thyself, My Soul, with Gladness

Johann Franck, 1618-1677
Tr. Catherine Winkworth, 1827-1878

SCHMÜCKE DICH 8.8.8.8.D.
Johann Crüger, 1598-1662

1 Deck thy-self, my soul, with glad-ness, Leave the gloom-y haunts of sad - ness;
2 Sun, who all my life dost bright-en; Light who dost my soul en - light - en;
3 Je - sus, Bread of Life, I pray thee, Let me glad - ly here o - bey thee;

Come in - to the day-light's splen-dor, There with joy thy prais-es ren - der
Joy, the sweet-est man e'er know-eth; Fount, whence all my be - ing flow - eth:
Nev - er to my hurt in - vit - ed, Be thy love with love re - quit - ed:

Un - to him whose grace un - bound-ed Hath this won-drous ban-quet found-ed:
At thy feet I cry, my Mak - er, Let me be a fit par - tak - er
From this ban-quet let me meas-ure, Lord, how vast and deep its treas-ure,

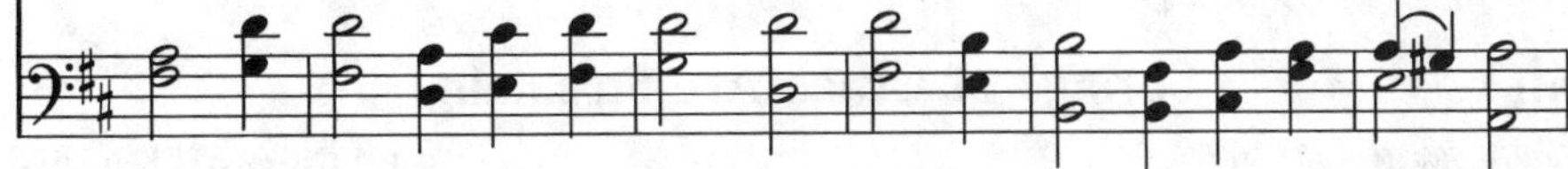

High o'er all the heav'ns he reign-eth, Yet to dwell with thee he deign-eth.
Of this bless-ed food from heav-en, For our good, thy glo-ry, giv - en.
Thru the gifts thou here dost give me, As thy guest in heav'n re-ceive me. A-men.

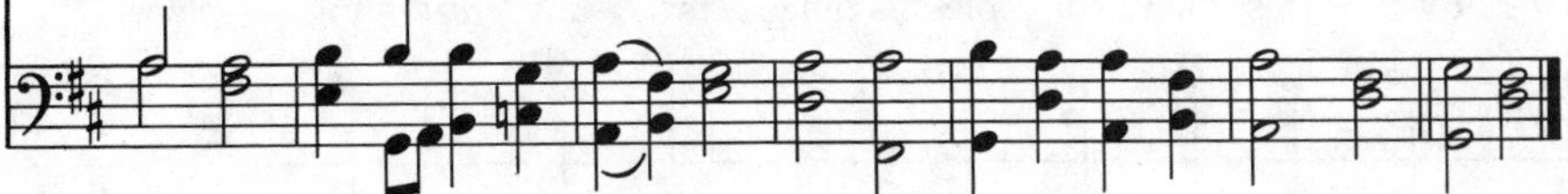

509 Bread of the World, in Mercy Broken

Reginald Heber, 1783-1826

EUCHARISTIC HYMN 9.8.9.8.
John S. B. Hodges, 1830-1915

1 Bread of the world, in mer - cy bro - ken, Wine of the
2 Look on the heart by sor - row bro - ken, Look on the

soul, in mer - cy shed, By whom the words of life were spo - ken,
tears by sin - ners shed, And be thy feast to us the to - ken

And in whose death our sins are dead:
That by thy grace our souls are fed. A - men.

510 Springs of Grace Are Streaming

Carl A. Stenholm, 1843-1884
Tr. E. Gustav Johnson, 1893-

LIVING WATER 6.5.6.5.
Source unknown

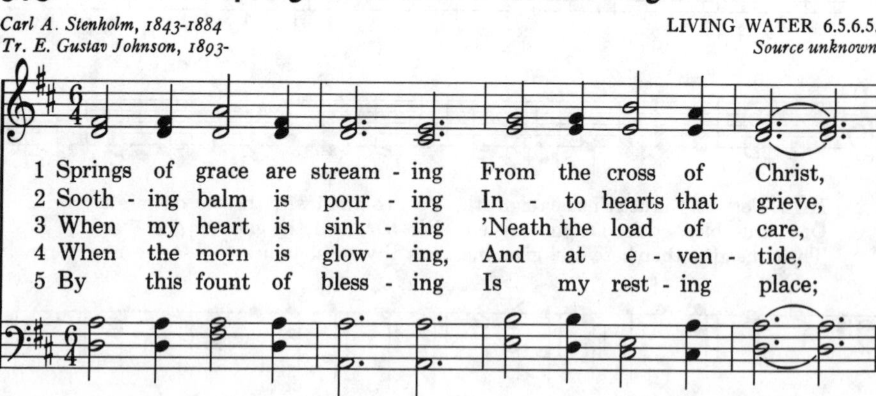
1 Springs of grace are stream - ing From the cross of Christ,
2 Sooth - ing balm is pour - ing In - to hearts that grieve,
3 When my heart is sink - ing 'Neath the load of care,
4 When the morn is glow - ing, And at e - ven - tide,
5 By this fount of bless - ing Is my rest - ing place;

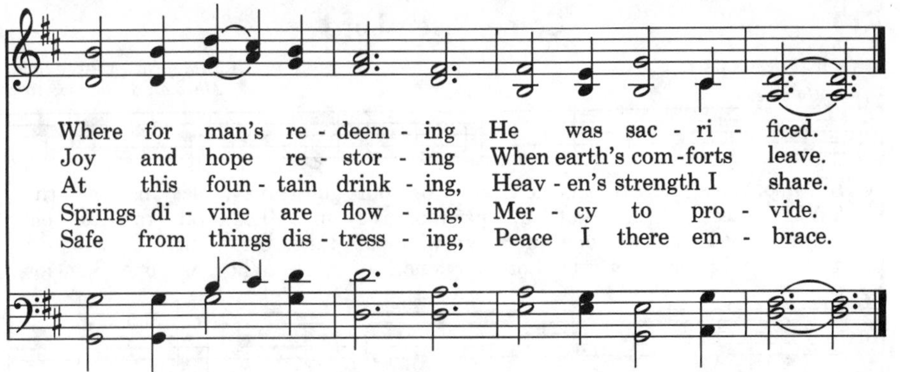
Where for man's re - deem - ing He was sac - ri - ficed.
Joy and hope re - stor - ing When earth's com-forts leave.
At this foun - tain drink - ing, Heav - en's strength I share.
Springs di - vine are flow - ing, Mer - cy to pro - vide.
Safe from things dis - tress - ing, Peace I there em - brace.

For the Bread Which Thou Hast Broken 511

Louis F. Benson, 1855-1930

KINGDOM 8.7.8.7.
V. Earle Copes, 1921-

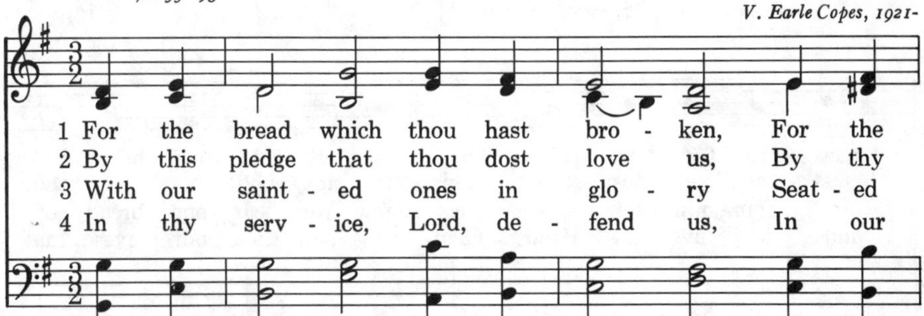

1 For the bread which thou hast bro - ken, For the
2 By this pledge that thou dost love us, By thy
3 With our saint - ed ones in glo - ry Seat - ed
4 In thy serv - ice, Lord, de - fend us, In our

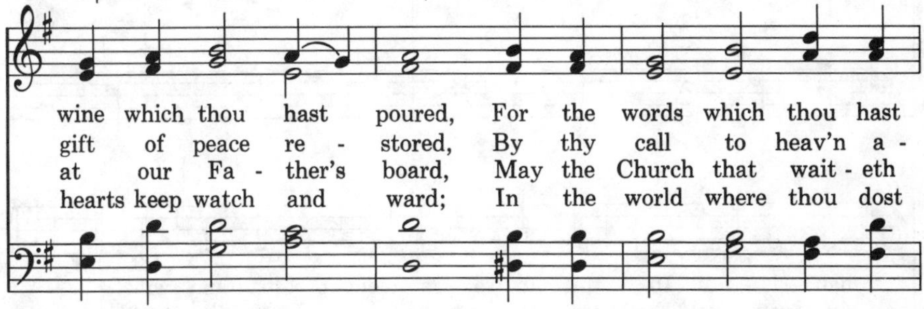

wine which thou hast poured, For the words which thou hast
gift of peace re - stored, By thy call to heav'n a -
at our Fa - ther's board, May the Church that wait - eth
hearts keep watch and ward; In the world where thou dost

spo - ken, Now we give thee thanks, O Lord.
bove us, Hal - low all our lives, O Lord.
for thee Keep love's tie un - bro - ken, Lord.
send us Let thy king - dom come, O Lord. A - men.

512 Come, Risen Lord

George W. Briggs, 1875-1959 SURSUM CORDA 10.10.10.10.
Alfred M. Smith, 1879-1970

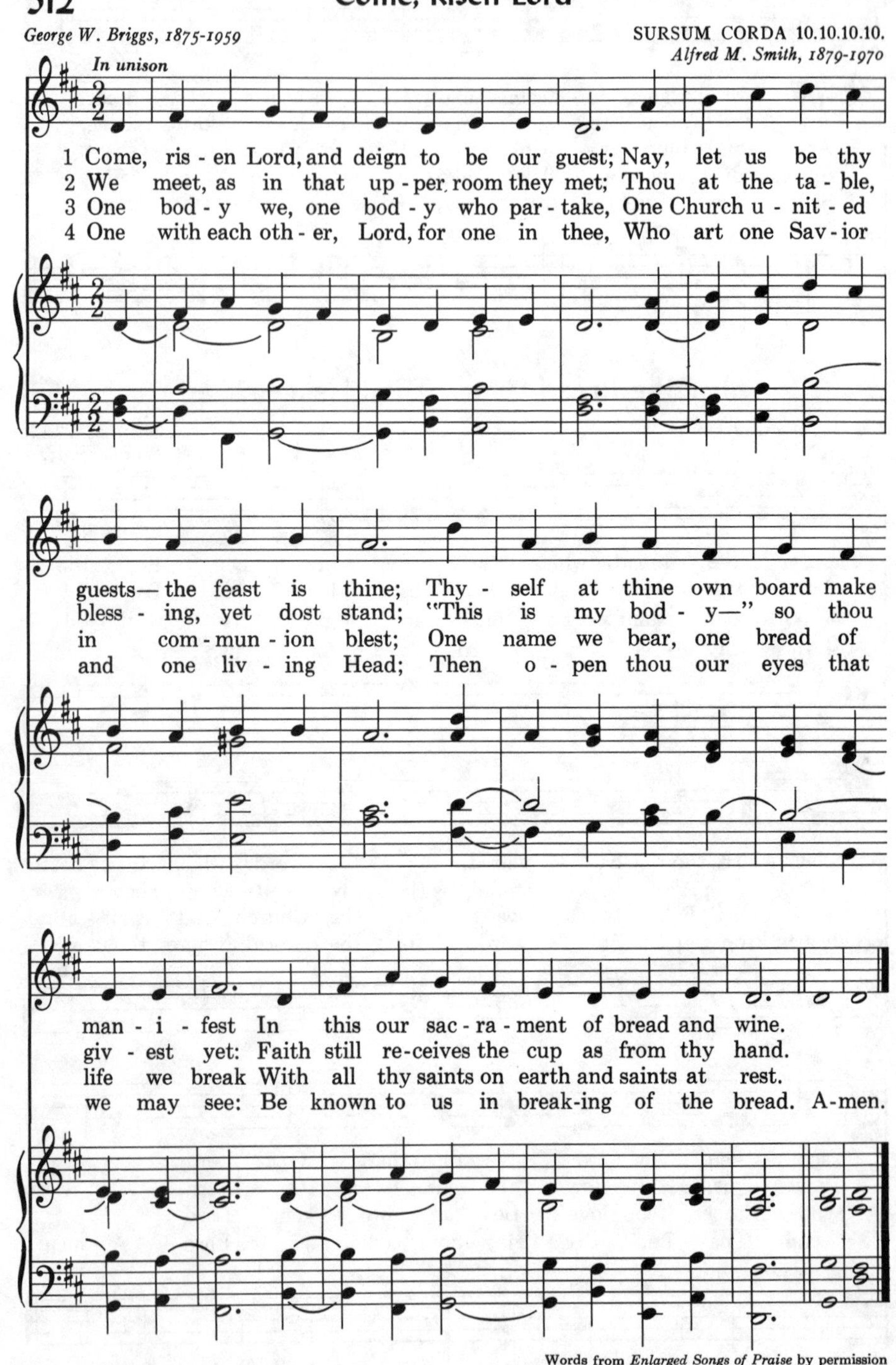

In unison
1 Come, ris - en Lord, and deign to be our guest; Nay, let us be thy
2 We meet, as in that up - per room they met; Thou at the ta - ble,
3 One bod - y we, one bod - y who par - take, One Church u - nit - ed
4 One with each oth - er, Lord, for one in thee, Who art one Sav - ior
guests— the feast is thine; Thy - self at thine own board make
bless - ing, yet dost stand; "This is my bod - y—" so thou
in com - mun - ion blest; One name we bear, one bread of
and one liv - ing Head; Then o - pen thou our eyes that
man - i - fest In this our sac - ra - ment of bread and wine.
giv - est yet: Faith still re - ceives the cup as from thy hand.
life we break With all thy saints on earth and saints at rest.
we may see: Be known to us in break - ing of the bread. A - men.

 Alternate tune: MORECAMBE, *No. 513*

Not Worthy, Lord, to Gather Up the Crumbs

Edward H. Bickersteth, 1825-1906

MORECAMBE 10.10.10.10.
Frederick C. Atkinson, 1841-1897

1 Not wor - thy, Lord, to gath - er up the crumbs
2 I am not wor - thy to be thought thy child,
3 I hear thy voice— thou bidd'st me come and rest;
4 My praise can on - ly breathe it - self in prayer,

With trem - bling hand that from thy ta - ble fall,
Nor sit the last and low - est at thy board;
I come, I kneel, I clasp thy pierc - ed feet;
My prayer can on - ly lose it - self in thee;

A wea - ry, heav - y - la - den sin - ner comes
Too long a wan - d'rer and too oft be - guiled,
Thou bidd'st me take my place, a wel - come guest
Dwell thou for - ev - er in my heart, and there,

To plead thy prom - ise and o - bey thy call.
I on - ly ask one rec - on - cil - ing word.
A - mong thy saints, and of thy ban - quet eat.
Lord, let me sup with thee—sup thou with me. A - men.

514 Here, O My Lord, I See Thee Face to Face

Horatius Bonar, 1808-1889
PENITENTIA 10.10.10.10.
Edward Dearle, 1806-1891
1 Here, O my Lord, I see thee face to face,
2 Here would I feed up - on the bread of God,
3 I have no help but thine, nor do I need
4 Mine is the sin, but thine the right - eous - ness,
Here would I touch and han - dle things un - seen;
Here drink with thee the roy - al wine of heav'n;
An - oth - er arm save thine to lean up - on;
Mine is the guilt, but thine the cleans - ing blood;
Here grasp with firm - er hand e - ter - nal grace,
Here would I lay a - side each earth - ly load,
It is e - nough, my Lord, e - nough in - deed—
Here is my robe, my ref - uge, and my peace—
And all my wea - ri - ness up - on thee lean.
Here taste a - fresh the calm of sin for - giv'n.
My strength is in thy might, thy might a - lone.
Thy blood, thy right - eous - ness, O Lord, my God. A - men.

LORD'S SUPPER

Alternate tune: MORECAMBE, No. 513

O Bread of Life from Heaven

Latin hymn, c.1661
Tr. Philip Schaff, 1819-1893

INNSBRUCK 7.7.6.7.7.8.
German Melody
Adapted by Heinrich Isaak, c.1450-1517
Harm. by F. Melius Christiansen, 1871-1955

1 O bread of life from heav - en, To wea - ry pil - grims
2 O fount of grace re - deem - ing, O riv - er ev - er
3 Je - sus, this feast re - ceiv - ing, Thy word of truth be -

giv - en, O man - na from a - bove: The
stream - ing From Je - sus' ho - ly side: Come
liev - ing, We thee un - seen a - dore: Grant,

souls that hun - ger feed thou, The hearts that seek thee
thou, thy - self be - stow - ing On thirst - ing souls, and
when our race is end - ed, That we, to heav'n as -

lead thou, With thy most sweet and ten - der love.
flow - ing Till all their wants are sat - is - fied.
cend - ed, May see thy glo - ry ev - er - more. A - men.

516

According to Thy Gracious Word

James Montgomery, 1771-1854

MARTYRDOM C.M.
Hugh Wilson, 1764-1824

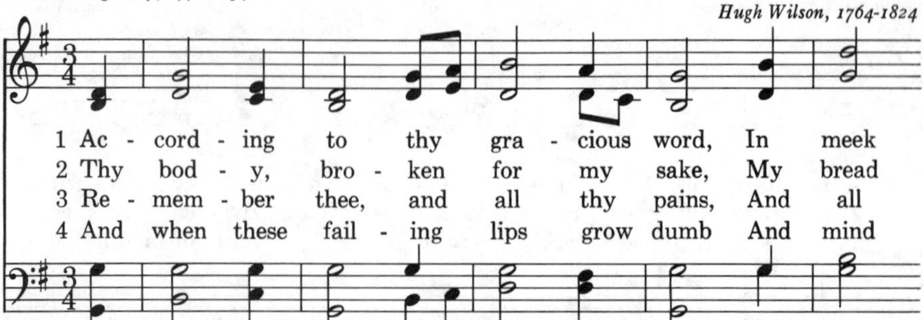

1 According to thy gracious word,
In meek humility,
This will I do, my dying Lord,
I will remember thee.

2 Thy body, broken for my sake,
My bread from heav'n shall be;
Thy testamental cup I take,
And thus remember thee:

3 Remember thee, and all thy pains,
And all thy love to me;
Yea, while a breath, a pulse, remains,
Will I remember thee.

4 And when these failing lips grow dumb
And mind and mem'ry flee,
When thou shalt in thy kingdom come,
Jesus, remember me. Amen.

517 Sons of God, Hear His Holy Word!

James Thiem, 1940-

SONS OF GOD 7.7.7.6. *with Refrain*
James Thiem, 1940-

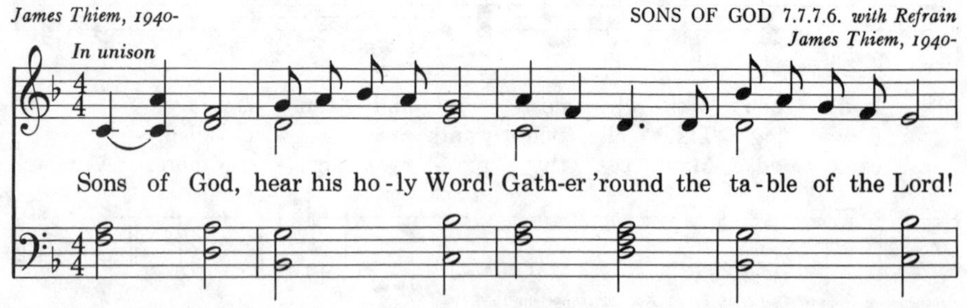
In unison
Sons of God, hear his ho-ly Word! Gath-er 'round the ta-ble of the Lord!

Eat his bod - y, drink his blood, And we'll sing a song of love: Al - le -
lu, al - le - lu, al - le - lu, al - le - lu - ia! ia!
1-6 To stanzas
7
Fine
1 Broth - ers, sis - ters, we are one, And our life has just be - gun;
2 Shout to - geth - er to the Lord, Who has prom - ised our re - ward:
3 Je - sus gave a new com - mand, That we love our fel - low - man,
4 If we want to live with him, We must al - so die with him,
5 Make the world a u - ni - ty, Make all men one fam - i - ly,
6 With the Church we cel - e - brate, Je - sus' com - ing we a - wait;
In the Spir - it we are young— We can live for - ev - er!
Hap - pi - ness a hun - dred - fold— And we'll live for - ev - er!
Till we reach the prom - ised land, Where we'll live for - ev - er!
Die to self - ish - ness and sin, And we'll rise for - ev - er!
Till we meet the Trin - i - ty And live with them for - ev - er!
So we make a hol - i - day— So we'll live for - ev - er!
D.C.

518 Let Us Break Bread Together

American Folk Hymn

LET US BREAK BREAD *Irregular*
American Folk Melody
Harm. by Norman E. Johnson, 1928-

1 Let us break bread to - geth - er on our knees; (on our knees;)
2 Let us drink wine to - geth - er on our knees; (on our knees;)
3 Let us praise God to - geth - er on our knees; (on our knees;)

Let us break bread to - geth - er on our knees; (on our knees;)
Let us drink wine to - geth - er on our knees; (on our knees;)
Let us praise God to - geth - er on our knees; (on our knees;)

REFRAIN

When I fall on my knees, With my face to the ris - ing sun,

O Lord, have mer - cy on me. (on me.)

O Lamb of God, Most Holy

Nikolaus Decius, c.1490-1541
Tr. Olof Olsson, 1841-1900

O LAMM GOTTES 7.7.7.7.7.7.7.
"Christliche Kirchen Ordnung," 1542

O Lamb of God, most ho - ly, On Cal - va -
ry an of - f'ring, De - spis - ed, meek and low - ly,
Thou in thy death and suf - f'ring Our sins didst
bear, our an - guish, The might of death didst
van - quish: Grant us thy peace, O Je - sus! A - men.

How Wonderful It Is

Nils Frykman, 1842-1911
Tr. E. Gustav Johnson, 1893-

GEMENSKAP 6.6.7.6.
Nils Frykman, 1842-1911

1 How won - der - ful it is To come in per - fect bliss,
2 Of great - er joy to me No oth - er thing can be,
3 I know that he is near, Our friend and Sav - ior dear;
4 My soul is now at ease, My bless - ings here in - crease,
5 His full a - bun - dant grace In truth I can em - brace,
6 O broth - ers, sing with joy, With praise your tongues em - ploy;
7 No mor - tal here be - low Can ev - er see or know

With saints in sweet com - mun - ion, To such a feast as this.
Than shar - ing with God's chil - dren This love and har - mo - ny.
I feel his ho - ly pres - ence, His lov - ing words I hear.
Since from all guilt the Sav - ior Has giv - en me re - lease.
And there - fore in his keep - ing My life and soul I place.
The good - ness of his bless - ing The world can - not de - stroy.
The glo - ry that in heav - en The Fa - ther will be - stow.

521 A Parting Hymn We Sing

Based on Matthew 26:30
Aaron R. Wolfe, 1821-1902, alt.

SCHUMANN S.M.
Mason and Webb's "Cantica Laudis," 1850

1 A part - ing hymn we sing A - round thy ta - ble, Lord;
2 Here have we seen thy face, And felt thy pres - ence near;
3 In self - for - get - ting love Be our com - mun - ion shown,

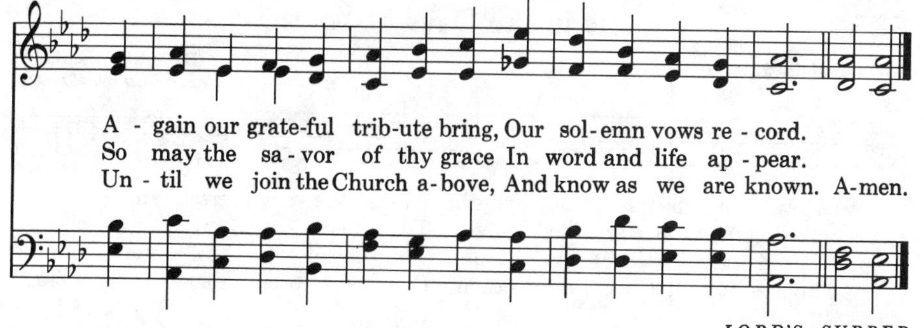

A - gain our grate-ful trib-ute bring, Our sol-emn vows re - cord.
So may the sa - vor of thy grace In word and life ap - pear.
Un - til we join the Church a-bove, And know as we are known. A-men.

LORD'S SUPPER

Shepherd of Tender Youth

522

Ascribed to Clement of Alexandria, c.170-220
Tr. Henry Martyn Dexter, 1821-1890

ITALIAN HYMN 6.6.4.6.6.6.4.
Felice de Giardini, 1716-1796

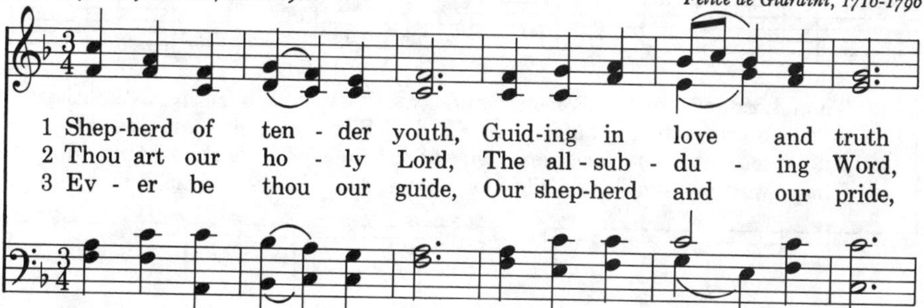

1 Shep-herd of ten - der youth, Guid-ing in love and truth
2 Thou art our ho - ly Lord, The all-sub - du - ing Word,
3 Ev - er be thou our guide, Our shep-herd and our pride,

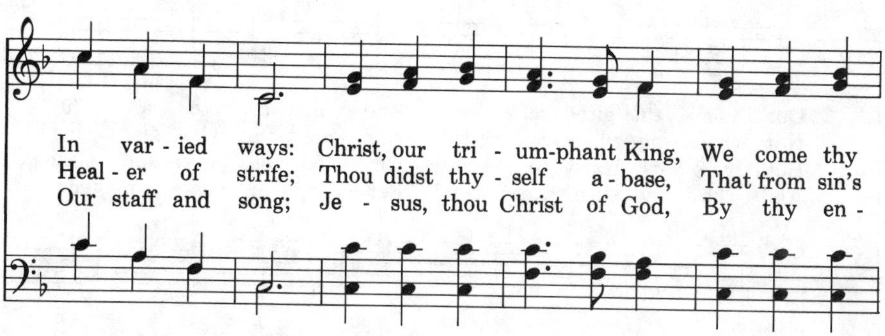

In var-ied ways: Christ, our tri - um-phant King, We come thy
Heal-er of strife; Thou didst thy - self a-base, That from sin's
Our staff and song; Je - sus, thou Christ of God, By thy en -

name to sing, And here our chil-dren bring To sound thy praise.
deep dis-grace Thou might-est save our race And give us life.
dur - ing word, Lead us where thou hast trod, Make our faith strong. A-men.

Another harmonization may be found at No. 275
Another harmonization in a higher setting may be found at No. 557

CONFIRMATION

523 Now in the Days of Youth

Walter J. Mathams, 1853-1932

DIADEMATA S.M.D.
George J. Elvey, 1816-1893

1 Now in the days of youth, When life flows fresh and free,
2 Teach us, wher-e'er we live, To act as in thy sight,
3 Teach us to love the true, The beau - ti - ful and pure,
4 Spir - it of Christ, do thou Our first bright days in - spire,

Thou Lord of all our hearts and lives, We give our-selves to thee;
And do what thou wouldst have us do, With ra - di - ant de - light;
And let us not for one short hour An e - vil thought en - dure;
That we may live the life of love And loft - i - est de - sire;

Our fer - vent gift re - ceive, And fit us to ful - fill,
Not choos - ing what is great, Nor spurn - ing what is small,
But give us grace to stand De - cid - ed, brave, and strong,
And be by thee pre - pared For larg - er years to come,

Thru all our days, in all our ways, Our heav'n-ly Fa-ther's will.
But tak - ing from thy hands our tasks, To glo - ri - fy them all.
The lov - ers of all ho - ly things, The foes of all things wrong.
And for the life in - ef - fa - ble With-in the Fa-ther's home. A-men.

CONFIRMATION

A lower setting may be found at No. 224

With Solemn Joy We Come, Dear Lord 524

Ernest Edwin Ryden, 1886-

ST. PETER C.M.

Alexander R. Reinagle, 1799-1877

1 With sol - emn joy we come, dear Lord, To make our vows this day; We find in thee our hope, our life—Thou art the liv - ing way.
2 In child - hood's pure and bless - ed morn Thy gift was shed from heav'n, When at the sa - cred font of life Our souls to thee were giv'n.
3 And through the years thy won - drous grace Has fol - lowed all the way; Thy love has nev - er let us go, Though we are prone to stray.
4 For - give, dear Lord, each fault and stain, And cleanse our hearts from sin; Help us to walk in hum - ble faith, And keep us pure with - in. A - men.

5 O blessed Savior, thine we are,
Thy name we would confess;
Thy Spirit pour into our hearts,
Our youthful lives to bless.

6 O keep us faithful, keep us true,
And seal us for thine own,
That we may stand at last with joy
Before thy great white throne. Amen.

Words from *The Lutheran Service Book and Hymnal*, by permission of the Commission on the Liturgy and Hymnal.

A lower setting may be found at No. 330

525 "Are Ye Able," Said the Master

Based on Mark 10:35-40
Earl B. Marlatt, 1892-

BEACON HILL 8.7.8.7. *with Refrain*
Harry S. Mason, 1881-1964

1 "Are ye a - ble," said the Mas - ter, "To be cru - ci - fied with me?"
2 "Are ye a - ble" to re - mem - ber, When a thief lifts up his eyes,
3 "Are ye a - ble?" still the Mas - ter Whis - pers down e - ter - ni - ty,
"Yea," the stur - dy dream - ers an - swered, "To the death we fol - low thee."
That his par - doned soul is wor - thy Of a place in par - a - dise?
And he - ro - ic spir - its an - swer Now, as then in Gal - i - lee:
REFRAIN
"Lord, we are a - ble!" our spir - its are thine; Re - mold them—
make us, like thee, di - vine. Thy guid - ing ra - diance a - bove us shall
be A bea - con to God, to love and loy - al - ty. A - men.

I Bind My Heart This Tide

526

Lauchlan MacLean Watt, 1867-1957
FEALTY 6.7.7.7.D.
Grace Wilbur Conant, 1880-1948
1 I bind my heart this tide To the Gal - i - le - an's side,
2 I bind my heart in thrall To the God, the Lord of all,
To the wounds of Cal - va - ry, To the Christ who died for me.
To the God, the poor man's friend, And the Christ whom he did send.
I bind my soul this day To the broth - er far a - way—
I bind my - self to peace, To make strife and en - vy cease:
And the broth-er near at hand In this town and in this land.
God, knit thou sure the cord Of my thrall-dom to my Lord! A-men.

Words used by permission of A. L. MacLean Watt.
Music used by permission of Fleming H. Revell Company.

527 Forth in Thy Name, O Lord, I Go

ROCKINGHAM L.M.

Charles Wesley, 1707-1788

Aaron Williams' "Supplement to Psalmody," c.1780
Adapted by Edward Miller, 1731-1807

1 Forth in thy name, O Lord, I go, My dai - ly
2 The task thy wis - dom hath as - signed O let me
3 Thee may I set at my right hand, Whose eyes my
4 Give me to bear thy eas - y yoke, And ev - 'ry
la - bor to pur - sue— Thee, on - ly thee, re - solved to
cheer - ful - ly ful - fill— In all my works thy pres - ence
in - most sub - stance see— And la - bor on at thy com-
mo - ment watch and pray—And still to things e - ter - nal
know In all I think or speak or do.
find, And prove thy good and per - fect will.
mand, And of - fer all my works to thee.
look, And has - ten to thy glo - rious day. A - men.
1 Be - hold us, Lord, a lit - tle space From dai - ly tasks set free,
2 A - round us rolls the cease-less tide Of busi-ness, toil, and care;
3 Yet these are not the on - ly walls Where-in thou mayst be sought:
4 Thine are the loom, the forge, the mart, The wealth of land and sea,
5 Then let us prove our heav'n-ly birth In all we do and know;
6 Work shall be prayer, if all be wrought As thou wouldst have it done;

A lower setting may be found at No. 535

528 Behold Us, Lord, a Little Space

DUNFERMLINE C.M.

John Ellerton, 1826-1893

"Scottish Psalter," 1615

And met with-in thy ho - ly place To rest a - while with thee.
And scarce-ly can we turn a - side For one brief hour of prayer.
On home-liest work thy bless-ing falls, In truth and pa-tience wrought.
The worlds of sci-ence and of art, Re-vealed and ruled by thee.
And claim the king-dom of the earth For thee and not thy foe.
And prayer, by thee in-spired and taught, It - self with work be one. A-men.

"Take Up Thy Cross," the Savior Said 529

Based on Luke 9:23
Charles W. Everest, 1814-1877

DISTRESS L.M.
William Walker's "Southern Harmony," 1835

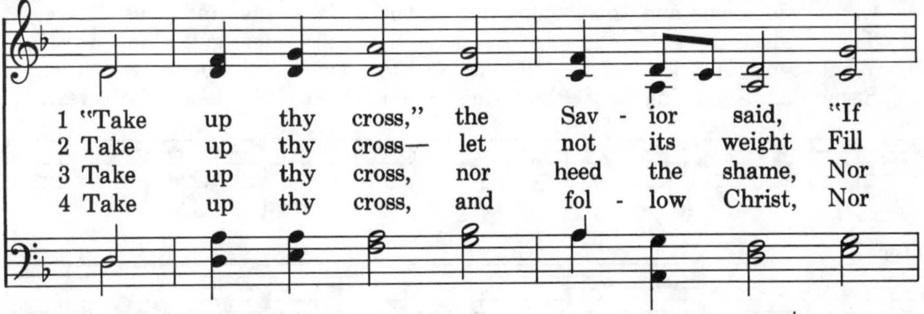

1 "Take up thy cross," the Sav - ior said, "If
2 Take up thy cross— let not its weight Fill
3 Take up thy cross, nor heed the shame, Nor
4 Take up thy cross, and fol - low Christ, Nor

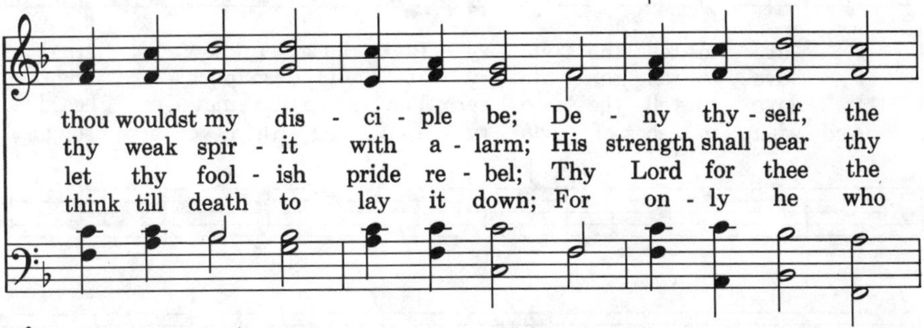

thou wouldst my dis - ci - ple be; De - ny thy - self, the
thy weak spir - it with a - larm; His strength shall bear thy
let thy fool - ish pride re - bel; Thy Lord for thee the
think till death to lay it down; For on - ly he who

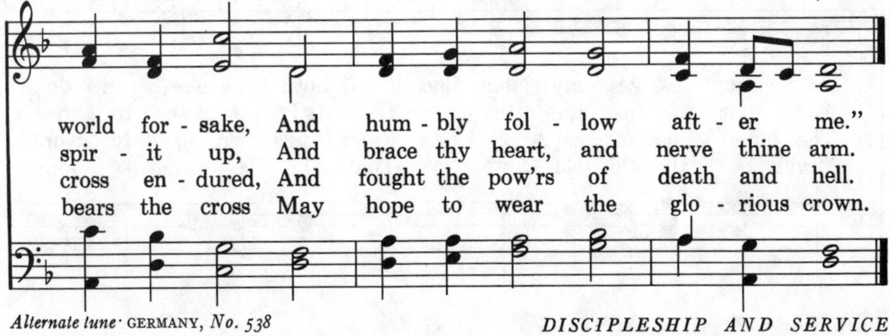

world for - sake, And hum - bly fol - low aft - er me."
spir - it up, And brace thy heart, and nerve thine arm.
cross en - dured, And fought the pow'rs of death and hell.
bears the cross May hope to wear the glo - rious crown.

Alternate tune: GERMANY, *No. 538*

530 I Love to Tell the Story

Katherine Hankey, 1834-1911

HANKEY 7.6.7.6.D. *with Refrain*
William G. Fischer, 1835-1912

1 I love to tell the sto - ry Of un - seen things a - bove,
2 I love to tell the sto - ry—More won - der - ful it seems
3 I love to tell the sto - ry—'Tis pleas - ant to re - peat
4 I love to tell the sto - ry—For those who know it best

Of Je - sus and his glo - ry, Of Je - sus and his love;
Than all the gold - en fan - cies Of all our gold - en dreams;
What seems, each time I tell it, More won - der - ful - ly sweet;
Seem hun - ger - ing and thirst - ing To hear it like the rest;

I love to tell the sto - ry— Be - cause I know 'tis true,
I love to tell the sto - ry— It did so much for me,
I love to tell the sto - ry— For some have nev - er heard
And when in scenes of glo - ry I sing the new, new song,

It sat - is - fies my long - ings As noth - ing else can do.
And that is just the rea - son I tell it now to thee.
The mes - sage of sal - va - tion From God's own ho - ly word.
'Twill be the old, old sto - ry That I have loved so long.

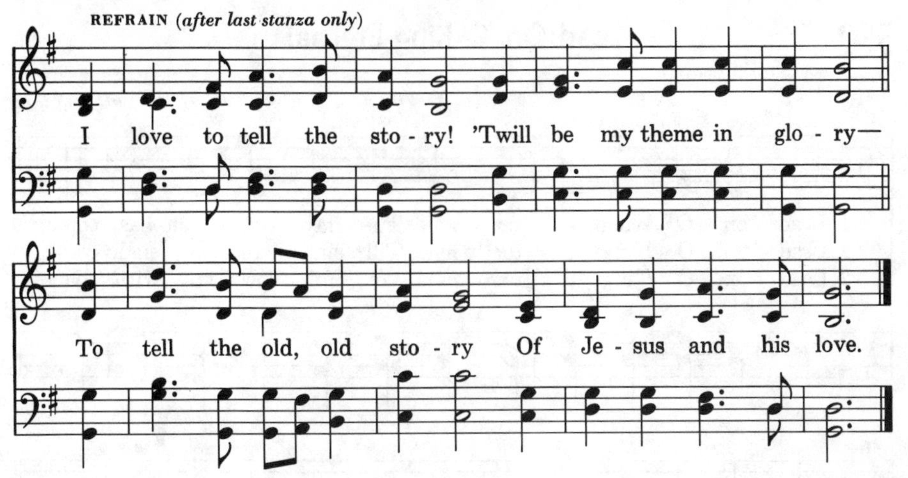
REFRAIN (after last stanza only)
I love to tell the sto - ry! 'Twill be my theme in glo - ry—
To tell the old, old sto - ry Of Je - sus and his love.

O Master, Let Me Walk with Thee 531

Washington Gladden, 1836-1918

MARYTON L.M.
H. Percy Smith, 1825-1898

1 O Master, let me walk with thee
In lowly paths of service free;
Tell me thy secret—help me bear
The strain of toil, the fret of care.

2 Help me the slow of heart to move
By some clear, winning word of love;
Teach me the wayward feet to stay,
And guide them in the homeward way.

3 Teach me thy patience: still with thee
In closer, dearer company,
In work that keeps faith sweet and strong,
In trust that triumphs over wrong.

4 In hope that sends a shining ray
Far down the future's broad'ning way,
In peace that only thou canst give,
With thee, O Master, let me live. Amen.

532 Lead On, O King Eternal

Ernest W. Shurtleff, 1862-1917

LANCASHIRE 7.6.7.6.D.
Henry T. Smart, 1813-1879

1 Lead on, O King e - ter - nal, The day of march has come;
2 Lead on, O King e - ter - nal, Till sin's fierce war shall cease,
3 Lead on, O King e - ter - nal, We fol - low, not with fears,

Hence-forth in fields of con - quest Thy tents shall be our home.
And ho - li - ness shall whis - per The sweet a - men of peace.
For glad - ness breaks like morn - ing Wher - e'er thy face ap - pears.

Through days of prep - a - ra - tion Thy grace has made us strong,
For not with swords' loud clash - ing, Nor roll of stir - ring drums—
Thy cross is lift - ed o'er us, We jour - ney in its light;

And now, O King e - ter - nal, We lift our bat - tle song.
With deeds of love and mer - cy The heavenly king - dom comes.
The crown a - waits the con - quest: Lead on, O God of might. A - men.

A higher setting may be found at No. 218

533 O Young and Fearless Prophet

S. Ralph Harlow, 1885-1972

WEBB 7.6.7.6.D.
George J. Webb, 1803-1887

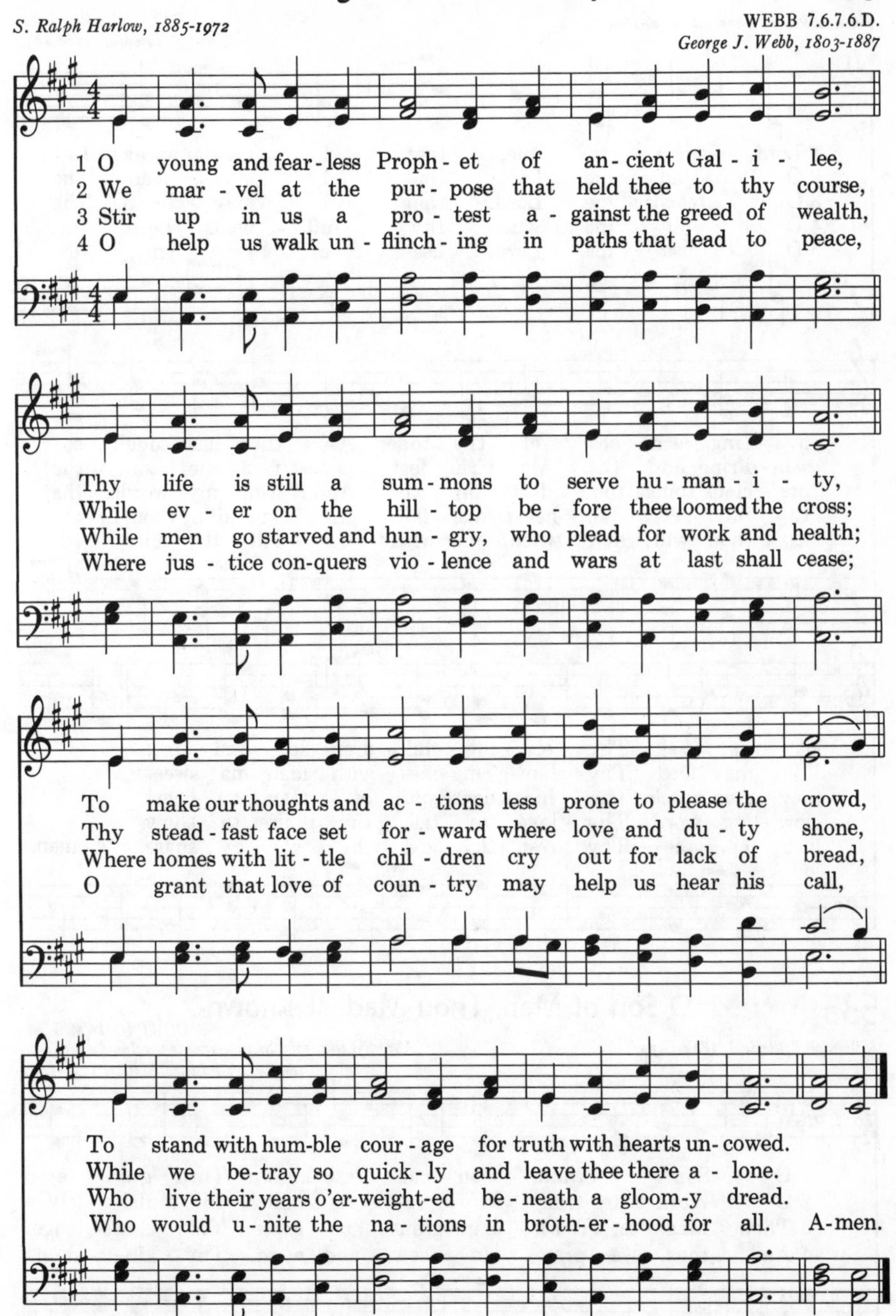

1 O young and fear-less Proph-et of an-cient Gal-i-lee,
2 We mar-vel at the pur-pose that held thee to thy course,
3 Stir up in us a pro-test a-gainst the greed of wealth,
4 O help us walk un-flinch-ing in paths that lead to peace,
Thy life is still a sum-mons to serve hu-man-i-ty,
While ev-er on the hill-top be-fore thee loomed the cross;
While men go starved and hun-gry, who plead for work and health;
Where jus-tice con-quers vio-lence and wars at last shall cease;
To make our thoughts and ac-tions less prone to please the crowd,
Thy stead-fast face set for-ward where love and du-ty shone,
Where homes with lit-tle chil-dren cry out for lack of bread,
O grant that love of coun-try may help us hear his call,
To stand with hum-ble cour-age for truth with hearts un-cowed.
While we be-tray so quick-ly and leave thee there a-lone.
Who live their years o'er-weight-ed be-neath a gloom-y dread.
Who would u-nite the na-tions in broth-er-hood for all. A-men.

A higher setting may be found at No. 374

534 Lord, Speak to Me

Frances Ridley Havergal, 1836-1879

CANONBURY L.M.
Robert Schumann, 1810-1856

1 Lord, speak to me, that I may speak In
2 O lead me, Lord, that I may lead The
3 O teach me, Lord, that I may teach The
4 O fill me with thy full - ness, Lord, Un -
5 O use me, Lord, use e - ven me, Just
liv - ing ech - oes of thy tone; As thou hast sought, so
wan - d'ring and the wa - v'ring feet; O feed me, Lord, that
pre - cious things thou dost im - part; And wing my words, that
til my ver - y heart o'er - flow In kin - dling thought and
as thou wilt, and when, and where, Un - til thy bless - ed
let me seek Thy err - ing chil - dren lost and lone.
I may feed Thy hun - g'ring ones with man - na sweet.
they may reach The hid - den depths of man - y a heart.
glow - ing word, Thy love to tell, thy praise to show.
face I see— Thy rest, thy joy, thy glo - ry share. A - men.

535 O Son of Man, Thou Madest Known

Milton S. Littlefield, 1864-1934

ROCKINGHAM L.M.
Aaron Williams' "Supplement to Psalmody," c.1780
Adapted by Edward Miller, 1731-1807

1 O Son of Man, thou mad - est known, Thru qui - et
2 O Work - man true, may we ful - fill In dai - ly
3 Thou Mas - ter Work - man, grant us grace The chal - lenge
4 And thus, we pray in deed and word, Thy king - dom

Alternate tunes: DISTRESS, No. 529; CANONBURY, No. 534

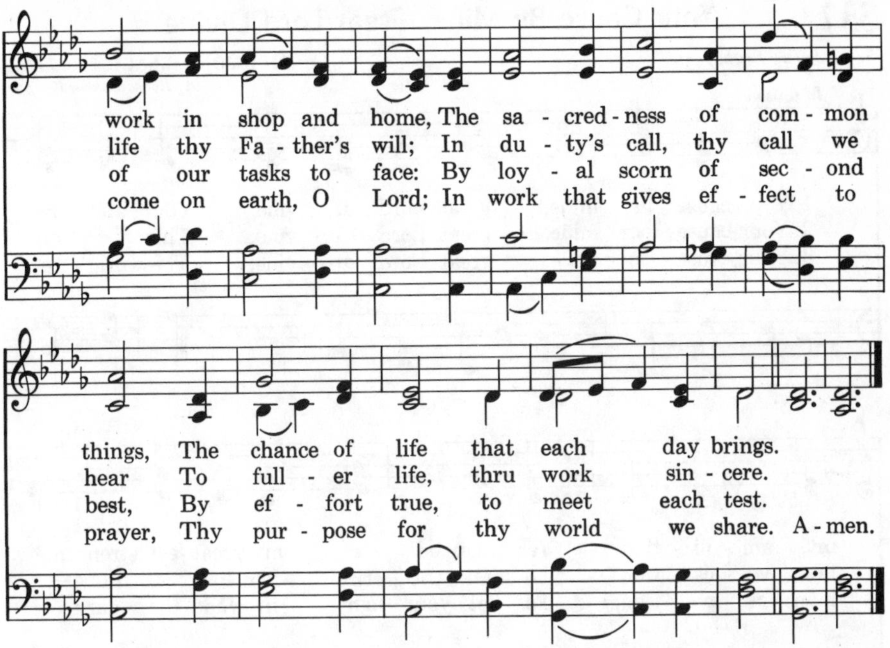

work in shop and home, The sa - cred - ness of com - mon
life thy Fa - ther's will; In du - ty's call, thy call we
of our tasks to face: By loy - al scorn of sec - ond
come on earth, O Lord; In work that gives ef - fect to

things, The chance of life that each day brings.
hear To full - er life, thru work sin - cere.
best, By ef - fort true, to meet each test.
prayer, Thy pur - pose for thy world we share. A - men.

We Bear the Strain of Earthly Care 536

Ozora Stearns Davis, 1866-1931

AZMON C.M.
Carl G. Gläser, 1784-1829
Mason's "Modern Psalmody," 1839

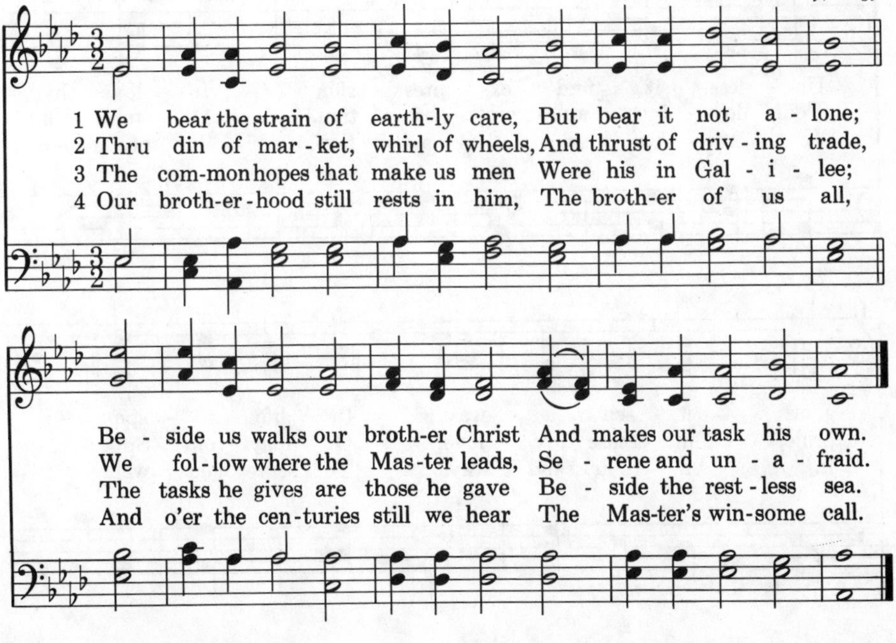

1 We bear the strain of earth-ly care, But bear it not a - lone;
2 Thru din of mar - ket, whirl of wheels, And thrust of driv - ing trade,
3 The com-mon hopes that make us men Were his in Gal - i - lee;
4 Our broth-er - hood still rests in him, The broth-er of us all,

Be - side us walks our broth-er Christ And makes our task his own.
We fol - low where the Mas-ter leads, Se - rene and un - a - fraid.
The tasks he gives are those he gave Be - side the rest - less sea.
And o'er the cen-turies still we hear The Mas-ter's win-some call.

537 Your Cause Be Mine, Great Lord Divine

Bryan Jeffery Leech, 1931-

RICHMOND BEACH 8.7.8.7.8.8.7.
A. Royce Eckhardt, 1937-

In unison
1 Your cause be mine, great Lord di - vine, Your aim be my am - bi - tion: For wast - ed is my great - est strength Un - less it find ex - pres - sion In love that gives it - self a - way, In life re - spon -
2 Your cause be mine, great Lord di - vine, This be my life's vo - ca - tion: To seek the prize when life is done— Your lov - ing ap - pro - ba - tion. Di - min - ish pride, in - crease my love, O may your Spir -
3 Your cause be mine, great Lord di - vine, The world's e - man - ci - pa - tion: To let your light in - vade the dark In ev - 'ry sit - u - a - tion, To prove you in a thou - sand ways, To serve you well

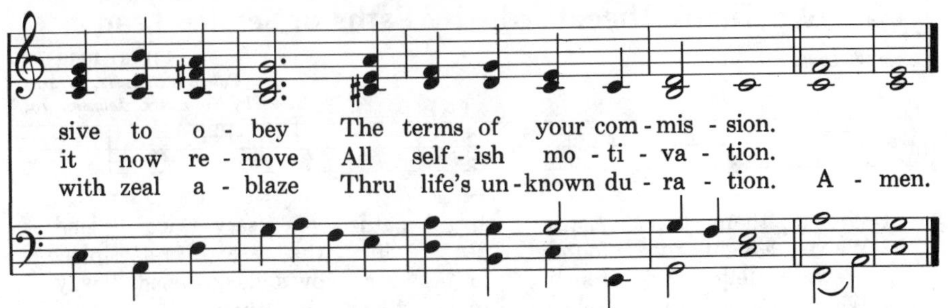
sive to o - bey The terms of your com - mis - sion.
it now re - move All self - ish mo - ti - va - tion.
with zeal a - blaze Thru life's un - known du - ra - tion. A - men.

Where Cross the Crowded Ways of Life 538

Frank Mason North, 1850-1935

GERMANY L.M.

William Gardiner's "Sacred Melodies," 1815

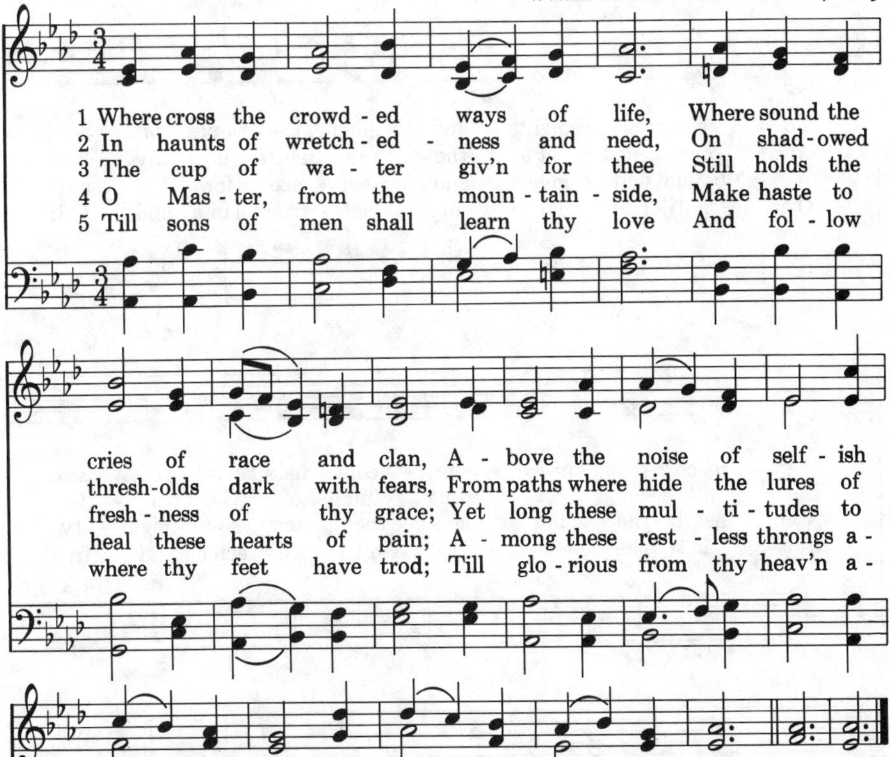

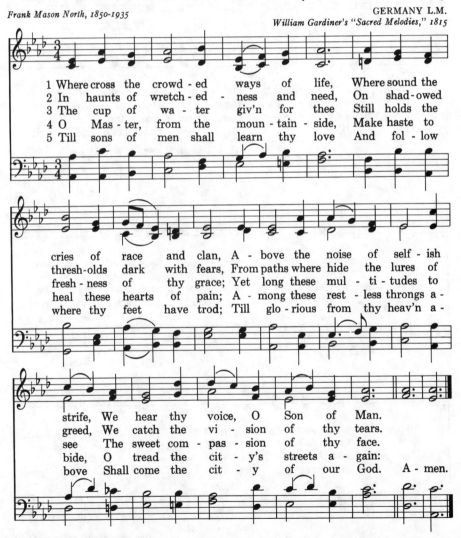

1 Where cross the crowd - ed ways of life, Where sound the
2 In haunts of wretch - ed - ness and need, On shad - owed
3 The cup of wa - ter giv'n for thee Still holds the
4 O Mas - ter, from the moun - tain - side, Make haste to
5 Till sons of men shall learn thy love And fol - low

cries of race and clan, A - bove the noise of self - ish
thresh - olds dark with fears, From paths where hide the lures of
fresh - ness of thy grace; Yet long these mul - ti - tudes to
heal these hearts of pain; A - mong these rest - less throngs a -
where thy feet have trod; Till glo - rious from thy heav'n a -

strife, We hear thy voice, O Son of Man.
greed, We catch the vi - sion of thy tears.
see The sweet com - pas - sion of thy face.
bide, O tread the cit - y's streets a - gain:
bove Shall come the cit - y of our God. A - men.

A higher setting may be found at No. 623

539 We Thank Thee, Lord, Thy Paths of Service Lead

Calvin W. Laufer, 1874-1938

FIELD 10.10.10.10.
Calvin W. Laufer, 1874-1938
Harm. by Norman E. Johnson, 1928-

1 We thank thee, Lord, thy paths of serv - ice lead
2 We've sought and found thee in the se - cret place
3 We've felt thy touch in sor - row's dark - ened way
4 We've seen thy glo - ry like a man - tle spread
To bla - zoned heights and down the slopes of need;
And mar - veled at the ra - diance of thy face;
A - bound with love and sol - ace for the day;
O'er hill and dale in saf - fron flame and red;
They reach thy throne, en - com - pass land and sea,
But oft - en in some far - off Gal - i - lee
And, 'neath the bur - dens there, thy sov - 'reign - ty
But, in the eyes of men re - deemed and free,
And he who jour - neys in them walks with thee.
Be - held thee fair - er yet while serv - ing thee.
Has held our hearts en-thralled while serv - ing thee.
A splen - dor great - er yet while serv - ing thee. A - men.

Alternate tune: MORECAMBE, *No. 265*

Christ Is the World's True Light

George Wallace Briggs, 1875-1959

ST. JOAN 6.7.6.7.6.6.6.6.
Percy E. B. Coller, 1895-

1 Christ is the world's true light, Its cap-tain of sal - va - tion,
2 In Christ all rac - es meet, Their an-cient feuds for - get - ting,
3 One Lord, in one great name U - nite us all who own thee,
The day-star clear and bright Of ev - 'ry man and na - tion;
The whole round world com-plete, From sun-rise to its set - ting:
Cast out our pride and shame That hin-der to en - throne thee;
New life, new hope a - wakes Wher-e'er men own his sway:
When Christ is throned as Lord, Men shall for - sake their fear,
The world has wait - ed long, Has trav-ailed long in pain:
Free-dom her bond - age breaks, And night is turned to day.
To plow-share beat the sword, To prun-ing - hook the spear.
To heal its an - cient wrong, Come, Prince of Peace, and reign. A-men.

541 Come, Labor On!

Jane L. Borthwick, 1813-1897, alt.
ORA LABORA 4.10.10.10.4.
T. Tertius Noble, 1867-1953
In unison
1 Come, la - bor on! Who dares stand i - dle on the har-vest plain
2 Come, la - bor on! Claim the high call - ing an-gels can-not share;
3 Come, la - bor on! A - way with gloom-y doubts and faith-less fear!
4 Come, la - bor on! No time for rest, till glows the west-ern sky,
While all a-round him waves the gold-en grain? And to each serv - ant
To young and old the gos - pel glad-ness bear; Re-deem the time, its
No arm so weak but may do serv-ice here; By fee-blest a - gents
Till the long shad-ows o'er our path-way lie, And a glad sound comes
does the Mas-ter say, "Go work to - day."
hours too swift - ly fly— The night draws nigh.
may our God ful - fill His right - eous will.
with the set-ting sun, "Well done, well done!"

MISSIONS

Eternal God, Whose Power Upholds

Henry Hallam Tweedy, 1868-1953

HALIFAX C.M.D.
George Frederick Handel, 1685-1759
Harm. by Norman E. Johnson, 1928-

1 E - ter - nal God, whose pow'r up - holds Both flow'r and flam - ing star,
2 O God of love, whose spir - it wakes In ev - 'ry hu - man breast,
3 O God of right-eous - ness and grace, Seen in the Christ, thy Son,

To whom there is no here nor there, No time, no near nor far,
Whom love, and love a - lone, can know, In whom all hearts find rest,
Whose life and death re - veal thy face, By whom thy will was done,

No a - lien race, no for - eign shore, No child un - sought, un - known,
Help us to spread thy gra - cious reign Till greed and hate shall cease,
In - spire thy her - alds of good news To live thy life di - vine,

O send us forth, thy proph-ets true, To make all lands thine own!
And kind-ness dwell in hu - man hearts, And all the earth find peace!
Till Christ is formed in all man-kind And ev - 'ry land is thine! A-men.

Alternate tunes: BETHLEHEM, *No. 78;* ELLACOMBE, *No. 80*

MISSIONS

543 Facing a Task Unfinished

Frank Houghton, 1894-1972

LLANGLOFFAN 7.6.7.6.D.
Welsh Melody

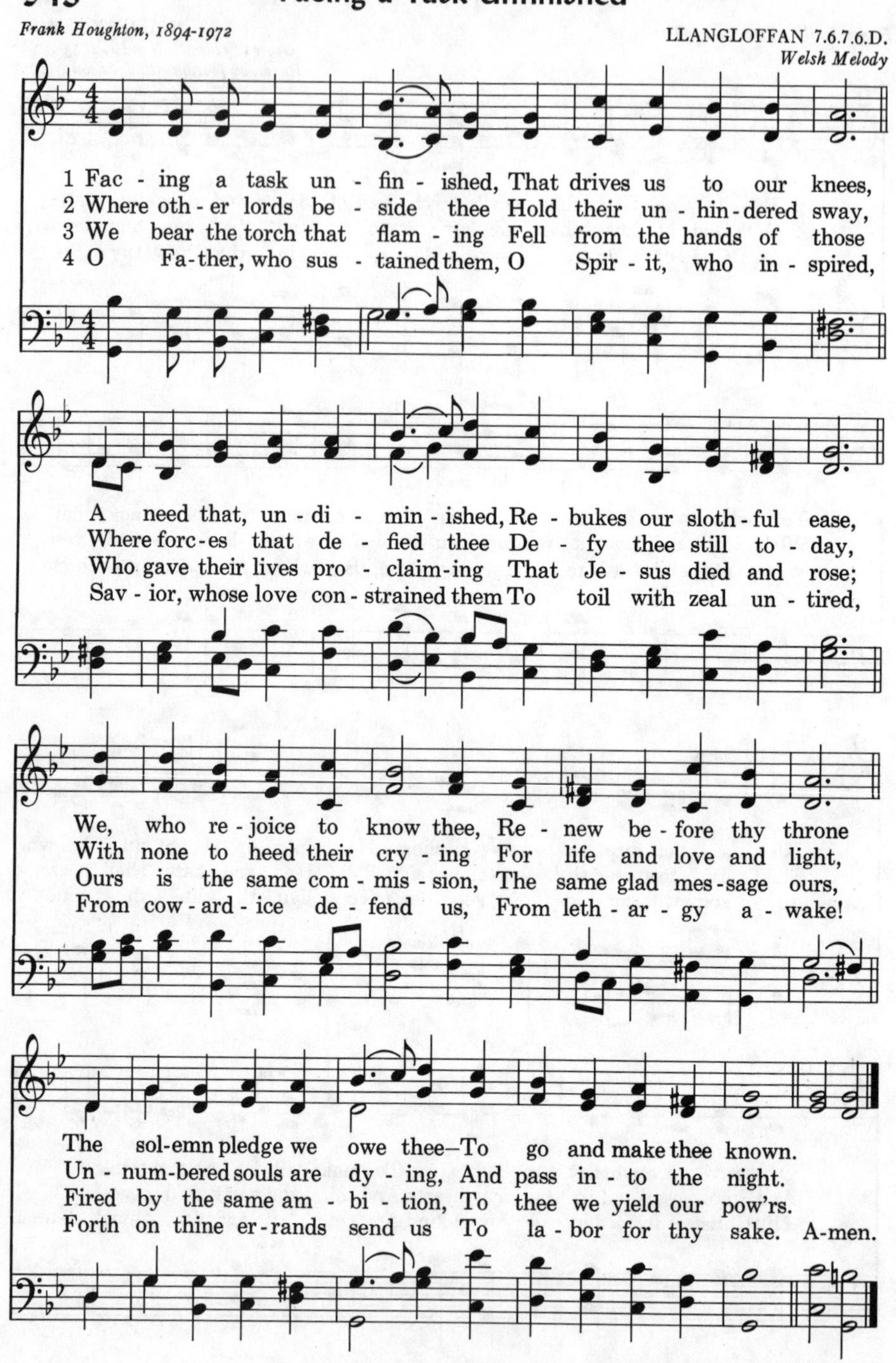
1 Fac - ing a task un - fin - ished, That drives us to our knees,
2 Where oth - er lords be - side thee Hold their un - hin - dered sway,
3 We bear the torch that flam - ing Fell from the hands of those
4 O Fa - ther, who sus - tained them, O Spir - it, who in - spired,
A need that, un - di - min - ished, Re - bukes our sloth - ful ease,
Where forc - es that de - fied thee De - fy thee still to - day,
Who gave their lives pro - claim - ing That Je - sus died and rose;
Sav - ior, whose love con - strained them To toil with zeal un - tired,
We, who re - joice to know thee, Re - new be - fore thy throne
With none to heed their cry - ing For life and love and light,
Ours is the same com - mis - sion, The same glad mes - sage ours,
From cow - ard - ice de - fend us, From leth - ar - gy a - wake!
The sol - emn pledge we owe thee—To go and make thee known.
Un - num - bered souls are dy - ing, And pass in - to the night.
Fired by the same am - bi - tion, To thee we yield our pow'rs.
Forth on thine er - rands send us To la - bor for thy sake. A - men.

MISSIONS

Hear the Voice of Jesus Calling

Daniel March, 1816-1909, alt.

RIPLEY 8.7.8.7.D.
From a Gregorian Chant
Adapted by Lowell Mason, 1792-1872

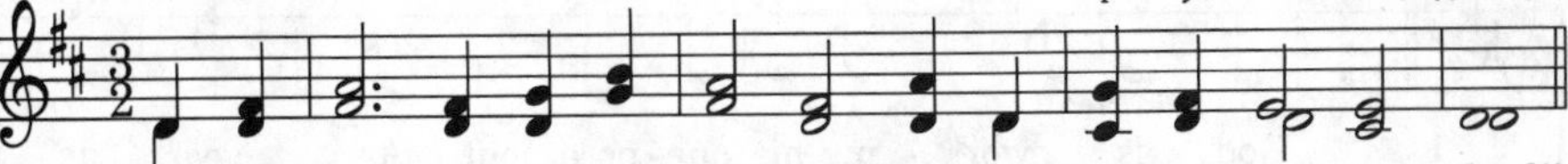

1 Hear the voice of Je - sus call - ing, "Who will go and work to - day?"
2 If you do not cross the o - cean And a dis - tant land ex - plore,
3 If you can - not be a watch-man Stand-ing high on Zi - on's wall,
4 Nev - er find your-self re - peat - ing, "There is noth-ing I can do;"

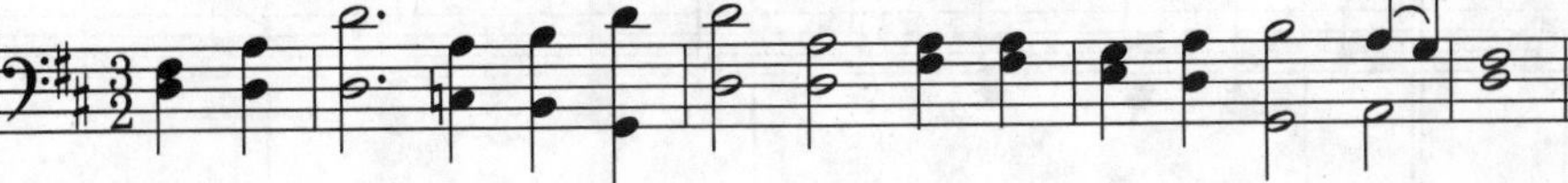

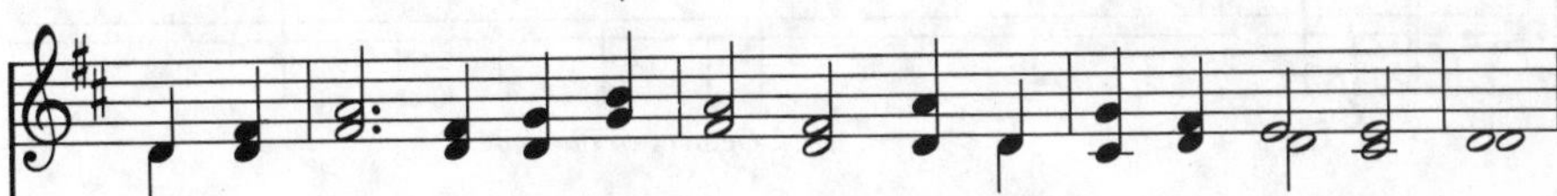

Fields are white and har-vests read - y, Who will bear the sheaves a - way?
You can find the pa - gan clos - er And the need - y at your door.
Point-ing men to find the Sav - ior, Who is life and peace to all,
While a world of men is dy - ing, There's a work God calls you to.

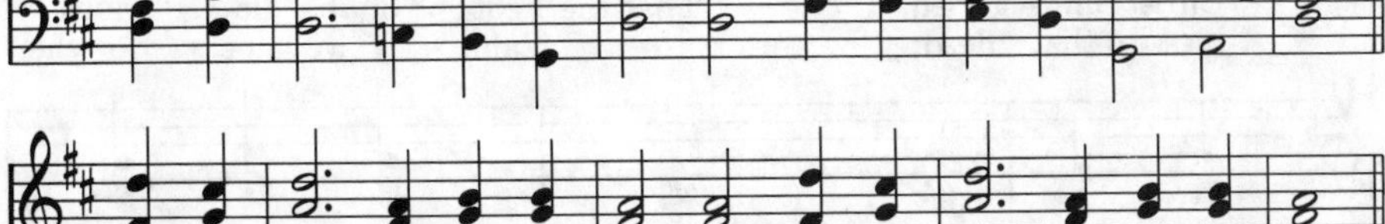

Loud and long the Mas-ter calls you, Rich re - ward he of - fers free;
Though your tal - ents may be mea - ger, Of - fer up the things you can,
With your gifts and in - ter - ces - sions You can do as he com-mands,
Glad - ly take the task he gives you, Let his will your pleas-ure be;

Who will an - swer, glad-ly say - ing, "Here am I, send me, send me."
And what - e'er you do for Je - sus Will be use - ful in his hand.
Join - ing with all faith-ful spokes-men Serv - ing him in dis - tant lands.
An - swer quick - ly, when he calls you, "Here am I, send me, send me."

Alternate tunes: ELLESDIE, *No. 412;* UPSALA, *No. 319*

545 God Is Working His Purpose Out

Arthur C. Ainger, 1841-1919

PURPOSE *Irregular*
Martin Shaw, 1875-1958

In unison
1 God is work - ing his pur - pose out As year suc -
2 From ut - most east to ut - most west, Wher - e'er man's
3 March we forth in the strength of God With the ban-ner of
4 All we can do is noth - ing worth Un - less God
Octaves to the end
ceeds to year; God is work - ing his
foot hath trod, By the mouth of man - y
Christ un - furled, That the light of the glo - rious
bless-es the deed; Vain - ly we hope for the
pur - pose out, And the time is draw - ing near; Near - er and
mes - sen - gers Goes forth the voice of God; Give ear to
gos - pel of truth May shine through-out the world; Fight we the
har - vest - tide Till God gives life to the seed; Yet near - er and

MISSIONS

near - er draws the time, The time that shall sure - ly be,
me, ye con - ti - nents, Ye isles, give ear to me,
fight with sorrow and sin To set their cap - tives free,
near - er draws the time, The time that shall sure - ly be,
When the earth shall be filled with the glo - ry of God
That the earth may be filled with the glo - ry of God
That the earth may be filled with the glo - ry of God
When the earth shall be filled with the glo - ry of God
St. 1, 2, 3
St. 4
As the wa - ters cov - er the sea.
As the wa - ters cov - er the sea.
As the wa - ters cov - er the sea.
As the wa - ters cov - er the sea.

546 Heralds of Christ, Who Bear the King's Commands

Based on Isaiah 40:3
Laura S. Copenhaver, 1868-1940
OLD 124th 10.10.10.10.10.
"Genevan Psalter," 1551
1 Her - alds of Christ, who bear the King's com-mands, Im - mor - tal
2 Thru des - ert ways, dark fen and deep mor - ass, Thru jun - gles,
3 Where once the twist - ing trail in dark-ness wound, Let march-ing
4 Lord, give us faith and strength the road to build, To see the
ti - dings in your mor - tal hands, Pass on and car - ry swift the
slug - gish seas and moun-tain pass, Build ye the road, and fal - ter
feet and joy - ous song re - sound; Where burn the fu - n'ral pyres and
prom - ise of the day ful - filled, When war shall be no more and
news ye bring: Make straight, make straight the high - way of the King,
not, nor stay: Pre - pare a - cross the earth the King's high - way,
cen - sers swing, Make straight, make straight the high - way of the King,
strife shall cease Up - on the high - way of the Prince of peace,
Make straight, make straight the high - way of the King.
Pre - pare a - cross the earth the King's high - way.
Make straight, make straight the high - way of the King.
Up - on the high - way of the Prince of peace. A - men.

MISSIONS

O Master of the Waking World

Frank Mason North, 1850-1935

MELITA 8.8.8.8.8.8.
John B. Dykes, 1823-1876

1 O Mas - ter of the wak - ing world, Who hast the na - tions
2 We hear the throb of surg - ing life, The clank of chains, the
3 Thy wit - ness in the souls of men, Thy Spir - it's cease - less,
in thy heart— The heart that bled and broke to send
curse of greed, The moan of pain, the fu - tile cries
brood - ing pow'r, In lands where shad - ows hide the light,
God's love to earth's re - mot - est part: Show us a - new in
Of su - per - sti - tion's cru - el creed: The peo - ples hun - ger
A - wait a new cre - a - tive hour: O might - y God, set
Cal - va - ry The won - drous pow'r that makes men free.
for thee, Lord, The world is wait - ing for thy word.
us a - flame To show the glo - ry of thy name. A - men.

A higher setting may be found at No. 584

548 O Zion, Haste, Thy Mission High Fulfilling

Mary A. Thomson, 1834-1923
TIDINGS 11.10.11.10. *with Refrain*
James Walch, 1837-1901
1 O Zi - on, haste, thy mis - sion high ful - fill - ing, To tell to all the world that God is light; That he who made all na - tions is not will - ing One soul should per - ish, lost in shades of night.
2 Pro - claim to ev - 'ry peo - ple, tongue, and na - tion That God in whom they live and move is love; Tell how he stooped to save his lost cre - a - tion, And died on earth that man might live a - bove.
3 Give of thy sons to bear the mes - sage glo - rious, Give of thy wealth to speed them on their way; Pour out thy soul for them in prayer vic - to - rious, And haste the com - ing of the glo - rious day.
REFRAIN
Pub - lish glad ti - dings, ti - dings of peace,
Ti - dings of Je - sus, re - demp - tion, and re - lease.

So Send I You—by Grace Made Strong

Based on John 20:21
E. Margaret Clarkson, 1915-

SO SEND I YOU 11.10.11.10.
John W. Peterson, 1921-

1 So send I you— by grace made strong to tri - umph O'er hosts of
hell, o'er dark-ness, death and sin, My name to bear, and in that
name to con - quer–So send I you, my vic - to - ry to win.

2 So send I you— to take to souls in bond - age The word of
truth that sets the cap - tive free, To break the bonds of sin, to
loose death's fet - ters–So send I you, to bring the lost to me.

3 So send I you—my strength to know in weak - ness, My joy in
grief, my per - fect peace in pain, To prove my pow'r, my grace, my
prom-ised pres - ence–So send I you, e - ter - nal fruit to gain.

4 So send I you— to bear my cross with pa - tience, And then one
day with joy to lay it down, To hear my voice, "Well done, my
faith - ful serv - ant–Come, share my throne, my king-dom and my
crown!" "As the Fa - ther hath sent me, So send I you."

Sts. 1,2,3

St. 4

550 Rescue the Perishing

Fanny J. Crosby, 1820-1915

RESCUE 6.5.10.D. *with Refrain*
William H. Doane, 1832-1915

1 Res - cue the per - ish - ing, Care for the dy - ing, Snatch them in
2 Tho they are slight-ing him, Still he is wait - ing, Wait - ing the
3 Down in the hu - man heart, Crushed by the tempt - er, Feel - ings lie
4 Res - cue the per - ish - ing—Du - ty de - mands it! Strength for thy
pit - y from sin and the grave; Weep o'er the
pen - i - tent child to re - ceive; Plead with them
bur - ied that grace can re - store; Touched by a
la - bor the Lord will pro - vide; Back to the
err - ing one, Lift up the fall - en, Tell them of
ear - nest - ly, Plead with them gen - tly, He will for -
lov - ing heart, Wak - ened by kind - ness, Chords that are
nar - row way Pa - tient - ly win them, Tell the poor
REFRAIN
Je - sus, the might - y to save.
give if they on - ly be - lieve.
bro - ken will vi - brate once more.
wan - d'rer a Sav - ior has died.
Res - cue the per - ish - ing,

Care for the dy - ing; Je - sus is mer - ci - ful, Je - sus will save.

Where Charity and Love Prevail 551

Latin: 9th Century
Para. by Omer Westendorf, 1916-

CHRISTIAN LOVE C.M.
Paul Benoit, 1893-

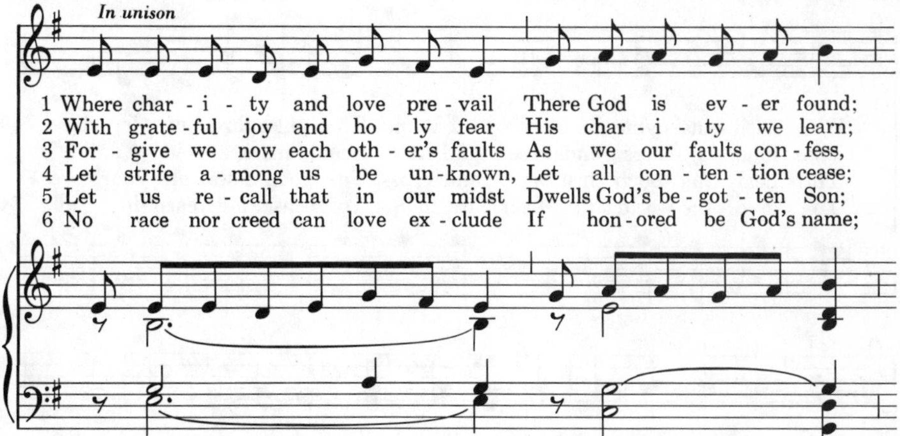

In unison

1 Where char - i - ty and love pre - vail There God is ev - er found;
2 With grate - ful joy and ho - ly fear His char - i - ty we learn;
3 For - give we now each oth - er's faults As we our faults con - fess,
4 Let strife a - mong us be un - known, Let all con - ten - tion cease;
5 Let us re - call that in our midst Dwells God's be - got - ten Son;
6 No race nor creed can love ex - clude If hon - ored be God's name;

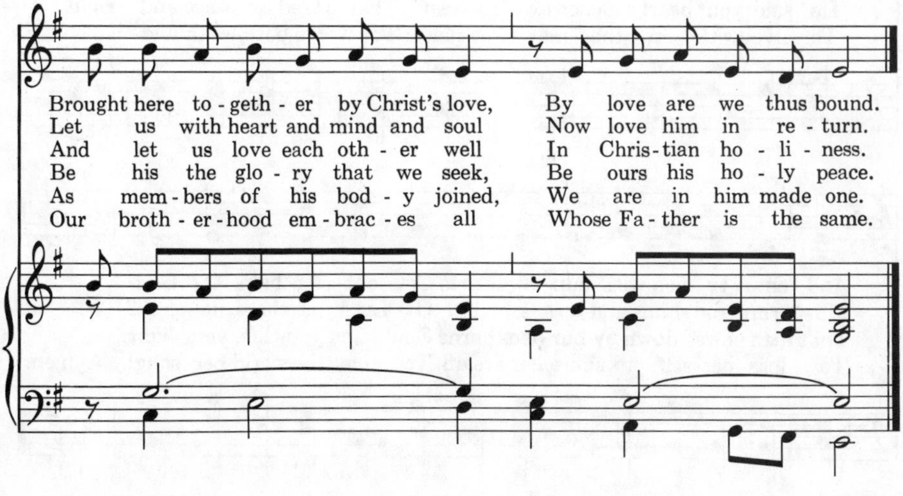

Brought here to - geth - er by Christ's love, By love are we thus bound.
Let us with heart and mind and soul Now love him in re - turn.
And let us love each oth - er well In Chris - tian ho - li - ness.
Be his the glo - ry that we seek, Be ours his ho - ly peace.
As mem - bers of his bod - y joined, We are in him made one.
Our broth - er - hood em - brac - es all Whose Fa - ther is the same.

552 The City Is Alive, O God

William W. Reid, Jr., 1923-

ALL SAINTS NEW C.M.D.
Henry S. Culler, 1824-1902

1 The cit - y is a - live, O God, With sound of hus - tling feet,
2 Is it your will, O lov - ing God, That rac - es live in strife?
3 In an - cient Gal - i - lee men heard Your serv - ant Christ de - clare
4 O God, in - spire your Church to - day To take Christ's serv - ant role,
With flash - ing lights and rap - id change That pulse thru ev - 'ry street;
That lone - li - ness and greed and hate Should mark a cit - y's life?
Thru heal - ing touch, thru word and cross, The good news of your care;
To love the world, to hear its claims, To sense its yearn - ing soul;
But oft there's in - hu - man - i - ty Be - hind the bright fa - cade,
Do you de - sire the rich man's wealth To keep the poor man poor?
He said your heart touched ev - 'ry heart That longed for peace and right,
To live with - in the mar - ket place, To serve both weak and strong,
And emp - ty men with hun - gry hearts Cry out for help, O God.
Must crime and slums and lust a - bound? O Lord, is there no cure?
That men bowed down by bur - dens borne Could find your life, your light.
To lose her - self, to share her dream, To give the world her song! A - men.

MISSIONS

Words from *Nine New Mission of the Church Hymns*, copyright 1969 by the Hymn Society of America. Used by permission.

We Have Heard the Joyful Sound

Priscilla J. Owens, 1829-1907

JESUS SAVES 7.3.7.3.7.7.7.3.
William J. Kirkpatrick, 1838-1921

1 We have heard the joy - ful sound: Je - sus saves! Je - sus saves!
2 Waft it on the roll - ing tide: Je - sus saves! Je - sus saves!
3 Sing a - bove the bat - tle strife: Je - sus saves! Je - sus saves!
4 Give the winds a might - y voice: Je - sus saves! Je - sus saves!
Spread the ti - dings all a - round: Je - sus saves! Je - sus saves!
Tell to sin - ners far and wide: Je - sus saves! Je - sus saves!
By his death and end - less life: Je - sus saves! Je - sus saves!
Let the na - tions now re - joice: Je - sus saves! Je - sus saves!
Bear the news to ev - 'ry land, Climb the steeps and cross the waves;
Sing, ye is - lands of the sea! Ech - o back, ye o - cean caves!
Sing it soft - ly thru the gloom, When the heart for mer - cy craves;
Shout sal - va - tion full and free, High - est hills and deep - est caves;
On - ward! 'tis our Lord's com - mand: Je - sus saves! Je - sus saves!
Earth shall keep her ju - bi - lee: Je - sus saves! Je - sus saves!
Sing in tri - umph o'er the tomb: Je - sus saves! Je - sus saves!
This our song of vic - to - ry: Je - sus saves! Je - sus saves!

554 Through All the World

Bryan Jeffery Leech, 1931-
CONRAD 10.4.6.6.6.6.10.4.
Paul F. Liljestrand, 1931-
In unison
1 Through all the world let ev-'ry na-tion sing To God, the King!
2 Through all the world let ev-'ry man ex-press True righ-teous-ness!
3 Through all the world let ev-'ry man em-brace The gift of grace!
4 If all the world in ev-'ry part shall hear And God re-vere,
As Lord may Christ pre-side Where now he is de-fied,
May Christ be now the norm To which all men con-form,
May Christ's great light con-sume Our cit-ies' dark-est gloom,
We must be moved to care And in his name to share
And sov-'reign place his throne In lands not yet his own.
His pas-sion cure the sin That fes-ters from with-in.
May Christ's great love ef-face Hos-til-i-ties of race.
The lib-er-at-ing Word Which must be told a-broad.

MISSIONS

Alternate tune: ALL THE WORLD, *No. 16*

Through all the world let ev-'ry na-tion sing To God, the King!
Through all the world let ev-'ry man ex-press True righ-teous-ness!
Through all the world let ev-'ry man em-brace The gift of grace!
Then all the world in ev-'ry part shall hear And God re-vere!

O Lord, the Maze of Earthly Ways 555

Based on Matthew 25:40
Carlton C. Buck, 1907-

BANGOR C.M.
William Tans'ur, 1706?-1783

1 O Lord, the maze of earth-ly ways Con-fus-es our in-tent;
Give us thy light to walk a-right Thru our be-wil-der-ment.

2 The bur-dened sigh and an-guished cry That so dis-turb and taunt
Are sounds of fear thru which we hear Hu-man-i-ty in want.

3 Give us the heart to do our part, To act the an-cient creed,
Ex-press our care, re-spond and share, To meet an-oth-er's need.

4 By help-ing men to live a-gain Most ful-ly, we serve thee;
A-gain to-day we hear thee say, "You've done it un-to me." A-men.

556 We've a Story to Tell to the Nations

H. Ernest Nichol, 1862-1928

MESSAGE 10.8.8.7. *with Refrain*
H. Ernest Nichol, 1862-1928

1 We've a sto - ry to tell to the na - tions That shall turn their hearts to the right, A sto - ry of truth and mer - cy, A sto - ry of peace and light, A sto - ry of peace and light.
2 We've a song to be sung to the na - tions That shall lift their hearts to the Lord, A song that shall con - quer e - vil And shat - ter the spear and sword, And shat - ter the spear and sword.
3 We've a mes - sage to give to the na - tions–That the Lord who reign - eth a - bove Hath sent us his Son to save us And show us that God is love, And show us that God is love.
4 We've a Sav - ior to show to the na - tions Who the path of sor - row hath trod, That all of the world's great peo - ples Might come to the truth of God, Might come to the truth of God.
REFRAIN
For the dark-ness shall turn to dawn-ing, And the dawn-ing to noon-day bright,

And Christ's great king-dom shall come on earth, The king-dom of love and light.

Christ for the World We Sing! 557

Samuel Wolcott, 1813-1886

ITALIAN HYMN 6.6.4.6.6.6.4.
Felice de Giardini, 1716-1796

1 Christ for the world we sing! The world to Christ we bring
2 Christ for the world we sing! The world to Christ we bring
3 Christ for the world we sing! The world to Christ we bring
4 Christ for the world we sing! The world to Christ we bring

With lov - ing zeal: The poor and them that mourn, The faint and
With fer - vent prayer: The way-ward and the lost, By rest - less
With one ac - cord: With us the work to share, With us re -
With joy - ful song: The new - born souls, whose days, Re-claimed from

o - ver-borne, Sin - sick and sor - row worn, Whom Christ doth heal.
pas - sions tossed, Re-deemed at count - less cost From dark de - spair.
proach to dare, With us the cross to bear For Christ our Lord.
er - ror's ways, In - spired with hope and praise, To Christ be - long.

Another harmonization in a lower setting may be found at No. 275

558 O Spirit of the Living God

James Montgomery, 1771-1854

MELCOMBE L.M.
Samuel Webbe, 1740-1816

1 O Spir - it of the liv - ing God, In
2 Give tongues of fire and hearts of love To
3 O Spir - it of the Lord, pre - pare All
4 Bap - tize the na - tions; far and nigh The

all thy plen - i - tude of grace, Wher - e'er the foot of
preach the rec - on - cil - ing word; Give pow'r and unc - tion
men of earth their God to meet; Breathe thou a - broad like
tri - umphs of the cross re - cord; The name of Je - sus

man hath trod, De - scend on our re - bel - lious race.
from a - bove, When - e'er the joy - ful sound is heard.
morn - ing air, Till hearts of stone be - gin to beat.
glo - ri - fy, Till ev - 'ry kin - dred call him Lord. A - men.

Alternate tune: WINCHESTER NEW, *No. 179*

559 Ye Christian Heralds, Go Proclaim

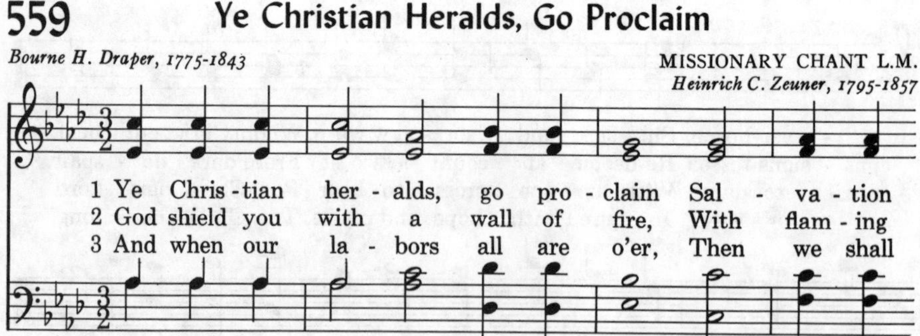
Bourne H. Draper, 1775-1843
MISSIONARY CHANT L.M.
Heinrich C. Zeuner, 1795-1857
1 Ye Chris - tian her - alds, go pro - claim Sal - va - tion
2 God shield you with a wall of fire, With flam - ing
3 And when our la - bors all are o'er, Then we shall

through Em - man - uel's name; To dis - tant climes the
zeal your hearts in - spire, Bid rag - ing winds their
meet to part no more, Meet with the blood - bought
ti - dings bear, And plant the Rose of Shar - on there.
fu - ry cease, And hush the tem - pests in - to peace.
throng to fall And crown our Je - sus Lord of all.

A lower setting may be found at No. 495

O Christ, Forget Not Them Who Stand 560

Margaret E. Sangster, 1838-1912

MISSIONARY CHANT L.M.
Heinrich C. Zeuner, 1795-1857

1 O Christ, forget not them who stand,
Thy vanguard in the distant land;
In flood, in flame, in dark, in dread,
Sustain, we pray, each lifted head.

2 Thine is the work they strive to do,
Their foes so many, they so few;
Be with thine own, thy loved, who stand,
Christ's vanguard, in the storm-swept land.
Amen.

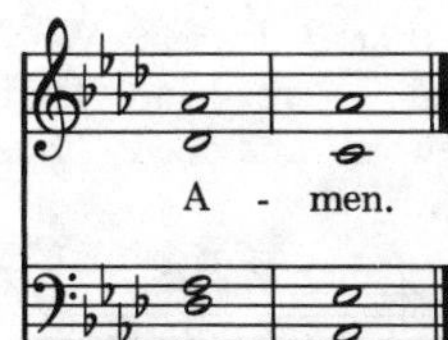
A - men.

561 Because I Have Been Given Much

Grace Noll Crowell, 1877-1969 ALGOT 8.4.8.4.8.8.8.
Norman E. Johnson, 1928-

In unison
1 Be - cause I have been giv - en much, I too must give;
Be - cause of thy great boun - ty, Lord, Each day I live,
I shall di - vide my gifts from thee With ev - 'ry broth - er
that I see Who has the need of help from me.
2 Be - cause I have been shel - tered, fed, By thy good care,
I can - not see an - oth - er's lack And I not share
My glow - ing fire, my loaf of bread, My roof's safe shel - ter
o - ver-head, That he too may be com - fort - ed.
3 Be - cause love has been lav - ished so Up - on me, Lord,
A wealth I know that was not meant For me to hoard,
I shall give love to those in need, Shall show that love by
word and deed: Thus shall my thanks be thanks in - deed. A - men.

Give to the Lord, As He Has Blessed Thee 562

James Boeringer, 1930-
CELEBRATION 9.8.9.8.8.8.
Swedish Folk Melody
1 Give to the Lord, as he has blessed thee, E - ven when
2 Give to the Lord, as he has blessed thee, Kept thee and
3 Give to the Lord, as he has blessed thee, Who pours forth
he seems far a - way; Know that his love has e'er pos-sessed thee,
guid - ed from thy birth; Look to the day when death will wrest thee
boun - ties rich and full; Let all thy self - ish aims con-fessed be,
Shel - ters and feeds thee ev - 'ry day. Heav - en and
From all thy treas - ures here on earth. God hath rich
Gain not the world and lose thy soul! Put all thou
earth are God's a - lone: Wilt thou hold back from him his own?
gifts for thee a - bove: Give of thy sub - stance now in love.
hast in God's own hands, In trust o - bey - ing his com-mands.

Words from *Ten New Stewardship Hymns*, copyright 1961 by the Hymn Society of America. Used by permission.

STEWARDSHIP

563 God, Whose Giving Knows No Ending

Robert Lansing Edwards, 1915- HASTINGS-ON-HUDSON 8.7.8.7.D.
Harold W. Friedell, 1905-1958

In unison
1 God, whose giv - ing knows no end - ing, All our life is from thy store:
2 Skills and time are ours for press-ing T'ward the goals of Christ, thy Son:
3 Treas-ure too thou hast en - trust-ed, Gain thru pow'rs thy grace con-ferred:
4 Lend thy joy to all our giv - ing, Let it light our pil - grim way:
Na - ture's won-der, Je - sus' wis-dom, Cost - ly cross, grave's shat-tered door.
Men at peace in health and free-dom, Rac - es joined, the Church made one.
Ours to use for home and kin-dred, And to spread the gos - pel word.
From the dark of anx-ious keep-ing, Loose us in - to gen-'rous day.
Gift - ed by thee, turn we to thee, Of - f'ring up our-selves in praise;
Now di - rect our dai - ly la - bor, Lest we strive for self a - lone;
O - pen wide our hands in shar-ing, As we heed Christ's age-less call,
Then when years on earth are o - ver, Rich t'ward thee and fel - low - man,
Thank-ful song shall rise for - ev - er, Gra-cious Do - nor of our days.
Born with tal-ents, make us serv-ants Fit to an-swer at thy throne.
Heal - ing, teach-ing, and re - claim-ing, Serv-ing thee who lov - est all.
Lord, ful - fill be-yond our dream-ing All our stew-ard - life be - gan. A-men.

Alternate tune: BEECHER, *No. 568*

STEWARDSHIP

Jesus, Who Transcends the Ages 564

Craig D. Erickson, 1948-

FRANKLIN SQUARE 8.7.8.7.D.
A. Royce Eckhardt, 1937-

1 Je - sus, who tran-scends the a - ges, Faith and love in us pre-pare;
2 When false loy - al - ty to na - tion Hate and lust in us con-jure,
3 We con - fess to pleas - ure - seek - ing, And to wealth—our pov - er - ty;
4 Je - sus, who tran-scends the a - ges, Faith and love in us pre-pare;
Save us from our own de - struc-tion And the mind - set of de - spair.
Lead us to a right con - vic - tion To af - firm what men ob - scure.
Both de - stroy what God has giv'n us, Foul - ing earth so wan - ton - ly.
May we know the name, "God's peo - ple," And to men his grace de - clare.
From our self - ish ways O lead us, Jar us from our leis - ured days;
And should some re - vile such ac - tion, Grant fresh wit - ness to the life
Help us strive with great - er ef - fort Na - ture's beau - ty to re - pair,
Though our task at times o'er-whelms us And we weep in fra - il - ty,
Come in us, and lead our spir - its In - to new cre - a - tive ways.
Of true peace in your sal - va - tion And the wrong of hu - man strife.
Mind - ful of our role as stew - ards O - ver wa - ter, land, and air.
Plant new hope, re - vive our spir - its! Dare us love more fer - vent - ly! A - men.

Alternate tune: HYMN TO JOY, *No. 352*

565 We Give Thee But Thine Own

William W. How, 1823-1897

SCHUMANN S.M.
Mason and Webb's "Cantica Laudis," 1850

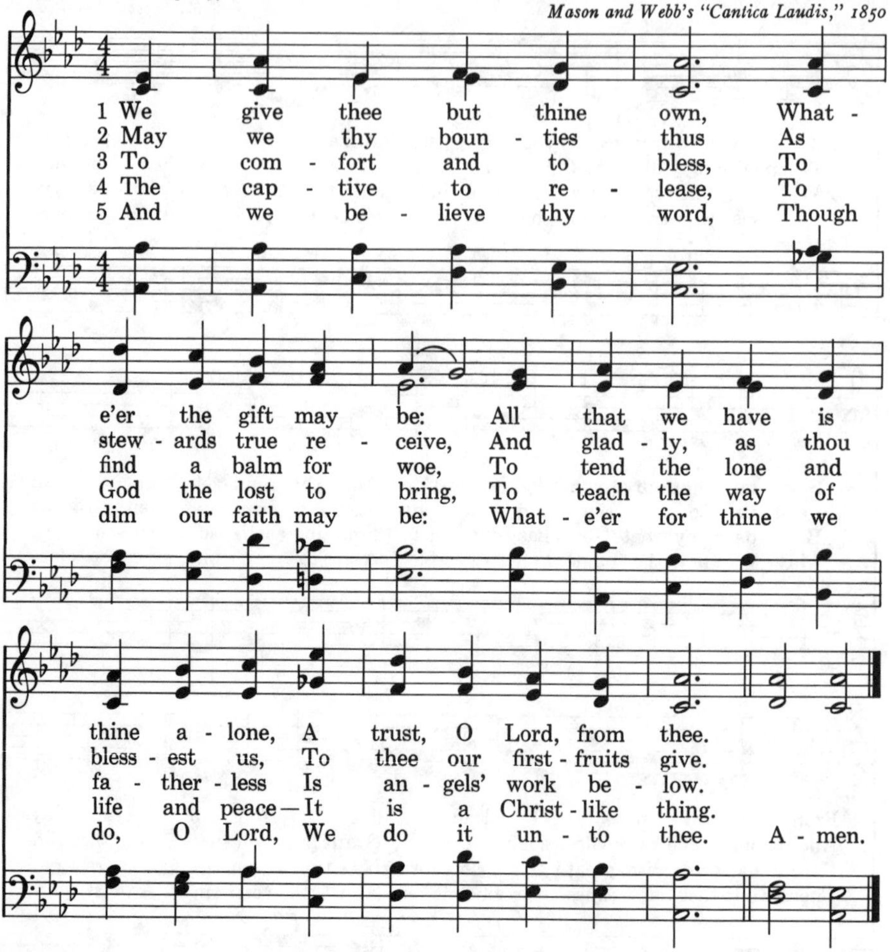

1 We give thee but thine own, What -
2 May we thy boun - ties thus As
3 To com - fort and to bless, To
4 The cap - tive to re - lease, To
5 And we be - lieve thy word, Though

e'er the gift may be: All that we have is
stew - ards true re - ceive, And glad - ly, as thou
find a balm for woe, To tend the lone and
God the lost to bring, To teach the way of
dim our faith may be: What - e'er for thine we

thine a - lone, A trust, O Lord, from thee.
bless - est us, To thee our first - fruits give.
fa - ther - less Is an - gels' work be - low.
life and peace—It is a Christ - like thing.
do, O Lord, We do it un - to thee. A - men.

566 All Labor Gained New Dignity

John Oxenham, 1852-1941

GELOBT SEI GOTT 8.8.8.4.
Melchior Vulpius, c. 1560-1616
Harm. by Norman E. Johnson, 1928-

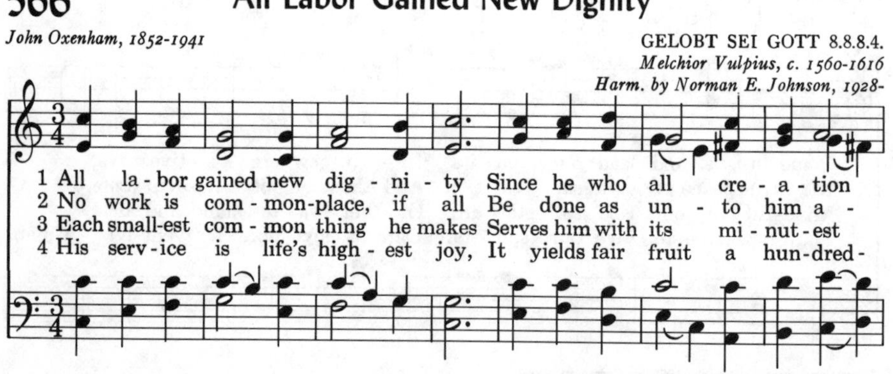
1 All la - bor gained new dig - ni - ty Since he who all cre - a - tion
2 No work is com - mon-place, if all Be done as un - to him a -
3 Each small-est com - mon thing he makes Serves him with its mi - nut - est
4 His serv - ice is life's high - est joy, It yields fair fruit a hun-dred -

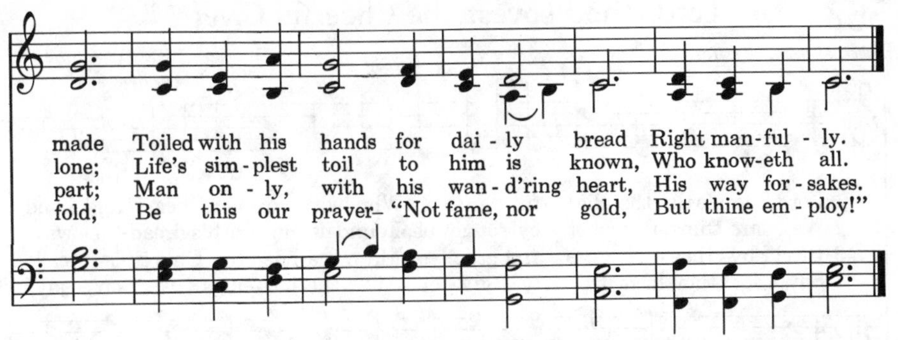
made Toiled with his hands for dai - ly bread Right man-ful - ly.
lone; Life's sim - plest toil to him is known, Who know-eth all.
part; Man on - ly, with his wan - d'ring heart, His way for - sakes.
fold; Be this our prayer– "Not fame, nor gold, But thine em - ploy!"

Savior, Thy Dying Love 567

S. Dryden Phelps, 1816-1895, alt.

SOMETHING FOR JESUS 6.4.6.4.6.6.6.4.
Robert Lowry, 1826-1899

1 Sav - ior, thy dy - ing love Thou gav - est me, Nor should I
2 Give me a faith - ful heart, Guid - ed by thee, That each de -
3 All that I am and have, Thy gifts so free, Ev - er in

aught with-hold, Dear Lord, from thee; In love my soul would bow, My heart ful-
part - ing day Hence-forth may see Some work of love be - gun, Some deed of
joy or grief, My Lord, for thee; And when thy face I see, My ran-somed

fill its vow, Some of-f'ring bring thee now, Some-thing for thee.
kind - ness done, Some wan-d'rer sought and won, Some-thing for thee.
soul shall be, Thru all e - ter - ni - ty, Some-thing for thee. A-men.

568 Lord, Thou Lovest the Cheerful Giver

Robert Murray, 1832-1910

BEECHER 8.7.8.7.D.
John Zundel, 1815-1882

1 Lord, thou lov'st the cheer-ful giv-er, Who with o-pen heart and hand
2 We are thine, thy mer-cy sought us, Found us in death's dread-ful way,
3 Blest by thee with gifts and grac-es, May we heed thy Church-'s call;
4 Sav-ior, thou hast free-ly giv-en All the bless-ings we en-joy,
Bless-es free-ly, as a riv-er That re-fresh-es all the land.
To the fold in safe-ty brought us, Nev-er-more from thee to stray.
Glad-ly in all times and plac-es Give to thee who giv-est all.
Earth-ly store and bread of heav-en, Love and peace with-out al-loy.
Grant us then the grace of giv-ing With a spir-it large and free,
Thine own life thou free-ly gav-est As an off-'ring on the cross
Thou hast bought us, and no long-er Can we claim to be our own;
Hum-bly now we bow be-fore thee And our all to thee re-sign;
That our life and all our liv-ing We may con-se-crate to thee.
For each sin-ner whom thou sav-est From e-ter-nal shame and loss.
Ev-er free and ev-er strong-er, We shall serve thee, Lord, a-lone.
For the king-dom, pow'r, and glo-ry Are, O Lord, for-ev-er thine. A-men.

Before Thy Throne, O God, We Kneel 569

William Boyd Carpenter, 1841-1918

ST. PETERSBURG 8.8.8.8.8.8.
Dmitri S. Bortniansky, 1751-1825
Harm. by A. Royce Eckhardt, 1937-

1 Be - fore thy throne, O God, we kneel: Give us a
2 Search out our hearts and make us true, Wish - ful to
3 For sins of heed - less word and deed, For pride am -
4 Let the fierce fires, which burn and try, Our in - most

con - science quick to feel, A read - y mind to un - der - stand
give to all their due; From love of pleas - ure, lust of gold,
bi - tious to suc - ceed; For craft - y trade and sub - tle snare
spir - its pur - i - fy: Con - sume the ill, purge out the shame;

The mean - ing of thy chast-'ning hand; What-e'er the pain and
From sins which make the heart grow cold, Wean us and train us
To catch the sim - ple un - a - ware; For lives be - reft of
O God! be with us in the flame; A new-born peo - ple

shame may be, Bring us, O Fa - ther, near - er thee.
with thy rod; Teach us to know our faults, O God.
pur - pose high, For - give, for - give, O Lord, we cry.
may we rise, More pure, more true, more no - bly wise. A - men.

Alternate tune: MELITA, *No. 547*

570 Christian, Rise and Act Thy Creed

F. A. Rollo Russell, 1849-1914
MONKLAND 7.7.7.7.
John Antes, 1740-1811
Adapted by John B. Wilkes, 1785-1869
1 Chris - tian, rise and act thy creed, Let thy prayer be in thy deed; Seek the right, per - form the true, Raise thy work and life a - new.
2 Hearts a - round thee sink with care, Thou canst help their load to bear; Thou canst bring in - spir - ing light, Arm their fal - t'ring wills to fight.
3 Let thine alms be hope and joy, And thy wor - ship God's em - ploy; Give him thanks in hum - ble zeal, Learn - ing all his will to feel.
571 Rise Up, O Men of God!
William P. Merrill, 1867-1954
FESTAL SONG S.M.
William H. Walter, 1825-1893
1 Rise up, O men of God! Have done with less - er things;
2 Rise up, O men of God! His king - dom tar - ries long;
3 Rise up, O men of God! The Church for you doth wait,
4 Lift high the cross of Christ, Tread where his feet have trod;

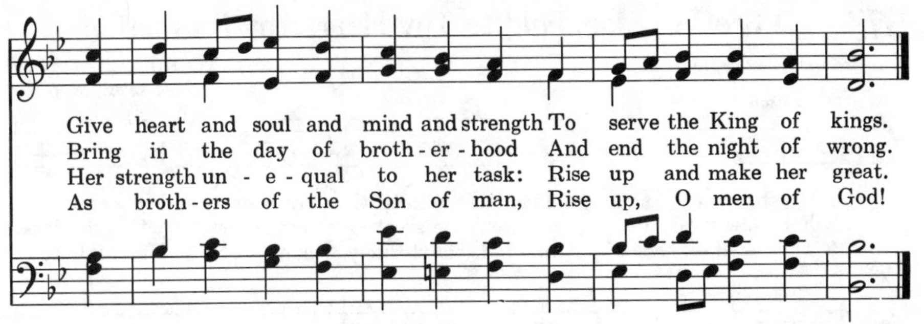
Give heart and soul and mind and strength To serve the King of kings.
Bring in the day of broth-er-hood And end the night of wrong.
Her strength un-e-qual to her task: Rise up and make her great.
As broth-ers of the Son of man, Rise up, O men of God!

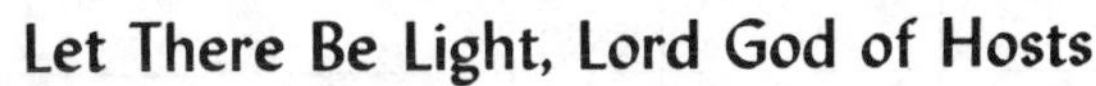
Let There Be Light, Lord God of Hosts

572

William M. Vories, 1880-1964

PENTECOST L.M.
William Boyd, 1847-1928

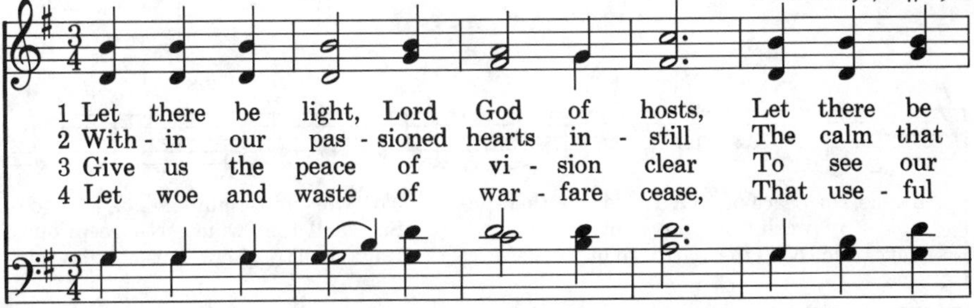

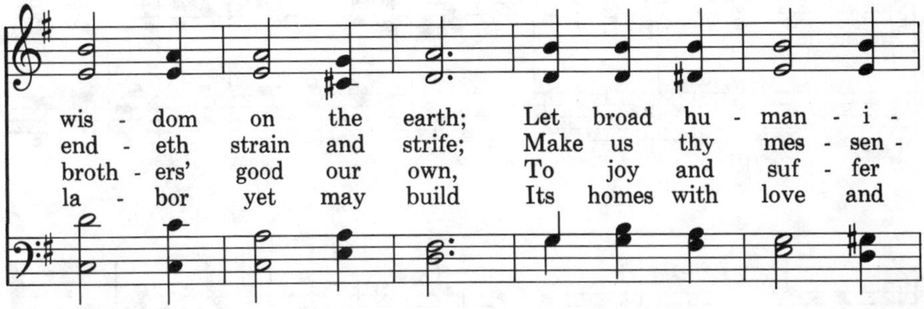

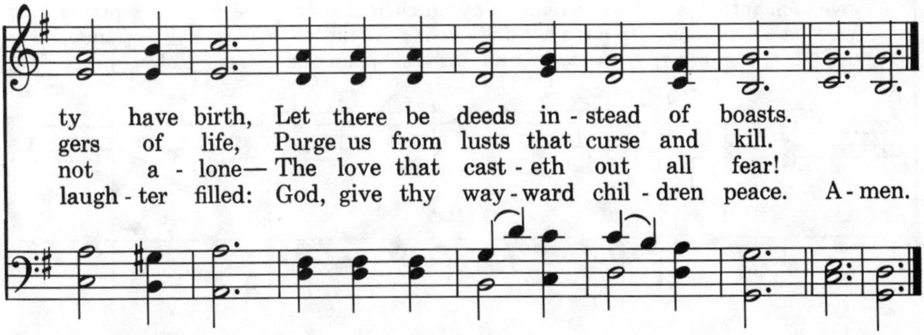

1 Let there be light, Lord God of hosts,
Let there be wis-dom on the earth;
Let broad hu-man-i-ty have birth,
Let there be deeds in-stead of boasts.

2 With-in our pas-sioned hearts in-still
The calm that end-eth strain and strife;
Make us thy mes-sen-gers of life,
Purge us from lusts that curse and kill.

3 Give us the peace of vi-sion clear
To see our broth-ers' good our own,
To joy and suf-fer not a-lone—
The love that cast-eth out all fear!

4 Let woe and waste of war-fare cease,
That use-ful la-bor yet may build
Its homes with love and laugh-ter filled:
God, give thy way-ward chil-dren peace. A-men.

Lower settings may be found at Nos. 336 and 501

573 O Brother Man, Fold to Thy Heart Thy Brother!

John Greenleaf Whittier, 1807-1892
CHARTERHOUSE 11.10.11.10.
David Evans, 1874-1948
In unison
1 O broth-er man, fold to thy heart thy broth - er! Where pit - y
2 Fol - low with rev - 'rent steps the great ex - am - ple Of him whose
3 Then shall all shack - les fall, the storm-y clang - or Of wild war
dwells, the peace of God is there; To wor-ship right - ly is to
ho - ly work was do - ing good; So shall the wide earth seem our
mu - sic o'er the earth shall cease; Love shall tread out the bale-ful
love each oth - er— Each smile a hymn, each kind-ly deed a prayer.
Fa-ther's tem - ple, Each lov - ing life a psalm of grat - i - tude.
fire of an - ger, And in its ash - es plant the tree of peace.

BROTHERHOOD

The Light of God Is Falling

Louis F. Benson, 1855-1930

GREENLAND 7.6.7.6.D.

Attr. to Johann Michael Haydn, 1737-1806

1 The light of God is fall - ing Up - on life's com-mon way,
2 Who shares life's joys and pleas - ures And walks the hon - est road,
3 Where hu - man lives are throng - ing In toil and pain and sin,
The Mas-ter's voice still call - ing, "Come, walk with me to - day;"
Who trades with heap-ing meas - ures And lifts his broth-er's load,
While clois-tered hearts are long - ing To bring the king-dom in,
No du - ty can seem low - ly To him who lives with thee,
Who turns the wrong down blunt - ly And lends the right a hand,
O Christ, the eld - er broth - er Of proud and beat - en men,
And all of life grows ho - ly, O Christ of Gal - i - lee!
He dwells in God's own coun - try, He tills the ho - ly land.
When they have found each oth - er, Thy king-dom will come then!

Words used by permission of Barbara Benson Jefferys.

BROTHERHOOD

575 The Voice of God Is Calling

Based on Isaiah 6:8
John Haynes Holmes, 1879-1964
MEIRIONYDD 7.6.7.6.D.
Welsh Melody
Attr. to William Lloyd, 1786-1852
1 The voice of God is call - ing Its sum-mons un - to men;
2 "I hear my peo - ple cry - ing In cot and mine and slum;
3 We heed, O Lord, thy sum - mons, And an - swer: "Here are we!"
4 From ease and plen - ty save us, From pride of place ab - solve;
As once he spake in Zi - on, So now he speaks a - gain!
No field or mart is si - lent, No cit - y street is dumb.
Send us up - on thine er - rand, Let us thy serv - ants be.
Purge us of low de - sire, Lift us to high re - solve;
"Whom shall I send to suc - cor My peo - ple in their need?
I see my peo - ple fall - ing In dark-ness and de - spair;
Our strength is dust and ash - es, Our years a pass - ing hour;
Take us, and make us ho - ly, Teach us thy will and way;
Whom shall I send to loos - en The bonds of shame and greed?"
Whom shall I send to shat - ter The fet-ters which they bear?"
But thou canst use our weak-ness To mag - ni - fy thy pow'r.
Speak, and, be-hold, we an - swer! Com-mand, and we o - bey! A-men.

BROTHERHOOD

A lower setting may be found at No. 196

Our Father, by Whose Name

F. Bland Tucker, 1895-

RHOSYMEDRE 6.6.6.6.8.8.8.
John D. Edwards, 1806-1885

1 Our Fa - ther, by whose name All fa - ther - hood is known,
2 O Christ, thy - self a child With - in an earth - ly home,
3 O Spir - it, who dost bind Our hearts in u - ni - ty,
Who dost in love pro - claim Each fam - i - ly thine own,
With heart still un - de - filed, Thou didst to man - hood come;
Who teach - est us to find The love from self set free,
Bless thou all par - ents— guard - ing well, With con - stant love as
Our chil - dren bless, in ev - 'ry place, That they may all be -
In all our hearts such love in - crease, That ev - 'ry home, by
sen - ti - nel, The homes in which thy peo - ple dwell.
hold thy face, And know - ing thee may grow in grace.
this re - lease, May be the dwell - ing place of peace. A - men.

577 Thou Gracious God Whose Mercy Lends

Oliver Wendell Holmes, 1809-1894

CANONBURY L.M.
Robert Schumann, 1810-1856

1 Thou gra - cious God whose mer - cy lends The
2 Wilt thou not hear us while we raise, In
3 For all the bless - ings life has brought, For
4 The noon - tide sun - shine of the past, These
5 We thank thee, Fa - ther: let thy grace Our

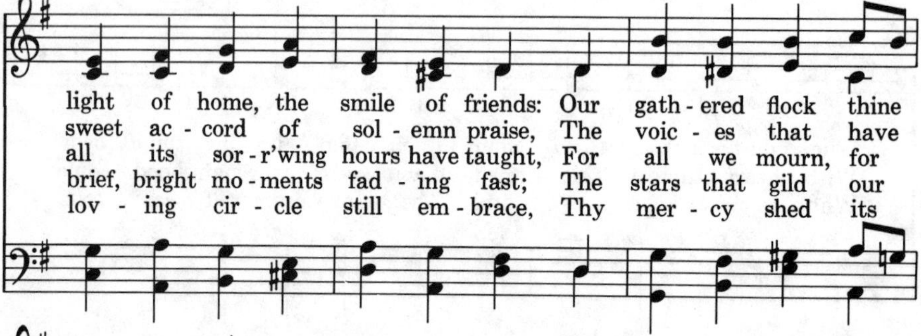

light of home, the smile of friends: Our gath - ered flock thine
sweet ac - cord of sol - emn praise, The voic - es that have
all its sor - r'wing hours have taught, For all we mourn, for
brief, bright mo - ments fad - ing fast; The stars that gild our
lov - ing cir - cle still em - brace, Thy mer - cy shed its

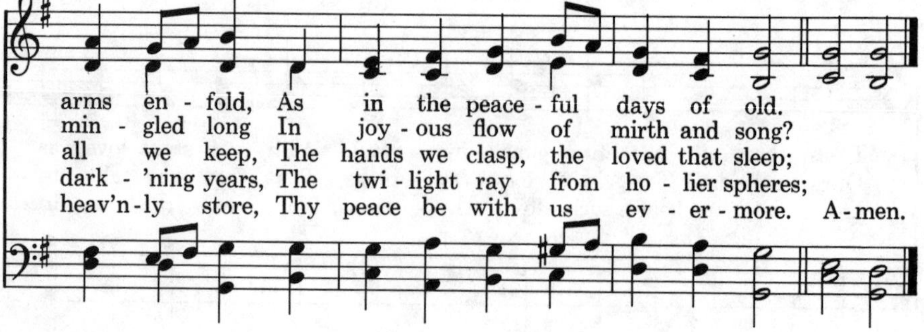

arms en - fold, As in the peace - ful days of old.
min - gled long In joy - ous flow of mirth and song?
all we keep, The hands we clasp, the loved that sleep;
dark - 'ning years, The twi - light ray from ho - lier spheres;
heav'n - ly store, Thy peace be with us ev - er - more. A - men.

578 O Perfect Love

Dorothy F. Gurney, 1858-1932

O PERFECT LOVE 11.10.11.10.
Joseph Barnby, 1838-1896

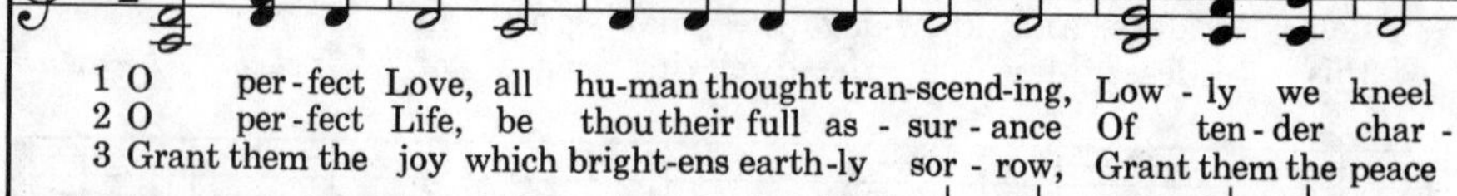

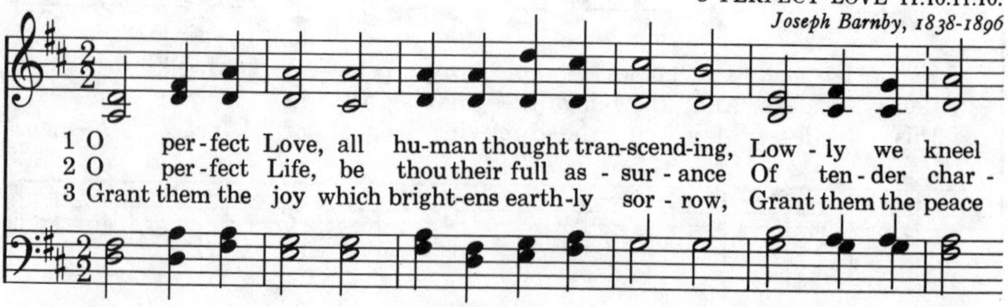

1 O per - fect Love, all hu - man thought tran - scend - ing, Low - ly we kneel
2 O per - fect Life, be thou their full as - sur - ance Of ten - der char -
3 Grant them the joy which bright - ens earth - ly sor - row, Grant them the peace

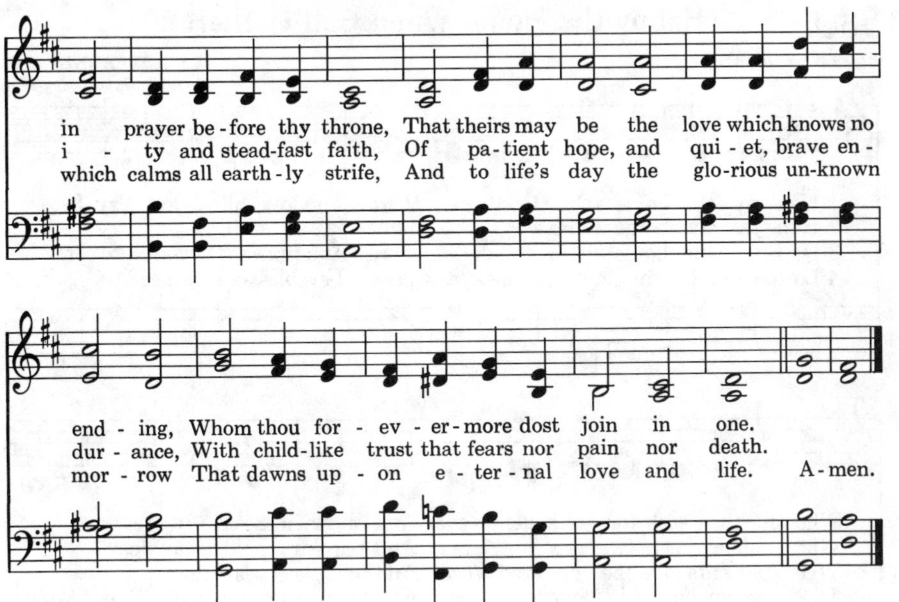
in prayer be-fore thy throne, That theirs may be the love which knows no
i - ty and stead-fast faith, Of pa-tient hope, and qui - et, brave en -
which calms all earth-ly strife, And to life's day the glo-rious un-known
end - ing, Whom thou for - ev - er-more dost join in one.
dur - ance, With child-like trust that fears nor pain nor death.
mor - row That dawns up - on e - ter - nal love and life. A-men.

O Happy Home, Where Thou Art Loved 579

Carl J. P. Spitta, 1801-1859
Tr. Sarah B. Findlater, 1823-1907

O PERFECT LOVE 11.10.11.10.
Joseph Barnby, 1838-1896

1 O happy home, where thou art loved the dearest,
Thou loving friend and Savior of our race,
And where among the guests there never cometh
One who can hold such high and honored place!

2 O happy home, where each one serves thee, lowly,
Whatever his appointed work may be,
Till ev'ry common task seems great and holy,
When it is done, O Lord, as unto thee!

3 O happy home, whose little ones are given
Early to thee, in humble faith and prayer—
To thee, their friend, who from the heights of heaven
Guides them, and guards with more than mother's care!

4 Until at last, when earth's day's work is ended,
All meet thee in the blessed home above,
From whence thou camest, where thou hast ascended,
Thy everlasting home of peace and love! Amen.

580

Happy the Home When God Is There

Henry Ware, Jr., 1794-1843

ST. AGNES C.M.
John B. Dykes, 1823-1876

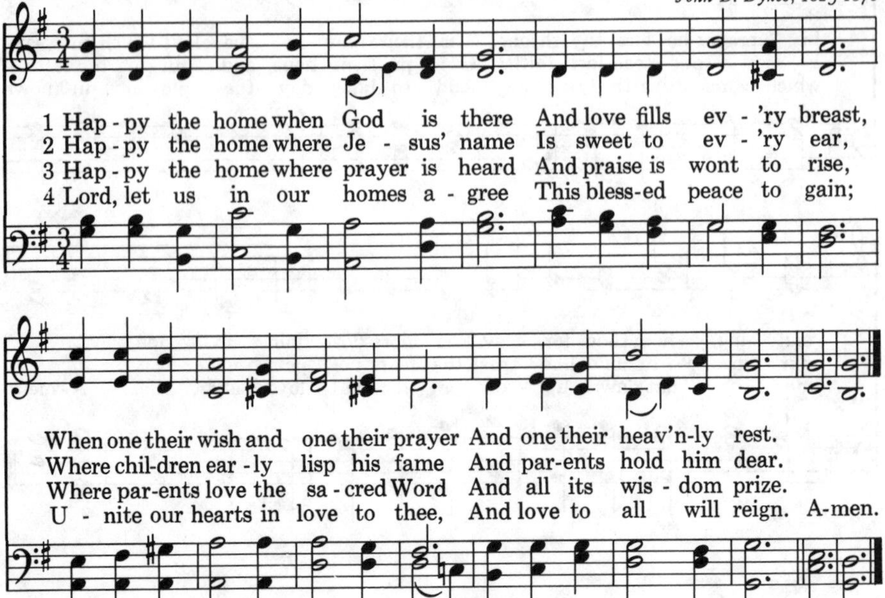

1 Hap-py the home when God is there And love fills ev-'ry breast,
When one their wish and one their prayer And one their heav'n-ly rest.

2 Hap-py the home where Je-sus' name Is sweet to ev-'ry ear,
Where chil-dren ear-ly lisp his fame And par-ents hold him dear.

3 Hap-py the home where prayer is heard And praise is wont to rise,
Where par-ents love the sa-cred Word And all its wis-dom prize.

4 Lord, let us in our homes a-gree This bless-ed peace to gain;
U-nite our hearts in love to thee, And love to all will reign. A-men.

FAMILY AND HOME

581 My Country, 'Tis of Thee

Samuel F. Smith, 1808-1895
AMERICA 6.6.4.6.6.6.4.
"Thesaurus Musicus," 1744
1 My coun-try, 'tis of thee, Sweet land of lib-er-ty, Of thee I sing: Land where my fa-thers died, Land of the
2 My na-tive coun-try, thee, Land of the no-ble free, Thy name I love: I love thy rocks and rills, Thy woods and
3 Let mu-sic swell the breeze, And ring from all the trees Sweet free-dom's song: Let mor-tal tongues a-wake, Let all that
4 Our fa-thers' God, to thee, Au-thor of lib-er-ty, To thee we sing; Long may our land be bright With free-dom's

NATION

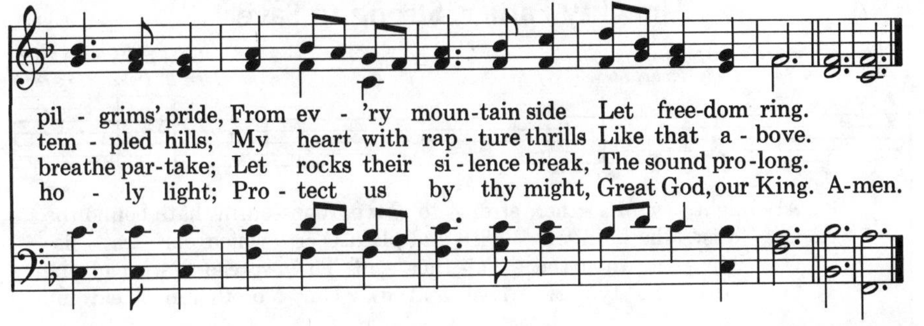
pil - grims' pride, From ev - 'ry moun-tain side Let free-dom ring.
tem - pled hills; My heart with rap - ture thrills Like that a - bove.
breathe par-take; Let rocks their si - lence break, The sound pro - long.
ho - ly light; Pro - tect us by thy might, Great God, our King. A-men.

God Bless Our Native Land 582

Siegfried A. Mahlmann, 1771-1826, Sts. 1,2
William E. Hickson, 1803-1870, St. 3

AMERICA 6.6.4.6.6.6.4.
"Thesaurus Musicus," 1744

1 God bless our native land—
Firm may she ever stand
Through storm and night:
When the wild tempests rave,
Ruler of wind and wave,
Do thou our country save
By thy great might.

2 For her our prayers shall rise
To God above the skies—
On him we wait:
Thou who art ever nigh,
Guarding with watchful eye,
To thee aloud we cry,
God save the state!

3 And not to us alone,
But be thy mercies known
From shore to shore:
Lord, make the nations see
That men should brothers be,
And form one family
The wide world o'er. Amen.

God Save Our Gracious Queen 583

Source unknown, Sts. 1,2
Robert Murray, 1832-1910, St. 3

AMERICA 6.6.4.6.6.6.4.
"Thesaurus Musicus," 1744

1 God save our gracious Queen,
Long live our noble Queen:
God save the Queen.
Send her victorious,
Happy and glorious,
Long to reign over us:
God save the Queen.

2 Thy choicest gifts in store
On her be pleased to pour:
Long may she reign.
May she defend our laws,
And ever give us cause
To sing with heart and voice,
God save the Queen.

3 Our loved dominion bless
With peace and happiness
From shore to shore;
And let our nation be
Loyal, united, free,
True to herself and thee
For evermore. Amen.

584 Almighty Father, Strong to Save

William Whiting, 1825-1878, Sts. 1,4, alt.
Robert Nelson Spencer, 1877-1961, Sts. 2,3

MELITA 8.8.8.8.8.8.
John B. Dykes, 1823-1876

1 Al - might - y Fa - ther, strong to save, Whose arm hath bound the
2 O Christ, the Lord of hill and plain, O'er which our traf - fic
3 O Spir - it, whom the Fa - ther sent To spread a - broad the
4 O Trin - i - ty of love and pow'r, Our breth - ren shield in
rest - less wave, Who bidd'st the might - y o - cean deep
runs a - main By moun - tain pass or val - ley low:
fir - ma - ment: O Wind of heav - en, by thy might
dan - ger's hour; From rock and tem - pest, fire and foe,
Its own ap - point - ed lim - its keep: O hear us when we
Wher - ev - er, Lord, thy breth - ren go, Pro - tect them by thy
Save all who dare the ea - gle's flight, And keep them by thy
Pro - tect them where - so - e'er they go: Thus ev - er - more shall
cry to thee For those in per - il on the sea.
guard - ing hand From ev - 'ry per - il on the land.
watch - ful care From ev - 'ry per - il in the air.
rise to thee Glad praise from air and land and sea. A - men.

A lower setting may be found at No. 547

God of Our Fathers, Whose Almighty Hand

Daniel C. Roberts, 1841-1907
NATIONAL HYMN 10.10.10.10.
George W. Warren, 1828-1902
3
Trumpets
before each stanza
1 God of our fa - thers, whose al - might - y hand
2 Thy love di - vine hath led us in the past,
3 From war's a - larms, from dead - ly pes - ti - lence,
4 Re - fresh thy peo - ple on their toil - some way,
Leads forth in beau - ty all the star - ry band
In this free land by thee our lot is cast;
Be thy strong arm our ev - er - sure de - fense;
Lead us from night to nev - er - end - ing day;
Of shin - ing worlds in splen - dor thru the skies,
Be thou our rul - er, guard - ian, guide, and stay,
Thy true re - li - gion in our hearts in - crease,
Fill all our lives with love and grace di - vine,
Our grate - ful songs be - fore thy throne a - rise.
Thy word our law, thy paths our cho - sen way.
Thy boun - teous good - ness nour - ish us in peace.
And glo - ry, laud, and praise be ev - er thine! A - men.

586 God of the Nations, Who from Dawn of Days

W. Russell Bowie, 1882-1969

TOULON 10.10.10.10.
Abridged from "Genevan Psalter," 1551

1 God of the na - tions, who from dawn of days
2 Thine an - cient might de - stroyed the Phar - aoh's boast,
3 Thy hand has led a - cross the hun - gry sea
4 Then for thy grace to grow in broth - er - hood,
Hast led thy peo - ple in their wid - 'ning ways,
Thou wast the shield for Is - rael's march - ing host,
The ea - ger peo - ples flock - ing to be free,
For hearts a - flame to serve thy des - tined good,
Through whose deep pur - pose stran - ger - thou - sands stand
And, all the a - ges through, past crum - bling throne
And from the breeds of earth, thy si - lent sway
For faith, and will to win what faith shall see,
Here in the bor - ders of our prom - ised land:
And bro - ken fet - ter, thou hast brought thine own.
Fash - ions the na - tion of the broad - 'ning day.
God of thy peo - ple, hear us cry to thee! A - men.

Words used by permission of Jean Bowie Evans.
A lower setting may be found at No. 181

NATION

Not Alone for Mighty Empire 587

William Pierson Merrill, 1867-1954

IN BABILONE 8.7.8.7.D.
Dutch Melody
Harm. by Julius Röntgen, 1855-1933

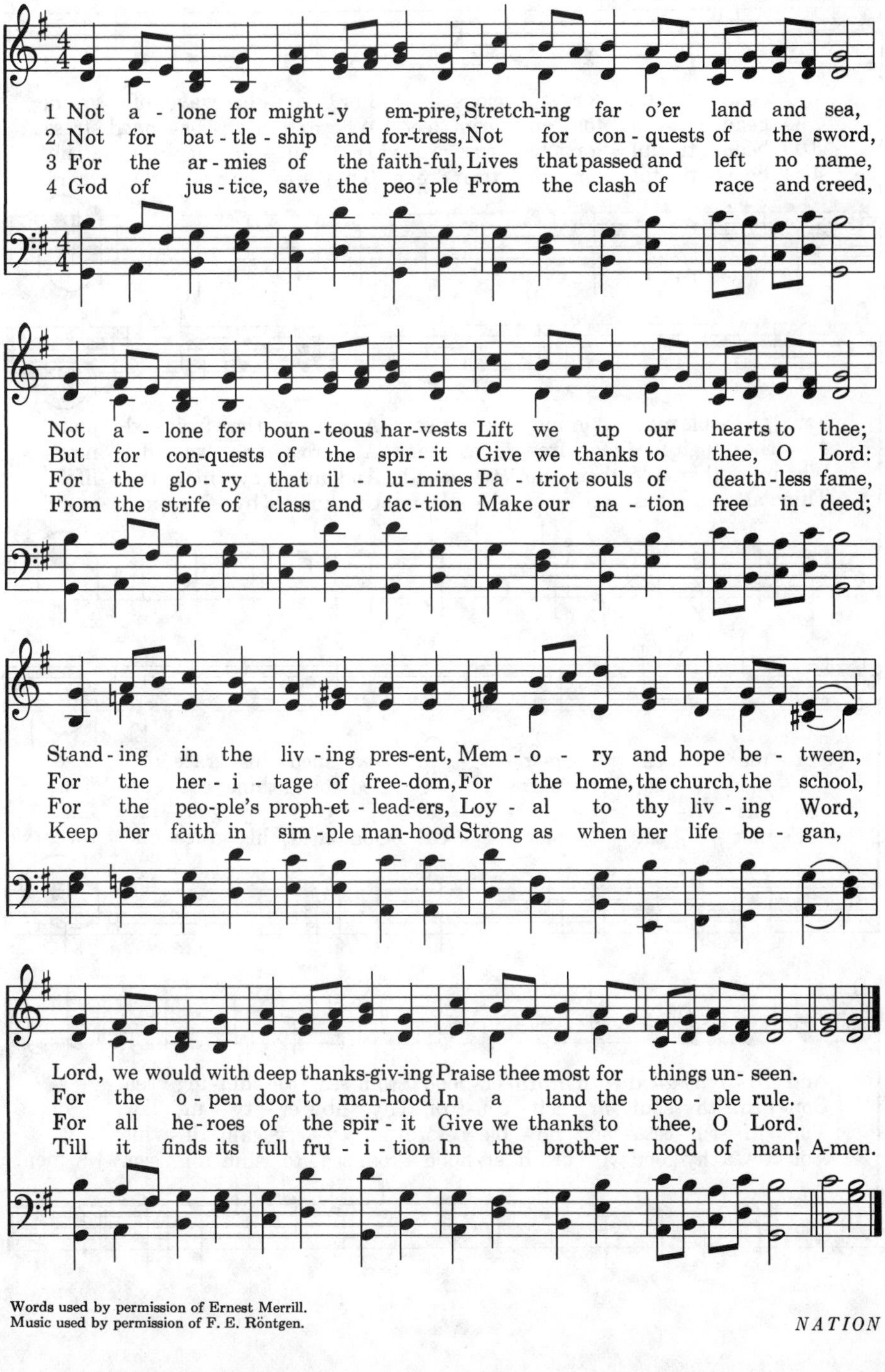

1 Not a - lone for might-y em-pire, Stretch-ing far o'er land and sea,
2 Not for bat - tle - ship and for-tress, Not for con - quests of the sword,
3 For the ar - mies of the faith-ful, Lives that passed and left no name,
4 God of jus - tice, save the peo - ple From the clash of race and creed,

Not a - lone for boun - teous har-vests Lift we up our hearts to thee;
But for con-quests of the spir - it Give we thanks to thee, O Lord:
For the glo - ry that il - lu-mines Pa - triot souls of death-less fame,
From the strife of class and fac-tion Make our na - tion free in - deed;

Stand - ing in the liv - ing pres-ent, Mem - o - ry and hope be - tween,
For the her - i - tage of free-dom, For the home, the church, the school,
For the peo-ple's proph-et - lead-ers, Loy - al to thy liv - ing Word,
Keep her faith in sim - ple man-hood Strong as when her life be - gan,

Lord, we would with deep thanks-giv-ing Praise thee most for things un - seen.
For the o - pen door to man-hood In a land the peo - ple rule.
For all he-roes of the spir - it Give we thanks to thee, O Lord.
Till it finds its full fru - i - tion In the broth-er - hood of man! A-men.

588 O Beautiful for Spacious Skies

Katharine Lee Bates, 1859-1929
MATERNA C.M.D.
Samuel A. Ward, 1848-1903
1 O beau - ti - ful for spa-cious skies, For am - ber waves of grain,
2 O beau - ti - ful for pil - grim feet, Whose stern, im-pas-sioned stress
3 O beau - ti - ful for he - roes proved In lib - er - at - ing strife,
4 O beau - ti - ful for pa - triot dream That sees be-yond the years
For pur - ple moun-tain maj - es - ties A - bove the fruit - ed plain!
A thor-ough-fare for free - dom beat A - cross the wil - der - ness!
Who more than self their coun - try loved, And mer - cy more than life!
Thine al - a - bas - ter cit - ies gleam, Un-dimmed by hu - man tears!
A - mer - i - ca! A - mer - i - ca! God shed his grace on thee,
A - mer - i - ca! A - mer - i - ca! God mend thine ev - ery flaw,
A - mer - i - ca! A - mer - i - ca! May God thy gold re - fine,
A - mer - i - ca! A - mer - i - ca! God shed his grace on thee,
And crown thy good with broth - er - hood From sea to shin - ing sea.
Con - firm thy soul in self - con - trol, Thy lib - er - ty in law.
Till all suc - cess be no - ble - ness, And ev - ery gain di - vine.
And crown thy good with broth - er - hood From sea to shin - ing sea. A - men.

589 O God of Earth and Altar

Gilbert K. Chesterton, 1874-1936
LLANGLOFFAN 7.6.7.6.D.
Welsh Melody
1 O God of earth and al - tar, Bow down and hear our cry;
2 From all that ter - ror teach - es, From lies of tongue and pen,
3 Tie in a liv - ing teth - er The prince and priest and thrall;
Our earth - ly rul - ers fal - ter, Our peo - ple drift and die;
From all the eas - y speech - es That com - fort cru - el men,
Bind all our lives to - geth - er, Smite us and save us all;
The walls of gold en - tomb us, The swords of scorn di - vide;
From sale and prof - a - na - tion Of hon - or and the sword,
In ire and ex - ul - ta - tion A - flame with faith, and free,
Take not thy thun - der from us, But take a - way our pride.
From sleep and from dam - na - tion, De - liv - er us, good Lord!
Lift up a liv - ing na - tion, A sin - gle sword to thee. A - men.

Words by permission of Oxford University Press.

NATION

590 Thou, by Heavenly Hosts Adored

Henry Harbaugh, 1817-1867, alt.

ST. GEORGE'S WINDSOR 7.7.7.7.D.

George J. Elvey, 1816-1893

1 Thou, by heav'n-ly hosts a-dored, Gra-cious, might-y, sov-'reign Lord,
God of na-tions, King of kings, Head of all cre-a-ted things,
By the Church with joy con-fessed, God o'er all for-ev-er blest,
Plead-ing at thy throne we stand: Save thy peo-ple, bless our land.

2 From all pub-lic sin and shame, From am-bi-tion's grasp-ing aim,
From re-bel-lion, death and war, From de-stroy-ing na-ture's store,
From dread fam-ine's aw-ful stroke, From op-pres-sion's gall-ing yoke,
From the judg-ments of thy hand: Spare thy peo-ple, spare our land.

3 Let our rul-ers ev-er be Men that love and hon-or thee,
Let the pow'rs by thee or-dained Be in right-eous-ness main-tained;
In the peo-ple's hearts in-crease Love of pi-e-ty and peace:
Thus u-nit-ed, we shall stand One wide, free, and hap-py land. A-men.

NATION

A lower setting may be found at No. 618

Thou Judge by Whom Each Empire Fell

Percy Dearmer, *1867-1936*

NUN FREUT EUCH 8.7.8.7.8.8.7.
Joseph Klug's "Geistliche Lieder," Wittenberg, 1535

1 Thou Judge by whom each em-pire fell When pride of pow'r o'er - came it,
2 Search, Lord, our spir - its in thy sight, In best and worst re - veal us;
3 Lo, fear-ing naught we come to thee, Tho by our fault con - found-ed;
Con - vict us now, if we re - bel— Our na-tion judge, and shame it.
Shed on our souls a blaze of light, And judge, that thou may'st heal us.
Tho self - ish, mean, and base we be, Thy jus-tice is un - bound-ed—
In each sharp cri - sis, Lord, ap - pear, For - give, and show our
The pres - ent be our judg - ment day, When all our lack thou
So large it naught but love re - quires, And, judg - ing, par - dons,
du - ty clear: To serve thee by re - pen - tance.
dost sur - vey: Show us our - selves and save us.
frees, in - spires: De - liv - er us from e - vil! A - men.

Words from *Enlarged Songs of Praise* by permission of Oxford University Press.

NATION

592 Mine Eyes Have Seen the Glory

Julia Ward Howe, 1819-1910 BATTLE HYMN OF THE REPUBLIC 15.15.15.6. *with Refrain*
American Melody, c. 1852

1 Mine eyes have seen the glo - ry of the com - ing of the Lord,
2 I have seen him in the watch-fires of a hun - dred cir - cling camps,
3 He has sound - ed forth the trum - pet that shall nev - er call re - treat,
4 In the beau - ty of the lil - ies Christ was born a - cross the sea,
He is tram - pling out the vin - tage where the grapes of wrath are stored;
They have build - ed him an al - tar in the eve - ning dews and damps;
He is sift - ing out the hearts of men be - fore his judg - ment seat;
With a glo - ry in his bos - om that trans - fig - ures you and me;
He hath loosed the fate - ful light - ning of his ter - ri - ble swift sword,
I can read his right - eous sen - tence by the dim and flar - ing lamps,
O be swift, my soul, to an - swer him, be ju - bi - lant, my feet!
As he died to make men ho - ly let us die to make men free!
His truth is march - ing on.
His day is march - ing on.
Our God is march - ing on.
While God is march - ing on.
REFRAIN
Glo - ry! glo - ry! Hal - le -

lu - jah! Glo - ry! glo - ry! Hal - le - lu - jah!
Glo - ry! glo - ry! Hal - le - lu - jah! His truth is march - ing on.

O Day of God, Draw Nigh 593

Robert B. Y. Scott, 1899- , *alt.*

ST. MICHAEL (Old 134th) S.M.
"Genevan Psalter," 1551
Adapted by William Crotch, 1775-1847

1 O Day of God, draw nigh In beau - ty and in power;
Come with thy time-less judg-ment now To match our pres-ent hour.

2 Bring to our trou - bled minds, Un - cer - tain and a - fraid,
The qui - et of a stead-fast faith, Calm of a call o - beyed.

3 Bring jus - tice to our land, That all may dwell se - cure,
And fine - ly build for days to come Foun-da-tions that en - dure.

4 Bring to our world of strife Thy sov-ereign word of peace,
That war may haunt the earth no more And des - o - la - tion cease.

5 O Day of God, draw nigh As at cre - a - tion's birth;
Let there be light a - gain, and set Thy judg-ments in the earth. A-men.

594 God the Omnipotent

Henry F. Chorley, 1808-1872, Sts. 1,2, alt.
John Ellerton, 1826-1893, Sts. 3,4, alt.

RUSSIAN HYMN 11.10.11.9.
Alexis F. Lvov, 1799-1870

1 God the Om - nip - o - tent, King, who or - dain - est
2 God the All - mer - ci - ful, earth hath for - sak - en
3 God the All - right - eous One, man hath de - fied thee,
4 God the All - prov - i - dent, earth by thy chas - t'ning
Thun - der thy clar - ion, the light - ning thy sword,
Thy ways all - ho - ly, and slight - ed thy word;
Yet to e - ter - ni - ty stand - eth thy word;
Yet shall to free - dom and truth be re - stored;
Show forth thy pit - y on high where thou reign - est:
Bid not thy wrath in its ter - rors a - wak - en:
False - hood and wrong shall not tar - ry be - side thee:
Thru the thick dark - ness thy king - dom is has - t'ning:
Give to us peace in our time, O Lord.
Give to us peace in our time, O Lord.
Give to us peace in our time, O Lord.
Thou wilt give peace in thy time, O Lord. A - men.

O God of Every Nation

William W. Reid, Jr., 1923-

ST. THEODULPH 7.6.7.6.D.
Melchior Teschner, 1584-1635

1 O God of ev - 'ry na - tion, Of ev - 'ry race and land,
2 From search for wealth and pow - er And scorn of truth and right,
3 Lord, strength-en all who la - bor That men may find re - lease
4 Keep bright in us the vi - sion Of days when war shall cease,
Re - deem thy whole cre - a - tion With thine al-might-y hand:
From trust in bombs that show - er De - struc-tion thru the night,
From fear of rat-tling sa - ber, From dread of war's in - crease:
When ha-tred and di - vi - sion Give way to love and peace,
Where hate and fear di - vide us And bit - ter threats are hurled,
From pride of race and sta - tion And blind-ness to thy way,
When hope and cour-age fal - ter, Thy still, small voice be heard;
Till dawns the morn-ing glo - rious When broth-er-hood shall reign,
In love and mer-cy guide us, And heal our strife-torn world.
De - liv - er ev - 'ry na - tion, E - ter-nal God, we pray.
With faith that none can al - ter, Thy serv-ants un - der - gird.
And Christ shall rule vic - to - rious O'er all the world's do-main. A-men.

596 Son of God, Eternal Savior

Somerset Corry Lowry, 1855-1932

EBENEZER 8.7.8.7.D.
Thomas J. Williams, 1869-1944

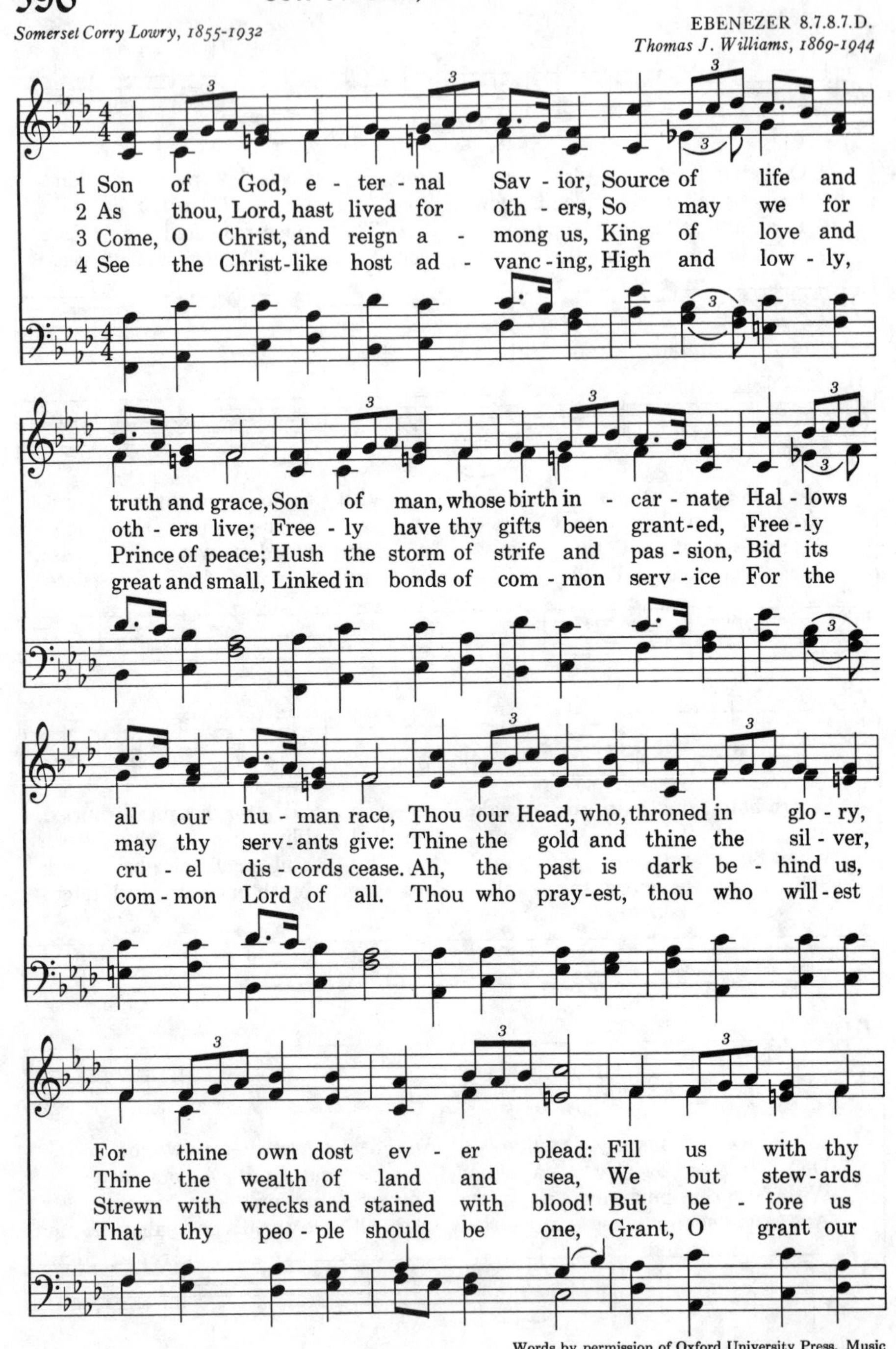

1 Son of God, e - ter - nal Sav - ior, Source of life and
2 As thou, Lord, hast lived for oth - ers, So may we for
3 Come, O Christ, and reign a - mong us, King of love and
4 See the Christ-like host ad - vanc - ing, High and low - ly,
truth and grace, Son of man, whose birth in - car - nate Hal - lows
oth - ers live; Free - ly have thy gifts been grant - ed, Free - ly
Prince of peace; Hush the storm of strife and pas - sion, Bid its
great and small, Linked in bonds of com - mon serv - ice For the
all our hu - man race, Thou our Head, who, throned in glo - ry,
may thy serv - ants give: Thine the gold and thine the sil - ver,
cru - el dis - cords cease. Ah, the past is dark be - hind us,
com - mon Lord of all. Thou who pray - est, thou who will - est
For thine own dost ev - er plead: Fill us with thy
Thine the wealth of land and sea, We but stew - ards
Strewn with wrecks and stained with blood! But be - fore us
That thy peo - ple should be one, Grant, O grant our
3

WORLD FRIENDSHIP AND PEACE

A lower setting may be found at No. 432

love and pit - y, Heal our wrongs and help our need.
of thy boun - ty, Held in sol - emn trust for thee.
gleams the vi - sion Of the com - ing broth - er - hood.
hope's fru - i - tion: Here on earth thy will be done. A-men.

O God of Love, O King of Peace

597

Henry W. Baker, 1821-1877

QUEBEC L.M.
Henry Baker, 1835-1910

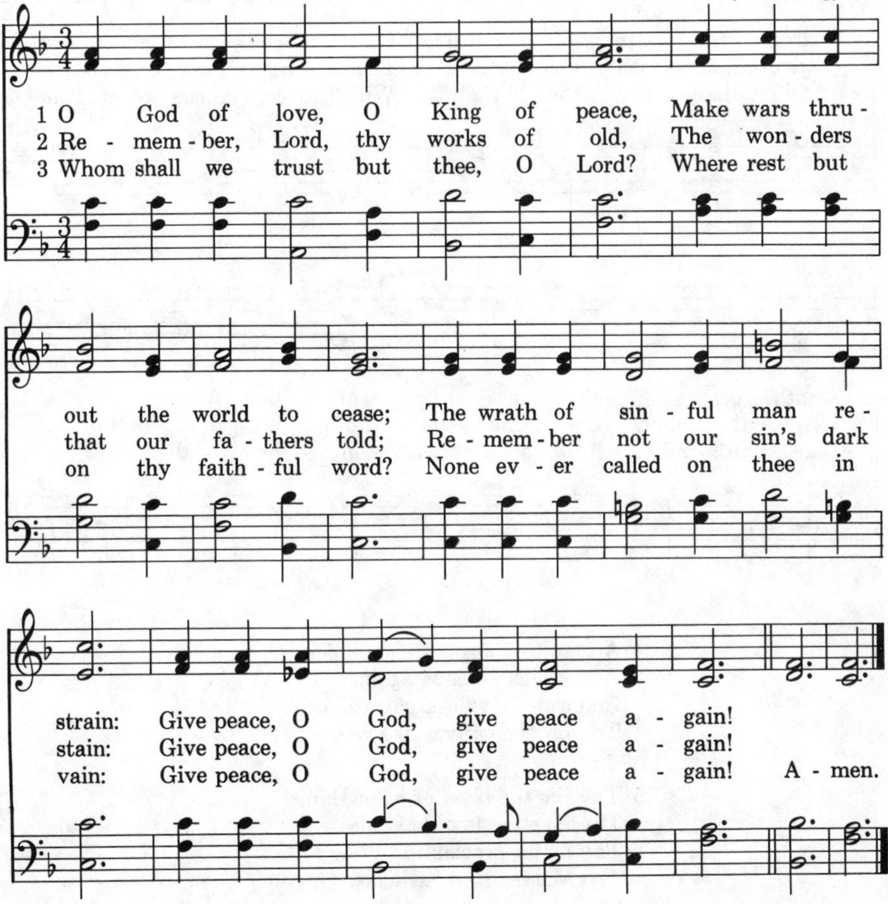

1 O God of love, O King of peace, Make wars thru -
2 Re - mem - ber, Lord, thy works of old, The won - ders
3 Whom shall we trust but thee, O Lord? Where rest but

out the world to cease; The wrath of sin - ful man re -
that our fa - thers told; Re - mem - ber not our sin's dark
on thy faith - ful word? None ev - er called on thee in

strain: Give peace, O God, give peace a - gain!
stain: Give peace, O God, give peace a - gain!
vain: Give peace, O God, give peace a - gain! A - men.

A lower setting may be found at No. 600

598 O Thou Whose Feet Have Climbed Life's Hill

Louis F. Benson, 1855-1930

ST. MAGNUS C.M.
Jeremiah Clark, c.1670-1707

1 O thou whose feet have climbed life's hill And trod the path of youth, Our Sav - ior and our broth - er still, Now lead us in - to truth.
2 The call is thine: be thou the Way, And give us men who guide; Let wis - dom broad - en with the day, Let hu - man faith a - bide.
3 Who learn of thee the truth shall find, Who fol - low, gain the goal; With rev - 'rence crown the ear - nest mind, And speak with - in the soul.
A - men.

4 Awake the purpose high which strives,
And, falling, stands again;
Confirm the will of eager lives
To quit themselves like men.

5 Thy life the bond of fellowship,
Thy love the law that rules,
Thy name, proclaimed by ev'ry lip,
The Master of our schools. Amen.

A higher setting may be found at No. 229

Shine Thou upon Us, Lord

John Ellerton, 1826-1893

LEONI 6.6.6.6.D.
Hebrew Melody
Adapted by Meyer Lyon, 1751-1797

1 Shine thou up - on us, Lord, True light of men to - day,
2 Breathe thou up - on us, Lord, Thy Spir - it's liv - ing flame,
3 Speak thou for us, O Lord, In all we say of thee:
4 Live thou with - in us, Lord— Thy mind and will be ours:

And through the writ - ten Word Thy ver - y self dis - play,
That so with one ac - cord Our lips may tell thy name;
Ac - cord - ing to thy Word Let all our teach - ing be,
Be thou be - loved, a - dored And served with all our pow'rs,

That so, from hearts which burn With gaz - ing on thy face,
Give thou the hear - ing ear, Fix thou the wan-d'ring thought,
That so thy lambs may know Their own true Shep-herd's voice,
That so our lives may teach Thy chil - dren what thou art,

Thy lit - tle ones may learn The won - ders of thy grace.
That those we teach may hear The great things thou hast wrought.
Wher - e'er he leads them go, And in his love re - joice.
And plead, by more than speech, For thee with ev - 'ry heart. A-men.

600 My Lord, I Do Not Ask to Stand

Norman E. Richardson, 1878-1945 QUEBEC L.M.
Florence I. Judson-Bradley *Henry Baker, 1835-1910*

1 My Lord, I do not ask to stand As king or
2 To teach a ten - der voice to pray, Two child - ish
3 O grant thy pa - tience to im - part Thy ho - ly
4 As step by step we tread the way, Trust - ing and

prince of high de - gree; I on - ly pray that hand in
eyes thy face to see, Two feet to guide in thy straight
law, thy words of truth; Give, Lord, thy grace, that my whole
con - fi - dent and free, A child and I shall day by

hand A child and I may come to thee.
way— This fer - vent - ly I ask of thee.
heart May o - ver - flow with love for youth.
day Find sweet com - pan - ion - ship with thee. A - men.

EDUCATION

A higher setting may be found at No. 597

601 Behold a Host Arrayed in White

Based on Revelation 7:9 BEHOLD A HOST 8.8.8.6. 12L.
Hans Adolph Brorson, 1694-1764 *Norwegian Folk Song*
Tr. Carl Doving, 1867-1937, alt. *Harm. by Edvard Grieg, 1843-1907*

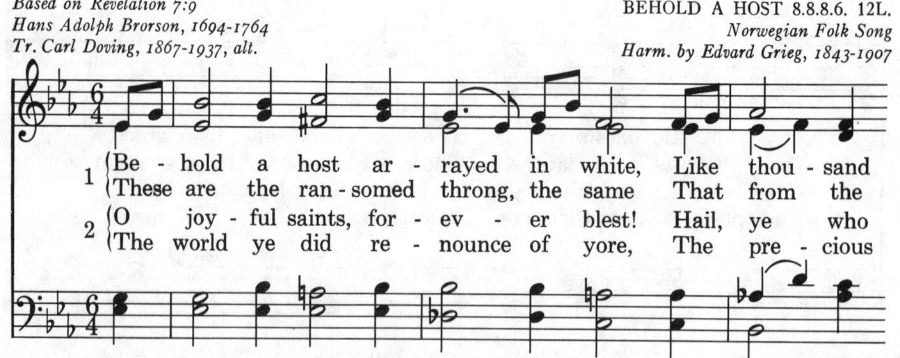
1 Be - hold a host ar - rayed in white, Like thou - sand
These are the ran - somed throng, the same That from the
2 O joy - ful saints, for - ev - er blest! Hail, ye who
The world ye did re - nounce of yore, The pre - cious

LIFE EVERLASTING

snow - clad moun - tains bright! With palms they stand— who
trib - u - la - tion came, And in the flood of
have at - tained your rest! In life and death ye
seed ye weep - ing bore; Now reap the joy with -
are this band Be - fore the throne of light?
Je - sus' blood Are cleansed from guilt and shame:
kept the faith, Though ye were sore op - prest.
out al - loy In bliss for - ev - er - more.
And now, ar - rayed in robes made white, They serve the
Lift up your voice, ye ran - somed throng, And swell the
Lord by day and night; And an - thems swell where
ev - er - last - ing song: Praise, hon - or, laud, to
God doth dwell With an - gels in the height.
thee, our God, And to the Lamb be - long.

LIFE EVERLASTING

602 For All the Saints

William W. How, 1823-1897

SINE NOMINE 10.10.10. *with Alleluias*
Ralph Vaughan Williams, 1872-1958

In unison
1 For all the saints who from their la - bors rest, Who
2 Thou wast their rock, their for - tress, and their might, Thou,
3 O may thy sol - diers, faith - ful, true, and bold,
4 O blest com - mu - nion, fel - low - ship di - vine!
5 But lo! there breaks a yet more glo - rious day: The
6 From earth's wide bounds, from o - cean's far - thest coast, Thru
thee by faith be - fore the world con - fessed, Thy
Lord, their cap - tain in the well-fought fight;
Fight as the saints who no - bly fought of old, And
We fee - bly strug - gle, they in glo - ry shine; Yet
saints tri - um - phant rise in bright ar - ray; The
gates of pearl streams in the count - less host,
name, O Je - sus, be for - ev - er blest:
Thou, in the dark - ness drear, their one true light:
win with them the vic - tor's crown of gold:
all are one in thee, for all are thine:
King of glo - ry pass - es on his way:
Sing - ing to Fa - ther, Son, and Ho - ly Ghost:

Abide with Me 603

Henry F. Lyte, 1793-1847, alt.

EVENTIDE 10.10.10.10.
William H. Monk, 1823-1889

Al - le - lu - ia! Al - le - lu - ia! A-men.
1 A - bide with me—fast falls the e - ven - tide; The dark-ness deep-ens—
2 Swift to its close ebbs out life's lit - tle day; Earth's joys grow dim, its
3 I need thy pres - ence ev - 'ry pass-ing hour; What but thy grace can
4 I fear no foe, with thee at hand to bless; Ills have no weight and
5 Hold thou thy cross be - fore my clos-ing eyes; Shine thru the gloom and
Lord, with me a - bide; When oth - er help - ers fail and com-forts flee,
glo - ries pass a - way; Change and de - cay in all a-round I see;
foil the temp-ter's pow'r? Who like thy - self my guide and stay can be?
tears no bit - ter - ness; Where is death's sting? where, grave, thy vic - to - ry?
point me to the skies; Heav'n's morn-ing breaks and earth's vain shad-ows flee;
Help of the help - less, O a - bide with me.
O thou who chang - est not, a - bide with me.
Thru cloud and sun - shine, O a - bide with me.
I tri - umph still if thou a - bide with me.
In life, in death, O Lord, a - bide with me. A - men.

604 In Heaven Above

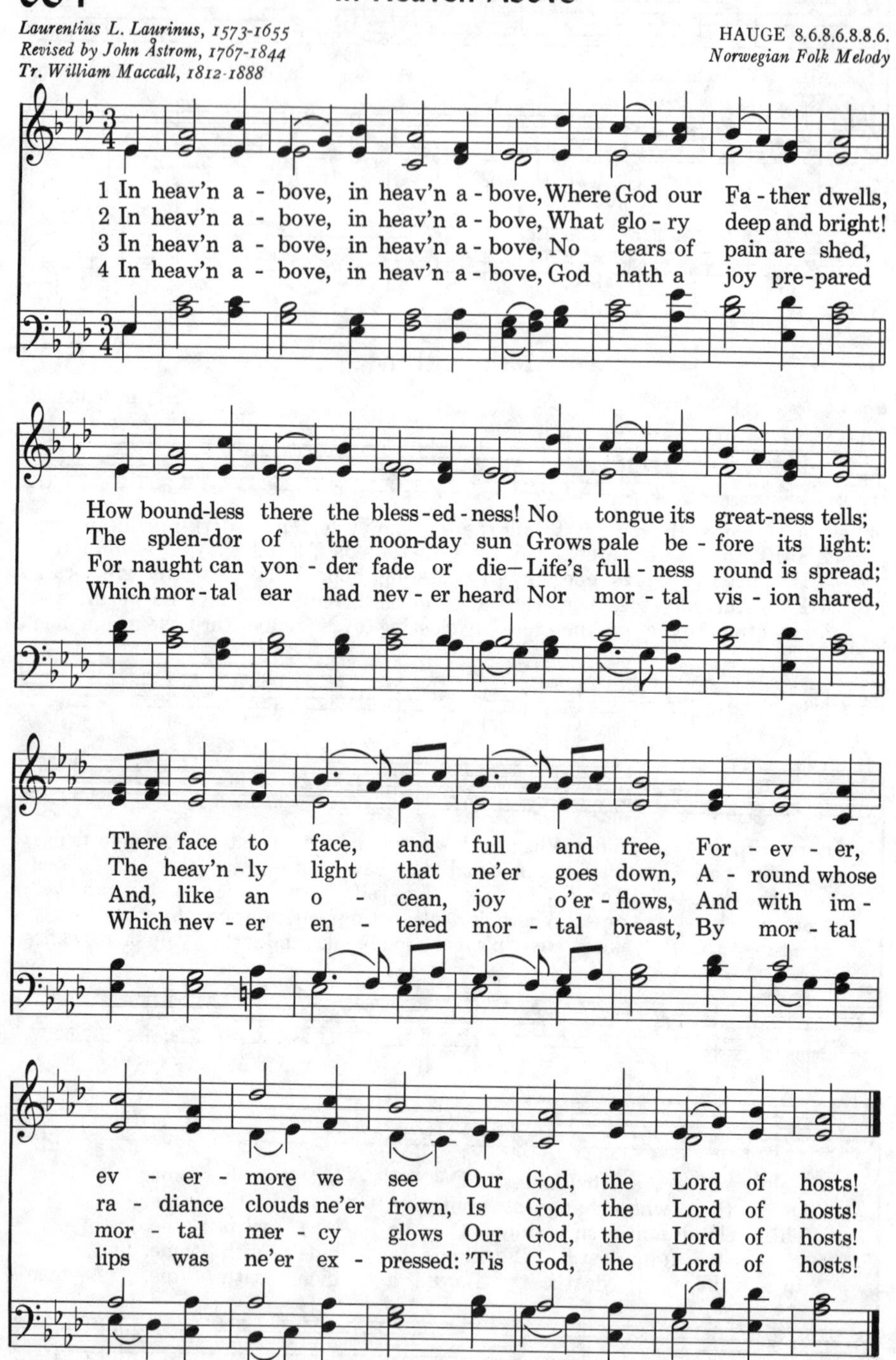
Laurentius L. Laurinus, 1573-1655
Revised by John Åstrom, 1767-1844
Tr. William Maccall, 1812-1888
HAUGE 8.6.8.6.8.8.6.
Norwegian Folk Melody
1 In heav'n a - bove, in heav'n a - bove, Where God our Fa - ther dwells,
2 In heav'n a - bove, in heav'n a - bove, What glo - ry deep and bright!
3 In heav'n a - bove, in heav'n a - bove, No tears of pain are shed,
4 In heav'n a - bove, in heav'n a - bove, God hath a joy pre-pared
How bound-less there the bless - ed - ness! No tongue its great-ness tells;
The splen-dor of the noon-day sun Grows pale be - fore its light:
For naught can yon - der fade or die— Life's full - ness round is spread;
Which mor - tal ear had nev - er heard Nor mor - tal vis - ion shared,
There face to face, and full and free, For - ev - er,
The heav'n - ly light that ne'er goes down, A - round whose
And, like an o - cean, joy o'er - flows, And with im -
Which nev - er en - tered mor - tal breast, By mor - tal
ev - er - more we see Our God, the Lord of hosts!
ra - diance clouds ne'er frown, Is God, the Lord of hosts!
mor - tal mer - cy glows Our God, the Lord of hosts!
lips was ne'er ex - pressed: 'Tis God, the Lord of hosts!

In Heaven All Is Gladness

Johan N. Brun, 1745-1816
Tr. Composite

GLÄDJE 7.6.7.6.D.
Oscar Ahnfelt, 1813-1882

1 In heav-en all is glad-ness—Here trou-bles press, and fears;
2 This world is not my home-land, In tents I pass my days;
3 Would I ex-change con-di-tions With one whose all's be-low?
4 My hope for life e-ter-nal Rests on foun-da-tion sure;
Here, oft-en bowed and sigh-ing, I eat "the bread of tears."
T'ward yon-der shore of glo-ry With yearn-ing eyes I gaze.
No, rath-er I'd be sow-ing Good seed, tho tears may flow,
My cross I there-fore glad-ly Will yet a-while en-dure.
Here joy and sor-row min-gle For Christ's be-lov-ed bride;
While seeks the world its fol-ly, I view the cit-a-del
If at my jour-ney's end-ing I but in joy may reap,
Soon there shall be no sor-row, No plaints nor sighs for me,
But 'tis not so up yon-der, For there doth joy a-bide.
Where, free from care and sor-row, For-ev-er I shall dwell.
When world-ly joys are o-ver And some, too late, must weep.
When, with un-cov-ered vi-sion, My Sav-ior I shall see.

606 Jerusalem the Golden

St. Bernard of Cluny, 12th century
Tr. John M. Neale, 1818-1866, alt.

EWING 7.6.7.6.D.
Alexander Ewing, 1830-1895

1 Je - ru - sa - lem the gold - en, With milk and hon - ey blest,
2 They stand, those halls of Zi - on, All ju - bi - lant with song,
3 There is the throne of Da - vid, And there, from care re - leased,
4 O sweet and bless - ed coun - try, The home of God's e - lect!
Be - neath thy con - tem - pla - tion Sink heart and voice op - pressed.
And bright with man - y an an - gel, And all the mar - tyr throng.
The shout of them that tri - umph, The song of them that feast,
O sweet and bless - ed coun - try, That ea - ger hearts ex - pect!
I know not, O I know not, What joys a - wait us there,
The Prince is ev - er in them, The day - light is se - rene;
And they, who with their lead - er, Have con - quered in the fight,
Je - sus, in mer - cy bring us To that dear land of rest,
What ra - dian - cy of glo - ry, What bliss be - yond com - pare.
The pas - tures of the bless - ed Are decked in glo - rious sheen.
For - ev - er and for - ev - er Are clad in robes of white.
Who art, with God the Fa - ther And Spir - it, ev - er blest! A - men.

On Jordan's Stormy Banks I Stand

Samuel Stennett, 1727-1795

PROMISED LAND C.M. *with Refrain*
American Folk Melody
Adapted by Rigdon M. McIntosh, 1836-1899
Harm. by Norman E. Johnson, 1928-

1 On Jor-dan's storm-y banks I stand, And cast a wish-ful eye
2 O'er all those wide ex-tend-ed plains Shines one e-ter-nal day;
3 When shall I reach that hap-py place And be for-ev-er blest?
4 Filled with de-light, my rap-tured soul Would here no long-er stay;

To Ca-naan's fair and hap-py land, Where my pos-ses-sions lie.
There God the Son for-ev-er reigns And scat-ters night a-way.
When shall I see my Fa-ther's face And in his bos-om rest?
Tho Jor-dan's waves a-round me roll, Fear-less I'd launch a-way.

REFRAIN

I am bound for the prom-ised land, I am bound for the prom-ised land;

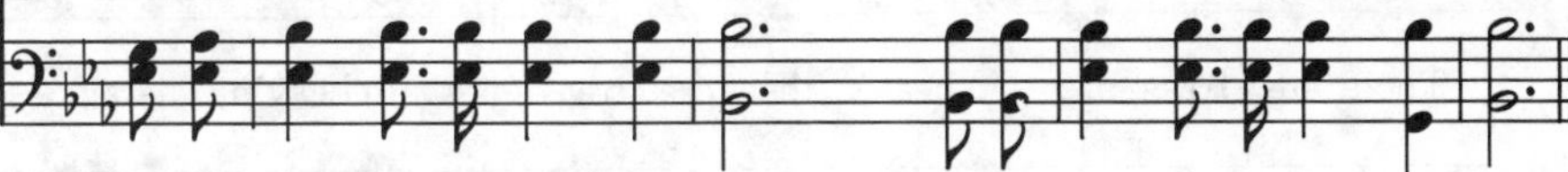

O who will come and go with me? I am bound for the prom-ised land.

May be played in E-flat minor

608 There Are Treasures for Children in Heaven

From the Swedish
Tr. Ernest Edwin Ryden, 1886-

TREASURES 12.9.12.9. *with Refrain*
Source unknown

1 There are treas-ures for chil-dren in heav-en a-bove, For the
2 They shall join in the an-thems of glo-ry and praise, They shall
chil-dren who trust in their Lord; They shall dwell in the light of his
sing with the an-gels so fair; And no sor-row or sigh-ing shall
fa-vor and love, They shall praise him with joy-ous ac-cord.
hush their sweet lays, When they meet their Re-deem-er up there.
REFRAIN
There are treas-ures in heav'n, there are treas-ures in heav'n, There are
treas-ures for chil-dren in heav'n; In the man-sions so bright, where the

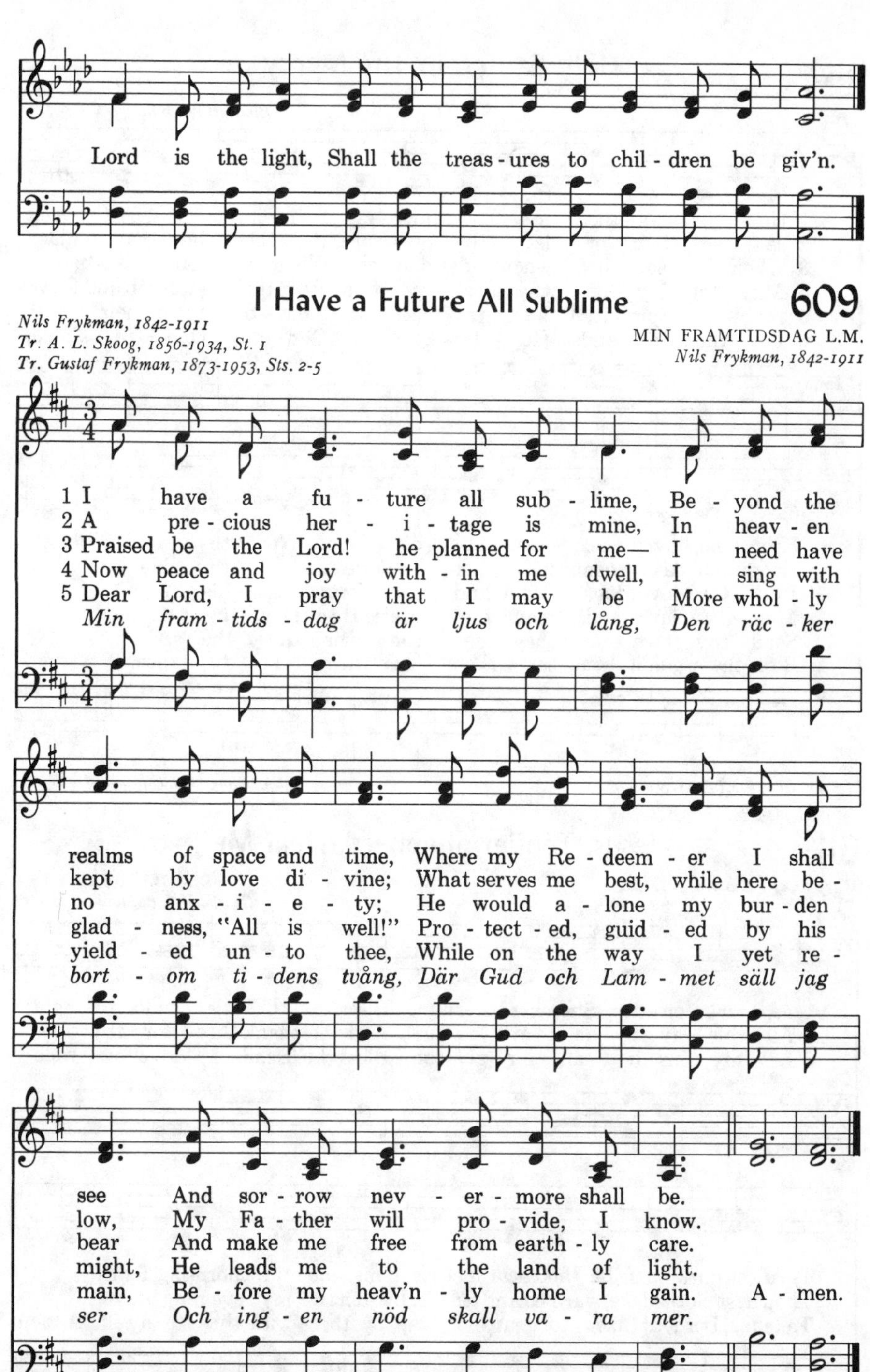
Lord is the light, Shall the treas - ures to chil - dren be giv'n.
I Have a Future All Sublime
609
Nils Frykman, 1842-1911
Tr. A. L. Skoog, 1856-1934, St. 1
Tr. Gustaf Frykman, 1873-1953, Sts. 2-5
MIN FRAMTIDSDAG L.M.
Nils Frykman, 1842-1911
1 I have a fu - ture all sub - lime, Be - yond the
2 A pre - cious her - i - tage is mine, In heav - en
3 Praised be the Lord! he planned for me— I need have
4 Now peace and joy with - in me dwell, I sing with
5 Dear Lord, I pray that I may be More whol - ly
Min fram - tids - dag är ljus och lång, Den räc - ker
realms of space and time, Where my Re - deem - er I shall
kept by love di - vine; What serves me best, while here be -
no anx - i - e - ty; He would a - lone my bur - den
glad - ness, "All is well!" Pro - tect - ed, guid - ed by his
yield - ed un - to thee, While on the way I yet re -
bort - om ti - dens tvång, Där Gud och Lam - met säll jag
see And sor - row nev - er - more shall be.
low, My Fa - ther will pro - vide, I know.
bear And make me free from earth - ly care.
might, He leads me to the land of light.
main, Be - fore my heav'n - ly home I gain. A - men.
ser Och ing - en nöd skall va - ra mer.

610 Holy Father, in Thy Mercy

Isabel S. Stevenson, 1843-1890 BULLINGER 8.5.8.3.
Ethelbert W. Bullinger, 1837-1913

1 Ho - ly Fa - ther, in thy mer - cy, Hear our ear - nest prayer:
2 Je - sus, Sav - ior, let thy pres-ence Be their light and guide;
3 When in sor - row, when in dan - ger, When in lone - li - ness,
4 May the joy of thy sal - va - tion Be their strength and stay;
5 Ho - ly Spir - it, let thy teach-ing Sanc - ti - fy their life;
6 Fa - ther, Son, and Ho - ly Spir - it, God the One - in - Three,

Keep our loved ones, now far dis - tant, 'Neath thy care.
Keep, O keep them, in their weak-ness, At thy side.
In thy love look down and com - fort Their dis - tress.
May they love and may they praise thee Day by day.
Send thy grace that they may con - quer In the strife.
Bless them, guide them, save them, keep them Near to thee. A-men.

ABSENT FRIENDS *A higher setting may be found at No. 380*

611 Jesus, Tender Shepherd, Hear Me

Mary Lundie Duncan, 1814-1840 BROCKLESBURY 8.7.8.7.
Charlotte A. Barnard, 1830-1869

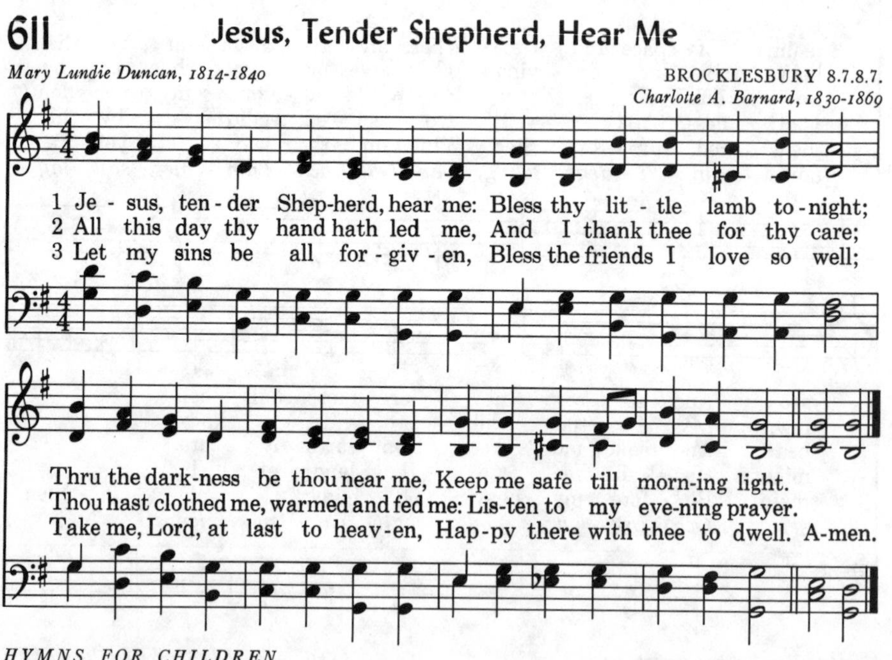
1 Je - sus, ten - der Shep-herd, hear me: Bless thy lit - tle lamb to-night;
2 All this day thy hand hath led me, And I thank thee for thy care;
3 Let my sins be all for - giv - en, Bless the friends I love so well;
Thru the dark-ness be thou near me, Keep me safe till morn-ing light.
Thou hast clothed me, warmed and fed me: Lis-ten to my eve-ning prayer.
Take me, Lord, at last to heav-en, Hap-py there with thee to dwell. A-men.

HYMNS FOR CHILDREN

Jesus Loves Me! This I Know

Anna B. Warner, 1820-1915

JESUS LOVES ME 7.7.7.7. *with Refrain*
William B. Bradbury, 1816-1868

1 Je - sus loves me! this I know, For the Bi - ble tells me so;
2 Je - sus loves me! he who died Heav-en's gate to o - pen wide;
3 Je - sus, take this heart of mine, Make it pure and whol - ly thine;

Lit - tle ones to him be - long, They are weak but he is strong.
He will wash a - way my sin, Let his lit - tle child come in.
Thou hast bled and died for me, I will hence-forth live for thee.

REFRAIN

Yes, Je - sus loves me! Yes, Je - sus loves me!

Yes, Je - sus loves me! The Bi - ble tells me so.

613 I Am So Glad That Our Father in Heaven

Philip P. Bliss, 1838-1876

GLADNESS 10.10.10.10. *with Refrain*
Philip P. Bliss, 1838-1876

1 I am so glad that our Fa - ther in heav'n Tells of his
2 Tho I for - get him and wan - der a - way, Still he doth
3 O if there's on - ly one song I can sing When in his
love in the book he has giv'n; Won - der - ful things in the
love me wher - ev - er I stray; Back to his dear lov - ing
beau - ty I see the great King, This shall my song in e -
Bi - ble I see— This is the dear - est, that Je - sus loves me.
arms would I flee When I re - mem - ber that Je - sus loves me.
ter - ni - ty be: "O what a won - der that Je - sus loves me!"
REFRAIN
I am so glad that Je - sus loves me, Je - sus loves me, Je - sus loves me;
I am so glad that Je - sus loves me, Je - sus loves e - ven me.

I Love to Hear the Story

Emily Huntington Miller, 1833-1913
GLÄDJE 7.6.7.6.D.
Oscar Ahnfelt, 1813-1882
1 I love to hear the sto - ry Which an - gel voic - es tell,
2 I'm glad my bless - ed Sav - ior Was once a child like me,
3 To sing his love and mer - cy My sweet-est songs I'll raise,
How once the King of glo - ry Came down on earth to dwell;
To show how pure and ho - ly His lit - tle ones should be;
And, though I can - not see him, I know he hears my praise;
I am both weak and sin - ful, But this I sure - ly know,
And if I try to fol - low His foot-steps here be - low,
For he has kind - ly prom - ised That e - ven I may go
The Lord came down to save me, Be - cause he loved me so.
He nev - er will for - get me, Be - cause he loves me so.
To sing a - mong his an - gels, Be - cause he loves me so.

615 Loving Shepherd of Thy Sheep
Jane E. Leeson, 1807-1882
KARI 7.7.7.7.
Norwegian Folk Song
Harm. by Norman E. Johnson, 1928-
1 Lov - ing Shep-herd of thy sheep, Keep thy lamb, in safe - ty keep;
2 I would praise thee ev - 'ry day, Glad - ly all thy will o - bey,
3 Lov - ing Shep-herd, ev - er near, Teach thy lamb thy voice to hear;
4 Where thou lead - est I would go, Walk-ing in thy steps be - low,
Noth-ing can thy pow'r with-stand, None can pluck me from thy hand.
Like thy bless - ed ones a - bove, Hap-py in thy pre-cious love.
Suf - fer not my steps to stray From the straight and nar-row way.
Till, be - fore my Fa-ther's throne, I shall know as I am known. A-men.
Harm. copyright 1973 by Covenant Press.
616 I Think, When I Read That Sweet Story
Based on Mark 10:13-16
Jemima T. Luke, 1813-1906, alt.
SWEET STORY Irregular
Greek Melody
Adapted by William B. Bradbury, 1816-1868
1 I think, when I read that sweet sto - ry of old, When
2 I wish that his hands had been placed on my head, That his
3 Yet still to his foot - stool in prayer I may go And
Je - sus was here a - mong men, How he called lit - tle chil-dren as
arms had been thrown a - round me, And that I might have seen his kind
ask for a share in his love; And if I thus ear - nest - ly

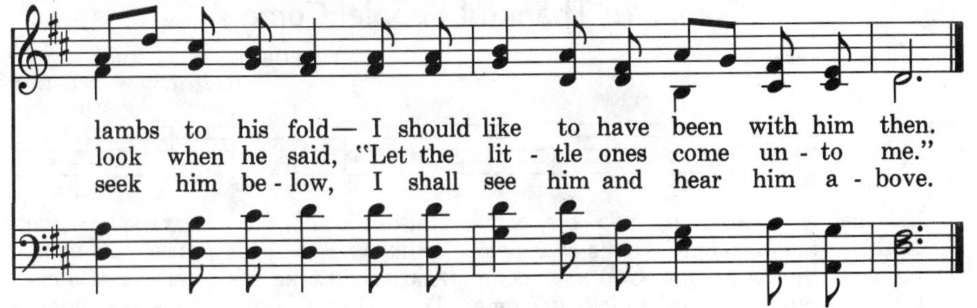
lambs to his fold— I should like to have been with him then.
look when he said, "Let the lit - tle ones come un - to me."
seek him be - low, I shall see him and hear him a - bove.

Savior, Teach Me, Day by Day

617

Jane E. Leeson, 1807-1882

POSEN 7.7.7.7.

Georg C. Strattner, 1650-1705

1 Sav - ior, teach me, day by day, Love's sweet les - son
2 With a child's glad heart of love, At thy bid - ding
3 Teach me thus thy steps to trace, Strong to fol - low
4 Love in lov - ing finds em - ploy, In o - be - dience

to o - bey; Sweet - er les - son can - not be—
may I move, Prompt to serve and fol - low thee—
in thy grace, Learn - ing how to love from thee—
all her joy; Ev - er new that joy will be,

Lov - ing him who first loved me.
Lov - ing him who first loved me.
Lov - ing him who first loved me.
Lov - ing him who first loved me. A - men.

618 Come, Ye Thankful People, Come

Henry Alford, 1810-1871

ST. GEORGE'S WINDSOR 7.7.7.7.D.
George J. Elvey, 1816-1893

1 Come, ye thank-ful peo-ple, come, Raise the song of har-vest-home;
2 All the world is God's own field, Fruit un-to his praise to yield;
3 For the Lord our God shall come, And shall take his har-vest home;
4 E - ven so, Lord, quick-ly come To thy fi - nal har-vest-home;

All is safe-ly gath-ered in, Ere the win-ter storms be-gin:
Wheat and tares to-geth-er sown, Un-to joy or sor-row grown:
From his field shall in that day All of-fens-es purge a-way,
Gath-er thou thy peo-ple in, Free from sor-row, free from sin:

God, our Mak-er, doth pro-vide For our wants to be sup-plied;
First the blade, and then the ear, Then the full corn shall ap-pear;
Give his an-gels charge at last In the fire the tares to cast,
There for-ev-er pu-ri-fied, In thy pres-ence to a-bide;

Come to God's own tem-ple, come, Raise the song of har-vest-home.
Lord of har-vest, grant that we Whole-some grain and pure may be.
But the fruit-ful ears to store In his gar-ner ev-er-more.
Come, with all thine an-gels, come, Raise the glo-rious har-vest-home. A-men.

A higher setting may be found at No. 590

Sing to the Lord of Harvest

John S. B. Monsell, 1811-1875

WIE LIEBLICH IST DER MAIEN 7.6.7.6.D.
Johann Steurlein, 1546-1613
Harm. by Healey Willan, 1880-1968

1 Sing to the Lord of har - vest, Sing songs of love and praise;
2 By him the clouds drop rich - ness, The des-erts bloom and spring,
3 Heap on his sa - cred al - tar The gifts his good-ness gave,
4 To God, the gra - cious Fa - ther, Who made us ver - y good,

With joy - ful hearts and voic - es Your al - le - lu - ias raise!
The hills leap up in glad - ness, The val-leys laugh and sing.
The gold - en sheaves of har - vest, The souls he died to save.
To Christ, who, when we wan - dered, Re-stored us with his blood,

By him the roll - ing sea - sons In fruit-ful or - der move;
He fill - eth with his full - ness All things with large in - crease;
Your hearts lay down be - fore him When at his feet you fall,
And to the Ho - ly Spir - it, Who does up - on us pour

Sing to the Lord of har - vest A song of hap - py love.
He crowns the year with good-ness, With plen - ty and with peace.
And with your lives a - dore him Who gave his life for all.
His bless - ed dews and sun-shine, Be praise for - ev - er - more. A-men.

620 We Plow the Fields and Scatter the Good Seed

Matthias Claudius, 1740-1815
Tr. Jane M. Campbell, 1817-1878, alt.

WIR PFLÜGEN 7.6.7.6.D. *with Refrain*
Johann A. P. Schulz, 1747-1800

1 We plow the fields and scat - ter The good seed on the land,
2 He on - ly is the mak - er Of all things near and far,
3 We thank thee, then, O Fa - ther, For all things bright and good—
But it is fed and wa - tered By God's al - might - y hand;
He paints the way-side flow - er, He lights the eve - ning star;
The seed-time and the har - vest, Our life, our health, our food;
He sends the snow in win - ter, The warmth to swell the grain,
The winds and waves o - bey him, By him the birds are fed:
Ac - cept the gifts we of - fer For all thy love im - parts,
The breez - es and the sun - shine, And soft, re-fresh - ing rain.
Much more, to us his chil - dren, He gives our dai - ly bread.
And, what thou most de - sir - est, Our hum - ble, thank-ful hearts.

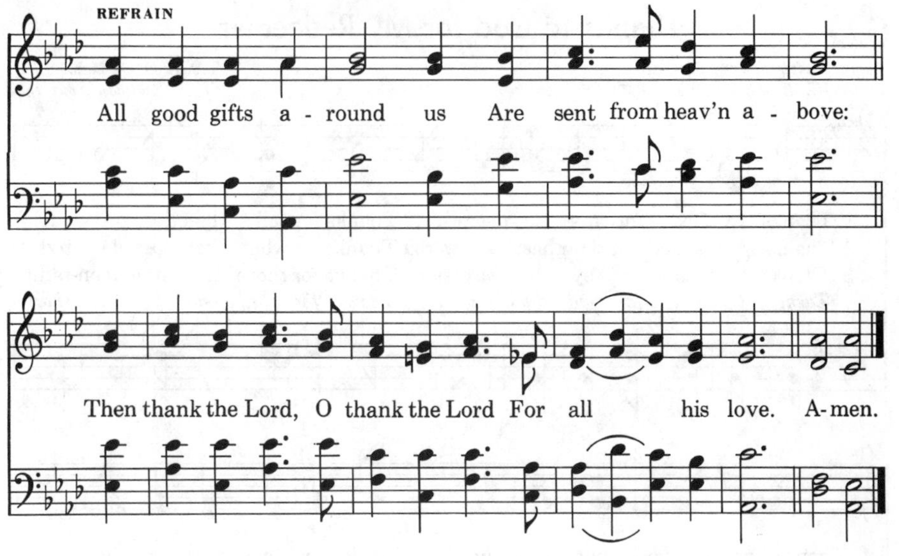
REFRAIN
All good gifts a - round us Are sent from heav'n a - bove:
Then thank the Lord, O thank the Lord For all his love. A-men.

Praise to God, Immortal Praise 621

Anna L. Barbauld, 1743-1825

SABBATSDAG 7.7.7.7.
Joel Blomqvist, 1840-1930
Harm. by James P. Davies, 1913-

1 Praise to God, im - mor - tal praise, For the love that crowns our days!
2 For the bless-ings of the field, For the stores the gar - dens yield,
3 All that spring with boun-teous hand Scat - ters o'er the smil - ing land,
4 These to thee, our God, we owe, Source whence all our bless - ings flow,

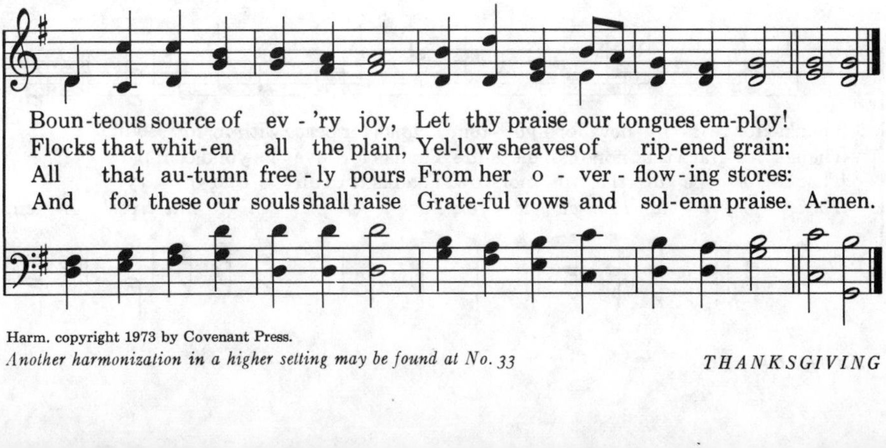

Boun-teous source of ev - 'ry joy, Let thy praise our tongues em-ploy!
Flocks that whit - en all the plain, Yel-low sheaves of rip-ened grain:
All that au-tumn free - ly pours From her o - ver - flow - ing stores:
And for these our souls shall raise Grate-ful vows and sol-emn praise. A-men.

Another harmonization in a higher setting may be found at No. 33

622 Thanks to God for My Redeemer

August Ludvig Storm, 1862-1914
Tr. Carl E. Backstrom, 1901-

TACK O GUD 8.7.8.7.D.
J. A. Hultman, 1861-1942

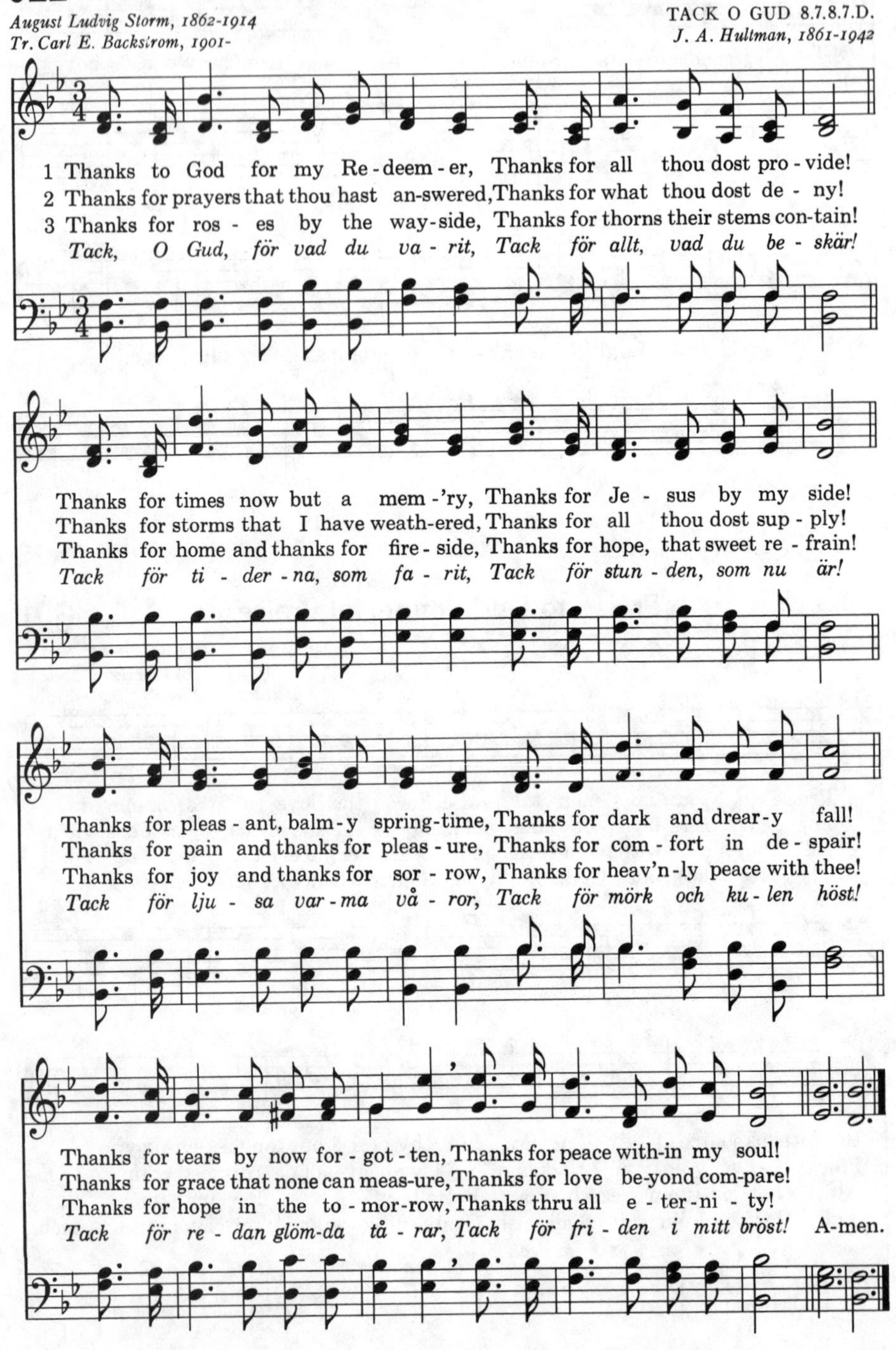
1 Thanks to God for my Re-deem-er, Thanks for all thou dost pro-vide!
2 Thanks for prayers that thou hast an-swered, Thanks for what thou dost de-ny!
3 Thanks for ros-es by the way-side, Thanks for thorns their stems con-tain!
Tack, O Gud, för vad du va-rit, Tack för allt, vad du be-skär!
Thanks for times now but a mem-'ry, Thanks for Je-sus by my side!
Thanks for storms that I have weath-ered, Thanks for all thou dost sup-ply!
Thanks for home and thanks for fire-side, Thanks for hope, that sweet re-frain!
Tack för ti-der-na, som fa-rit, Tack för stun-den, som nu är!
Thanks for pleas-ant, balm-y spring-time, Thanks for dark and drear-y fall!
Thanks for pain and thanks for pleas-ure, Thanks for com-fort in de-spair!
Thanks for joy and thanks for sor-row, Thanks for heav'n-ly peace with thee!
Tack för lju-sa var-ma vå-ror, Tack för mörk och ku-len höst!
Thanks for tears by now for-got-ten, Thanks for peace with-in my soul!
Thanks for grace that none can meas-ure, Thanks for love be-yond com-pare!
Thanks for hope in the to-mor-row, Thanks thru all e-ter-ni-ty!
Tack för re-dan glöm-da tå-rar, Tack för fri-den i mitt bröst! A-men.

Great God, We Sing That Mighty Hand 623

Philip Doddridge, 1702-1751, alt.
GERMANY L.M.
William Gardiner's "Sacred Melodies," 1815
1 Great God, we sing that might - y hand By which sup - port - ed still we stand; The o - p'ning year thy mer - cy shows, That mer - cy crowns it till it close.
2 By day, by night, at home, a - broad, Still are we guard - ed by our God, By his in - ces - sant boun - ty fed, By his un - err - ing coun - sel led.
3 With grate - ful hearts the past we own: The fu - ture, all to us un - known, We to thy guard - ian care com - mit And peace - ful leave be - fore thy feet.
4 In scenes ex - alt - ed or de - pressed, Thou art our joy, and thou our rest; Thy good - ness all our hopes shall raise, A - dored thru all our chang - ing days. A - men.

5 When death shall interrupt our songs
And seal in silence mortal tongues,
In fairer realms, O God shall we
Thy praises sing eternally. Amen.

A lower setting may be found at No. 395

624 Another Year Is Dawning

Frances Ridley Havergal, 1836-1879

AURELIA 7.6.7.6.D.
Samuel S. Wesley, 1810-1876

1 An - oth - er year is dawn - ing: Dear Fa - ther, let it be,
2 An - oth - er year of mer - cies, Of faith - ful - ness and grace;
3 An - oth - er year of serv - ice, Of wit - ness for thy love;
In work - ing or in wait - ing, An - oth - er year with thee;
An - oth - er year of glad - ness In the shin - ing of thy face;
An - oth - er year of train - ing For ho - lier work a - bove.
An - oth - er year of prog - ress, An - oth - er year of praise,
An - oth - er year of lean - ing Up - on thy lov - ing breast;
An - oth - er year is dawn - ing: Dear Fa - ther, let it be,
An - oth - er year of prov - ing Thy pres - ence all the days;
An - oth - er year of trust - ing, Of qui - et, hap - py rest;
On earth or else in heav - en, An - oth - er year for thee. A - men.

We Dedicate This Temple

625

Ernest K. Emurian, 1912-

AURELIA 7.6.7.6.D.
Samuel S. Wesley, 1810-1876

1 We dedicate this temple, O Father, unto thee,
The God of ancient ages And ages yet to be:
That here our hearts may worship And here our songs ascend
In loving adoration And praise that knows no end.

2 We dedicate this temple To Christ, the Lord of love,
Who brought God's revelation, The kingdom from above:
That we may learn his goodness, His godliness and grace,
Who holds all men and nations Within his love's embrace.

3 We dedicate this temple, O Spirit from on high,
To thee, in our thanksgiving That thou art always nigh
To comfort us in sorrow, To strengthen in distress:
That we, thru truth and mercy, May walk in holiness.

4 We dedicate this temple, This labor of our hands,
To Father, Son and Spirit, Whose temple ever stands
In hearts that learn to love thee And minds that comprehend,
In wills empow'red to witness Thy kingdom without end! Amen.

O Living Christ, Chief Cornerstone

626

Maud M. Cuninggim, 1874-1965

ST. ANNE C.M.
Attr. to William Croft, 1678-1727

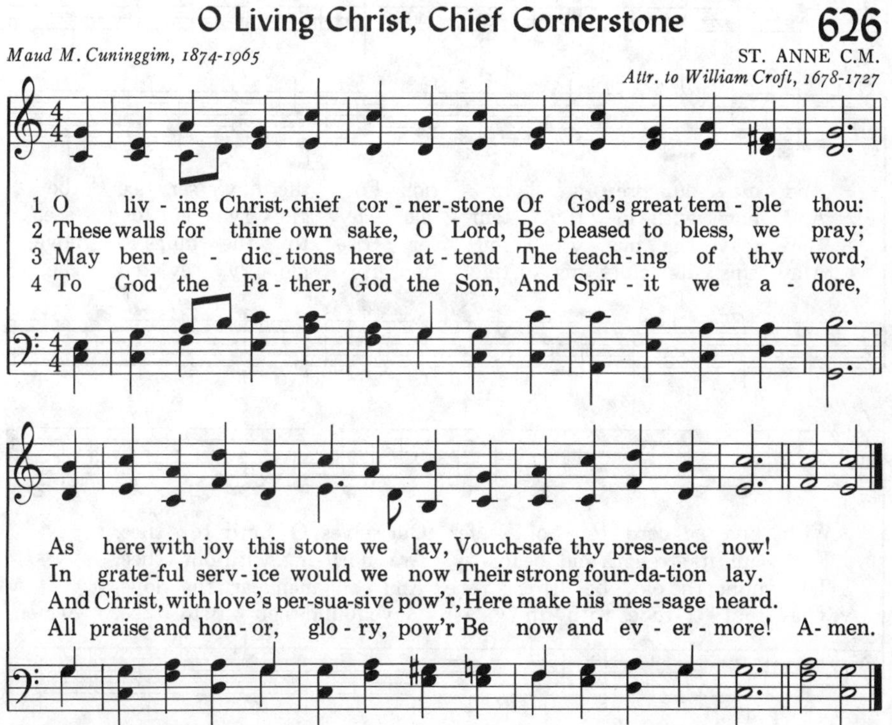
1 O liv - ing Christ, chief cor - ner-stone Of God's great tem - ple thou:
2 These walls for thine own sake, O Lord, Be pleased to bless, we pray;
3 May ben - e - dic - tions here at - tend The teach - ing of thy word,
4 To God the Fa - ther, God the Son, And Spir - it we a - dore,
As here with joy this stone we lay, Vouch-safe thy pres-ence now!
In grate-ful serv - ice would we now Their strong foun-da-tion lay.
And Christ, with love's per-sua-sive pow'r, Here make his mes-sage heard.
All praise and hon - or, glo - ry, pow'r Be now and ev - er - more! A- men.

Alternate tunes: AZMON, *No. 242;* MANOAH, *No. 160*

627 O Thou Whose Hand Has Brought Us

Frederic W. Goadby, 1845-1880

ST. THEODULPH 7.6.7.6.D.
Melchior Teschner, 1584-1635

1 O thou whose hand has brought us Un - to this joy - ful day,
2 For this thy house we praise thee, Reared by thine own com - mand,
3 And oft as here we gath - er And hearts in wor - ship blend,
4 And as the years roll o - ver And strong af - fec - tions twine
Ac - cept our glad thanks - giv - ing, And lis - ten as we pray;
For ev - 'ry gen - 'rous spir - it And ev - 'ry will - ing hand;
May truth re - veal its pow - er And fer - vent prayer as - cend;
And ten - der mem - 'ries gath - er A - bout this sa - cred shrine,
And may our prep - a - ra - tion For this day's serv - ice be
And now with - in thy tem - ple Thy glo - ry let us see,
Here may the bus - y toil - er Rise to the things a - bove,
May this its chief dis - tinc - tion, Its glo - ry, ev - er be,
With one ac - cord to of - fer Our - selves, O Lord, to thee.
For all its strength and beau - ty Are noth - ing with - out thee.
The young, the old, be strength - ened And all men learn thy love.
That mul - ti - tudes with - in it Have found their way to thee. A - men.

Glory to God! Praise to Thy Holy Name! 628

C. George Ericson, 1890-

NATIONAL HYMN 10.10.10.10.
George W. Warren, 1828-1902

Trumpets before each stanza
1 Glo - ry to God! praise to thy ho - ly name!
2 For this new church, a to - ken of thy grace,
3 Thy bless-ings, God, be - stow on us, we pray—
4 Our church we hum - bly ded - i - cate this day,
Thru chang - ing years thou ev - er art the same;
With joy - ful hearts we ren - der thee our praise;
May Christ, who is the Truth, the Life, the Way,
Thy pres - ence, Lord, will make it thine al - way;
In faith we wor - ship here be - fore thy face,
Its strength and beau - ty, all that eye can see,
Be ev - er loved and preached with pow'r di - vine—
With one ac - cord we give our - selves to thee,
Thy word pro - claim, and pro - mis - es em - brace.
Is emp - ti - ness un - less in - dwelt by thee.
Our lives re - deem and keep for - ev - er thine.
All to thy glo - ry, bless - ed Tri - ni - ty. A - men.

629 Now Praise We Great and Famous Men

William G. Tarrant, 1853-1928

CONSTANCE 8.7.8.7.D.
Arthur S. Sullivan, 1842-1900

1 Now praise we great and fa-mous men, The fa-thers named in sto - ry,
2 Praise we the great of heart and mind, The sing- ers sweet-ly gift - ed,
3 Praise we the glo-rious names we know, And they whose names have per-ished,

And praise the Lord, who now as then Re - veals in man his glo - ry.
Whose mu - sic like a might - y wind The souls of men up - lift - ed.
Lost in the haze of long a - go, In si - lent love yet cher-ished.

Praise we the wise and brave and strong Who graced their gen-er - a - tion,
Praise we the peace-ful men of skill Who build-ed homes of beau-ty,
In peace their bod - ies lie at rest—Ful-filled their day's en-deav-or;

Who helped the right, and fought the wrong, And made our folk a na - tion.
And, rich in art, made rich - er still The broth-er - hood of du - ty.
They blessed the earth, and they are blessed Of God and man for - ev - er.

COMMEMORATION

Our Father, by Whose Servants

George Wallace Briggs, 1875-1959

AURELIA 7.6.7.6.D.
Samuel S. Wesley, 1810-1876

1 Our Fa-ther, by whose serv-ants Our house was built of old,
Whose hand hath crowned their chil-dren With bless-ings man-i-fold,
For thine un-fail-ing mer-cies Far-strewn a-long our way,
With all who passed be-fore us, We praise thy name to-day.
2 The change-ful years un-rest-ing Their si-lent course have sped,
New com-rades ev-er bring-ing In com-rades' steps to tread:
And some are long for-got-ten— Long spent their hopes and fears;
Safe rest they in thy keep-ing, Who chang-est not with years.
3 They reap not where they la-bored, We reap what they have sown;
Our har-vest may be gar-nered By a-ges yet un-known.
The days of old have dow'red us With gifts be-yond all praise:
Our Fa-ther, make us faith-ful To serve the com-ing days.
4 Be-fore us and be-side us, Still hold-en in thine hand,
A cloud un-seen of wit-ness, Our eld-er com-rades stand:
One fam-i-ly un-bro-ken, We join, with one ac-claim,
One heart, one voice up-lift-ing, To glo-ri-fy thy name. A-men.

Words used by permission of The Grammar School, Loughborough, England.

COMMEMORATION

THE COVENANT HYMNAL

SERVICE MUSIC

CALLS TO WORSHIP
DOXOLOGIES AND GLORIAS
PRAYERS
OFFERTORIES
COMMUNION
BENEDICTIONS
AMENS

SUPPLEMENTARY HYMNS FOR USE AS SERVICE MUSIC

CALLS TO WORSHIP

243 Come, Christians, join
244 Come, let us praise
628 Glory to God! praise
7 God himself is with us
5 Holy majesty! before
112 Let all mortal flesh
16 Let all the world
627 O thou whose hand
52 Open now thy gates
81 Praise the Lord, all
56 Praise the Lord, each
21 Praise the Lord, his
27 Sing to the Lord
23 Stand up and bless
31 We praise thee, O
551 Where charity and

DOXOLOGIES AND GLORIAS

2 All creatures of our (St. 5)
271 All glory be to God
42 All praise to thee, my God (St. 4)
272 Ancient of Days (St. 5)
442 As pants the hart (St. 5)
474 Christ is made the (St. 4)
275 Come, thou almighty (St. 4)
276 Glory to the Father (St. 4)
18 Now thank we all our (St. 3)
35 O splendor of God's (St. 4)
3 Praise God, from
270 We believe in one

PRAYERS

83 Are you dismayed
320 Blessed Savior, thee I
341 Dear Lord and Father
337 Father, hear the
468 Great Shepherd of thy
344 Heavenly Father, hear
303 I lay my sins on Jesus
304 Just as I am
307 Kind and merciful God (all Sts.)
314 Lord Jesus, think on
370 Lord of our life
86 O love of God most
346 Our Father in heaven (Sts. 1, 2)
312 Out of the depths
403 Peace, perfect peace
264 Spirit divine, attend
343 Sweet hour of prayer
447 There is a place

OFFERTORIES

568 Lord, thou lovest
567 Savior, thy dying love
565 We give thee but

COMMUNION

521 A parting hymn we
509 Bread of the world (Sts. 1, 2)
512 Come, risen Lord
508 Deck thyself, my soul
511 For the bread
519 O Lamb of God

BENEDICTIONS

489 Blest be the tie (Sts. 1, 4)
527 Forth in thy name
61 God be with you
62 God be with you
60 Lord, dismiss us
58 Savior, again to thy
59 The Lord be with us
45 Thy holy wings

Use only the first stanza unless otherwise indicated. For special seasons of the Christian year and other occasions select hymns from appropriate categories in the hymnal.

Praise Ye the Lord 631

Duncan Howlett, 1906-

SINE NOMINE 10.10.12. *with Alleluias*
Ralph Vaughan Williams, 1872-1958

Music appears at No. 602

Praise ye the Lord, his mighty works acclaim:
His years are endless, yet is he the same.
O sing his praise, give glory to his holy name:
Alleluia, Alleluia. Amen.

Praise We the Father and the Son 632

Paul Sjolund, 1935-

HYMN TO THE TRINITY
Paul Sjolund, 1935-

In unison
Praise we the Fa-ther and the Son, and the Ho-ly
Spir - it. Thanks be to thee whose liv - ing Word
doth lead and guide us. Praise we thy maj - es - ty,
O bless-ed Trin - i - ty! A - men, A - men.

633 Christ, We Do All Adore Thee

Adoramus Te
English version by Theodore Baker, 1851-1934

From "The Seven Last Words of Christ"
Theodore Dubois, 1837-1924

Christ, we do all a - dore thee, and we do praise thee for - ev - er;
Christ, we do all a - dore thee, and we do praise thee for - ev - er,
For on the ho - ly cross hast thou the world from sin re - deem-ed.
Christ, we do all a - dore thee, and we do praise thee for - ev - er.

*Organ

Christ, we do all a - dore thee!

**May be omitted*

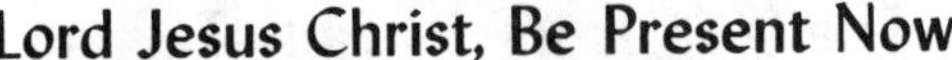

Lord Jesus Christ, Be Present Now

634

Johann Niedling's "Lutherisch Handbüchlein," 1638?
Tr. Catherine Winkworth, 1827-1878, alt.

HERR JESU CHRIST L.M.
"Pensum Sacrum," Goerlitz, 1648

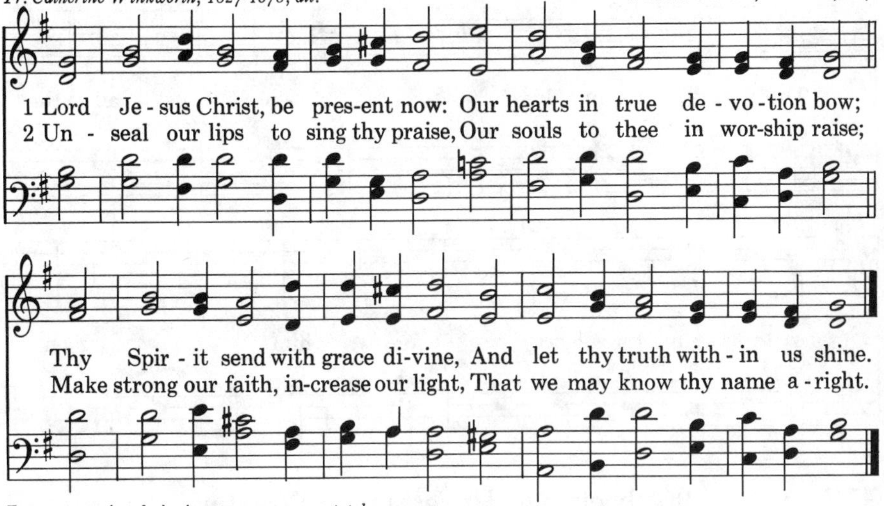

1 Lord Je - sus Christ, be pres-ent now: Our hearts in true de - vo - tion bow;
Thy Spir - it send with grace di-vine, And let thy truth with - in us shine.

2 Un - seal our lips to sing thy praise, Our souls to thee in wor-ship raise;
Make strong our faith, in-crease our light, That we may know thy name a - right.

For congregational singing, transpose one step lower

O Come, Let Us Worship

635

Psalm 95:6,7

J. Harold Moyer, 1927-

O come, let us wor-ship and bow down, let us kneel be-fore the Lord our mak - er;
For he is our God,
For he is our God, and we are the peo - ple of his pas - ture and the sheep of his hand.

636 The Lord Is in His Holy Temple

Habakkuk 2:20 *Source unknown*

The Lord is in his ho - ly tem - ple: let all the
earth keep si - lence be - fore him. A - men.

637 Brethren, We Have Met to Worship

George Atkins, 19th century

HOLY MANNA 8.7.8.7.D.
Attr. to William Moore, 19th century
"Columbian Harmony," 1825
Harm. by Norman E. Johnson, 1928-

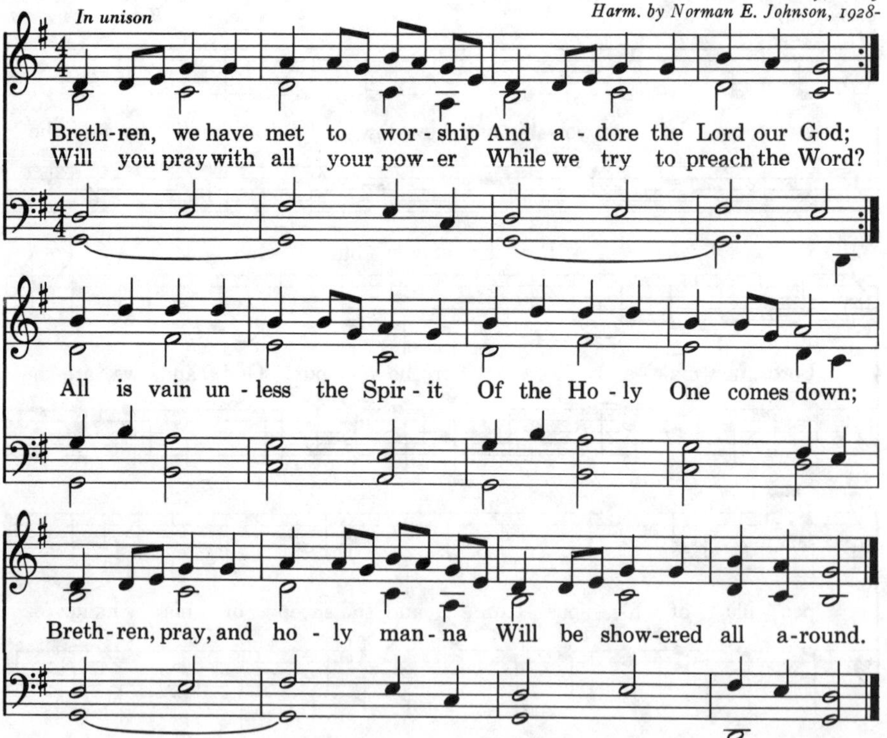

In unison

Breth-ren, we have met to wor - ship And a - dore the Lord our God;
Will you pray with all your pow - er While we try to preach the Word?
All is vain un - less the Spir - it Of the Ho - ly One comes down;
Breth - ren, pray, and ho - ly man - na Will be show-ered all a-round.

Praise God, from Whom All Blessings Flow 638

Thomas Ken, 1637-1711

OLD 100th (Altered rhythm) L.M.
Attr. to Louis Bourgeois, c.1510-c.1561
"Genevan Psalter," 1551

Praise God, from whom all bless-ings flow; Praise him, all crea-tures here be - low;
Praise him a-bove, ye heav'n-ly host; Praise Fa-ther, Son, and Ho-ly Ghost. A- men.

Praise God, from Whom All Blessings Flow 639

Thomas Ken, 1637-1711

OLD 100th (Original rhythm) L.M.
Attr. to Louis Bourgeois, c.1510-c.1561
"Genevan Psalter," 1551

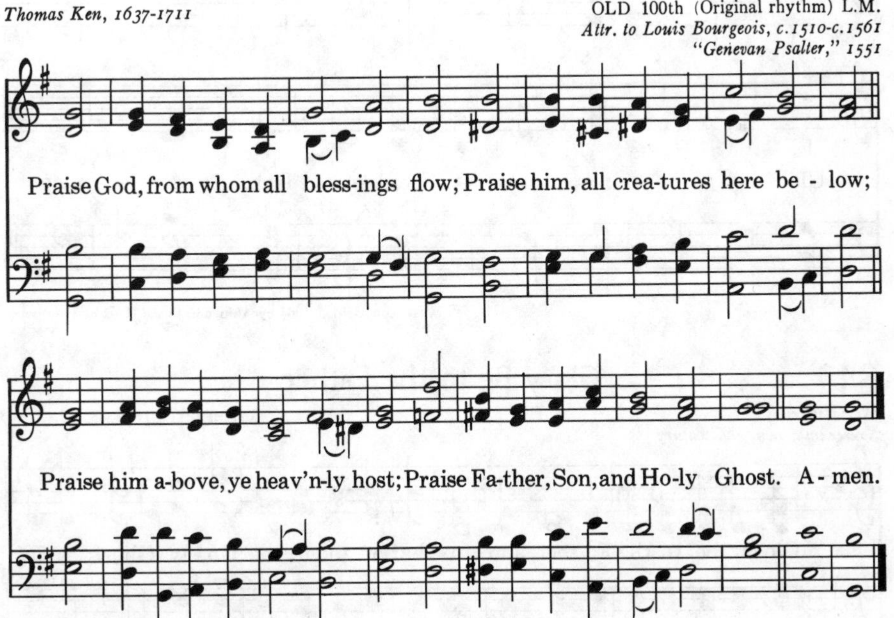

Praise God, from whom all bless-ings flow; Praise him, all crea-tures here be - low;
Praise him a-bove, ye heav'n-ly host; Praise Fa-ther, Son, and Ho-ly Ghost. A- men.

The traditional harmonization may be found at No. 4

640 Alleluia!
Giovanni P. da Palestrina, c.1525-1594
Al - le - lu - ia! Al - le - lu - ia! Al - le - lu - ia!
641 Holy, Holy, Holy
Sanctus
Communion Service in E Minor
Philip R. Dietterich, 1931-
In unison
Ho - ly, ho - ly, ho - ly, Lord God of hosts;
Heav - en and earth are full of thy glo - ry;
Glo - ry be to thee, O Lord most high. A - men.
Music copyright © 1964 by Abingdon Press. Used by permission.
642 Glory Be to the Father
Gloria Patri
Source unknown, 2nd century
Henry W. Greatorex, 1813-1858
Glo-ry be to the Fa-ther, and to the Son, and to the Ho - ly Ghost: as it

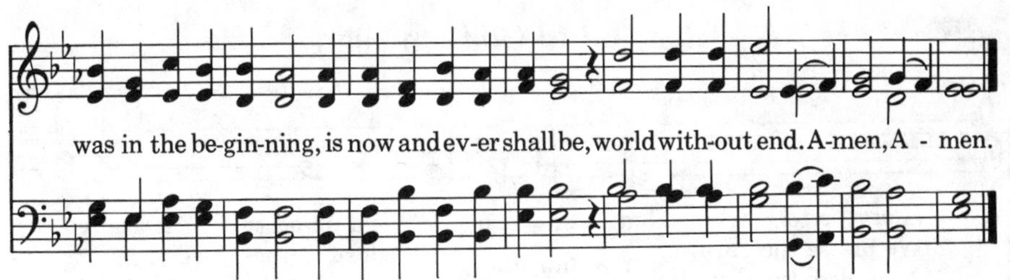
was in the be-gin-ning, is now and ev-er shall be, world with-out end. A-men, A - men.

Glory Be to the Father 643

Gloria Patri *Old Scottish Chant*
Source unknown, 2nd century

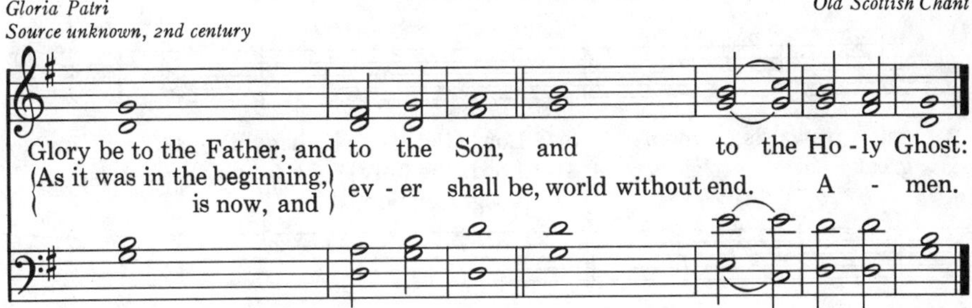
Glory be to the Father, and to the Son, and to the Ho - ly Ghost:
As it was in the beginning, is now, and ev - er shall be, world without end. A - men.

Glory Be to the Father 644

Gloria Patri *Charles Meineke, 1782-1850*
Source unknown, 2nd century

Glo - ry be to the Fa - ther, and to the Son, and to the

Ho - ly Ghost: as it was in the be - gin - ning, is

now and ev - er shall be, world with-out end. A - men, A - men.

645 Glory Be to God On High

Gloria in excelsis

Old Scottish Chant

1 Glory be to God on high, and on earth peace, good will towards men.
2 We praise thee, we bless thee, we worship thee, we glorify thee, we give thanks to thee for thy great glory,
3 O Lord God, heav'n-ly King, God the Father almighty.
4 O Lord, the only begotten Son, Jesus Christ; O Lord God, Lamb of God, Son of the Father,
5 That takest away the sins of the world, have mercy upon us.
6 Thou that takest away the sins of the world, receive our prayer.
7 Thou that sittest at the right hand of God the Father, have mercy upon us.
8 For thou only art holy, thou only art the Lord;
9 Thou only, O Christ, with the Holy Ghost, art most high in the glory of God the Father. A-men.

Create in Me a Clean Heart, O God 646

Psalm 51:10,11 *Carl F. Mueller, 1892-*

Cre - ate in me a clean heart, O God, and re -
new a right spir - it with - in me. A - men.

O Thou Who Hearest Prayer 647

Source unknown

WALES 6.6.6.6.8.8.
Welsh Melody

O thou who hear-est prayer, Give ear un-to our cry; O let thy
chil-dren share Thy bless-ing from on high. We plead the prom-ise
of thy Word—O grant us peace, al-might-y Lord! A-men.

648 May the Words of Our Mouths

Psalm 19:14, alt. — *Alan Walker, 1927-*

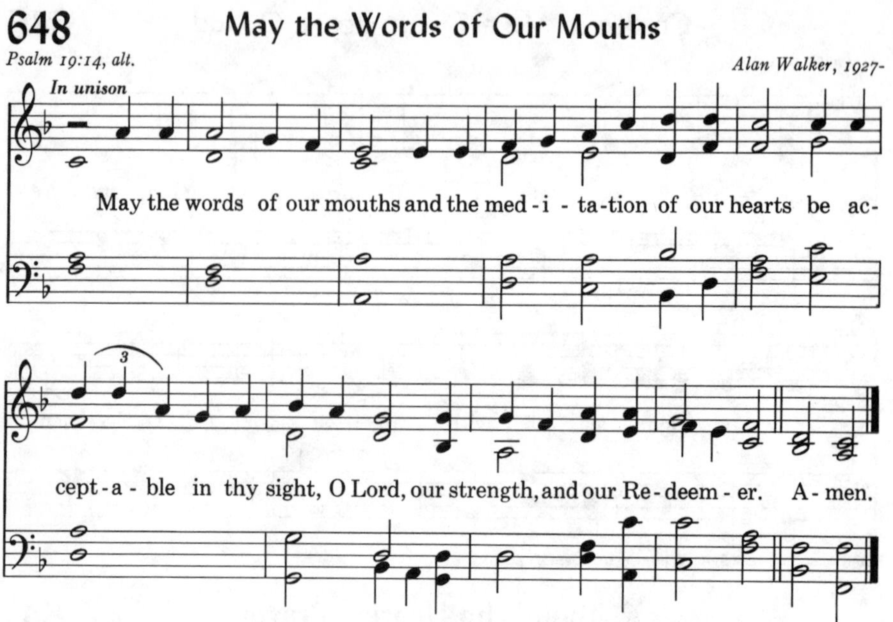
In unison
3
May the words of our mouths and the med - i - ta-tion of our hearts be ac-
cept - a - ble in thy sight, O Lord, our strength, and our Re - deem - er. A - men.

649 Our Father Who Art in Heaven

Matthew 6:9-13 — *Ancient Chant*

1 Our Father who art in heaven, hal-lowed be thy name;
2 Give us this day our dai - ly bread;
3 And lead us not into temptation, but de-liv - er us from evil:

Thy kingdom come, thy will be done on earth as it is in heaven.
And forgive us our debts as we for - give our debtors.
(For thine is the kingdom, and the power, and the glory for-) ev - er. A - men.

O Send Out Thy Light

650

Psalm 43:3 — *Austin C. Lovelace, 1919-*

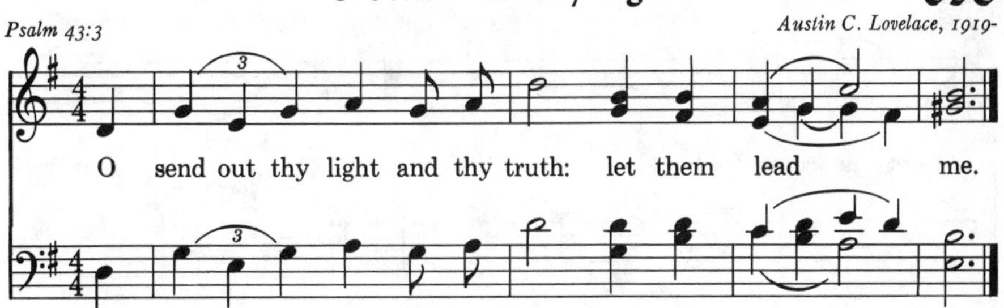
3
3
O send out thy light and thy truth: let them lead me.

Heart and Mind, Possessions, Lord 651

Krishnarao Rathnaji Sangle, 1834-1908
Tr. Alden H. Clark, 1878-1960, and others

TANA MANA DHANA (Marathi) *Irregular*
Ancient Indian Melody
Adapted by Marion Jean Chute, 1901-

1 Heart and mind, pos - ses - sions, Lord, I of - fer un - to thee:
2 Heart and mind, pos - ses - sions, Lord, I of - fer un - to thee:

All these were thine, Lord— thou didst give them all to me.
Thou art the Way, the Truth, thou art the Life.

Won-drous are thy do - ings un - to me. Plans, and my thoughts, and
Sin - ful, I com - mit my - self to thee. Je - sus Christ is fill - ing

ev - 'ry - thing I ev - er do are de - pend - ent on thy
all the heart of me. He can give me vic - t'ry o'er

will and love a - lone. I com - mit my spir - it un - to thee.
all that threat-ens me. Je - sus Christ is fill - ing all my heart.

652 Let Us Come Boldly

Hebrews 4:16 *Norman E. Johnson, 1928-*

Let us come bold - ly to the throne of grace, that we
may ob - tain mer - cy, and find grace to help in time of need.

653 Lead Me, Lord

Psalms 5:8 and 4:8 *Samuel S. Wesley, 1810-1876*

Lead me, Lord, lead me in thy righ-teous-ness; make thy way
plain be - fore my face: For it is thou, Lord— thou,
Lord, on - ly—that mak - est me dwell in safe - ty.

*Optional ending

Cast Thy Burden upon the Lord

Based on Psalm 55:22

From "Elijah," 1846
Felix Mendelssohn, 1809-1847

Cast thy bur - den up - on the Lord, and he shall sus -
tain thee; He nev - er will suf - fer the
right - eous to fall: he is at thy right hand. Thy
mer - cy, Lord, is great and far a - bove the heav'ns: Let
none be made a - sham - ed that wait up - on thee. A - men.

Suitable also as a Call to Worship

655 God Be in My Head

"*Sarum Primer*," 1558

GOD BE IN MY HEAD *Irregular*
H. Walford Davies, 1869-1941

p
org.
p
God be in my head, and in my un-der-stand-ing;
p
God be in mine eyes, and in my look-ing; God be in my mouth, and in my
speak - ing; God be in my heart, and in my think - ing;
pp
God be at mine end, and at my de - part - ing.
pp

All Things Are Thine: No Gift Have We
656
John Greenleaf Whittier, 1807-1892
GERMANY L.M.
William Gardiner's "Sacred Melodies," 1815
All things are thine: no gift have we, Lord of all gifts, to of - fer thee;
And hence with grate-ful hearts to - day Thine own be - fore thy feet we lay.
All Things Come of Thee
657
I Chronicles 29:14b
Attr. to Ludwig van Beethoven, 1770-1827
All things come of thee, O Lord, and of thine own have we giv-en thee. A-men.
Grant Us, Lord, the Grace of Giving
658
Robert Murray, 1832-1910, alt.
STUTTGART 8.7.8.7.
Attr. to Christian F. Witt, 1660-1716
"Psalmodia Sacra," Gotha, 1715
Grant us, Lord, the grace of giv - ing With a spir - it large and free,
That our-selves and all our liv - ing We may of - fer un - to thee. A-men.

A lower setting may be found at No. 337

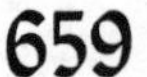

659 O Christ, Thou Lamb of God

Agnus Dei, alt.

"Kirchenordnung," Braunschweig, 1528
Arr. by Healey Willan, 1880-1968

In unison

O Christ, thou Lamb of God, that tak - est a - way the sins of the world, have mer - cy up - on us. O Christ, thou Lamb of God, that tak - est a - way the sins of the world, grant us thy peace. A - - - men.

660 Lord, Have Mercy upon Us

Kyrie eleison
From "The Book of Common Prayer," 1549

Richard Warner, 1908-

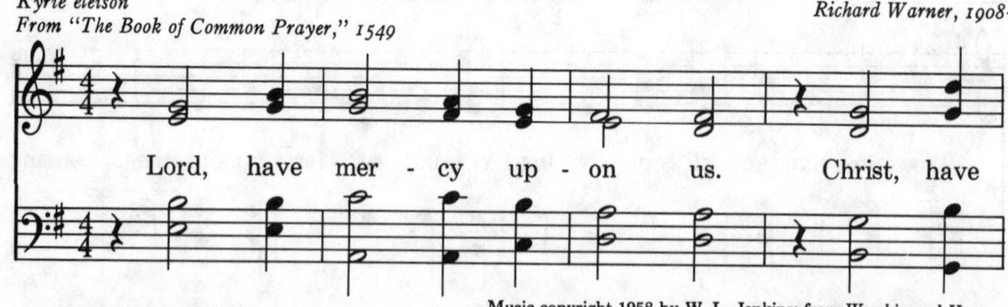
Lord, have mer - cy up - on us. Christ, have

mer - cy up - on us. Lord, have mer - cy up - on us.
O Lamb of God, that tak - est a - way the sins of the
1. world, have mer - cy up - on us! 2. world, grant us thy peace!
May the grace of Christ, our Sav - ior, And the Fa - ther's bound - less love,
With the Ho - ly Spir - it's fa - vor, Rest up - on us from a - bove. A - men.

O Lamb of God 661

Agnus Dei

Norman E. Johnson, 1928-

COMMUNION

May the Grace of Christ, Our Savior 662

John Newton, 1725-1807

SARDIS 8.7.8.7.

Arr. from Ludwig van Beethoven, 1770-1827

663 Amen

Louis Bourgeois, c. 1510-c. 1561

664 Twofold Amen

Dresden

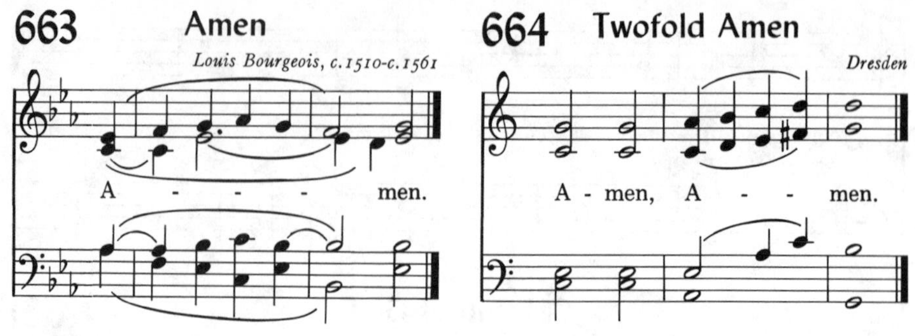

A - - - men.
A - men, A - - men.

665 Twofold Amen

Vincent Persichetti, 1915-

666 Threefold Amen

Danish

A - - men, A - - men.
A - men, A - men, A - men.

From *Hymns and Responses* by Vincent Persichetti.

667 Sevenfold Amen

John Stainer, 1840-1901

A - men, A - - - men,

A - men, A - men, A - men, A - - - men, A -

A - men, A - men,

A - - men,

- - men, A - - - men, A - men.

A - men,

THE COVENANT HYMNAL

SCRIPTURE READINGS

PSALMS
OLD TESTAMENT
NEW TESTAMENT

668

Blessed is the man who walks not in the counsel of the wicked, / **nor stands in the way of sinners, nor sits in the seat of scoffers;** / but his delight is in the law of the Lord, / **and on his law he meditates day and night.** / He is like a tree planted by streams of water, / **that yields its fruit in its season,** / and its leaf does not wither. / **In all that he does, he prospers.**

The wicked are not so, / **but are like chaff which the wind drives away.** / Therefore the wicked will not stand in the judgment, / **nor sinners in the congregation of the righteous;** / for the Lord knows the way of the righteous, / **but the way of the wicked will perish.**

Psalm 1

669

Answer me when I call, O God of my right! / **Thou hast given me room when I was in distress. Be gracious to me, and hear my prayer.**

O men, how long shall my honor suffer shame? / **How long will you love vain words, and seek after lies?** / But know that the Lord has set apart the godly for himself; / **the Lord hears when I call to him.**

Be angry, but sin not: commune with your own hearts on your beds, and be silent. / **Offer right sacrifices, and put your trust in the Lord.**

There are many who say, "O that we might see some good! Lift up the light of thy countenance upon us, O Lord!" / **Thou hast put more joy in my heart than they have when their grain and wine abound.**

In peace I will both lie down and sleep; / **for thou alone, O Lord, makest me dwell in safety.**

Psalm 4

670

O Lord, our Lord, / **how majestic is thy name in all the earth!**

Thou whose glory above the heavens is chanted by the mouth of babes and infants, / **thou hast founded a bulwark because of thy foes, to still the enemy and the avenger.**

When I look at thy heavens, the work of thy fingers, the moon and the stars which thou hast established; / **what is man that thou art mindful of him, and the son of man that thou dost care for him?**

Yet thou hast made him little less than God, / **and dost crown him with glory and honor.** / Thou hast given him dominion over the works of thy hands; / **thou hast put all things under his feet,** / all sheep and oxen, / **and also the beasts of the field,** / the birds of the air, / **and the fish of the sea.** / whatever passes along the paths of the sea.

O Lord, our Lord, how majestic is thy name in all the earth!

Psalm 8

671

Protect me, God, because I come to you for safety. **/ I say to the Lord, "You are my Lord; all the good things I have come from you."**

How excellent are the Lord's faithful people! **/ My greatest pleasure is to be with them.**

Those who rush to other gods bring many troubles on themselves. **/ I will not take part in their sacrifices; I will not worship their gods.**

You, Lord, are all I have, **/ and you give me all I need; /** my life is in your hands. **/ How wonderful are your gifts to me; how good they are!**

I praise the Lord, because he guides me, **/ and in the night my conscience warns me. /** I am always aware of the Lord's presence; **/ he is near, and nothing can shake me.**

And so I am full of happiness and joy, **/ and I always feel secure; /** because you will not allow me to go to the world of the dead, **/ you will not abandon to the depths below the one you love.**

You will show me the path that leads to life; **/ your presence fills me with joy, and your help brings pleasure forever.**

Psalm 16 (TEV)

672

How clearly the sky reveals God's glory! **/ How plainly it shows what he has done! /** Each day announces it to the following day; **/ each night repeats it to the next. /** No speech or words are used, **/ no sound is heard; /** yet their voice goes out to all the world, **/ their message reaches the ends of the earth. /** God set up a tent in the sky for the sun; **/ it comes out like a bridegroom striding from his house, /** like an athlete, eager to run a race. **/ It starts at one end of the sky /** and goes around to the other. **/ Nothing can hide from its heat.**

The law of the Lord is perfect; **/ it gives new life. /** The commands of the Lord are trustworthy, **/ giving wisdom to those who lack it. /** The rules of the Lord are right, **/ and those who obey them are happy. /** His commandments are completely just **/ and give understanding to the mind. /** The worship of the Lord is good; **/ it will continue forever. /** The judgments of the Lord are just, **/ they are always fair. /** They are more desirable than gold, even the finest gold. **/ They are sweeter than honey, even the purest honey. /** They give knowledge to me, your servant; **/ I am rewarded for obeying them.**

No one can see his own errors; deliver me from hidden faults! **/ Keep me safe, also, from open sins; don't let them rule over me. /** Then I shall be perfect **/ and free from terrible sin.**

May my words and my thoughts be acceptable to you, O Lord, my refuge and my redeemer!

Psalm 19 (TEV)

673

The Lord is my shepherd; I shall not want. He maketh me to lie down in green pastures: he leadeth me beside the still waters. He restoreth my soul: he leadeth me in the paths of righteousness for his name's sake. Yea, though I walk through the valley of the shadow of death, I will fear no evil: for thou art with me; thy rod and thy staff they comfort me. Thou preparest a table before me in the presence of mine enemies: thou anointest my head with oil; my cup runneth over. Surely goodness and mercy shall follow me all the days of my life: and I will dwell in the house of the Lord for ever.

Psalm 23 (AV)

674

The earth is the Lord's and the fulness thereof, **/ the world and those who dwell therein;** / for he has founded it upon the seas, **/ and established it upon the rivers.**

Who shall ascend the hill of the Lord? And who shall stand in his holy place? **/ He who has clean hands and a pure heart, who does not lift up his soul to what is false, and does not swear deceitfully.** / He will receive blessings from the Lord, **/ and vindication from the God of his salvation.** / Such is the generation of those who seek him, **/ who seek the face of the God of Jacob.**

Lift up your heads, O gates! and be lifted up, O ancient doors! **/ that the King of glory may come in.** / Who is the King of glory? **/ The Lord, strong and mighty, the Lord, mighty in battle!** / Lift up your heads, O gates! and be lifted up, O ancient doors! **/ that the King of glory may come in.** / Who is this King of glory? **/ The Lord of hosts, he is the King of glory!**

Psalm 24

675

To thee, O Lord, I lift up my soul. **/ O my God, in thee I trust,** / let me not be put to shame; **/ let not my enemies exult over me.** / Yea, let none that wait for thee be put to shame; **/ let them be ashamed who are wantonly treacherous.**

Make me to know thy ways, O Lord; **/ teach me thy paths.** / Lead me in thy truth, and teach me, **/ for thou art the God of my salvation; for thee I wait all the day long.**

Be mindful of thy mercy, O Lord, and of thy steadfast love, **/ for they have been from of old.** / Remember not the sins of my youth, or my transgressions; **/ according to thy steadfast love remember me, for thy goodness' sake, O Lord!** / Good and upright is the Lord; **/ therefore he instructs sinners in the way.** / He leads the humble in what is right. **/ and teaches the humble his way.** / All the paths of the Lord are steadfast love and faithfulness, **/ for those who keep his covenant and his testimonies.**

Psalm 25:1-10

676

The Lord is my light and my salvation; **/ whom shall I fear?** / The

Lord is the stronghold of my life; / **of whom shall I be afraid?**

When evildoers assail me, uttering slanders against me, / **my adversaries and foes, they shall stumble and fall.**

Though a host encamp against me, / **my heart shall not fear;** / though war arise against me, / **yet I will be confident.**

One thing have I asked of the Lord, that will I seek after: / **that I may dwell in the house of the Lord all the days of my life,** / to behold the beauty of the Lord, / **and to inquire in his temple.**

For he will hide me in his shelter in the day of trouble; / **he will conceal me under the cover of his tent, he will set me high upon a rock.**

And now my head shall be lifted up above my enemies round about me; and I will offer in his tent sacrifices with shouts of joy; / **I will sing and make melody to the Lord.**

Hear, O Lord, when I cry aloud, / **be gracious to me and answer me!** / Thou hast said, "Seek ye my face." / **My heart says to thee, "Thy face, Lord, do I seek."** / Hide not thy face from me.

Turn not thy servant away in anger, thou who hast been my help. / Cast me not off, forsake me not, O God of my salvation! / **For my father and my mother have forsaken me, but the Lord will take me up.**

Teach me thy way, O Lord; and lead me on a level path because of my enemies. / **Give me not up to the will of my adversaries; for false witnesses have risen against me, and they breathe out violence.**

I believe that I shall see the goodness of the Lord in the land of the living! / **Wait for the Lord; be strong, and let your heart take courage; yea, wait for the Lord!**
Psalm 27

677

Blessed is he whose transgression is forgiven, / **whose sin is covered.** / Blessed is the man to whom the Lord imputes no iniquity, / **and in whose spirit there is no deceit.**

When I declared not my sin, / **my body wasted away through my groaning all day long.** / For day and night thy hand was heavy upon me; / **my strength was dried up as by the heat of summer.**

I acknowledged my sin to thee, and I did not hide my iniquity; / **I said, "I will confess my transgressions to the Lord"; then thou didst forgive the guilt of my sin.** / Therefore let every one who is godly offer prayer to thee; / **at a time of distress, in the rush of great waters, they shall not reach him.** / Thou art a hiding place for me, thou preservest me from trouble; / **thou dost encompass me with deliverance.**

I will instruct you and teach you the way you should go; / **I will counsel you with my eye upon you.** / Be not like a horse or a mule, without understanding, / **which must be curbed with bit and bridle, else it will not keep with you.**

Many are the pangs of the wicked;

/ but steadfast love surrounds him who trusts in the Lord. / Be glad in the Lord, and rejoice, O righteous, **/ and shout for joy, all you upright in heart!**

Psalm 32

678

Let all the earth fear the Lord, **/ let all the inhabitants of the world stand in awe of him! /** For he spoke, and it came to be; **/ he commanded, and it stood forth.**

The Lord brings the counsel of the nations to nought; **/ he frustrates the plans of the peoples. /** The counsel of the Lord stands for ever, **/ the thoughts of his heart to all generations. /** Blessed is the nation whose God is the Lord, **/ the people whom he has chosen as his heritage!**

The Lord looks down from heaven, he sees all the sons of men; **/ from where he sits enthroned he looks forth on all the inhabitants of the earth, /** he who fashions the hearts of them all, **/ and observes all their deeds. /** A king is not saved by his great army; **/ a warrior is not delivered by his great strength. /** The war horse is a vain hope for victory, **/ and by its great might it cannot save.**

Behold, the eye of the Lord is on those who fear him, **/ on those who hope in his steadfast love, /** that he may deliver their soul from death, **/ and keep them alive in famine.**

Our soul waits for the Lord; **/ he is our help and shield. /** Yea, our heart is glad in him, **/ because we trust in his holy name. /** Let thy steadfast love, O Lord, be upon us, **/ even as we hope in thee.**

Psalm 33:8-22

679

I will bless the Lord continually; **/ his praise shall be always on my lips. /** In the Lord I will glory; **/ the humble shall hear and be glad. /** O glorify the Lord with me, **/ and let us exalt his name together.**

I sought the Lord's help and he answered me; **/ he set me free from all my terrors. /** Look towards him and shine with joy; **/ no longer hang your heads in shame. /** Here was a poor wretch who cried to the Lord; **/ he heard him and saved him from all his troubles. /** The angel of the Lord is on guard round those who fear him, and rescues them. **/ Taste, then, and see that the Lord is good. Happy the man who finds refuge in him!**

Fear the Lord, all you his holy people; **/ for those who fear him lack nothing. /** Unbelievers suffer want and go hungry, **/ but those who seek the Lord lack no good thing. /** Come, my children, listen to me: **/ I will teach you the fear of the Lord. /** Which of you delights in life and desires a long life to enjoy all good things? **/ Then keep your tongue from evil and your lips from uttering lies; /** turn from evil and do good, **/ seek peace and pursue it. /** The eyes of the Lord are upon the righteous, **/ and his ears are open to their cries. /** The Lord sets his face against evildoers **/ to blot out their memory from the earth.**

When men cry for help, the Lord hears them and sets them free from all their troubles. **/ The Lord is close to those whose courage is broken and he saves those whose spirit is crushed. /** The good man's misfortunes may be many, **/ the Lord delivers him out of them all. /** He guards every bone of his body, **/ and not one of them is broken. /** Their own misdeeds are death to the wicked, **/ and those who hate the righteous are brought to ruin. /** The Lord ransoms the lives of his servants, **/ and none who seek refuge in him are brought to ruin.**

Psalm 34 (NEB)

680

I waited patiently for the Lord; **/ he inclined to me and heard my cry. /** He drew me up from the desolate pit, out of the miry bog, **/ and set my feet upon a rock, making my steps secure. /** He put a new song in my mouth, **/ a song of praise to our God. /** Many will see and fear, **/ and put their trust in the Lord.**

Blessed is the man who makes the Lord his trust, **/ who does not turn to the proud, to those who go astray after false gods! /** Thou hast multiplied, O Lord my God, thy wondrous deeds and thy thoughts toward us; **/ none can compare with thee! /** Were I to proclaim and tell of them, **/ they would be more than can be numbered.**

Sacrifice and offering thou dost not desire; but thou hast given me an open ear. **/ Burnt offering and sin offering thou hast not required. /** Then I said, "Lo, I come; in the roll of the book it is written of me; **/ I delight to do thy will, O my God; thy law is within my heart."**

I have told the glad news of deliverance in the great congregation; **/ lo, I have not restrained my lips, as thou knowest, O Lord. /** I have not hid thy saving help within my heart, I have spoken of thy faithfulness and thy salvation; **/ I have not concealed thy steadfast love and thy faithfulness from the great congregation.**

Do not thou, O Lord, withold thy mercy from me, **/ let thy steadfast love and thy faithfulness ever preserve me!**

Psalm 40:1-11

681

As a deer longs for a stream of cool water, so I long for you, God. **/ I thirst for you, the living God; when can I go and worship in your presence? /** Day and night I cry, and tears are my only food; **/ all the time my enemies ask me, "Where is your God?"**

My heart breaks when I remember the past, when I went with the crowds to the house of God, **/ and led them as they walked along, a happy crowd, singing and shouting praise to God. /** Why am I so sad? Why am I troubled? **/ I will put my hope in God, and once again I will praise him, my Savior and my God.**

My heart is breaking, so I will remember him; **/ in my exile in the region of the Jordan, near Mount Hermon and Mount Mizar, I will remember him. /** The ocean depths call out to each other, and the waterfalls of God are roaring! **/ They are like the waves of sorrow with which he floods my soul. /**

May the Lord show his constant love every day! **/ May I sing praise to him every night, and pray to God, who gives me life.**

To God, my defender, I say, **/ "Why have you forgotten me? Why must I go on suffering from the cruelty of my enemies?"** / I am crushed by their insults, as they keep on asking me, **/ "Where is your God?"**

Why am I so sad? Why am I troubled? **/ I will put my hope in God, and once again I will praise him, my Savior and my God.**

Psalm 42 (TEV)

682

God is our refuge and strength, **/ a very present help in trouble. /** Therefore we will not fear though the earth should change, **/ though the mountains shake in the heart of the sea; /** though its waters roar and foam, **/ though the mountains tremble with its tumult.**

There is a river whose streams make glad the city of God, **/ the holy habitation of the Most High. /** God is in the midst of her, she shall not be moved; **/ God will help her right early. /** The nations rage, the kingdoms totter; **/ he utters his voice, the earth melts. /** The Lord of hosts is with us; **/ the God of Jacob is our refuge.**

Come, behold the works of the Lord, **/ how he has wrought desolations in the earth. /** He makes wars cease to the end of the earth; **/ he breaks the bow, and shatters the spear, he burns the chariots with fire! /** "Be still, and know that I am God. I am exalted among the nations, I am exalted in the earth!" **/ The Lord of hosts is with us; the God of Jacob is our refuge.**

Psalm 46

683

Have mercy on me, O God, according to thy steadfast love; **/ according to thy abundant mercy blot out my transgressions. /** Wash me thoroughly from my iniquity, **/ and cleanse me from my sin!**

For I know my transgressions, **/ and my sin is ever before me. /** Against thee, thee only, have I sinned, and done that which is evil in thy sight, **/ so that thou art justified in thy sentence and blameless in thy judgment. /** Behold I was brought forth in iniquity, **/ and in sin did my mother conceive me.**

Behold, thou desirest truth in the inward being; **/ therefore teach me wisdom in my secret heart. /** Purge me with hyssop, and I shall be clean; **/ wash me, and I shall be whiter than snow. /** Fill me with joy and gladness; let the bones which thou hast broken rejoice. **/ Hide thy face from my sins, and blot out all my iniquities.**

Create in me a clean heart, O God, **/ and put a new and right spirit within me. /** Cast me not away from thy presence, **/ and take not thy holy Spirit from me. /** Restore to me the joy of thy salvation, **/ and uphold me with a willing spirit.**

Then I will teach transgressors thy ways, **/ and sinners will return to thee. /** Deliver me from bloodguiltiness, O God, thou God of my salvation, **/ and my tongue will sing aloud of thy deliverance.**

O Lord, open thou my lips, **/ and my mouth shall show forth thy praise. /** For thou hast no delight in sacrifice; **/ were I to give a burnt offering, thou wouldst not be pleased. /** The sacrifice acceptable to God is a broken spirit; **/ a broken and contrite heart, O God, thou wilt not despise.**

Psalm 51:1-17

684

For God alone my soul waits in silence; **/ from him comes my salvation. /** He only is my rock and my salvation, my fortress; / **I shall not be greatly moved.**

How long will you set upon a man to shatter him, all of you, like a leaning wall, a tottering fence? **/ They only plan to thrust him down from his eminence. /** They take pleasure in falsehood. **/ They bless with their mouths, but inwardly they curse.**

For God alone my soul waits in silence, **/ for my hope is from him. /** He only is my rock and my salvation, my fortress; **/ I shall not be shaken. /** On God rests my deliverance and my honor; **/ my mighty rock, my refuge is God.**

Trust in him at all times, O People; pour out your heart before him; **/ God is a refuge for us.**

Men of low estate are but a breath, **/ men of high estate are a delusion; /** in the balances they go up; **/ they are together lighter than a breath. /** Put no confidence in extortion, set no vain hopes on robbery; **/ if riches increase, set not your heart on them.**

Once God has spoken; twice have I heard this: that power belongs to God; **/ and that to thee, O Lord, belongs steadfast love. For thou dost requite a man according to his work.**

Psalm 62

685

Make a joyful noise to God, all the earth; **/ sing the glory of his name; give to him glorious praise! /** Say to God, "How terrible are thy deeds! So great is thy power that thy enemies cringe before thee. **/ All the earth worships thee; /** they sing praises to thee, **/ sing praises to thy name."**

Come and see what God has done: **/ he is terrible in his deeds among men. /** He turned the sea into dry land; **/ men passed through the river on foot. /** There did we rejoice in him, who rules by his might for ever, whose eyes keep watch on the nations— **/ let not the rebellious exalt themselves.**

Bless our God, O peoples, **/ let the sound of his praise be heard, /** who has kept us among the living, **/ and has not let our feet slip. /** For thou, O God, hast tested us; **/ thou hast tried us as silver is tried. /** Thou didst bring us into the net; **/ thou didst lay affliction on our loins; /** thou didst let men ride over our heads; we went through fire and through water; **/ yet thou hast brought us forth to a spacious place.**

Come and hear, all you who fear God, and I will tell what he has done for me. / **I cried aloud to him, and he was extolled with my tongue.** / If I had cherished iniquity in my heart, the Lord would not have listened. / **But truly God has listened; he has given heed to the voice of my prayer.**

Blessed be God, because he has not rejected my prayer / **or removed his steadfast love from me!**

Psalm 66:1-12, 16-20

686

May God be gracious to us and bless us and make his face to shine upon us, / **that thy way may be known upon earth, thy saving power among all nations.** / Let the peoples praise thee, O God; / **let all the peoples praise thee!** / Let the nations be glad and sing for joy, / **for thou dost judge the peoples with equity and guide the nations upon earth.** / Let the peoples praise thee, O God; / **let all the peoples praise thee!**

The earth has yielded its increase; / **God, our God, has blessed us.** / God has blessed us; / **let all the ends of the earth fear him!**

Psalm 67

687

How lovely is thy dwelling place, O Lord of hosts! / **My soul longs, yea, faints for the courts of the Lord; my heart and flesh sing for joy to the living God.**

Even the sparrow finds a home, and the swallow a nest for herself, / **where she may lay her young, at thy altars, O Lord of hosts, my king and my God.** / Blessed are those who dwell in thy house, / **ever singing thy praise!**

Blessed are the men whose strength is in thee, in whose heart are the highways to Zion. / **As they go through the valley of Baca they make it a place of springs; the early rain also covers it with pools.** / They go from strength to strength; / **the God of gods will be seen in Zion.**

O Lord, God of Hosts, hear my prayer; / **give ear, O God of Jacob!** / Behold our shield, O God; / **look upon the face of thine anointed!**

For a day in thy courts is better than a thousand elsewhere. / **I would rather be a door-keeper in the house of my God than dwell in the tents of wickedness.** / For the Lord God is a sun and shield; / **he bestows favor and honor.** / No good thing does the Lord withhold from those who walk uprightly. / **O Lord of hosts, blessed is the man who trusts in thee!**

Psalm 84

688

Incline thy ear, O Lord, and answer me, / **for I am poor and needy.** / Preserve my life, for I am godly; / **save thy servant who trusts in thee.** / Thou art my God; / **be gracious to me, O Lord, for to thee do I cry all the day.** / Gladden the soul of thy servant, / **for to thee, O Lord, do I lift up my soul.** / For thou, O Lord, art good and forgiving, abounding in steadfast love to all who call on thee. / **Give ear, O Lord, to my**

prayer; hearken to my cry of supplication. / In the day of my trouble I call on thee, **/ for thou dost answer me.**

There is none like thee among the gods, O Lord, nor are there any works like thine. **/ All the nations thou hast made shall come and bow down before thee, O Lord, and shall glorify thy name.** / For thou art great and doest wondrous things, **/ thou alone art God.** / Teach me thy way, O Lord, that I may walk in thy truth; **/ unite my heart to fear thy name.** / I give thanks to thee, O Lord my God, with my whole heart, **/ and I will glorify thy name for ever.**

Psalm 86:1-12

689

Lord, thou hast been our dwelling place in all generations. **/ Before the mountains were brought forth, or ever thou hadst formed the earth and the world, from everlasting to everlasting thou art God.**

Thou turnest man back to the dust, and sayest, "Turn back, O children of men!" **/ For a thousand years in thy sight are but as yesterday when it is past, or as a watch in the night.**

Thou dost sweep men away; **/ they are like a dream, like grass which is renewed in the morning:** / in the morning it flourishes and is renewed; **/ in the evening it fades and withers.**

For we are consumed by thy anger; **/ by thy wrath we are overwhelmed.** / Thou hast set our iniquities before thee, **/ our secret sins in the light of thy countenance.**

For all our days pass away under thy wrath, **/ our years come to an end like a sigh.** / The years of our life are threescore and ten, or even by reason of strength fourscore; **/ yet their span is but toil and trouble; they are soon gone, and we fly away.**

Who considers the power of thy anger, and thy wrath according to the fear of thee? **/ So teach us to number our days that we may get a heart of wisdom.**

Return, O Lord! How long? Have pity on thy servants! **/ Satisfy us in the morning with thy steadfast love, that we may rejoice and be glad all our days.** / Make us glad as many days as thou hast afflicted us, and as many years as we have seen evil. **/ Let thy work be manifest to thy servants, and thy glorious power to their children.** / Let the favor of the Lord our God be upon us, and establish thou the work of our hands upon us, **/ yea, the work of our hands establish thou it.**

Psalm 90

690

He who dwells in the shelter of the Most High, who abides in the shadow of the Almighty, will say to the Lord, **/ "My refuge and my fortress; my God, in whom I trust."** / For he will deliver you from the snare of the fowler and from the deadly pestilence; **/ he will cover you with his pinions,** / and under his wings you will find refuge; **/ his faithfulness is a shield and buckler.** / You will not fear the terror of the night, nor the arrow that flies by day, **/ nor the pestilence that stalks in darkness, nor the destruction**

that wastes at noonday. / A thousand may fall at your side, / **ten thousand at your right hand;** / but it will not come near you. / **You will only look with your eyes and see the recompense of the wicked.**

Because you have made the Lord your refuge, the Most High your habitation, / **no evil shall befall you, no scourge come near your tent.**

For he will give his angels charge of you to guard you in all your ways. / **On their hands they will bear you up, lest you dash your foot against a stone.** / You will tread on the lion and the adder, / **the young lion and the serpent you will trample under foot.**

Because he cleaves to me in love, I will deliver him; / **I will protect him, because he knows my name.** / When he calls to me, I will answer him; / **I will be with him in trouble,** / I will rescue him and honor him. / **With long life I will satisfy him, and show him my salvation.**

Psalm 91

691

O come, let us sing to the Lord; / **let us make a joyful noise to the rock of our salvation!** / Let us come into his presence with thanksgiving; / **let us make a joyful noise to him with songs of praise!** / For the Lord is a great God, / **and a great King above all gods.** / In his hand are the depths of the earth; / **the heights of the mountains are his also.** / The sea is his, for he made it; / **for his hands formed the dry land.**

O come, let us worship and bow down, / **let us kneel before the Lord, our Maker!** / For he is our God, / **and we are the people of his pasture, and the sheep of his hand.**

Psalm 95:1-7

692

O sing to the Lord a new song; / **sing to the Lord, all the earth!** / Sing to the Lord, bless his name; / **tell of his salvation from day to day.** / Declare his glory among the nations, his marvelous works among all the peoples! / **For great is the Lord, and greatly to be praised; he is to be feared above all gods.** / For all the gods of the peoples are idols; / **but the Lord made the heavens.** / Honor and majesty are before him; / **strength and beauty are in his sanctuary.**

Ascribe to the Lord, O families of the peoples, ascribe to the Lord glory and strength! / **Ascribe to the Lord the glory due his name;** / bring an offering, and come into his courts! / **Worship the Lord in holy array; tremble before him, all the earth!**

Say among the nations, / **"The Lord reigns! Yea, the world is established, it shall never be moved; he will judge the peoples with equity."** / Let the heavens be glad, / **and let the earth rejoice;** / let the sea roar, / **and all that fills it;** / let the field exult, / **and everything in it!** / Then shall all the trees of the wood sing for joy before the Lord, for he comes, / **for he comes to judge the earth.** / He will judge the world with righteousness, / **and the peoples with his truth.**

Psalm 96

693

Make a joyful noise to the Lord, all the lands! / **Serve the Lord with gladness! Come into his presence with singing!** / Know that the Lord is God! / **It is he that made us, and we are his; we are his people, and the sheep of his pasture.**

Enter his gates with thanksgiving, and his courts with praise! / **Give thanks to him, bless his name!**

For the Lord is good; / **his steadfast love endures for ever, and his faithfulness to all generations.**

Psalm 100

694

Bless the Lord, O my soul; / **and all that is within me, bless his holy name!** / Bless the Lord, O my soul, and forget not all his benefits, / **who forgives all your iniquity,** / who heals all your diseases, / **who redeems your life from the Pit,** / who crowns you with steadfast love and mercy, / **who satisfies you with good as long as you live so that your youth is renewed like the eagle's.**

The Lord works vindication and justice for all who are oppressed. / **He made known his ways to Moses, his acts to the people of Israel.** / The Lord is merciful and gracious, / **slow to anger and abounding in steadfast love.** / He will not always chide, / **nor will he keep his anger for ever.** / He does not deal with us according to our sins, / **nor requite us according to our iniquities.** / For as the heavens are high above the earth, / **so great is his steadfast love toward those who fear him;** / as far as the east is from the west, / **so far does he remove our transgressions from us.** / As a father pities his children, / **so the Lord pities those who fear him.** / For he knows our frame; / **he remembers that we are dust.**

As for man, his days are like grass; / **he flourishes like a flower of the field;** / for the wind passes over it, and it is gone, / **and its place knows it no more.** / But the steadfast love of the Lord is from everlasting to everlasting upon those who fear him, and his righteousness to children's children, / **to those who keep his covenant and remember to do his commandments.**

The Lord has established his throne in the heavens, / **and his kingdom rules over all.** / Bless the Lord, O you his angels, / **you mighty ones who do his word, hearkening to the voice of his word!** / Bless the Lord, all his hosts, / **his ministers that do his will!** / Bless the Lord, all his works, in all places of his dominion. / **Bless the Lord, O my soul!**

Psalm 103

695

I love the Lord, because he has heard my voice and my supplications. / **Because he inclined his ear to me, therefore I will call on him as long as I live.** / The snares of death encompassed me; / **the pangs of Sheol laid hold on me;** / I suffered distress and anguish. / **Then I called on the name of the Lord; "O Lord, I beseech thee, save my life!"**

Gracious is the Lord, and righteous;

/ our God is merciful. / The Lord preserves the simple; **/ when I was brought low, he saved me. /** Return, O my soul, to your rest; **/ for the Lord has dealt bountifully with you.**

For thou hast delivered my soul from death, **/ my eyes from tears, /** my feet from stumbling; **/ I walk before the Lord in the land of the living. /** I kept my faith, even when I said, "I am greatly afflicted"; **/ I said in my consternation, "Men are all a vain hope."**

What shall I render to the Lord for all his bounty to me? **/ I will lift up the cup of salvation and call on the name of the Lord, /** I will pay my vows to the Lord in the presence of all his people. **/ Precious in the sight of the Lord is the death of his saints. /** O Lord, I am thy servant; **/ I am thy servant, the son of thy handmaid. /** Thou hast loosed my bonds. **/ I will offer to thee the sacrifice of thanksgiving and call on the name of the Lord. /** I will pay my vows to the Lord in the presence of all his people, **/ in the courts of the house of the Lord, /** in your midst, O Jerusalem. **/ Praise the Lord!**

Psalm 116

696

O give thanks to the Lord, for he is good; his steadfast love endures for ever!

Let Israel say, "His steadfast love endures for ever." / Let the house of Aaron say, "His steadfast love endures for ever." **/ Let those who fear the Lord say, "His steadfast love endures for ever."**

Out of my distress I called on the Lord; the Lord answered and set me free. **/ With the Lord on my side I do not fear. What can man do to me? /** The Lord is on my side to help me; I shall look in triumph on those who hate me. **/ It is better to take refuge in the Lord than to put confidence in man. /** It is better to take refuge in the Lord than to put confidence in princes.

The Lord is my strength and my song; he has become my salvation.

Hark, glad songs of victory in the tents of the righteous: **/ "The right hand of the Lord does valiantly, the right hand of the Lord is exalted, the right hand of the Lord does valiantly!" /** I shall not die, but I shall live, and recount the deeds of the Lord. **/ The Lord has chastened me sorely, but he has not given me over to death.**

Open to me the gates of righteousness, that I may enter through them and give thanks to the Lord.

This is the gate of the Lord; the righteous shall enter through it.

The stone which the builders rejected has become the chief cornerstone. **/ This is the Lord's doing; it is marvelous in our eyes. /** This is the day which the Lord has made; **/ Let us rejoice and be glad in it.**

Thou art my God, and I will give thanks to thee; **/ Thou art my God, I will extol thee.**

O give thanks to the Lord, for he is good; **/ For his steadfast love endures for ever!**

Psalm 118

697

Teach me, O Lord, the way of thy statutes; **/ and I will keep it to the end. /** Give me understanding, **/ that I may keep thy law and observe it with my whole heart. /** Lead me in the path of thy commandments, for I delight in it. **/ Incline my heart to thy testimonies, and not to gain! /** Turn my eyes from looking at vanities; **/ and give me life in thy ways. /** Confirm to thy servant thy promise, which is for those who fear thee. **/ Turn away the reproach which I dread; for thy ordinances are good. /** Behold, I long for thy precepts; **/ in thy righteousness give me life!**

Psalm 119:33-40

698

I lift up my eyes to the hills. **/ From whence does my help come? /** My help comes from the Lord, who made heaven and earth. **/ He will not let your foot be moved, /** he who keeps you will not slumber. **/ Behold, he who keeps Israel will neither slumber nor sleep.**

The Lord is your keeper; **/ the Lord is your shade on your right hand. /** The sun shall not smite you by day, **/ nor the moon by night.**

The Lord will keep you from all evil; he will keep your life. **/ The Lord will keep your going out and your coming in from this time forth and for evermore.**

Psalm 121

699

Out of the depths I cry to thee, O Lord! Lord, hear my voice! **/ Let thy ears be attentive to the voice of my supplications!**

If thou, O Lord, shouldst mark iniquities, Lord, who could stand? **/ But there is forgiveness with thee, that thou mayest be feared.**

I wait for the Lord, my soul waits, **/ and in his word I hope; /** my soul waits for the Lord more than watchmen for the morning, **/ more than watchmen for the morning.**

O Israel, hope in the Lord! **/ For with the Lord there is steadfast love, /** and with him is plenteous redemption. **/ And he will redeem Israel from all his iniquities.**

Psalm 130

700

Give thanks to the Lord, for he is good, **/ his love is everlasting! /** Give thanks to the God of gods, **/ his love is everlasting! /** Give thanks to the Lord of lords, **/ his love is everlasting!**

He alone performs great marvels, **/ his love is everlasting! /** His wisdom made the heavens, **/ his love is everlasting! /** He set the earth on the waters, **/ his love is everlasting!**

He made the great lights, **/ his love is everlasting! /** The sun to govern the day, **/ his love is everlasting! /** Moon and stars to govern the night, **/ his love is everlasting!**

He struck down the first-born of Egypt, **/ his love is everlasting! /** And brought Israel out, **/ his love is**

everlasting! / With mighty hand and outstretched arm, **/ his love is everlasting!**

He split the Sea of Reeds, **/ his love is everlasting!** / Led Israel through the middle, **/ his love is everlasting!** / Drowned Pharoah and his army, / **his love is everlasting!**

He led his people through the wilderness, **/ his love is everlasting! /** He remembered us when we were down, **/ his love is everlasting! /** And snatched us from our oppressors, **/ his love is everlasting!**

He provides for all living creatures, **/ his love is everlasting!** / Give thanks to the God of Heaven, **/ his love is everlasting!**

Psalm 136:1-16;23-26 (JB)

701

I give thee thanks, O Lord, with my whole heart; **/ before the gods I sing thy praise;** / I bow down toward thy holy temple **/ and give thanks to thy name for thy steadfast love and thy faithfulness;** / for thou hast exalted above everything thy name and thy word. **/ On the day I called, thou didst answer me, my strength of soul thou didst increase.**

All the kings of the earth shall praise thee, O Lord, for they have heard the words of thy mouth; / **and they shall sing of the ways of the Lord, for great is the glory of the Lord.** / For though the Lord is high, he regards the lowly; **/ but the haughty he knows from afar.**

Though I walk in the midst of trouble, **/ thou dost preserve my life; /** thou dost stretch out thy hand against the wrath of my enemies, **/ and thy right hand delivers me. /** The Lord will fulfil his purpose for me; **/ thy steadfast love, O Lord, endures for ever. Do not forsake the work of thy hands.**

Psalm 138

702

Lord, you have examined me, and you know me. **/ You know everything I do; from far away you understand all my thoughts.** / You see me, whether I am working or resting; **/ you know all my actions.** / Even before I speak you already know what I will say. **/ You are all around me, on every side; you protect me with your power.** / Your knowledge of me is overwhelming; **/ it is too deep for me to understand.** / Where could I go to escape from your Spirit? **/ Where could I get away from your presence?** / If I went up to heaven, you would be there; **/ if I lay down in the world of the dead, you would be there.** / If I flew away beyond the east, or lived in the farthest place in the west, **/ you would be there to lead me, you would be there to help me.** / I could ask the darkness to hide me, **/ or the light around me to turn into night,** / but even the darkness is not dark for you, and the night is as bright as the day. **/ Darkness and light are the same to you.**

You created every part of me; **/ you put me together in my mother's womb.** / I praise you because you are to be feared; **/ all you do is strange and wonderful. I know it with all my heart.** / You saw my bones being formed, carefully put together in my mother's womb, when I was growing there in secret. **/ You saw me before I was born. /** The days that had been created for me had all been recorded in your book, before any of them had ever begun. **/ God, how difficult your thoughts are for me; how many of them there are! /** If I counted them, they would be more than the grains of sand. **/ When I awake, I am still with you.**

Examine me, God, **/ and know my mind; /** test me, **/ and discover my thoughts. /** Find out if there is any deceit in me, **/ and guide me in the eternal way.**

Psalm 139:1-18, 23, 24 (TEV)

703

Hear my prayer, O Lord; give ear to my supplications! **/ In thy faithfulness answer me, in thy righteousness! /** Enter not into judgment with thy servant; **/ for no man living is righteous before thee.**

For the enemy has pursued me; **/ he has crushed my life to the ground; /** he has made me sit in darkness like those long dead. **/ Therefore my spirit faints within me; my heart within me is appalled.**

I remember the days of old, I meditate on all that thou hast done; **/ I muse on what thy hands have wrought. /** I stretch out my hands to thee; **/ my soul thirsts for thee like a parched land.**

Make haste to answer me, O Lord! **/ My spirit fails! /** Hide not thy face from me, lest I be like those who go down to the Pit. **/ Let me hear in the morning of thy steadfast love, for in thee I put my trust. /** Teach me the way I should go, **/ for to thee I lift up my soul.**

Deliver me, O Lord, from my enemies! **/ I have fled to thee for refuge! /** Teach me to do thy will, for thou art my God! **/ Let thy good spirit lead me on a level path!**

For thy name's sake, Lord, preserve my life! **/ In thy righteousness bring me out of trouble!**

Psalm 143

704

I will extol thee, my God and King, and bless thy name for ever and ever. **/ Every day I will bless thee, and praise thy name for ever and ever. /** Great is the Lord, and greatly to be praised, **/ and his greatness is unsearchable.**

One generation shall laud thy works to another, **/ and shall declare thy mighty acts. /** On the glorious splendor of thy majesty, and on thy wondrous works, I will meditate. **/ Men shall proclaim the might of thy terrible acts, and I will declare thy greatness. /** They shall pour forth the fame of thy abundant goodness, **/ and shall sing aloud of thy righteousness.**

The Lord is gracious and merciful, **/ slow to anger and abounding in steadfast love. /** The Lord is good to all, **/ and his compassion is over all that he has made.**

All thy works shall give thanks to thee, O Lord, **/ and all thy saints shall bless thee! /** They shall speak of the glory of thy kingdom, and tell of thy power, **/ to make known to the sons of men thy mighty deeds, and the glorious splendor of thy kingdom.** / Thy kingdom is an everlasting kingdom, **/ and thy dominion endures throughout all generations.**

The Lord is faithful in all his words, **/ and gracious in all his deeds.** / The Lord upholds all who are falling, **/ and raises up all who are bowed down.** / The eyes of all look to thee, and thou givest them their food in due season. **/ Thou openest thy hand, thou satisfiest the desire of every living thing.** / The Lord is just in all his ways, **/ and kind in all his doings.** / The Lord is near to all who call upon him, **/ to all who call upon him in truth.** / He fulfils the desire of all who fear him, **/ he also hears their cry, and saves them.** / The Lord preserves all who love him; **/ but all the wicked he will destroy.**

My mouth will speak the praise of the Lord, **/ and let all flesh bless his holy name for ever and ever.**

Psalm 145

705

Praise the Lord! **/ Praise the Lord, my soul!** / I will praise him as long as I live; **/ I will sing to my God all my life.**

Don't put your trust in human leaders, or anyone else who cannot save you. **/ When they die they return to the soil; on that day all their plans come to an end.**

Happy is the man who has the God of Jacob to help him, **/ and depends on the Lord his God, who created heaven, earth, and sea, and all that is in them.** / He always keeps his promises, **/ he judges in favor of the oppressed and gives food to the hungry.**

The Lord sets prisoners free **/ and gives sight to the blind.** / He raises all who are humbled; **/ he loves his righteous people.** / He protects the foreigners who live in the land; **/ he helps widows and orphans, but ruins the plans of the wicked.**

The Lord will be king forever! Your God, Zion, will reign for all time!

Praise the Lord!

Psalm 146 (TEV)

706

Praise the Lord! Praise the Lord from the heavens, praise him in the heights! **/ Praise him, all his angels, praise him, all his host!**

Praise him, sun and moon, **/ praise him, all you shining stars!** / Praise him, you highest heavens, **/ and you waters above the heavens!**

Let them praise the name of the Lord! **/ For he commanded and they were created.** / And he established them for ever and ever; **/ he fixed their bounds which cannot be passed.**

Praise the Lord from the earth, / **you sea monsters and all deeps,** / fire and hail, snow and frost, / **stormy wind fulfilling his command!**

Mountains and all hills, **/ fruit trees**

and all cedars! / Beasts and all cattle, **/ creeping things and flying birds!**

Kings of earth and all peoples, **/ princes and all rulers of the earth! /** Young men and maidens together, **/ old men and children!**

Let them praise the name of the Lord, for his name alone is exalted; **/ his glory is above earth and heaven. /** He has raised up a horn for his people, **/ praise for all his saints, /** for the people of Israel who are near to him. **/ Praise the Lord!**

Psalm 148

707

Praise the Lord! Praise God in his sanctuary; **/ praise him in his mighty firmament!** / Praise him for his mighty deeds; **/ praise him according to his exceeding greatness!**

Praise him with trumpet sound; **/ praise him with lute and harp! /** Praise him with timbrel and dance; **/ praise him with strings and pipe!** / Praise him with sounding cymbals; **/ praise him with loud clashing cymbals!** / Let everything that breathes praise the Lord! **/ Praise the Lord!**

Psalm 150

708

And God spoke all these words, saying, "I am the Lord your God, who brought you out of the land of Egypt, out of the house of bondage.

"You shall have no other gods before me.

"You shall not make yourself a graven image, or any likeness of anything that is in heaven above, or that is in the earth beneath, or that is in the water under the earth; you shall not bow down to them or serve them; for I the Lord your God am a jealous God, visiting the iniquity of the fathers upon the children to the third and the fourth generation of those who hate me, but showing steadfast love to thousands of those who love me and keep my commandments.

"You shall not take the name of the Lord your God in vain; for the Lord will not hold him guiltless who takes his name in vain.

"Remember the sabbath day, to keep it holy. Six days you shall labor, and do all your work; but the seventh day is a sabbath to the Lord your God; in it you shall not do any work, you, or your son, or your daughter, your manservant, or your maidservant, or your cattle, or the sojourner who is within your gates; for in six days the Lord made heaven and earth, the sea, and all that is in them, and rested the seventh day; therefore the Lord blessed the sabbath day and hallowed it.

"Honor your father and your mother, that your days may be long in the land which the Lord your God gives you.

"You shall not kill.

"You shall not commit adultery.

"You shall not steal.

"You shall not bear false witness against your neighbor.

"You shall not covet your neighbor's house; you shall not covet your neighbor's wife, or his manservant, or his maidservant, or his ox, or his ass, or anything that is your neighbor's."

Exodus 20:1-17

709

"Listen, O Israel; the Lord is our God, the Lord alone; so you must love the Lord your God with all your mind and all your heart and all your strength. These instructions that I am giving you today are to be fixed in your mind; you must impress them on your children, and talk about them when you are sitting at home, and when you go off on a journey, when you lie down and when you get up; you must bind them on your hand as a sign, and they must be worn on your forehead as a mark; you must inscribe them on the doorposts of your house and on your gates.

Deuteronomy 6:4-9 (AT)

710

And David said: "Blessed art thou, O Lord, the God of Israel our father, for ever and ever. Thine, O Lord, is the greatness, and the power, and the glory, and the victory, and the majesty; for all that is in the heavens and in the earth is thine; thine is the kingdom, O Lord, and thou art exalted as head above all. Both riches and honor come from thee, and thou rulest over all. In thy hand are power and might; and in thy hand it is to make great and to give strength to all. And now we thank thee, our God, and praise thy glorious name.

1 Chronicles 29:10b-13

711

Then Joshua gathered all the tribes of Israel to Shechem, and summoned the elders, the heads, the judges, and the officers of Israel; and they presented themselves before God. And Joshua said to all the people, "Thus says the Lord, the God of Israel, 'Your fathers lived of old beyond the Euphrates, Terah, the father of Abraham and of Nahor; and they served other gods. Then I took your father Abraham from beyond the River and led him through all the land of Canaan, and made his offspring many. I gave him Isaac; and to Isaac I gave Jacob and Esau. And I gave Esau the hill country of Seir to possess, but Jacob and his children went down to Egypt. And I sent Moses and Aaron and I plagued Egypt with what I did in the midst of it; and afterwards I brought you out.

'Then I brought your fathers out of Egypt, and you came to the sea; and the Egyptians pursued your fathers with chariots and horsemen to the Red Sea. And when they cried to the Lord, he put darkness between you and the Egyptians, and made the sea come upon them and cover them; and your eyes saw what I did to Egypt; and you lived in the wilderness a long time.

'Then I brought you to the land of the Amorites, who lived on the other side of the Jordan; they fought with you, and I gave them into your hand, and you took possession of their land, and I destroyed them before you.... And you went over the Jordan and came to Jericho, and the men of Jericho fought against you...and I gave them into your hand.... I gave you a land on which you had not labored, and cities which you had not built, and you dwell therein; you eat the fruit of vineyards and oliveyards which you did not plant.'

"Now therefore fear the Lord, and serve him in sincerity and in faithfulness; put away the gods which your fathers served beyond the River, and in Egypt, and serve the Lord. And if you be unwilling to serve the Lord, choose this day whom you will serve, whether the gods your fathers served in the region beyond the River, or the gods of the Amorites in whose land you dwell; but as for me and my house, we will serve the Lord."

Joshua 24:1-8,11,13-15

712

Happy is the man who finds wisdom, and the man who gets understanding, for the gain from it is better than gain from silver and its profit better than gold. She is more precious than jewels, and nothing you desire can compare with her. Long life is in her right hand; in her left hand are riches and honor. Her ways are ways of pleasantness, and all her paths are peace. She is a tree of life to those who lay hold of her; those who hold her fast are called happy.

The Lord by wisdom founded the earth; by understanding he established the heavens; by his knowledge the deeps broke forth, and the clouds drop down the dew.

My son, keep sound wisdom and discretion; let them not escape from your sight, and they will be life for your soul and adornment for your neck. Then you will walk on your way securely and your foot will not stumble. If you sit down, you will not be afraid; when you lie down, your sleep will be sweet. Do not be afraid of sudden panic, or of the ruin of the wicked, when it comes; for the Lord will be your confidence and will keep your foot from being caught.

Proverbs 3:13-26

713

Listen, my sons, to a father's instruction, consider attentively how to gain understanding; for it is sound learning I give you; so do not forsake my teaching. I too have been a father's son, tender in years, my mother's only child. He taught me and said to me: Hold fast to my words with all your heart, keep my commands and you will have life. Do not forget or turn a deaf ear to what I say.

The first thing is to acquire wisdom; gain understanding though it cost you all you have. Do not forsake her, and she will keep you safe; love her, and she will guard you; cherish her, and she will lift you high; if only you embrace her, she will bring you to honour. She will set a garland of grace on your head and bestow on you a crown of glory.

Listen, my son, take my words to heart, and the years of your life shall be multiplied. I will guide you in the paths of wisdom and lead you in honest ways. As you walk you will not slip, and, if you run, nothing will bring you down. Cling to instruction and never let it go; observe it well, for it is your life. Do not take to the course of the wicked or follow the way of evil men; do not set foot on it, but avoid it; turn aside and go on your way. For they cannot sleep unless they have done some wrong; unless they have been someone's downfall they lose their sleep. The bread they eat is the fruit of crime and they drink wine got by violence. The course of the righteous is like morning light, growing brighter till it is broad day; but the ways of the wicked are like darkness at night, and they do not know what has been their downfall.

Proverbs 4:1-19 (NEB)

714

Remember also your Creator in the days of your youth, before the evil days come, and the years draw nigh, when you will say, "I have no pleasure in them"; before the sun and the light, and the moon, and the stars are darkened and the clouds return after the rain; in the day when the keepers of the house tremble, and the strong men are bent, and the grinders cease because they are few, and those that look through the windows are dimmed, and the doors on the street are shut; when the sound of the grinding is low, and one rises up at the voice of a bird, and all the daughters of song are brought low; they are afraid also of what is high, and terrors are in the way; the almond tree blossoms, the grasshopper drags itself along and desire fails; because man goes to his eternal home, and the mourners go about the streets; before the silver cord is snapped, or the golden bowl is broken, or the pitcher is broken at the fountain, or the wheel broken at the cistern, and the dust returns to the earth as it was, and the spirit returns to God who gave it. Vanity of vanities, says the Preacher; all is vanity.

The end of the matter; all has been heard. Fear God, and keep his commandments; for this is the whole duty of man. For God will bring every deed into judgment, with every secret thing, whether good or evil.

Ecclesiastes 12:1-8,13,14

715

It shall come to pass in the latter days that the mountain of the house of the Lord shall be established as the highest of the mountains, and shall be raised above the hills; and all the nations shall flow to it, and many peoples shall come and say: "Come, let us go up to the mountain of the Lord, to the house of the God of Jacob; that he may teach us his ways and that we may walk in his paths." For out of Zion shall go forth the law, and the word of the Lord from Jerusalem. He shall judge between the nations, and shall decide for many peoples; and they shall beat their swords into plowshares, and their spears into pruning hooks; nation shall not lift up sword against nation, neither shall they learn war any more.

Isaiah 2:2-4

716

In the year that King Uzziah died I saw the Lord sitting upon a throne, high and lifted up; and his train filled the temple. Above him stood the seraphim; each had six wings: with two he covered his face, and with two he covered his feet, and with two he flew. And one called to another and said:

"Holy, holy, holy is the Lord of hosts;
the whole earth is full of his glory."

And the foundations of the thresholds shook at the voice of him who called, and the house was filled with smoke. And I said: "Woe is me! For I am lost; for I am a man of unclean lips, and I dwell in the midst of a people of unclean lips; for my eyes have seen the King, the Lord of hosts!"

Then flew one of the seraphim to me, having in his hand a burning coal which he had taken with tongs from the altar. And he touched my mouth, and said: "Behold, this has touched your lips; your guilt is taken away, and your sin is forgiven." And I heard the voice of the Lord saying, "Whom shall I send, and who will go for us?" Then I said, "Here I am! Send me."

Isaiah 6:1-8

717

The people who walked in darkness have seen a great light; those who dwelt in a land of deep darkness, on them has light shined. Thou hast multiplied the nation, thou hast increased its joy; they rejoice before thee as with joy at the harvest, as men rejoice when they divide the spoil. For the yoke of his burden, and the staff for his shoulder, the rod of his oppressor, thou hast broken as on the day of Midian. For every boot of the tramping warrior in battle tumult and every garment rolled in blood will be burned as fuel for the fire. For to us a child is born, to us a son is given; and the government will be upon his shoulder, and his name will be called "Wonderful Counselor, Mighty God, Everlasting Father, Prince of Peace." Of the increase of his government and of peace there will be no end, upon the throne of David, and over his kingdom, to establish it, and to uphold it with justice and with righteousness from this time forth and for evermore. The zeal of the Lord of hosts will do this.

Isaiah 9:2-7

718

There shall come forth a shoot from the stump of Jesse, and a branch shall grow out of his roots. And the Spirit of the Lord shall rest upon him, the spirit of wisdom and understanding, the spirit of counsel and might, the spirit of knowledge and the fear of the Lord. And his delight shall be in the fear of the Lord.

He shall not judge by what his eyes see, or decide by what his ears hear; but with righteousness he shall judge the poor, and decide with equity for the meek of the earth; and he shall smite the earth with the rod of his mouth, and with the breath of his lips he shall slay the wicked. Righteousness shall be the girdle of his waist, and faithfulness the girdle of his loins. The wolf shall dwell with the lamb, and the leopard shall lie down with the kid, and the calf and the lion and the fatling together, and a little child shall lead them. The cow and the bear shall feed; their young shall lie down together; and the lion shall eat straw like the ox. The sucking child shall play over the hole of the asp, and the weaned child shall put his hand on the adder's den. They shall not hurt or destroy in all my holy mountain; for the earth shall be full of the knowledge of the Lord as the waters cover the sea.

Isaiah 11:1-9

719

The wilderness and the dry land shall be glad, the desert shall rejoice and blossom; like the crocus it shall blossom abundantly, and rejoice with joy and singing. The glory of Lebanon shall be given to it, the majesty of Carmel and Sharon. They shall see the glory of the Lord, the majesty of our God.

Strengthen the weak hands, and make firm the feeble knees. Say to those who are of a fearful heart, "Be strong, fear not! Behold, your God will come with vengeance, with the recompense of God. He will come and save you."

Then the eyes of the blind shall be opened, and the ears of the deaf unstopped; then shall the lame man leap like a hart, and the tongue of the dumb sing for joy. For waters shall break forth in the wilderness, and streams in the desert; the burning sand shall become a pool, and the thirsty ground springs of water; the haunt of jackals shall become a swamp, the grass shall become reeds and rushes.

And a highway shall be there, and it shall be called the Holy Way; the unclean shall not pass over it, and fools shall not err therein. No lion shall be there, nor shall any ravenous beast come up upon it; they shall not be found there, but the redeemed shall walk there. And the ransomed of the Lord shall return, and come to Zion with singing, with everlasting joy upon their heads; they shall obtain joy and gladness, and sorrow and sighing shall flee away.

Isaiah 35

720

Comfort, comfort my people; —it is the voice of your God; speak tenderly to Jerusalem and tell her this, that she has fulfilled her term of bondage, that her penalty is paid; she has received at the Lord's hand double measure for all her sins.

There is a voice that cries: Prepare a road for the Lord through the wilderness, clear a highway across the desert for our God. Every valley shall be lifted up, every mountain and hill brought down; rugged places shall be made smooth and mountain-ranges become a plain. Thus shall the glory of the Lord be revealed, and all mankind together shall see it; for the Lord himself has spoken.

A voice says, 'Cry', and another asks, 'What shall I cry?' 'That all mankind is grass, they last no longer than a flower of the field. The grass withers, the flower fades, when the breath of the Lord blows upon them; the grass withers, the flowers fade, but the word of our God endures for evermore.'

You who bring Zion good news, up with you to the mountain-top; lift up your voice and shout, you who bring good news to Jerusalem, lift it up fearlessly; cry to the cities of Judah, 'Your God is here.' Here is the Lord God coming in might, coming to rule with his right arm. His recompense comes with him, he carries his reward before him. He will tend his flock like a shepherd and gather them together with his arm; he will carry the lambs into his bosom and lead the ewes to water.

Isaiah 40:1-11 (NEB)

721

Have you not known? Have you not heard? Has it not been told you from the beginning? Have you not understood from the foundations of the earth? It is he who sits above the circle of the earth, and its inhabitants are like grasshoppers; who stretches out the heavens like a curtain, and spreads them like a tent to dwell in; who brings princes to nought, and makes the rulers of the earth as nothing.

Scarcely are they planted, scarcely sown, scarcely has their stem taken root in the earth, when he blows upon them, and they wither, and the tempest carries them off like stubble.

To whom then will you compare me, that I should be like him? says the Holy One. Lift up your eyes on high and see: who created these? He who brings out their host by number, calling them all by name; by the greatness of his might, and because he is strong in power not one is missing.

Why do you say, O Jacob, and speak, O Israel, "My way is hid from the Lord, and my right is disregarded by my God"? Have you not known? Have you not heard? The Lord is the everlasting God, the Creator of the ends of the earth. He does not faint or grow weary, his understanding is unsearchable. He gives power to the faint, and to him who has no might he increases strength. Even youths shall faint and be weary, and young men shall fall exhausted; but they who wait for the Lord shall renew their strength, they shall mount up with wings like eagles, they shall run and not be weary, they shall walk and not faint.

Isaiah 40:21-31

722

Behold my servant, whom I uphold, my chosen, in whom my soul delights; I have put my spirit upon him, he will bring forth justice to the nations. He will not cry or lift up his voice, or make it heard in the street; a bruised reed he will not break, and a dimly burning wick he will not quench; he will faithfully bring forth justice. He will not fail or be discouraged till he has established justice in the earth; and the coastlands wait for his law.

Thus says God, the Lord, who created the heavens and stretched them out, who spread forth the earth and what comes from it, who gives breath to the people upon it and spirit to those who walk in it: "I am the Lord, I have called you in righteousness, I have taken you by the hand and kept you; I have given you as a covenant to the people, a light to the nations, to open the eyes that are blind, to bring out the prisoners from the dungeon, from the prison those who sit in darkness. I am the Lord, that is my name; my glory I give to no other, nor my praise to graven images. Behold, the former things have come to pass, and new things I now declare; before they spring forth I tell you of them."

Sing to the Lord a new song, his praise from the end of the earth!
Isaiah 42:1-10a

723

Behold, my servant shall prosper, he shall be exalted and lifted up, and shall be very high. As many were astonished at him—his appearance was so marred, beyond human semblance, and his form beyond that of the sons of men—so shall he startle many nations; kings shall shut their mouths because of him; for that which has not been told them they shall see, and that which they have not heard they shall understand.

Who has believed what we have heard? And to whom has the arm of the Lord been revealed? For he grew up before him like a young plant, and like a root out of dry ground; he had no form or comeliness that we should look at him, and no beauty that we should desire him. He was despised and rejected by men; a man of sorrows, and acquainted with grief; and as one from whom men hide their faces he was despised, and we esteemed him not.

Surely he has borne our griefs and carried our sorrows; yet we esteemed him stricken, smitten by God, and afflicted. But he was wounded for our transgressions, he was bruised for our iniquities; upon him was the chastisement that made us whole, and with his stripes we are healed. All we like sheep have gone astray; we have turned every one to his own way; and the Lord has laid on him the iniquity of us all. He was oppressed, and he was afflicted, yet he opened not his mouth; like a lamb that is led to the slaughter, and like a sheep that before his shearers is dumb, so he opened not his mouth. By oppression and judgment he was taken away; and as for his generation, who considered that he was cut off out of the land of the living, stricken for the transgression of my people? And they made his grave with the wicked and with a rich man in his death, although he had done no violence, and there was no deceit in his mouth.

Yet it was the will of the Lord to bruise him; he has put him to grief; when he makes himself an offering for sin, he shall see his offering, he shall prolong his days; the will of the Lord shall prosper in his hand; he shall see the fruit of the travail of his soul and be satisfied; by his knowledge shall the righteous one, my servant, make many to be accounted righteous; and he shall bear their iniquities. Therefore I will divide him a portion with the great, and he shall divide the spoil with the strong; because he poured out his soul to death, and was numbered with the transgressors; yet he bore the sin of many, and made intercession for the transgressors.

Isaiah 52:13-53:12

724

"Ho, every one who thirsts, come to the waters; and he who has no money, come, buy and eat! Come, buy wine and milk without money and without price. Why do you spend your money for that which is not bread, and your labor for that which does not satisfy? Hearken diligently to me, and eat what is good, and delight yourselves in fatness. Incline your ear, and come to me; hear, that your soul may live; and I will make with you an everlasting covenant, my steadfast, sure love for David. Behold, I made him a witness to the peoples, a leader and commander for the peoples. Behold, you shall call nations that you know not, and nations that knew you not shall run to you, because of the Lord your God, and of the Holy One of Israel, for he has glorified you.

"Seek the Lord while he may be found, call upon him while he is near; let the wicked forsake his way, and the unrighteous man his thoughts; let him return to the Lord, that he may have mercy on him, and to our God, for he will abundantly pardon. For my thoughts are not your thoughts, neither are your ways my ways, says the Lord. For as the heavens are higher than the earth, so are my ways higher than your ways and my thoughts than your thoughts.

"For as the rain and the snow come down from heaven, and return not thither but water the earth, making it bring forth and sprout, giving seed to the sower and bread to the eater, so shall my word be that goes forth from my mouth; it shall not return to me empty, but it shall accomplish that which I purpose, and prosper in the thing for which I sent it.

"For you shall go out in joy, and be led forth in peace; the mountains and the hills before you shall break forth into singing, and all the trees of the field shall clap their hands. Instead of the thorn shall come up the cypress; instead of the brier shall come up the myrtle; and it shall be to the Lord for a memorial, for an everlasting sign which shall not be cut off."

Isaiah 55

725

"Behold, the days are coming, says the Lord, when I will make a new covenant with the house of Israel and the house of Judah, not like the covenant which I made with their fathers when I took them by the hand to bring them out of the land of Egypt, my covenant which they broke, though I was their husband, says the Lord. But this is the covenant which I will make with the house of Israel after those days, says the Lord: I will put my law within them, and I will write it upon their hearts; and I will be their God, and they shall be my people. And no longer shall each man teach his neighbor and each his brother, saying, 'Know the Lord,' for they shall all know me, from the least of them to the greatest, says the Lord; for I will forgive their iniquity, and I will remember their sin no more."

Jeremiah 31:31-34

726

The steadfast love of the Lord never ceases, his mercies never come to an end; they are new every morning; great is thy faithfulness.

"The Lord is my portion," says my soul, "therefore I will hope in him."

The Lord is good to those who wait for him, to the soul that seeks him. It is good that one should wait quietly for the salvation of the Lord. It is good for a man that he bear the yoke in his youth.

Let him sit alone in silence when he has laid it on him; let him put his mouth in the dust—there may yet be hope; let him give his cheek to the smiter, and be filled with insults.

For the Lord will not cast off for ever, but, though he cause grief, he will have compassion according to the abundance of his steadfast love; for he does not willingly afflict or grieve the sons of men.

Lamentations 3:22-33

727

It shall come to pass in the latter days that the mountain of the house of the Lord shall be established as the highest of the mountains, and shall be raised up above the hills; and peoples shall flow to it, and many nations shall come and say: "Come, let us go up to the mountain of the Lord, to the house of the God of Jacob; that he may teach us his ways and we may walk in his paths." For out of Zion shall go forth the law, and the word of the Lord from Jerusalem. He shall judge between many peoples, and shall decide for strong nations afar off; and they shall beat their swords into plowshares, and their spears into pruning hooks; nation shall not lift up sword against nation, neither shall they learn war any more; but they shall sit every man under his vine and under his fig tree, and none shall make them afraid; for the mouth of the Lord of hosts has spoken.

For all the peoples walk each in the name of its god, but we will walk in the name of the Lord our God for ever and ever.

In that day, says the Lord, I will assemble the lame and gather those who have been driven away, and those whom I have afflicted; and the lame I will make the remnant; and those who were cast off, a strong nation; and the Lord will reign over them in Mount Zion from this time forth and for evermore.

Micah 4:1-7

728

Hear what the Lord says: Arise, plead your case before the mountains, and let the hills hear your voice. Hear, you mountains, the controversy of the Lord, and you enduring foundations of the earth; for the Lord has a controversy with his people, and he will contend with Israel.

"O my people, what have I done to you? In what have I wearied you? Answer me! For I brought you up from the land of Egypt, and redeemed you from the house of bondage; and I sent before you Moses, Aaron, and Miriam. O my people, remember what Balak king of Moab devised, and what Balaam the son of Beor answered him, and what happened from Shittim to Gilgal, that you may know the saving acts of the Lord."

"With what shall I come before the Lord, and bow myself before God on high? Shall I come before him with burnt offerings, with calves a year old? Will the Lord be pleased with thousands of rams, with ten thousands of rivers of oil? Shall I give my first-born for my transgression, the fruit of my body for the sin of my soul?" He has showed you, O man, what is good; and what does the Lord require of you but to do justice, and to love kindness, and to walk humbly with your God?

Micah 6:1-8

729

But the souls of the righteous are in the hand of God, and no torment will ever touch them. In the eyes of the foolish they seemed to have died, and their departure was thought to be an affliction, and their going from us to be their destruction; but they are at peace.

For though in the sight of men they were punished, their hope is full of immortality. Having been disciplined a little, they will receive great good, because God tested them and found them worthy of himself; like gold in the furnace he tried them, and like a sacrificial burnt offering he accepted them.

In the time of their visitation they will shine forth, and will run like sparks through the stubble. They will govern nations and rule over peoples, and the Lord will reign over them for ever. Those who trust in him will understand truth, and the faithful will abide with him in love, because grace and mercy are upon his elect, and he watches over his holy ones.

Wisdom of Solomon 3:1-9

730

Now when Jesus was born in Bethlehem of Judea in the days of Herod the king, behold, wise men from the East came to Jerusalem, saying, "Where is he who has been born king of the Jews? For we have seen his star in the East, and have come to worship him." When Herod the king heard this, he was troubled, and all Jerusalem with him; and assembling all the chief priests and scribes of the people, he inquired of them where the Christ was to be born. They told him, "In Bethlehem of Judea; for so it is written by the prophet: 'And you, O Bethlehem, in the land of Judah, are by no means least among the rulers of Judah; for from you shall come a ruler who will govern my people Israel.' "

Then Herod summoned the wise men secretly and ascertained from them what time the star had appeared; and he sent them to Bethlehem, saying, "Go and search diligently for the child, and when you have found him bring me word, that I too may come and worship him." When they had heard the king they went their way; and lo, the star which they had seen in the East went before them, till it came to rest over the place where the child was. When they saw the star, they rejoiced exceedingly with great joy; and going into the house they saw the child with Mary his mother, and they fell down and worshiped him. Then, opening their treasures, they offered him gifts, gold and frankincense and myrrh. And being warned in a dream not to return to Herod, they departed to their own country by another way.

Matthew 2:1-12

731

Seeing the crowds, he went up on the mountain, and when he sat down his disciples came to him. And he opened his mouth and taught them, saying:

"Blessed are the poor in spirit, for theirs is the kingdom of heaven.

"Blessed are those who mourn, for they shall be comforted.

"Blessed are the meek, for they shall inherit the earth.

"Blessed are those who hunger and thirst for righteousness, for they shall be satisfied.

"Blessed are the merciful, for they shall obtain mercy.

"Blessed are the pure in heart, for they shall see God.

"Blessed are the peacemakers, for they shall be called sons of God.

"Blessed are those who are persecuted for righteousness' sake, for theirs is the kingdom of heaven.

"Blessed are you when men revile you and persecute you and utter all kinds of evil against you falsely on my account. Rejoice and be glad, for your reward is great in heaven, for so men persecuted the prophets who were before you."

Matthew 5:1-12

732

"Be careful not to perform your religious duties in public so that people will see what you do. If you do these things publicly you will not have any reward from your Father in heaven.

"So when you give something to a needy person, do not make a big show of it, as the hypocrites do in the synagogues and on the streets. They do it so that people will praise them. Remember this! They have already been paid in full. But when you help a needy person, do it in such a way that even your closest friend will not know about it, but it will be a private matter. And your Father, who sees what you do in private, will reward you.

"When you pray, do not be like the hypocrites! They love to stand up and pray in the synagogues and on the street corners so that everyone will see them. Remember this! They have already been paid in full. But when you pray, go to your room and close the door, and pray to your Father, who is unseen. And your Father, who sees what you do in private, will reward you.

"In your prayers do not use a lot of meaningless words, as the pagans do, who think that God will hear them because of their long prayers. Do not be like them; your Father already knows what you need before you ask him. This, then, is how you should pray:

'Our Father in heaven:
May your holy name be honored;
may your Kingdom come;
may your will be done on earth as it is in heaven.
Give us today the food we need.
Forgive us the wrongs that we have done, as we forgive the wrongs that others have done us.
Do not bring us to hard testing, but keep us safe from the Evil One.'

"If you forgive others the wrongs they have done you, your Father in heaven will also forgive you. But if you do not forgive the wrongs of others, then your Father in heaven will not forgive the wrongs you have done."

Matthew 6:1-15 (TEV)

733

"Do not lay up for yourselves treasures on earth, where moth and rust consume and where thieves break in and steal, but lay up for yourselves treasures in heaven, where neither moth nor rust consumes and where thieves do not break in and steal. For where your treasure is, there will your heart be also.

"The eye is the lamp of the body. So, if your eye is sound, your whole body will be full of light; but if your eye is not sound, your whole body will be full of darkness. If then the light in you is darkness, how great is the darkness!

"No one can serve two masters; for either he will hate the one and love the other, or he will be devoted to the one and despise the other. You cannot serve God and mammon.

"Therefore I tell you, do not be anxious about your life, what you shall eat or what you shall drink, nor about your body, what you shall put on. Is not life more than food, and the body more than clothing? Look at the birds of the air: they neither sow nor reap nor gather into barns, and yet your heavenly Father feeds them. Are you not of more value than they? And which of you by being anxious can add one cubit to his span of life? And why are you anxious about clothing? Consider the lilies of the field, how they grow; they neither toil nor spin; yet I tell you, even Solomon in all his glory was not arrayed like one of these. But if God so clothes the grass of the field, which today is alive and tomorrow is thrown into the oven, will he not much more clothe you, O men of little faith? Therefore do not be anxious, saying, 'What shall we eat?' or 'What shall we drink?' or 'What shall we wear?' For the Gentiles seek all these things; and your heavenly Father knows that you need them all. But seek first his kingdom and his righteousness, and all these things shall be yours as well.

"Therefore do not be anxious about tomorrow, for tomorrow will be anxious for itself. Let the day's own trouble be sufficient for the day.

Matthew 6:19-34

734

Now when Jesus came into the district of Caesarea Philippi, he asked his disciples, "Who do men say that the Son of man is?" And they said, "Some say John the Baptist, others say Elijah, and others Jeremiah or one of the prophets." He said to them, "But who do you say that I am?" Simon Peter replied, "You are the Christ, the Son of the living God." And Jesus answered him, "Blessed are you, Simon Bar-Jona! For flesh and blood has not revealed this to you, but my Father who is in heaven. And I tell you, you are Peter, and on this rock I will build my church, and the powers of death shall not prevail against it. I will give you the keys of the kingdom of heaven, and whatever you bind on earth shall be bound in heaven, and whatever you loose on earth shall be loosed in heaven."

Matthew 16:13-19

735

And when they had approached Jerusalem and had come to Bethphage, to the Mount of Olives, then Jesus sent two disciples, saying to them, "Go into the village opposite you, and immediately you will find a donkey tied there and a colt with her; untie them, and bring them to me. And if anyone says something to you, you shall say, 'The Lord has need of them;' and immediately he will send them."

Now this took place that what was spoken through the prophet might be fulfilled, saying, "Say to the daughter of Zion, 'Behold your King is coming to you, gentle, and mounted upon a donkey, even upon a colt, the foal of a beast of burden.' " And the disciples went and did just as Jesus had directed them, and brought the donkey and the colt, and laid on them their garments; on which he sat. And most of the multitude spread their garments in the road, and others were cutting branches from the trees, and spreading them in the road.

And the multitudes going before him, and those who followed after were crying out, saying, "Hosanna to the Son of David; Blessed is he who comes in the name of the Lord; Hosanna in the highest!" And when he had entered Jerusalem, all the city was stirred, saying, "Who is this?" And the multitudes were saying, "This is the prophet Jesus, from Nazareth in Galilee."

Matthew 21:1-11 (NASB)

736

"When the Son of man comes in his glory, and all the angels with him, then he will sit on his glorious throne. Before him will be gathered all the nations, and he will separate them one from another as a shepherd separates the sheep from the goats, and he will place the sheep at his right hand, but the goats at the left.

Then the King will say to those at his right hand, 'Come, O blessed of my Father, inherit the kingdom prepared for you from the foundation of the world; for I was hungry and you gave me food, I was thirsty and you gave me drink, I was a stranger and you welcomed me, I was naked and you clothed me, I was sick and you visited me, I was in prison and you came to me.' Then the righteous will answer him, 'Lord, when did we see thee hungry and feed thee, or thirsty and give thee drink? And when did we see thee a stranger and welcome thee, or naked and clothe thee? And when did we see thee sick or in prison and visit thee?' And the King will answer them, 'Truly, I say to you, as you did it to one of the least of these my brethren, you did it to me.'

Then he will say to those at his left hand, 'Depart from me, you cursed, into the eternal fire prepared for the devil and his angels; for I was hungry and you gave me no food, I was thirsty and you gave me no drink, I was a stranger and you did not welcome me, naked and you did not clothe me, sick and in prison and you did not visit me.' Then they also will answer, 'Lord, when did we see thee hungry or thirsty or a stranger or naked or sick or in prison, and did not minister to thee?' Then he will answer them, 'Truly, I say to you, as you did it not to one of the least of these, you did it not to me.' And they will go away into eternal punishment, but the righteous into eternal life."

Matthew 25:31-46

737

After the Sabbath, as Sunday morning was dawning, Mary Magdalene and the other Mary went to look at the grave. Suddenly there was a strong earthquake; an angel of the Lord came down from heaven, rolled the stone away, and sat on it. His appearance was like lightning and his clothes were white as snow. The guards were so afraid that they trembled and became like dead men.

The angel spoke to the women. "You must not be afraid," he said. "I know you are looking for Jesus, who was nailed to the cross. He is not here; he has been raised, just as he said. Come here and see the place where he lay. Quickly, now, go and tell his disciples, 'He has been raised from death, and now he is going to Galilee ahead of you; there you will see him!' Remember what I have told you."

So they left the grave in a hurry, afraid and yet filled with joy, and ran to tell his disciples.

Suddenly Jesus met them and said, "Peace be with you." They came up to him, took hold of his feet, and worshiped him. "Do not be afraid," Jesus said to them. "Go and tell my brothers to go to Galilee, and there they will see me."

Matthew 28:1-10 (TEV)

738

The eleven disciples went to the hill in Galilee where Jesus had told them to go. When they saw him they worshiped him, even though some of them doubted. Jesus drew near and said to them, "I have been given all authority in heaven and on earth. Go, then, to all peoples everywhere and make them my disciples: baptize them in the name of the Father, the Son, and the Holy Spirit, and teach them to obey everything I have commanded you. And remember! I will be with you always, to the end of the age."

Matthew 28:16-20 (TEV)

739

And one of the scribes came up and heard them disputing with one another, and seeing that he answered them well, asked him, "Which commandment is the first of all?" Jesus answered, "The first is, 'Hear, O Israel: The Lord our God, the Lord is one; and you shall love the Lord your God with all your heart, and with all your soul, and with all your mind, and with all your strength.' The second is this, 'You shall love your neighbor as yourself.' There is no other commandment greater than these." And the scribe said to him, "You are right, Teacher; you have truly said that he is one, and there is no other but he; and to love him with all the heart, and with all the understanding, and with all the strength, and to love one's neighbor as oneself, is much more than all whole burnt offerings and sacrifices." And when Jesus saw that he answered wisely, he said to him, "You are not far from the kingdom of God." And after that no one dared to ask him any question.

Mark 12:28-34

740

"My soul magnifies the Lord, and my spirit rejoices in God my Savior, for he has regarded the low estate of his handmaiden. For behold, henceforth all generations will call me blessed; for he who is mighty has done great things for me, and holy is his name. And his mercy is on those who fear him from generation to generation. He has shown strength with his arm, he has scattered the proud in the imagination of their hearts, he has put down the mighty from their thrones, and exalted those of low degree; he has filled the hungry with good things, and the rich he has sent empty away. He has helped his servant Israel, in remembrance of his mercy, as he spoke to our fathers, to Abraham and to his posterity for ever."

Luke 1:46b-55

741

"Blessed be the Lord God of Israel, for he has visited and redeemed his people, and has raised up a horn of salvation for us in the house of his servant David, as he spoke by the mouth of his holy prophets from of old, that we should be saved from our enemies, and from the hand of all who hate us; to perform the mercy promised to our fathers, and to remember his holy covenant, the oath which he swore to our father Abraham, to grant us that we, being delivered from the hand of our enemies, might serve him without fear, in holiness and righteousness before him all the days of our life. And you, child, will be called the prophet of the Most High; for you will go before the Lord to prepare his ways, to give knowledge of salvation to his people in the forgiveness of their sins, through the tender mercy of our God, when the day shall dawn upon us from on high to give light to those who sit in darkness and in the shadow of death, to guide our feet into the way of peace."

Luke 1:68-79

742

At that time Emperor Augustus sent out an order for all the citizens of the Empire to register themselves for the census. When this first census took place, Quirinius was the governor of Syria. Everyone, then, went to register himself, each to his own town.

Joseph went from the town of Nazareth, in Galilee, to Judea, to the town named Bethlehem, where King David was born. Joseph went there because he was a descendant of David. He went to register himself with Mary, who was promised in marriage to him. She was pregnant, and while they were in Bethlehem, the time came for her to have her baby. She gave birth to her first son, wrapped him in cloths and laid him in a manger—there was no room for them to stay in the inn.

There were some shepherds in that part of the country who were spending the night in the fields, taking care of their flocks. An angel of the Lord appeared to them, and the glory of the Lord shone over them. They were terribly afraid, but the angel said to them, "Don't be afraid! I am here with good news for you, which will bring great joy to all the people. This very day in David's town your Savior was born—Christ the Lord! What will prove it to you is this: you will find a baby wrapped in cloths and lying in a manger."

Suddenly a great army of heaven's angels appeared with the angel, singing praises to God, "Glory to God in the highest heaven, and peace on earth to those with whom he is pleased!"

When the angels went away from them back into heaven, the shepherds said to one another, "Let us go to Bethlehem and see this thing that has happened, that the Lord has told us."

So they hurried off and found Mary and Joseph, and saw the baby lying in the manger. When the shepherds saw him they told them what the angel had said about this child. All who heard it were filled with wonder at what the shepherds told them. Mary remembered all these things and thought deeply about them. The shepherds went back, singing praises to God for all they had heard and seen; it had been just as the angel had told them.

Luke 2:1-20 (TEV)

743

And he came to Nazareth, where he had been brought up; and he went to the synagogue, as his custom was, on the sabbath day. And he stood up to read; and there was given to him the book of the prophet Isaiah. He opened the book and found the place where it was written, "The Spirit of the Lord is upon me, because he has anointed me to preach good news to the poor. He has sent me to proclaim release to the captives and recovering of sight to the blind, to set at liberty those who are oppressed, to proclaim the acceptable year of the Lord." And he closed the book, and gave it back to the attendant, and sat down; and the eyes of all in the synagogue were fixed on him. And he began to say to them, "Today this scripture has been fulfilled in your hearing."

Luke 4:16-21

744

"But I tell you who hear me: Love your enemies, do good to those who hate you, bless those who curse you, and pray for those who mistreat you. If anyone hits you on one cheek, let him hit the other one too; if someone takes your coat, let him have your shirt as well. Give to everyone who asks you for something, and when someone takes what is yours, do not ask for it back. Do for others just what you want them to do for you.

"If you love only the people who love you, why should you receive a blessing? Even sinners love those who love them! And if you do good only to those who do good to you, why should you receive a blessing? Even sinners do that! And if you lend only to those from whom you hope to get it back, why should you receive a blessing? Even sinners lend to sinners, to get back the same amount! No! Love your enemies and do good to them; lend and expect nothing back. You will have a great reward, and you will be sons of the Most High God. For he is good to the ungrateful and the wicked. Be merciful, just as your Father is merciful.

"Do not judge others, and God will not judge you; do not condemn others, and God will not condemn you; forgive others, and God will forgive you. Give to others, and God will give to you; you will receive a full measure, a generous helping, poured into your hands—all that you can hold. The measure you use for others is the one God will use for you."

Luke 6:27-38 (TEV)

745

And behold, a lawyer stood up to put him to the test, saying, "Teacher, what shall I do to inherit eternal life?" He said to him, "What is written in the law? How do you read?" And he answered, "You shall love the Lord your God with all your heart, and with all your soul, and with all your strength, and with all your mind; and your neighbor as yourself." And he said to him, "You have answered right; do this, and you will live."

But he, desiring to justify himself, said to Jesus, "And who is my neighbor?" Jesus replied, "A man was going down from Jerusalem to Jericho, and he fell among robbers, who stripped him and beat him, and departed, leaving him half dead. Now by chance a priest was going down that road; and when he saw him he passed by on the other side. So likewise a Levite, when he came to the place and saw him, passed by on the other side. But a Samaritan, as he journeyed, came to where he was; and when he saw him, he had compassion, and went to him and bound up his wounds, pouring on oil and wine; then he set him on his own beast and brought him to an inn, and took care of him. And the next day he took out two denarii and gave them to the innkeeper, saying, 'Take care of him; and whatever more you spend, I will repay you when I come back.' Which of these three, do you think, proved neighbor to the man who fell among the robbers?" He said, "The one who showed mercy on him." And Jesus said to him, "Go and do likewise."

Luke 10:25-37

746

Jesus went on to say, "There was a man who had two sons. The younger one said to him, 'Father, give me now my share of the property.' So the man divided the property between his two sons. After a few days the younger son sold his part of the property and left home with the money. He went to a country far away, where he wasted his money in reckless living. He spent everything he had. Then a severe famine spread over that country, and he was left without a thing. So he went to work for one of the citizens of that country, who sent him out to his farm to take care of the pigs. He wished he could fill himself with the bean pods the pigs ate, but no one gave him anything to eat. At last he came to his senses and said, 'All my father's hired workers have more than they can eat, and here I am, about to starve! I will get up and go to my father and say, "Father, I have sinned against God and against you. I am no longer fit to be called your son; treat me as one of your hired workers." ' So he got up and started back to his father.

"He was still a long way from home when his father saw him; his heart was filled with pity and he ran, threw his arms around his son, and kissed him. 'Father,' the son said, 'I have sinned against God and against you. I am no longer fit to be called your son.' But the father called his servants: 'Hurry!' he said. 'Bring the best robe and put it on him. Put a ring on his finger and shoes on his feet. Then go get the prize calf and kill it, and let us celebrate with a feast! Because this son of mine was dead, but now he is alive; he was lost, but now he has been found.' And so the feasting began.

"The older son, in the meantime, was out in the field. On his way back, when he came close to the house, he heard the music and dancing. He called one of the servants and asked him, 'What's going on?' 'Your brother came back home,' the servant answered, 'and your father killed the prize calf, because he got him back safe and sound.' The older brother was so angry that he would not go into the house; so his father came out and begged him to come in. 'Look,' he answered back to his father, 'all these years I have worked like a slave for you, and I never disobeyed your orders. What have you given me? Not even a goat for me to have a feast with my friends! But this son of yours wasted all your property on prostitutes, and when he comes back home you kill the prize calf for him!' 'My son,' the father answered, 'you are always here with me and everything I have is yours. But we had to have a feast and be happy, because your brother was dead, but now he is alive; he was lost, but now he has been found.' "

Luke 15:11-32 (TEV)

747

That very day two of them were going to a village named Emmaus, about seven miles from Jerusalem, and talking with each other about all these things that had happened. While they were talking and discussing together, Jesus himself drew near and went with them. But their eyes were kept from recognizing him.

And he said to them, "What is this conversation which you are holding with each other as you walk?" And they stood still, looking sad. Then one of them, named Cleopas, answered him, "Are you the only visitor to Jerusalem who does not know the things that have happened there in these days?" And he said to them, "What things?" And they said to him, "Concerning Jesus of Nazareth, who was a prophet mighty in deed and word before God and all the people, and how our chief priests and rulers delivered him up to be condemned to death, and crucified him. But we had hoped that he was the one to redeem Israel. Yes, and besides all this, it is now the third day since this happened. Moreover, some women of our company amazed us. They were at the tomb early in the morning and did not find his body; and they came back saying that they had even seen a vision of angels, who said that he was alive. Some of those who were with us went to the tomb, and found it just as the women had said; but him they did not see."

And he said to them, "O foolish men, and slow of heart to believe all that the prophets have spoken! Was it not necessary that the Christ should enter into his glory?" And beginning with Moses and all the prophets, he interpreted to them in all the scriptures the things concerning himself.

So they drew near to the village to which they were going. He appeared to be going further, but they constrained him, saying, "Stay with us, for it is toward evening and the day is now far spent." So he went in to stay with them. When he was at table with them, he took the bread and blessed, and broke it, and gave it to them. And their eyes were opened and they recognized him; and he vanished out of their sight. They said to each other, "Did not our hearts burn within us while he talked to us on the road, while he opened to us the scriptures?" And they rose that same hour and returned to Jerusalem; and they found the eleven gathered together and those who were with them, who said, "The Lord has risen indeed, and has appeared to Simon!" Then they told what had happened on the road, and how he was known to them in the breaking of the bread.

Luke 24:13-35

748

When all things began, the Word already was. The Word dwelt with God, and what God was, the Word was. The Word, then, was with God at the beginning, and through him all things came to be; no single thing was created without him. All that came to be was alive with his life, and that life was the light of men. The light shines on in the dark, and the darkness has never mastered it.

There appeared a man named John, sent from God; he came as a witness to testify to the light, that all might become believers through him. He was not himself the light; he came to bear witness to the light. The real light which enlightens every man was even then coming into the world.

He was in the world; but the world, though it owed its being to him, did not recognize him. He entered his own realm, and his own would not receive him. But to all who did receive him, to those who have yielded him their allegiance, he gave the right to become children of God, not born of any human stock, or by the fleshly desire of a human father, but the offspring of God himself. So the Word became flesh; he came to dwell among us, and we saw his glory, such glory as befits the Father's only Son, full of grace and truth.

John 1:1-14 (NEB)

749

"And as Moses lifted up the serpent in the wilderness, so must the Son of man be lifted up, that whoever believes in him may have eternal life."

For God so loved the world that he gave his only Son, that whoever believes in him should not perish but have eternal life. For God sent the Son into the world, not to condemn the world, but that the world might be saved through him. He who believes in him is not condemned; he who does not believe is condemned already, because he has not believed in the name of the only Son of God. And this is the judgment, that the light has come into the world, and men loved darkness rather than light, because their deeds were evil. For every one who does evil hates the light, and does not come to the light, lest his deeds should be exposed. But he who does what is true comes to the light, that it may be clearly seen that his deeds have been wrought in God.

John 3:14-21

750

So Jesus again said to them, "Truly, truly, I say to you, I am the door of the sheep. All who came before me are thieves and robbers; but the sheep did not heed them. I am the door; if any one enters by me, he will be saved, and will go in and out and find pasture. The thief comes only to steal and kill and destroy; I came that they may have life, and have it abundantly. I am the good shepherd. The good shepherd lays down his life for the sheep. He who is a hireling and not a shepherd, whose own the sheep are not, sees the wolf coming and leaves the sheep and flees; and the wolf snatches them and scatters them. He flees because he is a hireling and cares nothing for the sheep. I am the good shepherd; I know my own and my own know me, as the Father knows me and I know the Father; and I lay down my life for the sheep. And I have other sheep, that are not of this fold; I must bring them also, and they will heed my voice. So there shall be one flock, one shepherd. For this reason the Father loves me, because I lay down my life, that I may take it again. No one takes it from me, but I lay it down of my own accord. I have power to lay it down, and I have power to take it again; this charge I have received from my Father."

John 10:7-18

751

"Let not your hearts be troubled; believe in God, believe also in me. In my Father's house are many rooms; if it were not so, would I have told you that I go to prepare a place for you? And when I go and prepare a place for you, I will come again and will take you to myself, that where I am you may be also. And you know the way where I am going." Thomas said to him, "Lord, we do not know where you are going; how can we know the way?" Jesus said to him, "I am the way, and the truth, and the life; no one comes to the Father, but by me. If you had known me, you would have known my Father also; henceforth you know him and have seen him."

Philip said to him, "Lord, show us the Father, and we shall be satisfied." Jesus said to him, "Have I been with you so long, and yet you do not know me, Philip? He who has seen me has seen the Father; how can you say, 'Show us the Father'? Do you not believe that I am in the Father and the Father in me? The words that I say to you I do not speak on my own authority; but the Father who dwells in me does his works. Believe me that I am in the Father and the Father in me; or else believe me for the sake of the works themselves.

"Truly, truly, I say to you, he who believes in me will also do the works that I do; and greater works than these will he do, because I go to the Father. Whatever you ask in my name, I will do it, that the Father may be glorified in the Son; if you ask anything in my name, I will do it.

John 14:1-14

752

"I am the true vine, and my Father is the vinedresser. Every branch of mine that bears no fruit, he takes away, and every branch that does bear fruit he prunes, that it may bear more fruit. You are already made clean by the word which I have spoken to you. Abide in me, and I in you. As the branch cannot bear fruit by itself, unless it abides in the vine, neither can you, unless you abide in me. I am the vine, you are the branches. He who abides in me, and I in him, he it is that bears much fruit, for apart from me you can do nothing. If a man does not abide in me, he is cast forth as a branch and withers; and the branches are gathered, thrown into the fire and burned. If you abide in me, and my words abide in you, ask whatever you will, and it shall be done for you. By this my Father is glorified, that you bear much fruit, and so prove to be my disciples. As the Father has loved me, so have I loved you; abide in my love. If you keep my commandments, you will abide in my love, just as I have kept my Father's commandments and abide in his love. These things I have spoken to you, that my joy may be in you, and that your joy may be full.

"This is my commandment, that you love one another as I have loved you. Greater love has no man than this, that a man lay down his life for his friends. You are my friends if you do what I command you. No longer do I call you servants, for the servant does not know what his master is doing; but I have called you friends, for all that I have heard from my Father I have made known to you. You did not choose me, but I chose you and appointed you that you should go and bear fruit and that your fruit should abide; so that whatever you ask the Father in my name, he may give it to you. This I command you, to love one another."

John 15:1-17

753

When the day of Pentecost had come, they were all together in one place. And suddenly a sound came from heaven like the rush of a mighty wind, and it filled all the house where they were sitting. And there appeared to them tongues as of fire, distributed and resting on each one of them. And they were all filled with the Holy Spirit and began to speak in other tongues, as the Spirit gave them utterance.

But Peter, standing with the eleven, lifted up his voice and addressed them, "Men of Judea and all who dwell in Jerusalem, let this be known to you, and give ear to my words.

"Jesus of Nazareth, a man attested to you by God with mighty works and wonders and signs which God did through him in your midst, as you yourselves know—this Jesus, delivered up according to the definite plan and foreknowledge of God, you crucified and killed by the hands of lawless men. But God raised him up, having loosed the pangs of death, because it was not possible for him to be held by it.

"Let all the house of Israel therefore know assuredly that God has made him both Lord and Christ, this Jesus whom you crucified."

Now when they heard this they were cut to the heart, and said to

Peter and the rest of the apostles, "Brethren, what shall we do?" And Peter said to them, "Repent, and be baptized every one of you in the name of Jesus Christ for the forgiveness of your sins; and you shall receive the gift of the Holy Spirit. For the promise is to you and to your children and to all that are far off, every one whom the Lord our God calls to him." And he testified with many other words and exhorted them, saying, "Save yourselves from this crooked generation." So those who received his word were baptized, and there were added that day about three thousand souls. And they devoted themselves to the apostles' teaching and fellowship, to the breaking of bread and the prayers.

Acts 2:1-4, 14, 22b-24, 36-42

754

"You know the word which he sent to Israel, preaching good news of peace by Jesus Christ (he is Lord of all), the word which was proclaimed throughout all Judea, beginning from Galilee after the baptism which John preached: how God anointed Jesus of Nazareth with the Holy Spirit and with power; how he went about doing good and healing all that were oppressed by the devil, for God was with him. And we are witnesses to all that he did both in the country of the Jews and in Jerusalem. They put him to death by hanging him on a tree; but God raised him on the third day and made him manifest; not to all the people but to us who were chosen by God as witnesses, who are and drank with him after he rose from the dead. And he commanded us to preach to the people, and to testify that he is the one ordained by God to be judge of the living and the dead. To him all the prophets bear witness that every one who believes in him receives forgiveness of sins through his name."

Acts 10:36-43

755

So Paul stood before the whole Council of the Areopagus and made this speech:

"Men of Athens, I have seen for myself how extremely scrupulous you are in all religious matters, because I noticed, as I strolled round admiring your sacred monuments, that you had an altar inscribed: To An Unknown God. Well, the God whom I proclaim is in fact the one whom you already worship without knowing it.

"Since the God who made the world and everything in it is himself Lord of heaven and earth, he does not make his home in shrines made by human hands. Nor is he dependent on anything that human hands can do for him, since he can never be in need of anything; on the contrary, it is he who gives everything—including life and breath—to everyone. From one single stock he not only created the whole human race so that they could occupy the entire earth, but he decreed how long each nation should flourish and what the boundaries of its territory should be. And he did this so that all nations might seek the deity and, by feeling their way towards him, succeed in finding him. Yet in fact he is not far from any of us, since it is in him that we live, and move, and exist, as indeed some of your own writers have said: 'We are all his children'.

"Since we are the children of God, we have no excuse for thinking that the deity looks like anything in gold, silver or stone that has been carved and designed by a man.

"God overlooked that sort of thing when men were ignorant, but now he is telling everyone everywhere that they must repent, because he has fixed a day when the whole world will be judged, and judged in righteousness, and he has appointed a man to be the judge. And God has publicly proved this by raising this man from the dead."

Acts 17:22-31 (JB)

756

Therefore, since we are justified by faith, we have peace with God through our Lord Jesus Christ. Through him we have obtained access to this grace in which we stand, and we rejoice in our hope of sharing the glory of God. More than that, we rejoice in our sufferings, knowing that suffering produces endurance, and endurance produces character, and character produces hope, and hope does not disappoint us, because God's love has been poured into our hearts through the Holy Spirit which has been given to us.

While we were still weak, at the right time Christ died for the ungodly. Why, one will hardly die for a righteous man—though perhaps for a good man one will dare even to die. But God shows his love for us in that while we were yet sinners Christ died for us. Since, therefore, we are now justified by his blood, much more shall we be saved by him from the wrath of God. For if while we were enemies we were reconciled to God by the death of his Son, much more, now that we are reconciled, shall we be saved by his life. Not only so, but we also rejoice in God through our Lord Jesus Christ, through whom we have now received our reconciliation.

Romans 5:1-11

757

We know that in everything God works for good with those who love him, who are called according to his purpose. For those whom he foreknew he also predestined to be conformed to the image of his Son, in order that he might be the first-born among many brethren. And those whom he predestined he also called; and those whom he called he also justified; and those whom he justified he also glorified.

What then shall we say to this? If God is for us, who is against us? He who did not spare his own Son but gave him up for us all, will he not also give us all things with him? Who shall bring any charge against God's elect? It is God who justifies; who is to condemn? Is it Christ Jesus, who died, yes, who was raised from the dead, who is at the right hand of God, who indeed intercedes for us? Who shall separate us from the love of Christ? Shall tribulation, or distress, or persecution, or famine, or nakedness, or peril, or sword? As it is written, "For thy sake we are being killed all the day long; we are regarded as sheep to be slaughtered." No, in all these things we are more than conquerors through him who loved us. For I am sure that neither death, nor life, nor angels, nor principalities, nor things present, nor things to come, nor powers, nor height, nor depth, nor anything else in all creation, will be able to separate us from the love of God in Christ Jesus our Lord.

Romans 8:28-39

758

The word is near you, on your lips and in your heart (that is, the word of faith which we preach); because, if you confess with your lips that Jesus is Lord and believe in your heart that God raised him from the dead, you will be saved. For man believes with his heart and so is justified, and he confesses with his lips and so is saved. The scripture says, "No one who believes in him will be put to shame." For there is no distinction between Jew and Greek; the same Lord is Lord of all and bestows his riches upon all who call upon him. For, "every one who calls upon the name of the Lord will be saved."

But how are men to call upon him in whom they have not believed? And how are they to believe in him of whom they have never heard? And how are they to hear without a preacher? And how can men preach unless they are sent? As it is written, "How beautiful are the feet of those who preach good news!" But they have not all heeded the gospel; for Isaiah says, "Lord, who has believed what he has heard from us?" So faith comes from what is heard, and what is heard comes by the preaching of Christ.

Romans 10:8b-17

759

With eyes wide open to the mercies of God, I beg you, my brothers, as an act of intelligent worship, to give him your bodies, as a living sacrifice, consecrated to him and acceptable by him. Don't let the world around you squeeze you into its own mould, but let God re-mould your minds from within, so that you may prove in practice that the plan of God for you is good, meets all his demands and moves towards the goal of true maturity.

Let us have no imitation Christian love. Let us have a genuine break with evil and a real devotion to good. Let us have real warm affection for one another as between brothers, and a willingness to let the other man have the credit. Let us not allow slackness to spoil our work and let us keep the fires of the spirit burning, as we do our work for the Lord. Base your happiness on your hope in Christ. When trials come endure them patiently; steadfastly maintain the habit of prayer.

Give freely to fellow Christians in want, never grudging a meal or a bed to those who need them. And as for those who try to make your life a misery, bless them. Don't curse, bless. Share the happiness of those who are happy, and the sorrow of those who are sad. Live in harmony with each other. Don't become snobbish but take a real interest in ordinary people. Don't become set in your own opinions. Don't pay back a bad turn by a bad turn, to anyone. See that your public behavior is above criticism. As far as your responsibility goes, live at peace with everyone.

Never take vengeance into your own hands, my dear friends: stand back and let God punish if he will. For it is written: Vengeance belongeth unto me: I will recompense. And these are God's words: If thine enemy hunger, feed him; If he thirst, give him to drink: For in so doing thou shalt heap coals of fire upon his head. Don't allow yourself to be overpowered by evil. Take the offensive—overpower evil with good!

Romans 12:1, 2, 9-21 (Phillips)

760

Now there are varieties of gifts, but the same Spirit; and there are varieties of service, but the same Lord; and there are varieties of working, but it is the same God who inspires them all in every one. To each is given the manifestation of the Spirit for the common good. To one is given through the Spirit the utterance of wisdom, and to another the utterance of knowledge according to the same Spirit, to another faith by the same Spirit, to another the gifts of healing by the one Spirit, to another the working of miracles, to another prophecy, to another the ability to distinguish between spirits, to another various kinds of tongues, to another the interpretation of tongues. All these are inspired by one and the same Spirit who apportions to each one individually as he wills.

For just as the body is one and has many members, and all the members of the body, though many, are one body, so it is with Christ. For by one Spirit we were all baptized into one body—Jews or Greeks, slaves or free—and all were made to drink of one Spirit.

1 Corinthians 12:4-13

761

If I speak in the tongues of men and of angels, but have not love, I am a noisy gong or a clanging cymbal. And if I have prophetic powers, and understand all mysteries and all knowledge, and if I have all faith, so as to remove mountains, but have not love, I am nothing. If I give away all I have, and if I deliver my body to be burned, but have not love, I gain nothing.

Love is patient and kind; love is not jealous or boastful; it is not arrogant or rude. Love does not insist on its own way; it is not irritable or resentful; it does not rejoice at wrong, but rejoices in the right. Love bears all things, believes all things, hopes all things, endures all things.

Love never ends; as for prophecy, it will pass away; as for tongues, they will cease; as for knowledge, it will pass away. For our knowledge is imperfect and our prophecy is imperfect; but when the perfect comes, the imperfect will pass away. When I was a child, I spoke like a child, I thought like a child, I reasoned like a child; when I became a man, I gave up childish ways. For now we see in a mirror dimly, but then face to face. Now I know in part; then I shall understand fully, even as I have been fully understood. So faith, hope, love abide, these three; but the greatest of these is love.

1 Corinthians 13

762

Now if Christ is preached as raised from the dead, how can some of you say that there is no resurrection of the dead? But if there is no resurrection of the dead, then Christ has not been raised; if Christ has not been raised, then our preaching is in vain and your faith is in vain. We are even found to be misrepresenting God, because we testified of God that he raised Christ, whom he did not raise if it is true that the dead are not raised. For if the dead are not raised, then Christ has not been raised. If Christ has not been raised, your faith is futile and you are still in your sins. Then those also who have fallen asleep in Christ have perished. If in this life only we have hoped in Christ, we are of all men most to be pitied.

But in fact Christ has been raised from the dead, the first fruits of those who have fallen asleep. For as by a man came death, by a man has come also the resurrection of the dead. For as in Adam all die, so also in Christ shall all be made alive. But each in his own order: Christ the first fruits, then at his coming those who belong to Christ. Then comes the end, when he delivers the kingdom to God the Father after destroying every rule and every authority and power. For he must reign until he has put all his enemies under his feet. The last enemy to be destroyed is death. "For God has put all things in subjection under his feet." But when it says, "All things are put in subjection under him," it is plain that he is excepted who put all things under him. When all things are subjected to him, then the Son himself will also be subjected to him who put all things under him, that God may be everything to everyone.

1 Corinthians 15:12-28

763

Lo! I tell you a mystery. We shall not all sleep, but we shall all be changed, in a moment, in the twinkling of an eye, at the last trumpet. For the trumpet will sound, and the dead will be raised imperishable, and we shall be changed. For this perishable nature must put on the imperishable, and this mortal nature must put on immortality. When the perishable puts on the imperishable, and the mortal puts on immortality, then shall come to pass the saying that is written:

"Death is swallowed up in victory."

"O death, where is thy victory?
O death, where is thy sting?"

The sting of death is sin, and the power of sin is the law. But thanks be to God, who gives us the victory through our Lord Jesus Christ.

Therefore, my beloved brethren, be steadfast, immovable, always abounding in the work of the Lord, knowing that in the Lord your labor is not in vain.

1 Corinthians 15:51-58

764

For what we preach is not ourselves, but Jesus Christ as Lord, with ourselves as your servants for Jesus' sake. For it is the God who said, "Let light shine out of darkness," who has shone in our hearts to give the light of the knowledge of the glory of God in the face of Christ.

But we have this treasure in earthen vessels, to show that the transcendent power belongs to God and not to us. We are afflicted in every way, but not crushed; perplexed, but not driven to despair; persecuted, but not forsaken; struck down, but not destroyed; always carrying in the body the death of Jesus, so that the life of Jesus may also be manifested in our bodies. For while we live we are always being given up to death for Jesus' sake, so that the life of Jesus may be manifested in our mortal flesh. So death is at work in us, but life in you.

2 Corinthians 4:5-12

765

For the love of Christ controls us, because we are convinced that one has died for all; therefore all have died. And he died for all, that those who live might live no longer for themselves but for him who for their sake died and was raised.

From now on, therefore, we regard no one from a human point of view; even though we once regarded Christ from a human point of view, we regard him thus no longer. Therefore, if any one is in Christ, he is a new creation; the old has passed away, behold, the new has come. All this is from God, who through Christ reconciled us to himself and gave us the ministry of reconciliation; that is, in Christ God was reconciling the world to himself, not counting their trespasses against them, and entrusting to us the message of reconciliation. So we are ambassadors for Christ, God making his appeal through us. We beseech you on behalf of Christ, be reconciled to God. For our sake he made him to be sin who knew no sin, so that in him we might become the righteousness of God.

2 Corinthians 5:14-21

766

The point is this: he who sows sparingly will also reap sparingly, and he who sows bountifully will also reap bountifully. Each one must do as he has made up his mind, not reluctantly or under compulsion, for God loves a cheerful giver. And God is able to provide you with every blessing in abundance, so that you may always have enough of everything and may provide in abundance for every good work. As it is written,

"He scatters abroad, he gives to the poor;
his righteousness endures for ever."

He who supplies seed to the sower and bread for food will supply and multiply your resources and increase the harvest of your righteousness. You will be enriched in every way for great generosity, which through us will produce thanksgiving to God; for the rendering of this service not only supplies the wants of the saints but also overflows in many thanksgivings to God. Under the test of this service, you will glorify God by your obedience in acknowledging the gospel of Christ, and by the generosity of your contribution for them and for all others; while they long for you and pray for you, because of the surpassing grace of God in you. Thanks be to God for his inexpressible gift!

2 Corinthians 9:6-15

767

For freedom Christ has set us free; stand fast therefore, and do not submit again to a yoke of slavery.

For you were called to freedom, brethren; only do not use your freedom as an opportunity for the flesh, but through love be servants of one another. For the whole law is fulfilled in one word, "You shall love your neighbor as yourself." But if you bite and devour one another take heed that you are not consumed by one another.

But I say, walk by the Spirit, and do not gratify the desires of the flesh. For the desires of the flesh are against the Spirit, and the desires of the Spirit are against the flesh; for these are opposed to each other, to prevent you from doing what you would. But if you are led by the Spirit you are not under the law. Now the works of the flesh are plain: immorality, impurity, licentiousness, idolatry, sorcery, enmity, strife, jealousy, anger, selfishness, dissension, party spirit, envy, drunkenness, carousing, and the like. I warn you, as I warned you before, that those who do such things shall not inherit the kingdom of God. But the fruit of the Spirit is love, joy, peace, patience, kindness, goodness, faithfulness, gentleness, self-control; against such there is no law. And those who belong to Christ Jesus have crucified the flesh with its passions and desires.

If we live by the Spirit, let us also walk by the Spirit.

Galatians 5:1,13-25

768

I urge you, then—I who am a prisoner because I serve the Lord: live a life that measures up to the standard God set when he called you. Be humble, gentle, and patient always. Show your love by being helpful to one another. Do your best to preserve the unity which the Spirit gives, by the peace that binds you together. There is one body and one Spirit, just as there is one hope to which God has called you. There is one Lord, one faith, one baptism; there is one God and Father of all men, who is Lord of all, works through all, and is in all.

Each one of us has been given a special gift, in proportion to what Christ has given.

It was he who "gave gifts to men"; he appointed some to be apostles, others to be prophets, others to be evangelists, others to be pastors and teachers. He did this to prepare all God's people for the work of Christian service, to build up the body of Christ. And so we shall all come together to that oneness in our faith and in our knowledge of the Son of God; we shall become mature men, reaching to the very height of Christ's full stature. Then we shall no longer be children, carried by the waves and blown about by every shifting wind of the teaching of deceitful men, who lead others to error by the tricks they invent. Instead, by speaking the truth in a spirit of love, we must grow up in every way to Christ, who is the head. Under his control all the different parts of the body fit together, and the whole body is held together by every joint with which it is provided. So when each separate part works as it should, the whole body grows and builds itself up through love.

Ephesians 4:1-7,11-16 (TEV)

769

Now if your experience of Christ's encouragement and love means anything to you, if you have known something of the fellowship of his Spirit, and all that it means in kindness and deep sympathy, do make my best hopes for you come true! Live together in harmony, live together in love, as though you had only one mind and one spirit between you. Never act from motives of rivalry or personal vanity, but in humility think more of each other than you do of yourselves. None of you should think only of his own affairs, but should learn to see things from other people's point of view.

Let Christ be your example as to what your attitude should be. For he, who had always been God by nature, did not cling to his prerogatives as God's equal, but stripped himself of all privilege by consenting to be a slave by nature and being born as mortal man. And, having become man, he humbled himself by living a life of utter obedience, even to the extent of dying, and the death he died was the death of a common criminal. That is why God has now lifted him so high, and has given him the name beyond all names, so that at the name of Jesus "every knee shall bow", whether in Heaven or earth or under the earth. And that is why, in the end, "every tongue shall confess" that Jesus Christ is the Lord, to the glory of God the Father.

Philippians 2:1-11 (Phillips)

770

May you be strengthened with all power, according to his glorious might, for all endurance and patience with joy, giving thanks to the Father, who has qualified us to share in the inheritance of the saints in light. He has delivered us from the dominion of darkness and transferred us to the kingdom of his beloved Son, in whom we have redemption, the forgiveness of sins.

He is the image of the invisible God, the first-born of all creation; for in him all things were created, in heaven and on earth, visible or invisible, whether thrones or dominions or principalities or authorities—all things were created through him and for him. He is before all things, and in him all things hold together. He is the head of the body, the church; he is the beginning, the first-born from the dead, that in everything he might be pre-eminent. For in him all the fulness of God was pleased to dwell, and through him to reconcile to himself all things, whether on earth or in heaven, making peace by the blood of his cross.

Colossians 1:11-20

771

You have been raised to life with Christ. Set your hearts, then, on the things that are in heaven, where Christ sits on his throne at the right side of God. Keep your minds fixed on things there, not on things here on earth. For you have died, and your life is hidden with Christ in God. Your real life is Christ, and when he appears, then you too will appear with him and share his glory!

You are the people of God; he loved you and chose you for his own. So then, you must put on compassion, kindness, humility, gentleness, and patience. Be helpful to one another, and forgive one another, whenever any of you has a complaint against someone else. You must forgive each other in the same way that the Lord has forgiven you. And to all these add love, which binds all things together in perfect unity. The peace that Christ gives is to be the judge in your hearts; for to this peace God has called you together in the one body. And be thankful. Christ's message, in all its richness, must live in your hearts. Teach and instruct each other with all wisdom. Sing psalms, hymns, and sacred songs; sing to God, with thanksgiving in your hearts. Everything you do or say, then, should be done in the name of the Lord Jesus, as you give thanks through him to God the Father.

Colossians 3:1-4,12-17 (TEV)

772

And what more shall I say? For time would fail me to tell of Gideon, Barak, Samson, Jephthah, of David and Samuel and the prophets—who through faith conquered kingdoms, enforced justice, received promises, stopped the mouths of lions, quenched raging fire, escaped the edge of the sword, won strength out of weakness, became mighty in war, put foreign armies to flight. Women received their dead by resurrection. Some were tortured, refusing to accept release, that they might rise again to a better life. Others suffered mocking and scourging, and even chains and imprisonment. They were stoned, they were sawn in two, they were killed with the sword; they went about in skins of sheep and goats, destitute, afflicted, ill-treated—of whom the world was not worthy—wandering over deserts and mountains, and in dens and caves of the earth.

And all these, though well attested by their faith, did not receive what was promised, since God had forseen something better for us, that apart from us they should not be made perfect.

Therefore, since we are surrounded by so great a cloud of witnesses, let us also lay aside every weight, and sin which clings so closely, and let us run with perseverance the race that is set before us, looking to Jesus the pioneer and perfecter of our faith, who for the joy that was set before him endured the cross, despising the shame, and is seated at the right hand of the throne of God.

Hebrews 11:32-12:2

773

My brethren, show no partiality as you hold the faith of our Lord Jesus Christ, the Lord of glory. For if a man with gold rings and in fine clothing comes into your assembly, and a poor man in shabby clothing also comes in, and you pay attention to the one who wears the fine clothing and say, "Have a seat here, please," while you say to the poor man, "Stand there," or, "Sit at my feet," have you not made distinctions among yourselves, and become judges with evil thoughts? Listen, my beloved brethren. Has not God chosen those who are poor in the world to be rich in faith and heirs of the kingdom which he has promised to those who love him?

If you really fulfil the royal law, according to the scripture, "You shall love your neighbor as yourself," you do well. But if you show partiality, you commit sin, and are convicted by the law as transgressors. So speak and so act as those who are to be judged under the law of liberty.

James 2:1-5,8,9,12

774

Blessed be the God and Father of our Lord Jesus Christ! By his great mercy we have been born anew to a living hope through the resurrection of Jesus Christ from the dead, and to an inheritance which is imperishable, undefiled, and unfading, kept in heaven for you, who by God's power are guarded through faith for a salvation ready to be revealed in the last time. In this you rejoice, though now for a little while you may have to suffer various trials, so that the genuineness of your faith, more precious than gold which though perishable is tested by fire, may redound to praise and glory and honor at the revelation of Jesus Christ. Without having seen him you love him; though you do not now see him you believe in him and rejoice with unutterable and exalted joy. As the outcome of your faith you obtain the salvation of your souls.

1 Peter 1:3-9

775

That which was from the beginning, which we have heard, which we have seen with our eyes, which we have looked upon and touched with our hands, concerning the word of life—the life was made manifest, and we saw it, and testify to it, and proclaim to you the eternal life which was with the Father and was made manifest to us—that which we have seen and heard we proclaim also to you, so that you may have fellowship with us; and our fellowship is with the Father and with his Son Jesus Christ. And we are writing this that our joy may be complete.

This is the message we have heard from him and proclaim to you, that God is light and in him is no darkness at all. If we say we have fellowship with him while we walk in darkness, we lie and do not live according to the truth; but if we walk in the light, as he is in the light, we have fellowship with one another, and the blood of Jesus his Son cleanses us from all sin. If we say we have no sin, we deceive ourselves, and the truth is not in us. If we confess our sins, he is faithful and just, and will forgive our sins and cleanse us from all unrighteousness. If we say we have not sinned, we make him a liar, and his word is not in us.

1 John 1:1-10

776

See how much the Father has loved us! His love is so great that we are called God's children—and so, in fact, we are. This is why the world does not know us: it has not known God. My dear friends, we are now God's children, but it is not yet clear what we shall become. But we know that when Christ appears, we shall become like him, because we shall see him as he really is. Everyone who has this hope in Christ keeps himself pure, just as Christ is pure.

Whoever sins is guilty of breaking God's law; because sin is a breaking of the law. You know that Christ appeared in order to take away men's sins, and that there is no sin in him. So everyone who lives in Christ does not continue to sin; but whoever continues to sin has never seen him or known him.

Let no one deceive you, children! Whoever does what is right is righteous, just as Christ is righteous. Whoever continues to sin belongs to the Devil, because the Devil has sinned from the very beginning. The Son of God appeared for this very reason, to destroy the Devil's works.

Whoever is a child of God does not continue to sin, because God's very nature is in him; and because God is his Father, he cannot continue to sin. Here is the clear difference between God's children and the Devil's children: anyone who does not do what is right, or does not love his brother, is not God's child.

1 John 3:1-10 (TEV)

777

My dear people, let us love one another since love comes from God and everyone who loves is begotten by God and knows God. Anyone who fails to love can never have known God, because God is love. God's love for us was revealed when God sent into the world his only Son so that we could have life through him; this is the love I mean: not our love for God, but God's love for us when he sent his Son to be the sacrifice that takes our sins away. My dear people, since God has loved us so much, we too should love one another. No one has ever seen God; but as long as we love one another God will live in us and his love will be complete in us. We can know that we are living in him and he is living in us because he lets us share his Spirit.

We ourselves saw and we testify that the Father sent his Son as saviour of the world. If anyone acknowledges that Jesus is the Son of God, God lives in him, and he in God. We ourselves have known and put our faith in God's love towards ourselves. God is love and anyone who lives in love lives in God, and God lives in him. Love will come to its perfection in us when we can face the day of judgment without fear; because even in this world we have become as he is. In love there can be no fear, but fear is driven out by perfect love: because to fear is to expect punishment, and anyone who is afraid is still imperfect in love. We are to love, then, because he loved us first. Anyone who says, "I love God", and hates his brother, is a liar, since a man who does not love the brother that he can see cannot love God, whom he has never seen. So this is the commandment that he has given us, that anyone who loves God must also love his brother.

1 John 4:7-21 (JB)

778

After this I looked, and behold, a great multitude which no man could number, from every nation, from all tribes and peoples and tongues, standing before the throne and before the Lamb, clothed in white robes, with palm branches in their hands, and crying out with a loud voice, "Salvation belongs to our God who sits upon the throne, and to the Lamb!" And all the angels stood round the throne and round the elders and the four living creatures, and they fell on their faces before the throne and worshiped God, saying, "Amen! Blessing and glory and wisdom and thanksgiving and honor and power and might be to our God for ever and ever! Amen."

Then one of the elders addressed me, saying, "Who are these, clothed in white robes, and whence have they come?" I said to him, "Sir, you know." And he said to me, "These are they who have come out of the great tribulation; they have washed their robes and made them white in the blood of the Lamb. Therefore are they before the throne of God, and serve him day and night within his temple; and he who sits upon the throne will shelter them with his presence. They shall hunger no more, neither thirst any more; the sun shall not strike them, nor any scorching heat. For the Lamb in the midst of the throne will be their shepherd, and he will guide them to springs of living water; and God will wipe away every tear from their eyes."

Revelation 7:9-17

779

Then I saw a new heaven and a new earth; for the first heaven and the first earth had passed away, and the sea was no more. And I saw the holy city, new Jerusalem, coming down out of heaven from God, prepared as a bride adorned for her husband; and I heard a great voice from the throne saying, "Behold, the dwelling of God is with men. He will dwell with them, and they shall be his people, and God himself will be with them; he will wipe away every tear from their eyes, and death shall be no more, neither shall there be mourning nor crying nor pain any more, for the former things have passed away."

And he who sat upon the throne said, "Behold, I make all things new." Also he said, "Write this, for these words are trustworthy and true." And he said to me, "It is done! I am the Alpha and the Omega, the beginning and the end. To the thirsty I will give from the fountain of the water of life without payment. He who conquers shall have this heritage, and I will be his God and he shall be my son."

Revelation 21:1-7

ABBREVIATIONS AND CREDITS

The Scripture quotations in this Hymnal, except where otherwise noted, are from the Revised Standard Version Bible (**RSV**), copyright 1946, 1952, and © 1971 by the Division of Christian Education of the National Council of the Churches of Christ in the U.S.A. and used by permission.

Those marked **NEB** are from **The New English Bible**, © The Delegates of the Oxford University Press and the Syndics of the Cambridge University Press 1961, 1970. Reprinted by permission.

Those marked **JB** are excerpts from **The Jerusalem Bible**, copyright © 1966 by Darton, Longman & Todd, Ltd. and Doubleday and Company, Inc. Used by permission of the publisher.

Those marked **Phillips** are from **The New Testament in Modern English**, reprinted with permission of The Macmillan Company, © J.B. Phillips 1958.

Those marked **TEV** are from the **Today's English Version of the New Testament**, © American Bible Society 1966, 1971. Used by permission.

The passage marked **NASB** is from the **New American Standard Bible: New Testament, Psalms**, © The Lockman Foundation, 1960, 1962, 1963, 1968, 1971. Used by permission.

The passage marked **AT** is from **The Bible: An American Translation**, edited by J.M. Powis Smith and Edgar J. Goodspeed, copyright 1935 by the University of Chicago, published by The University of Chicago Press. Used by permission.

The passage marked **AV** is from the Authorized (King James) Version of the Bible.

THE COVENANT HYMNAL

OTHER WORSHIP RESOURCES

780 We believe that God is Spirit, and they that worship him must worship him in spirit and in truth; **/ That God is light, and that if we walk in the light as he is in the light, we have fellowship one with another.** / We believe that God is love, **/ And that everyone who loves is born of God and knows God.**

We believe that Jesus Christ is the Son of God, **/ That God has given to us eternal life and this life is in his Son;** / That he is the resurrection and the life, **/ And that whoever believes on him, though he were dead, yet shall he live.**

We believe that the Holy Spirit has come, that he convinces the world of sin, of righteousness, and of judgment, and that he guides us into all truth. **/ We believe that we are children of God, and that he has given us of his Spirit.** / We believe that if we confess our sins, he is faithful and just to forgive us our sins and to cleanse us from all unrighteousness. **/ We believe that the world passes away and the lust thereof, but he who does the will of God abides forever.**

From the writings of John

781 This is the good news which we received, in which we stand, and by which we are saved: that Christ died for our sins according to the Scriptures, that he was buried, that he was raised on the third day; and that he appeared to Peter, then to the Twelve, and to many faithful witnesses.

We believe he is the Christ, the Son of the living God. He is the first and the last, the beginning and the end; he is our Lord and our God. Amen.

From the Apostle Paul

782 We believe there is no condemnation for those who are in Christ Jesus: and we know that in everything God works for good with those who love him, who are called according to his purpose. We are sure that neither death, nor life, nor angels, nor principalities, nor things present, nor things to come, nor powers, nor height, nor depth, nor anything else in all creation, will be able to separate us from the love of God in Christ Jesus our Lord. Amen.

From the Apostle Paul

783 I believe in God the Father Almighty, maker of heaven and earth:

And in Jesus Christ his only Son, our Lord; who was conceived by the Holy Spirit, born of the Virgin Mary, suffered under Pontius Pilate, was crucified, dead, and buried; he descended into hades; the third day he rose again from the dead; he ascended into heaven, and sitteth on the right hand of God, the Father Almighty; from thence he shall come to judge the quick and the dead.

I believe in the Holy Spirit, the holy Christian church, the communion of saints, the forgiveness of sins, the resurrection of the body, and the life everlasting. Amen.

The Apostles' Creed

784 I believe in one God the Father Almighty, maker of heaven and earth, and of all things visible and invisible:

And in one Lord Jesus Christ, the only-begotten Son of God, begotten of his Father before all worlds, God of God, Light of Light, very God of very God, begotten, not made, being of one substance with the Father, by whom all things were made;

Who for us men and for our salvation came down from heaven,
and was incarnate by the Holy Spirit of the Virgin Mary,
and was made man, and crucified also for us under Pontius Pilate;
He suffered and was buried, and the third day he rose again according to the Scriptures, and ascended into heaven, and sitteth on the right hand of the Father;
And he shall come again with glory to judge both the quick and the dead;
Whose kingdom shall have no end.

And I believe in the Holy Spirit, the Lord and giver of life, who proceedeth from the Father and the Son, who with the Father and the Son together is worshiped and glorified; who spoke by the prophets. And I believe in one catholic and apostolic church; I acknowledge one baptism for the remission of sins, and I look for the resurrection of the dead, and the life of the world to come. Amen.

The Nicene Creed

785 We believe in God, the Eternal Spirit, Father of our Lord Jesus Christ and our Father, and to his deeds we testify:

He calls the worlds into being,
creates man in his own image,
and sets before him the ways of life and death.
He seeks in holy love to save all people from aimlessness and sin.
He judges men and nations by his righteous will
declared through prophets and apostles.
In Jesus Christ, the man of Nazareth, our crucified and risen Lord,
he has come to us and shared our common lot,
conquering sin and death,
and reconciling the world to himself.
He bestows upon us his Holy Spirit,
creating and renewing the Church of Jesus Christ,
binding in covenant faithful people of all ages, tongues, and races.
He calls us into his Church,
to accept the cost and joy of discipleship,
to be his servants in the service of men,
to proclaim the gospel to all the world,
to resist the powers of evil,
to share in Christ's baptism and eat at his table,
to join him in his passion and victory.
He promises to all who trust him:
forgiveness of sins and fulness of grace,
courage in the struggle for justice and peace,
his presence in trial and rejoicing,
and eternal life in his kingdom which has no end.

Blessing and honor, glory and power be unto him. Amen.

Contemporary

786 The Lord God will swallow up death forever, and he will wipe away tears from all faces, and the reproach of his people he will take away from all the earth; for the Lord has spoken.

It will be said on that day: "Lo, this is our God; we have waited for him, that he might save us. This is the Lord; we have waited for him; let us be glad and rejoice in his salvation."

From the Prophet Isaiah

787 Have mercy on me, O God, according to thy steadfast love; according to thy abundant mercy blot out my transgressions. Wash me thoroughly from my iniquity, and cleanse me from my sin! For I know my transgressions, and my sin is ever before me.

Fill me with joy and gladness; let the bones which thou hast broken rejoice. Hide thy face from my sins, and blot out all my iniquities. Create in me a clean heart, O God, and put a new and right spirit within me. Cast me not away from thy presence, and take not thy holy Spirit from me. Restore to me the joy of thy salvation, and uphold me with a willing spirit.

From Psalm 51

788 Almighty and most merciful Father, we have erred, and strayed from thy ways like lost sheep. We have offended against thy holy laws. We have left undone those things which we ought to have done, and we have done those things which we ought not to have done; and there is no health in us.

But thou, O Lord, have mercy upon us, miserable offenders. Spare thou them, O Lord, which confess their faults. Restore thou them that are penitent, according to thy promises declared unto mankind in Christ Jesus our Lord. And grant, O most merciful Father, for his sake, that we may hereafter live a godly, righteous, and sober life—to the glory of thy holy name. Amen.

789 Almighty and most merciful God, we acknowledge and confess that we have sinned against thee in thought, word, and deed; that we have not loved thee with all our heart and soul, with all our mind and strength; and that we have not loved our neighbor as ourselves.

We beseech thee, O God, to be forgiving to what we have been, to help us to amend what we are, and of thy mercy to direct what we shall be, so that the love of goodness may ever be first in our hearts, that we may always walk in thy commandments and ordinances blameless, and follow unto our life's end in the footsteps of Jesus Christ our Lord. Amen.

790 Forgive us, most gracious God and Father, what we have done to increase the pain of the world. Pardon the unkind and impatient words, the thoughtless and careless failure, the selfish and unloving deed, the lack of sympathy, the withholding of compassion, and the reluctance to give aid when the opportunity came.

We confess our sins, and pray the Spirit of Christ to enter and possess us, and make our lives new in this act of worship. Amen.

791 We confess to you, Lord, what we are: we are not the people we like others to think we are; we are afraid to admit even to ourselves what lies in the depths of our souls. But we do not want to hide our true selves from you. We believe that you know us as we are, and yet you love us. Help us not to shrink from self-knowledge; teach us to respect ourselves for your sake; give us the courage to put our trust in your guiding and power.

We also confess to you, Lord, the unrest of the world, to which we contribute and in which we share. Forgive us that so many of us are indifferent to the needs of our fellow men. Forgive our reliance on weapons of terror, our discrimination against people of different races, and our preoccupation with material standards. And forgive us Christians for being so unsure of our good news, and so unready to tell it.

Raise us out of the paralysis of guilt into the freedom and energy of forgiven people. And for those who through long habit find forgiveness hard to accept, we ask you to break their bondage and set them free. Through Jesus Christ our Lord. Amen.

792 O God our Father, who hast set forth the way of life for us in your beloved Son: we confess with shame our slowness to learn of him, our failure to follow him, our reluctance to bear the cross. **/ Have mercy upon us and forgive us, O Lord.**

Forgive us, we pray you, the poverty of our worship, our neglect of fellowship and of the means of grace, our hesitating witness for

Christ, our evasion of our responsibilities in your service, our imperfect stewardship of your gifts. / **Have mercy upon us and forgive us, O Lord.**

Forgive us that so little of your love has reached others through us, that we have been thoughtless in our judgments, hasty in condemnation, grudging in forgiveness, slow to seek reconciliation, unwilling to help our neighbor as we ought. / **Have mercy upon us and forgive us, O Lord.**

Have mercy on me, O God, according to your steadfast love; according to your abundant mercy blot out my transgressions. Wash me thoroughly from my iniquity, and cleanse me from my sin. Create in me a clean heart, O God, and put a new and right spirit within me. Amen.

793 Lord God our Father, most wonderful, most gracious, and most glorious God, we praise and adore you for all that you have done for us in Jesus Christ. Because . . . the divine nature was his from the first, (and) he did not think to snatch at equality with you, but made himself nothing, assuming the nature of a slave: / **Father, we lift up our hearts, and bring you our worship and praise.**

Because you raised him to the heights, and bestowed on him the name above all names, that at the name of Jesus every knee should bow, in heaven, on earth, and in the depths, and every tongue confess that he is Lord: / **Father, we lift up our hearts, and bring you our worship and praise.**

Worthy is the Lamb that was slain to receive all power and wealth, wisdom and might, honor and glory and praise! / **Praise and honor, glory and might, to him who sits on the throne, and to the Lamb, for ever and ever. Amen.**

794 Lord, where is the end of your creation? What is the length of the list by which you provide for your people? How can there be so many different things, so many species, so much variety? Lord, how can there be so many names and so many color combinations?

We cannot comprehend your creative Spirit,
your endless imagination,
your sense of beauty,
and your great power.
We can only marvel. We too clap our hands, shout, sing, and praise you for your power and beauty. What a wonderland we live in! What a time to live! Spirit of the Lord, keep showing us new things. Amen.

795 Let us praise the Lord our God. **/ The Lord's name be praised.**

Let us praise God for the good world he has made; for things great and small, beautiful and awesome; for seen and unseen splendors: **/ We give thee thanks, O God.**

For human life; for the variety of our skills and interests; for our different ways of thinking and moving and speaking; for common hardships and common hopes we have from birth till dying: **/ We give thee thanks, O God.**

For work to do; for useful tasks that need study and strength; for the comradeship of labor; and for exchanges of good humor and encouragement: **/ We give thee thanks, O God.**

For marriage; for the mystery and joy of flesh made one; for mutual forgiveness and burdens shared; for secrets kept in love: **/ We give thee thanks, O God.**

For family; for living together and eating together; for family amusements and for the pleasure of common experiences: **/ We give thee thanks, O God.**

For children; for their energy and curiosity; for their brave play and their startling frankness; for their sudden sympathies: **/ We give thee thanks, O God.**

For the young; for their high hopes; for their irreverence toward worn-out values, their search for freedom, their solemn vows: **/ We give thee thanks, O God.**

For growing up and growing old; for wisdom deepened by experience; for rest in leisure and for time made precious by its passing: **/ We give thee thanks, O God.**

For thy grace in times of doubt and sorrow; for healing our diseases; for preserving our lives through temptation and danger: **We give thee thanks, O God.**

For the church into which we have been called; for the gospel of mercy we receive by Word and Sacrament; and for our life together in the Lord: **/ We praise thee, Lord God.**

For thy Holy Spirit, who guides our steps and brings us gifts of faith and love; who prays in us and prompts our worship of thee: **/ We praise thee, Lord God.**

Above all, O God, for thy Son Jesus Christ, who lived and died and lives again for our salvation; for our hope in him and for the joy of serving him: **/ We thank and praise thee for thy goodness, O Lord, our God and Father. Amen.**

796 You are God: we praise you;
You are the Lord: we hail you;
You are the eternal Father: all creation worships you.
To you all angels, all the powers of heaven, Cherubim and Seraphim continually sing: "Holy, holy, holy Lord, God of power and might, heaven and earth are full of your glory."
The glorious company of apostles praise you.
The worthy fellowship of prophets praise you.
The white-robed army of martyrs praise you.
The holy Church throughout the world proclaims you:
Father of majesty unbounded,
true and only Son, worthy of all worship,
and Holy Spirit, counsel and guide.
You, Christ, are king of glory, the Father's everlasting Son.
When you became man to deliver us you did not spurn the Virgin's womb.
You removed the sting of death and opened heaven to all believers.
You are seated in glory at God's right hand.
We believe you will come and be our judge.
Come then, deliver your people, bought with the price of your own blood, and bring us with your saints to glory everlasting.

797 O God, how great you are! On the first day of the week we commemorate your creation of the world and all that is in it. **/ Thank you for the light which wakes us morning by morning, and for that greater light which shines in Jesus Christ.**

O God, how great you are! On the first day of the week you raised Jesus from the dead. **/ Raise us with him to a new quality of faith and life.**

O God, how great you are! Again on the first day of the week you sent your Spirit on your disciples. **/ Do not deprive us of your Spirit, but renew him in us day by day.**

798 Here we are—with little power and less prestige, yet lifting up voices and feelings to You. You are hidden behind this curtain of sight, but we trust not removed from hearing our thoughts, instructing our minds, directing our energies, and sustaining us in obedience and service, in Jesus' name. Amen.

799 Almighty God, unto whom all hearts are open, all desires known, and from whom no secrets are hid; cleanse the thoughts of our hearts by the inspiration of thy Holy Spirit, that we may perfectly love thee, and worthily magnify thy holy name; through Christ our Lord. Amen.

800 Come, O Holy Spirit.
Come as Holy Fire and burn in us,
Come as Holy Wind and cleanse us within,
Come as Holy Light and lead us in the darkness,
Come as Holy Truth and dispel our ignorance,
Come as Holy Power and enable our weakness,
Come as Holy Life and dwell in us.
Convict us, convert us, consecrate us until we are set free from the service of ourselves, to be your servants to the world.

801 Spirit of purity and grace: we thank thee for the glory of our early visions and for thy rebukes of our low ambitions. Guide us, we pray thee, that we may no longer fear that which is ordinary. Let our common task glow again with the light of holy purpose, and give us some part in thy abiding work. Move us to speak and achieve the things that conform to thy purposes, ever uniting us more closely to Jesus, in whom we offer ourselves anew to thee. Amen.

802 Lord, make me an instrument of thy peace.
Where there is hatred, let me sow love;
Where there is injury, pardon;
Where there is doubt, faith;
Where there is despair, hope;
Where there is darkness, light;
Where there is sadness, joy.
O Divine Master, grant that I may not so much seek
To be consoled, as to console;
To be understood, as to understand;
To be loved, as to love.
For it is in giving that we receive;
It is in pardoning that we are pardoned;
It is in dying that we are born to eternal life.

803 We praise you, Father, that you have met us along the way with mercy and love and new life in Christ. / **With praise and dedication we offer ourselves.**

We thank you for our responsible calling, to be stewards of life in your kingdom. / **Help us to be good stewards of all you have placed in our care.**

We thank you, Lord, for the ability to learn and to do countless creative tasks. / **Motivate us to develop our skills and to use them in accord with the teaching of Jesus.**

We thank you for all the rich resources with which the world has been supplied. / **Make us determined so to use the soil, the air, the water—all nature's bounty—that future generations are not robbed by our irresponsibility.**

We thank you, Father, for the family we have. / **Teach us to live mindful of each other's need and each other's worth.**

We thank you for the human family, for the rich gift of each nationality and every culture. / **Grant us the spirit of Christ, to be brothers and sisters of all persons, to be ever mindful of the needs of others, and to be instruments of peace.**

We thank you for our wealth, great or small, and for opportunities money brings. / **May all our earning and spending, our saving and giving, be acceptable in your sight, Lord, and grant us the resolve to fulfil our pledge of giving, to the glory of your name, in the ministry of the word of Christ. Amen.**

804 Lord, call us into the church.
Call us in often,
and teach us the old words and old songs
with their new meanings.
Lord, give us new words
for the words we wear out.
Give us new songs
for those that have lost their spirit.
Give us new reasons for coming in
and for going out,
into our streets and to our homes.
As the house of the Lord once moved
like a tent through the wilderness,
so keep our churches from being rigid.
Make our congregation alive and free.
Give us ideas we never had before,
so that alleluia and gloria and amen
are like the experiences we know in daily living.
Alleluia! O Lord, be praised!
In worship and in work, be praised! Amen.

805 O God, we pray for thy Church, which is set today amid the perplexities of a changing order, and face to face with a great new task. We remember with love
the nurture she gave to our spiritual life in its infancy,
the tasks she set for our growing strength,
the influence of the devoted hearts she gathers,
the steadfast power for good she has exerted.
When we compare her with all other human institutions, we rejoice, for there is none like her.

But when we judge her by the mind of her Master, we bow in pity and contrition.
O baptize her afresh in the life-giving spirit of Jesus!
Put upon her lips the ancient gospel of her Lord.
Fill her with the prophet's scorn of tyranny, and with a Christlike tenderness for the heavy-laden and down-trodden.
Bid her cease from seeking her own life, lest she lose it.
Make her valiant to give up her life to humanity, that like her crucified Lord she may mount by the path of the cross to a higher glory. Amen.

806 This is the day you have made, Lord.
Help us to rejoice in it, and be glad!
Remind us of our privileges as your people:
to come to you in these moments,
to confess our sins,
to receive forgiveness, and give it,
to pray and sing and listen,
to renew our fainting spirits,
to rest in all your promises.
Open our eyes to see you, Lord.
Open our ears to hear your Word.
Visit us through your Holy Spirit
And help us to celebrate our faith.
Join our spirits to all in every age who have loved your appearing.
Lift us to higher ground,
Send us forth to serve,
And keep us in the way everlasting. Amen.

807 Jesus, our Master, whose heart was moved with compassion toward the weak and oppressed, and who was more willing to serve than to be served; we pray for all conditions of people:
for those lacking food, shelter, or clothing;
for the sick and all who are wasting away by disease;
for the blind, deaf, and lame;
for prisoners;
for those oppressed by injustice;
for those who have lost their way in society;
for the corrupted and morally fallen;
for the lonely and depressed;
for the worried and anxious;
for all living faithfully in obscurity;
for those fighting bravely in unpopular wars or causes;
for all who are serving diligently and dependably;
for those who stand in the valley of decision;
for those who are suffering the consequences of misdeeds repented of;
for all family circles broken by death;
for those faced by tasks too great for their powers.
Let the power of Jesus' spirit be strong within us, and those for whom we pray. Amen.

808 Lord Jesus Christ, healer of body, mind, and soul, we come to you on behalf of the sick and suffering. May those for whom we pray, especially   feel your presence and know at this moment your healing touch, bringing new life, strength, and health.

Surround those who wait, with the peace that passes all understanding, and those who serve, with wisdom and compassion. Grant to us gathered here such faith in you and your promises, that we may know our prayers have been heard, and that you will do what is best for all who trust in you. In your strength we pray. Amen.

809 Lord,
Restore the ones
caught in the routine
in the structure
in the system.
Release the ones
suppressed by the advice of others,
by the rules,
the guidelines,
the bylaws,
the schedules,
the time clocks, and
the deadlines.
Refresh us.
We are exhausted by the pressure;
We are dazed by the loose ends;
We are bewildered by the procedures;
We are confused by the temptations;
We are distraught by the deceptions
and chained by the job.
Return the lost.
Refresh the weary.
Release the enslaved.
Restore the caught.
Renew the bored.
Come, Christ, and our boredom will leave us.
Show us the people, Christ, and our hearts will be glad. Amen.

810 O God, our Father, this is a wonderful world that you have made. Thank you for it, and for giving us the responsibility to use it to the full, and to keep it as you planned it. Help us to be both wise and responsible, to keep the air clean, the water pure, and natural beauty beautiful.

Forgive us, Lord, for destroying land, fouling streams, and wasting natural resources. Help us to treat lovely things with respect and appreciation, so that the generations to come may enjoy the earth, as we have enjoyed it, through Jesus Christ our Lord. Amen.

811 Eternal God, send peace on earth, and by thy grace put down the pride, greed, and anger that turn man against man, and nation against nation. Speed the day when wars are ended and all men call thee Father; through Jesus Christ our Lord. Amen.

812 We await, O Lord, your challenge to us to go back to the world as your servants. Send us forth now,

sure of forgiveness for our sins;
sure of the freedom to be ourselves;
sure of joy and peace through life in Christ.
Send us out of this place,
united to one another in faith, hope, and love;
united to one another in service to man;
united to one another in and through your Son,
Jesus Christ our Lord. Amen.

813 Father, as we go to our homes and our work this coming week, we ask you to send the Holy Spirit into our lives.

Open our ears, to hear what you are saying in the things that happen to us, and in the people we meet.
Open our eyes, to see the needs of people around us.
Open our hands, to do our work well.
Open our lips, to tell others the good news of Jesus, and bring comfort, happiness, and laughter to other people.
Open our minds, to discover new truth about you and the world.
Open our hearts, to love you and our fellow men as you have loved us in Jesus.

To him, with you our Father and the Holy Spirit, one God, all honor and praise shall be given now and forever. Amen.

RESPONSES
baptism

814 For just as the body is one and has many members, and all the members of the body, though many, are one body, so it is with Christ. For by one Spirit we were all baptized into one body—Jews or Greeks, slaves or free—and all were made to drink of one Spirit.
1 Corinthians 12:12,13

815 God, our Father: We praise you for calling us to be a servant people, and for gathering us into the body of Christ. We thank you for choosing to add to our number brothers and sisters in faith. Together may we live in your Spirit, and so love one another, that we may have the mind of Jesus Christ our Lord, to whom we give honor and glory forever. Amen.

816 Holy God: remind us of the promises given in our own baptism, and renew our trust in you. Make us strong to obey your will, and to serve you with joy; for the sake of Jesus Christ our Lord. Amen.

817 You have offered your child to the strong and tender providence of God, and to the nurture of the church. We accept with humility of spirit, and seriousness of purpose, our responsibility for the spiritual well-being of this child. By our example and our words, we will support your parental role, in disposing this child to respond to the fulness that is in Christ. We earnestly pray that the life and witness of each of us will make your task both joyful and fruitful.

RESPONSES
communion

818 Lift up your hearts. **/ We lift them to the Lord.**
Let us give thanks to the Lord God. **/ It is good that we do.**

All glory is yours, Eternal God, who made the universe. We praise you for this earth, for life and breath, for beauty we have seen and wonders still to come. From the beginning your living Word has guided and corrected us. Your prophets have called us from disobedience, and prepared us for the coming of your Son.

We praise you for the Christ who chose to come as one of us, and lived among us full of grace and truth. For us he became poor, and knew the sadness in our days; and for us he died on the cross and was buried. In him we know forgiveness and lifting of burdens. He brings light to our darkness and opens our eyes to your great glory.

For you raised him from the dead and set him over all creation. Through your Holy Spirit we are members of his body, the church, and heirs of the promise of eternal life. Therefore with grateful hearts we join the faithful who, in all times and places, praise your name, saying:

Holy, holy, holy,
God of power and majesty,
Heaven and earth are full of your glory,
O God most high!

Holy Father, we thank you that the Lord Jesus, on the night when he was arrested, took bread, and when he had given thanks, he broke it, and said, "This is my body which is for you. Do this in remembering me." In the same way, he took the cup, after supper, saying, "This cup is the new covenant in my blood. Do this, as often as you drink it, in remembering me."

We remember you, Lord Jesus, as you commanded, confident we shall know you in the breaking of bread. We remember you, O Christ, confident you will seal the new covenant in our hearts as we drink this cup.

O Holy Spirit, who brought us here to proclaim the risen Lord, unite us in one body with him who loved us and gave himself for us.

O God, who called us from death to life; we give ourselves to you; and with the church through all ages, we thank you for your saving love in Jesus Christ our Lord. Amen.

819 Lord God, we are glad to come here today.
Gladly we come to give you thanks
for everything you have done for us.
Gladly we come to sing and pray
and listen to what you say to us.
But we are most glad and thankful
because you have invited us to come to the table of our Lord Jesus Christ.
We know as we come to worship you
that we do not live as we ought to live.
We do not deserve to be here at all.

Lord God, forgive us.
Pour out your Holy Spirit into our lives
to give us peace
and the strength to leave self behind,
take up the cross
and follow Christ
today, tomorrow, and always.
In his name we ask it. Amen.

820 It is good to give thanks to the Lord, to sing praises to his name, O Most High; to declare his steadfast love in the morning and his faithfulness by night. Brothers, let us love one another, for love is of God. He who loves knows God, for God is love.

We praise you, O God, that your love is ever new. O Lord, bless this new relationship, this new family about your table. Draw us all into your family, that we may be nourished by that Bread of Life which you give us so freely. Amen.

821 Almighty God, giver of the true Bread which comes down from heaven, even your Son, Jesus Christ our Lord: Grant that we who have received the Sacrament of his Body and Blood may abide in him, and he in us, that we may be filled with the power of his endless life; who lives and reigns with you and the Holy Ghost, one God, world without end. Amen.

822 Most merciful and gracious God, of whom the whole family in heaven and earth is named: Give to your children the seal of your approval, and your fatherly benediction; granting them grace to fulfill, with pure and steadfast love, the vows and covenant they here have made. Guide them together, we pray, in the way of righteousness and peace, that loving and serving you, with one heart and mind, all the days of their lives, they may be abundantly enriched with your everlasting favor, through Jesus Christ our Lord. Amen.

823 O God of this good day,
we rejoice that out of all the human family
you have brought together these two persons
and united them in marriage.
As they have often shared with your people
in the fellowship of the church where,
though many, we are one body in Christ,
so in the mystery and joy of flesh made one,
may they partake of the oneness found in you alone.
Fashion their love after that love which,
according to your word,
is slow to lose patience,
looks for ways of being constructive,
is not possessive,
knows no limits to its endurance,
no end to its trust,
no fading of its hope.
In good days and bad, strengthen and defend them
by your Word and Spirit.
Keep their love for you fervent and steady,
and their fellowship with your church creative and healthy,
that the blessings of this life
may be foretaste of the life to come.
Through Jesus Christ our Lord. Amen.

824 Dear friends, called of God to be his children, we give hearty thanks to him who has opened your hearts to receive Jesus Christ as your Savior and Lord, and has inclined you to unite with this church. Having been admitted to membership by decision of the church, we now welcome you into our fellowship, and call upon you in the presence of God and this congregation to confess your faith.

Minister: Do you believe the Bible to be the Word of God and the only perfect rule for faith, doctrine, and conduct?

Response: I do.

Minister: Do you confess Jesus Christ as your Savior and Lord?

Response: I do.

Minister: Do you purpose to remain steadfast in the faith unto the end, and as a true follower of Jesus Christ to walk in newness of life?

Response: I do.

Minister: Do you promise in watchfulness and prayer to diligently use the Word of God and the Holy Sacraments?

Response: I do.

Minister: Do you promise to join us in worship and service, and to give regularly of your substance for the work of the gospel as carried on by this church and the denomination to which it belongs?

Response: I do.

Congregation: Believing as you do, we, the members of this congregation welcome you with joy into our communion and fellowship. We pledge to you our affection, our help, and our prayers, that you with us may evermore increase in the knowledge and love of God.

825 Almighty God: by the love of Jesus Christ you draw men to faith, and welcome them into the church family. May we show your joy by embracing new brothers and sisters who with us believe, and with us will work to serve you. Keep us close together in your Spirit, breaking bread in faith and love, one with Jesus Christ our Lord and Master. Amen.

826 Go out into the world in peace; have courage;
hold on to what is good; return no man evil for evil;
strengthen the fainthearted; support the weak;
help the suffering; honor all men;
love and serve the Lord,
rejoicing in the power of the Holy Spirit.

With God's help we will.

And the blessing of God Almighty, the Father, the Son, and the Holy Spirit, be upon you, and remain with you forever. Amen.

827 This service is ended, **/ But our life in Jesus Christ our Lord goes on.**

We go now, in his name, into all the world. **/ Let our light so shine and our joy be so obvious, that all who see us will come to praise God!**

Amen. **/ Amen.**

828 May the grace of Christ which daily renews us, and the love of God which enables us to love all men, and the fellowship of the Holy Spirit which unites us in one body, make us eager to obey the will of God until we meet again, through Jesus Christ our Lord. Amen.

829 We believe God has made us his people:
to invite others to follow Christ,
to encourage one another to deeper commitment,
to proclaim forgiveness of sins and hope,
to reconcile men to God through word and deed,
to bear witness to the power of love over hate,
to proclaim Jesus the Lord over all,
to meet the daily tasks of life with purpose,
to suffer joyfully for the cause of right,
to the ends of the earth,
to the end of the age,
to the praise of his glory. Amen.

OTHER WORSHIP RESOURCES
credits

780 From **The Book of Common Worship**, Bishop Wilbur P. Thirkield and Dr. Oliver Huckle, © 1932 by E. P. Dutton & Co., Inc. Renewed © 1960 by Gilbert H. Thirkield. Used by permission of publishers. (This grant includes braille and other aids for the handicapped.)
785 Statement of Faith of the United Church of Christ, approved by the General Synod at Oberlin, Ohio, July 5-9, 1959. Used by permission.
788 From the **Book of Common Prayer of The Episcopal Church**. Used by permission.
789 From **Devotional Services for Public Worship**, compiled by John Hunter, p. 48. Published by E. P. Dutton & Co., Inc. Used by permission. (This grant includes braille and other aids for the handicapped.)
790 By James E. Dahlgren. Copyright 1973 by Covenant Press.
791 From **Contemporary Prayers for Public Worship**, Caryl Michlem, ed., published by Wm. B. Eerdmans Publishing Co. Used by permission.
792 From the **Book of Common Worship of the Church of S. India**. Used by permission.
793 From **Contemporary Prayers for Public Worship**, Caryl Michlem, ed., published by Wm. B. Eerdmans Publishing Co. Used by permission.
794 From **Lord, Be With** by Herbert Brokering, copyright 1969 by Concordia Publishing House. Used by permission.
795 From **The Worshipbook—Services**. Copyright © MCMLXX, The Westminster Press. Used by permission.
796 From **Prayers We Have in Common**, Fortress Press. Used by permission.
797 From **Contemporary Prayers for Public Worship**, Caryl Michlem, ed., published by Wm. B. Eerdmans Publishing Co. Used by permission.
798 From **Contemporary Worship Services** by James L. Christensen. Copyright © 1971 by Fleming H. Revell Company. Used by permission.
799 Adapted from **The First and Second Prayer Books of Edward VI**, Everyman's Library, No. 448, p. 212. Published by E. P. Dutton & Co., Inc. Used by permission. (This grant includes braille and other aids for the handicapped.)
800 From **A Prayer Companion**, Charles F. Whiston.
803 By James E. Dahlgren. Copyright 1973 by Covenant Press.
804 From **Lord, Be With** by Herbert Brokering, copyright 1969 by Concordia Publishing House. Used by permission.
805 From **Prayers of the Social Awakening** by Walter Rauschenbusch, Pilgrim Press.
806 By James R. Hawkinson. Copyright 1973 by Covenant Press.
807 From **Contemporary Worship Services** by James L. Christensen. Copyright © 1971 by Fleming H. Revell Company. Used by permission.
808 By Glen V. Wiberg. Copyright 1973 by Covenant Press.
809 From **Lord Be With** by Herbert Brokering, copyright 1969 by Concordia Publishing House. Used by permission.
810 By Earl C. Dahlstrom. Copyright 1973 by Covenant Press.
811 From **The Worshipbook—Services**. Copyright © MCMLXX, The Westminster Press. Used by permission.
812 From **Create and Celebrate**, by Jay C. Rochelle, Fortress Press. Used by permission.
813 From **Contemporary Prayers for Public Worship**, Caryl Michlem, ed., published by Wm. B. Eerdmans Publishing Co. Used by permission.
815 From **The Worshipbook—Services**. Copyright © MCMLXX, The Westminster Press. Used by permission.
816 From **The Worshipbook—Services**. Copyright © MCMLXX, The Westminster Press. Used by permission.
817 From **The Mennonite Hymnal**. Copyright © 1969 by Herald Press, Scottdale, Pa. 15683 and Faith and Life Press, Newton, Kan. 67114. Used by permission.
818 From **The Worshipbook—Services**. Copyright © MCMLXX, The Westminster Press. Used by permission.
819 From **Contemporary Prayers for Public Worship**, Caryl Michlem, ed., published by Wm. B. Eerdmans Publishing Co. Used by permission.
821 From the **Lutheran Service Book and Hymnal**, by permission of the Commission on the Liturgy and Hymnal.
822 From **A Book of Worship for Covenant Churches**, copyright 1960 by Covenant Press.
823 By Glen V. Wiberg. Copyright 1973 by Covenant Press.
824 From **A Book of Worship for Covenant Churches**, copyright 1960 by Covenant Press.
825 From **The Worshipbook—Services**. Copyright © MCMLXX, The Westminster Press. Used by permission.
829 From **The Mennonite Hymnal**. Copyright © 1969 by Herald Press, Scottdale, Pa. 15683 and Faith and Life Press, Newton, Kan. 67114. Used by permission.

THE COVENANT HYMNAL

LECTIONARY OF THE CHRISTIAN YEAR
(pericope)

ADVENT
CHRISTMASTIDE
EPIPHANY
PRE-LENT
LENT
EASTERTIDE
PENTECOST
TRINITY
SPECIAL DAYS

LECTIONARY OF THE CHRISTIAN YEAR

Worship is both private and public. It is done both individually and by congregations. When done individually, worship is mainly contemplative. When done in congregations, worship is celebrative, as the congregation rehearses, relives, and rejoices in its history as the People of God.

At the heart of the Christian celebration is the Christian Year (or sometimes called the Church Year). It is a way of giving titles to the various Sundays commemorative of the events in Jesus' life and teachings and certain observances in the life of the Church. This ancient practice of the Church, and one esteemed by our own fathers, holds before the congregation a balanced and sequential pilgrimage with Jesus as the events of salvation history unfold and take shape through him.

The two main festivals of the year are Christmas and Easter. Each festival is preceded by a period of preparation and each is followed by a sequel. In the first instance it is Advent, Christmas, and Epiphany. In the latter it is Lent, Easter, and Pentecost. Other festivals are also included such as the Transfiguration, Ascension Day, Trinity, and All Saints.

The first half of the Christian Year dramatizes the mighty acts of God in the life of Christ. The latter half of the year emphasizes the response of the People of God to what God has done in Christ by a new life of sacrificial service and joy.

The lectionary provides Bible readings for the Sundays in the Christian Year for a cycle of three years. The designations A, B, and C are used for the first, second, and third years. The basic structure of the lectionary is in large measure the one given us by our fathers. If followed, it is one way for the preacher to preach, and the congregation to hear, the whole counsel of God. It also assures the reading and hearing of Holy Scripture—both Old and New Testaments in their fulness.

LECTIONARY OF THE CHRISTIAN YEAR

ADVENT

Advent begins on the Sunday nearest November 30, and includes the four Sundays before Christmas. In this season the church joyfully remembers that Christ has come in the flesh, continues to come in the Word and the sacraments, and will come again in power and great glory.

SUNDAY OR FESTIVAL	*YEAR*	*PSALM*	*OLD TESTAMENT*	*EPISTLE*	*GOSPEL*
1st Sunday in Advent	A	96	Jer 31:31-34	Rom 13:11-14	Mt 21:1-9
	B	50	Is 40:9-11	Rev 3:14-22	Jn 18:33-38
	C	24	Is 62:10-12	1 Thess 3:11-4:8	Lk 4:16-22
2nd Sunday in Advent	A	95	Mal 4:1-6	Rom 15:4-13	Lk 21:25-31
	B	62	Is 11:1-10	Heb 10:32-39	Lk 12:35-40
	C	97	Is 63:15-64:4	Js 5:7-11	Lk 17:20-30
3rd Sunday in Advent	A	86	Is 40:1-8	1 Cor 4:1-5	Mt 11:2-10
	B	146	Mal 3:1-5	2 Pet 1:19-21	Mt 11:11-19
	C	33	Zeph 3:14-20	1 Pet 1:10-16	Lk 3:1-14
4th Sunday in Advent	A	145	Deut 18:15-22	Phil 4:4-7	Jn 1:19-28
	B	70	Is 51:3-6	1 Jn 1:1-4	Jn 3:22-36
	C	81	Is 52:7-10	Heb 12:18-29	Jn 5:30-40

CHRISTMASTIDE

During the twelve-day period beginning December 25 and ending January 5, the church celebrates the birth of our Lord Jesus Christ.

SUNDAY OR FESTIVAL	*YEAR*	*PSALM*	*OLD TESTAMENT*	*EPISTLE*	*GOSPEL*
Christmas Day	A	19	Is 9:2-7	Tit 2:11-14	Lk 2:1-20
	B	132	Is 62:1-5	Heb 1:1-12	Jn 1:1-14
	C	87	Mic 5:2-4	Col 1:15-20	Mt 1:18-25
1st Sunday after Christmas	A	85	Is 63:7-16	Gal 4:1-7	Lk 2:33-40
	B	110	Jer 31:10-14	Heb 2:10-18	Lk 2:22-32
	C	20	Jer 31:15-17	Rev 14:1-5	Mt 2:13-23

2nd Sunday After Christmas	A	103	1 Sam 2:1-10	Tit 3:3-7	Lk 1:46-55
	B	148	Prov 8:22-31	Eph 1:15-23	Jn 1:14-18
	C	135	2 Chron 6: 18-21	Rev 21:1-4	Jn 3:16-21

EPIPHANY

Beginning with the day of Epiphany (January 6), this season continues until Septuagesima Sunday. The church celebrates in this season the manifestation of Christ to all the world. This time of rejoicing is climaxed by remembering the Transfiguration of our Lord on the last Sunday of Epiphany.

SUNDAY OR FESTIVAL	*YEAR*	*PSALM*	*OLD TESTAMENT*	*EPISTLE*	*GOSPEL*
Epiphany	A	72	Is 60:1-7	Eph 3:1-12	Mt 2:1-12
	B	45	Is 2:2-5	2 Cor 4:1-6	Jn 8:12-20
	C	67	Is 49:1-6	Acts 11:1-18	Mt 12:15-21
1st Sunday after Epiphany	A	27	Eccles 12:1-7	Rom 12:1-5	Lk 2:41-52
	B	8	Is 42:1-9	Acts 10:34-43	Mt 3:13-17
	C	133	Gen 50:15-21	Col 1:24-29	Mt 12:46-50
		(or the readings for Epiphany, if observed on Sunday)			
2nd Sunday after Epiphany	A	148	Is 61:1-7	Rom 12:6-16	Jn 2:1-11
	B	36	1 Sam 3:1-10	1 Cor 6:12-20	Jn 4:5-26
	C	89:1-18	Is 41:8-13	1 Cor 1:26-31	Lk 19:1-10
3rd Sunday after Epiphany	A	107:1-22	2 Kings 5: 1-15	Rom 12:17-21	Mt 8:1-13
	B	126	Is 19:19-25	Heb 11:8-16	Jn 4:27-42
	C	26	Jon 3:1-5,10	1 Cor 7:17-24	Mk 1:14-20
4th Sunday after Epiphany	A	107:23-43	Ex 14:21-31	1 Pet 3:13-22	Mt 8:23-27
	B	85	Ezek 34: 25-31	Heb 11:23-28	Jn 6:66-69
	C	69	Is 43:1-7	2 Tim 1:3-10	Mt 14:22-33
5th Sunday after Epiphany	A	99	Ezek 33:10-16	Col 3:12-17	Mt 13:24-30
	B	112	Is 58:6-12	1 Cor 1:9-18	Mk 9:38-41
	C	104:24-35	Is 55:6-13	Eph 4:11-16	Mk 4:26-29
Last Sunday in Epiphany (The Transfiguration)	A	40	Ex 34:29-35	2 Cor 3:7-18	Mt 17:1-9
	B	29	Ex 24:12-18	2 Pet 1:16-21	Jn 13:31-35
	C	21	Is 61:10-11	Rev 1:9-18	Lk 9:28-36

PRE-LENT

After the Transfiguration the church follows her Lord as he prepares himself and his disciples for the journey to the cross. Septuagesima, Sexagesima, and Quinquagesima are Latin words designating approximately seventy, sixty, and fifty days before Easter.

SUNDAY OR FESTIVAL	*YEAR*	*PSALM*	*OLD TESTAMENT*	*EPISTLE*	*GOSPEL*
Septuagesima (3rd Sunday before Lent)	A	104:1-23	Jer 9:23-24	1 Cor 9:24-10:5	Mt 20:1-16
	B	86	Jer 1:4-10	1 Cor 3:5-23	Mt 19:27-30
	C	119:57-72	Ezek 2:1-7	Phil 3:7-14	Lk 17:7-10
Sexagesima (2nd Sunday before Lent)	A	139	Amos 8:11-12	2 Cor 11:19-12:9 (Alternate: 2 Cor 11:19-31)	Lk 8:4-15
	B	81	Is 45:4-13	1 Cor 2:1-10	Jn 12:35-43
	C	147	1 Sam 16:1-13	2 Tim 3:10-4:5	Mt 10:1-15
Quinquagesima (1st Sunday before Lent)	A	77	Jer 8:4-9	1 Cor 13:1-13	Lk 18:31-43
	B	15	Gen 12:1-9	2 Cor 4:7-12	Jn 12:20-33
	C	43	Jer 15:15-21	1 Cor 1:20-25	Mk 10:32-45

LENT

Beginning on Ash Wednesday and culminating in Holy Week, Lent includes forty week days and six Sundays. During this season the church proclaims, remembers, and responds in gratitude and faith to Christ's atoning death.

SUNDAY OR FESTIVAL	*YEAR*	*PSALM*	*OLD TESTAMENT*	*EPISTLE*	*GOSPEL*
Ash Wednesday	A	51	Joel 2:12-19	1 Jn 1:5-9	Mt 6:16-21
	B	37:1-11	Zech 7:4-10	Js 4:1-12	Mk 7:14-23
	C	30	Is 58:1-9a	2 Cor 5:20-6:2	Lk 5:27-32
1st Sunday in Lent	A	91	Gen 22:1-14	2 Cor 6:1-10	Mt 4:1-11
	B	130	Ex 17:1-7	Js 1:12-15	Mt 16:21-23
	C	35	Job 2:1-10	Rev 12:9-11	Lk 10:17-20
2nd Sunday in Lent	A	32	Ex 33:12-23	1 Thess 4:1-7	Mt 15:21-28
	B	39	2 Sam 12:7-13	Gal 2:15-20	Lk 7:36-50
	C	2	Ex 14:10-18	Heb 5:1-10	Mk 9:14-32

3rd Sunday in Lent	A	42	Jer 26:1-15	Eph 5:1-10	Lk 11:14-28
	B	56	Zech 3:1-5	Rev 3:7-13	Lk 22:31-38
	C	60	Ezek 12: 21-28	Heb 4:1-13	Lk 4:31-37
4th Sunday in Lent	A	111	Is 55:1-7	Gal 4:21-5:1	Jn 6:1-15
	B	4	Ex 16:2-12	2 Cor 5:11-17	Jn 6:25-36
	C	36	Ex 16:11-18	Phil 3:7-16	Jn 6:52-65
5th Sunday in Lent (Passion)	A	143	Num 21:4-9	Heb 9:11-15	Jn 8:46-59
	B	43	Hos 6:1-6	Heb 9:24-28	Jn 11:47-57
	C	102	Ex 34:4-10	Heb 7:23-38	Lk 13:31-35
6th Sunday in Lent (Palm)	A	24	Zech 9:9-12	Phil 2:5-11	Mt 21:1-11
	B	20	Is 50:4-8	Heb 12:1-6	Jn 12:1-16
	C	62	Is 59:14-21	1 Tim 1:12-17	Lk 19:28-40
Maundy Thursday	A	88	Ex 12:1-14	1 Cor 11: 20-32	Jn 13:1-15
	B	27	Ex 12:21-27	1 Cor 5:6-8	Lk 22:14-27
	C	61	Jer 32:36-41	Rev 19:6-10	Mk 14:12-26
Good Friday	A	22	Is 52:13-53:12	Rev 5:1-14	Jn 18:1-19:42 (Alternate: Jn 19: 17-30)
	B	31	Lam 1:7-12	Rev 1:4-8	Mk 14:1-15:46 (Alternate: Mk 15: 21-39)
	C	13	Lam 2:8-16	Heb 10:4-18	Lk 22:1-23:53 (Alternate: Lk 23: 33-49)

EASTERTIDE

Eastertide is a season which begins on Easter day and continues through Ascension day. During this period the church celebrates the ministry of the risen Lord.

SUNDAY OR FESTIVAL	*YEAR*	*PSALM*	*OLD TESTAMENT*	*EPISTLE*	*GOSPEL*
Easter Day	A	118:14-29	Is 25:6-9	1 Pet 1:3-9	Jn 20:1-18
	B	115	Ezek 37:1-14	1 Cor 15: 20-28	Mk 16:1-7
	C	93	Ex 15:1-11	Eph 1:15-23	Mt 28:1-10
Vespers:		16	Dan 3:8-25	Acts 10:34-43	Lk 24:13-35

2nd Sunday in Eastertide	A	61	Gen 32:22-30	1 Jn 5:4-12 (Alternate: Acts 2: 41-47)	Jn 20:19-31
	B	34	Job 19:25-27	Rev 1:9-19 (Alternate: Acts 4: 32-35)	Jn 21:1-14
	C	66	Ezek 36: 22-27	1 Pet 1:17-25 (Alternate: Acts 5:12-16	Jn 21:15-23
3rd Sunday in Eastertide	A	23	Ezek 34: 11-16	1 Pet 2:21-25 (Alternate: Acts 2: 22-28)	Jn 10:11-16
	B	95	Jer 23:1-8	Heb 13:20-21 (Alternate: Acts 3: 1-16)	Mt 9:35-38
	C	100	Ezek 34: 23-31	Rev 21:22-27 (Alternate: Acts 5:27-32)	Jn 10:1-10
4th Sunday in Eastertide	A	66	Is 40:25-31	1 Pet 2:11-20 (Alternate: Acts 2: 29-40)	Jn 16:16-22
	B	123	Is 49:8-15	2 Cor 4:16-18 (Alternate: Acts 4: 5-12)	Jn 17:1-8
	C	126	Is 65:17-25	2 Cor 5:1-10 (Alternate: Acts 13: 44-52)	Jn 14:1-14
5th Sunday in Eastertide	A	98	Is 29:9-14	Js 1:17-21 (Alternate: Acts 6: 1-7)	Jn 16:5-15
	B	65	Is 30:19-26	Heb 13:12-16 (Alternate: Acts 9: 26-31)	Jn 17:9-17
	C	84	Zech 8:18-23	1 Jn 3:18-24 (Alternate: Acts 14: 19-28)	Jn 15:12-17
6th Sunday in Eastertide	A	136	Is 55:6-11	Js 1:22-27 (Alternate: Acts 8: 4-17)	Jn 16:23-33
	B	133	1 Kings 3: 5-15	Col 4:2-6 (Alternate: Acts 10: 34-48)	Jn 17:18-23
	C	146	Jer 29:10-14	Acts 12:6-17 (Alternate: Acts 15: 1-2;22-29)	Lk 11:1-13

Ascension Day	A	47	2 Kings 2: 9-15	Acts 1:1-11	Jn 8:21-30
	B	68:1-20	Deut 33: 26-29	Heb 4:14-16	Jn 17:24-26
	C	110	Dan 7:9-14	Rom 8:31-39	Lk 24:49-53
Sunday after the Ascension (7th Sunday in Eastertide)	A	93	Is 32:14-20	1 Pet 4:7-11 (Alternate: Acts 1: 12-14)	Jn 15:26-16:4
	B	125	Zech 8:1-8	Col 3:1-10 (Alternate: Acts 1:15-17;21-26)	Mt 10:24-31
	C	138	Is 43:8-13	Rom 8:26-28 (Alternate: Acts 7: 55-60)	Jn 15:18-27
		(or the readings for Ascension day, if observed on Sunday)			

PENTECOST

Pentecost recalls the gift of the Holy Spirit to the church and the commencement of the church's ministry.

SUNDAY OR FESTIVAL	*YEAR*	*PSALM*	*OLD TESTAMENT*	*EPISTLE*	*GOSPEL*
Pentecost	A	150	Joel 2:28-32	Acts 2:1-11	Jn 14:22-31
	B	63	Is 57:15-21	Eph 2:17-22	Jn 7:37-39
	C	48	Is 44:1-8	Acts 2:37-47	Jn 14:15-21

TRINITY

In this extended season following Pentecost and concluding with Judgment Sunday, the church proclaims the meaning of God's work—Father, Son, and Holy Spirit—in the creation, redemption, and sanctification of man, the church, and the world.

SUNDAY OR FESTIVAL	*YEAR*	*PSALM*	*OLD TESTAMENT*	*EPISTLE*	*GOSPEL*
Trinity	A	29	Is 6:1-8	Rom 11:33-36	Mt 28:16-20
	B	80	Deut 6:4-9	1 Jn 3:1-10	Jn 15:1-11
	C	139	Ex 3:1-15	1 Tim 3:14-16	Jn 3:1-15
1st Sunday after Trinity	A	1	Is 5:8-16	1 Jn 4:13-21	Lk 16:19-31
	B	49	Deut 6:10-19	Js 4:13-17	Lk 12:13-21
	C	15	Prov 6:16-22	1 Tim 6:6-19	Mt 16:24-28

2nd Sunday after Trinity	A	55	Prov 9:1-10	1 Jn 3:11-18	Lk 14:15-24
	B	76	Ex 4:10-20	1 Cor 9:19-23	Lk 14:25-35
	C	12	Hos 11:1-9	2 Pet 1:3-11	Lk 9:51-62
3rd Sunday after Trinity	A	18:1-30	Is 12:1-6	1 Pet 5:6-11	Lk 15:1-10
	B	32	1 Kings 8: 37-43	Rom 4:1-8	Lk 15:11-32
	C	103	Jer 14:7-9	Eph 2:1-10	Mt 9:9-13
4th Sunday after Trinity	A	25	Num 6:22-27	Rom 8:18-25	Lk 6:36-42
	B	75	2 Chron 28: 8-11;14-15	Rom 2:1-11	Jn 8:2-11
	C	7	Amos 5:6-15	Rom 14:1-12	Lk 13:1-5
5th Sunday after Trinity	A	31	Lam 3:22-33	1 Pet 3:8-17	Lk 5:1-11
	B	119:1-24	Gen 12:1-4	Acts 8:26-40	Jn 1:35-51
	C	98	Josh 1:1-9	Acts 26:13-23	Mt 16:13-20
6th Sunday after Trinity	A	34	Mic 6:6-8	Rom 6:3-11	Mt 5:21-26
	B	119:89 -112	Deut 10: 12-22	Gal 3:23-29	Mt 5:17-20
	C	112	Lev 19:9-18	Js 2:8-17	Mt 5:38-42
7th Sunday after Trinity	A	100	Gen 1:26-2:3	Rom 6:12-23	Mk 8:1-9
	B	64	Gen 3:1-13	Rom 5:12-21	Mk 9:42-50
	C	113	Gen 4:3-16	Js 3:13-18	Mk 7:14-23
8th Sunday after Trinity	A	39	Jer 23:16-29	Rom 8:12-17	Mt 7:15-21
	B	1	Ezek 13:3-12	Rom 8:1-11	Mt 7:13-14
	C	19	Is 30:8-18	1 Jn 4:1-6	Mt 7:21-29
9th Sunday after Trinity	A	81	Prov 16:1-9	1 Cor 10:1-13	Lk 16:1-9
	B	122	1 Chron 29: 10-18	Heb 12:12-17	Lk 12:42-48
	C	37:16-40	Eccles 9: 13-18	2 Thess 3: 6-13	Lk 16:10-15
10th Sunday after Trinity	A	97	Jer 7:1-11	1 Cor 12:1-11	Lk 19:41-47
	B	90	Jer 18:1-11	Rom 11:17-24	Lk 4:24-30
	C	95	Gen 18:22-33	Heb 3:12-19	Mt 11:20-24
11th Sunday after Trinity	A	57	Dan 9:15-19	1 Cor 15:1-11	Lk 18:9-14
	B	62	Deut 1:19-36	Js 2:14-26	Mt 21:28-32
	C	52	Ezek 17: 22-34	1 Jn 1:5-2:2	Mt 23:1-12
12th Sunday after Trinity	A	65	Is 29:17-24	2 Cor 3:4-11	Mk 7:31-37
	B	12	Eccles 5:1-7	Js 3:6-12	Mt 12:33-37
	C	40	Jer 17:5-14	1 Cor 2:11-16	Mt 5:33-37
13th Sunday after Trinity	A	71	Zech 7:4-10	Rom 13:8-10	Lk 10:23-37
	B	41	Jer 22:13-16	1 Jn 4:7-12	Mt 5:43-6:4
	C	116	Deut 16:9-12	2 Cor 9:6-15	Mk 12:41-44
14th Sunday after Trinity	A	92	Prov 4:10-23	Gal 5:16-24	Lk 17:11-19
	B	147	Jer 31:7-9	Eph 1:3-14	Jn 5:1-14
	C	91	Hos 14:1-9	1 Tim 1:12-17	Mt 11:25-30

15th Sunday after Trinity	A	102	1 Kings 17: 8-16	Gal 5:25-6:10	Mt 6:24-34
	B	46	Prov 3:1-10	Acts 20:32-35	Lk 10:38-42
	C	145	Prov 30:4-9	Phil 4:8-13	Mt 6:19-23
16th Sunday after Trinity	A	116	Job 5:17-27	Eph 3:13-21	Lk 7:11-17
	B	16	Jon 2:1-9	2 Cor 4:7-15	Jn 11:1-7; 17-27
	C	86	2 Sam 12: 15-23	Phil 1:19-26	Jn 5:19-24
17th Sunday after Trinity	A	113	Prov 25:6-14	Eph 4:1-6	Lk 14:1-11
	B	51	Amos 5:21-24	Col 2:16-23	Mk 2:23-3:5
	C	105	Deut 7:6-11	Gal 5:1-14	Jn 8:31-36
18th Sunday after Trinity	A	138	2 Chron 1: 7-12	1 Cor 1:4-9	Mt 22:34-46
	B	73	Jer 32:6-15	Rom 10:1-13	Mt 13:44-46
	C	27	Deut 30: 11-20	1 Jn 2:7-17	Mk 10:17-27
19th Sunday after Trinity	A	112	Gen 28:10-17	Eph 4:17-28	Mt 9:1-8
	B	139	Mic 7:7-9	Acts 22:1-16	Jn 9:1-7; 24-38
	C	124	Is 1:18-20	Rom 7:14-25	Jn 7:40-52
20th Sunday after Trinity	A	36	Prov 2:1-9	Eph 5:15-20	Mt 22:1-14
	B	25	Hag 1:2-6	Heb 10:19-31	Mt 25:14-30
	C	80	Is 5:1-7	1 Pet 2:4-10	Mk 12:1-12
21st Sunday after Trinity	A	33	2 Sam 7:18-29	Eph 6:10-17	Jn 4:46-54
	B	86	Jon 3:10-4:11	2 Cor 13:5-9	Mt 16:1-4
	C	74	Is 51:9-16	Rom 5:1-8	Jn 10:22-30
22nd Sunday after Trinity	A	16	Prov 3:11-20	Phil 1:3-11	Mt 18:21-35
	B	143	Mic 7:18-20	Eph 4:25-32	Mt 18:15-22
	C	18	1 Sam 24:1-7; 16-19	1 Thess 5: 12-24	Mk 4:21-25
23rd Sunday after Trinity	A	146	Prov 8:10-21	Phil 3:17-21	Mt 22:15-22
	B	22:22-31	Obad 10-15	1 Tim 2:1-7	Mt 7:7-12
	C	9	Ex 18:13-23	Rom 13:1-7	Mt 17:24-27
24th Sunday after Trinity	A	131	1 Kings 17: 17-24	Col 1:9-14	Mt 9:18-26
	B	116	Is 26:13-19	1 Cor 15: 35-49	Jn 6:37-40
	C	118	Dan 12:1-3	1 Cor 15: 51-58	Lk 20:27-40
25th Sunday after Trinity	A	50	Job 14:1-6	1 Thess 4: 13-18	Mt 24:15-28
	B	99	Zeph 3:8-13	2 Thess 2: 1-12	Lk 13:22-30
	C	75	Eccles 3:1-11	2 Pet 3:1-10	Mt 24:1-14

26th Sunday after Trinity	A	130	Is 35:3-10	2 Pet 3:8-14	Mt 25:1-13
	B	97	Hab 3:1-6; 16-19	1 Pet 4:1-7	Mk 13:24-37
	C	82	Is 2:12-21	Rev 22:10-20	Mt 24:36-44
Last Sunday after Trinity (Judgment)	A	110	Dan 7:9-14	1 Thess 5: 1-11	Mt 25:31-46
	B	98	Ezek 34: 17-24	1 Cor 15: 22-28	Jn 5:22-29
	C	76	Ezek 18: 25-32	Rev 20:11-21:7	Mt 13:47-50

SPECIAL DAYS

It is fitting that the church remember special days that celebrate the universal and local heritage of the communion of saints and its place in the society of man.

SUNDAY OR FESTIVAL	*YEAR*	*PSALM*	*OLD TESTAMENT*	*EPISTLE*	*GOSPEL*
Covenant Founders' Day (February 20 or other church anniversaries)	A	44	Is 51:1-6	1 Pet 2:1-10	Mt 16:13-20
	B	48	Josh 4:1-7	2 Tim 2:15-22	Mt 21:12-16
	C	145	Is 42:5-9	2 Tim 1:3-7	Mt 9:14-17
Christian Family Day (Usually second Sunday in May)	A	128	1 Sam 1:19-20,24-28	Eph 6:1-4	Lk 1:5-17
	B	8	Gen 2:18-24	Eph 5:21-33	Mt 19:3-9
	C	127	Deut 6:1-9	1 Thess 2: 3-12	Mt 18:1-6
Reformation Day (October 31 or preceding Sunday)	A	46	Hab 2:1-4	Rom 3:21-28	Jn 8:31-36
	B	85	Amos 3:3-8	Acts 4:13-21	Jn 12:44-50
	C	118	Jer 23:16-29	1 Pet 4:12-19	Jn 2:13-22
All Saints' Day (November 1 or the following Sunday)	A	68	Deut 33:1-3	Rev 7:9-17	Mt 5:1-12
	B	112	Is 66:10-14	Rev 14:1-5, 12,13	Mt 5:13-16
	C	16	Prov 10:6-11	Heb 11:32-12:2	Lk 6:20-26

Thanksgiving Day	A	103	Deut 8:1-20	Acts 14:8-18	Lk 12:22-34
	B	136	Deut 26:1-11	Acts 17:22-31	Lk 17:11-19
	C	148	Gen 8:13-22	Js 1:16-18	Mt 6:25-34
New Year's Eve or Day	A	90	Num 14: 10b-19	Rev 2:1-5	Lk 13:6-9
	B	105	Ex 20:1-20	Rom 13:8-10	Mt 22:34-40
	C	121	Josh 24:14-24	Acts 16:25-34	Lk 12:32-34

ABBREVIATIONS

The following abbreviations are used for the books of the Bible in the references above.

OLD TESTAMENT

Gen	Genesis
Ex	Exodus
Lev	Leviticus
Num	Numbers
Deut	Deuteronomy
Josh	Joshua
Judg	Judges
Ruth	Ruth
1 Sam	1 Samuel
2 Sam	2 Samuel
1 Kings	1 Kings
2 Kings	2 Kings
1 Chron	1 Chronicles
2 Chron	2 Chronicles
Ezra	Ezra
Neh	Nehemiah
Esther	Esther
Job	Job
Ps	Psalms
Prov	Proverbs
Eccles	Ecclesiastes
Song	Song of Solomon
Is	Isaiah
Jer	Jeremiah
Lam	Lamentations
Ezek	Ezekiel
Dan	Daniel
Hos	Hosea
Joel	Joel
Amos	Amos
Obad	Obadiah
Jon	Jonah
Mic	Micah
Nahum	Nahum
Hab	Habakkuk
Zeph	Zephaniah
Hag	Haggai
Zech	Zechariah
Mal	Malachi

NEW TESTAMENT

Mt	Matthew
Mk	Mark
Lk	Luke
Jn	John
Acts	Acts of the Apostles
Rom	Romans
1 Cor	1 Corinthians
2 Cor	2 Corinthians
Gal	Galatians
Eph	Ephesians
Phil	Philippians
Col	Colossians
1 Thess	1 Thessalonians
2 Thess	2 Thessalonians
1 Tim	1 Timothy
2 Tim	2 Timothy
Tit	Titus
Philem	Philemon
Heb	Hebrews
Js	James
1 Pet	1 Peter
2 Pet	2 Peter
1 Jn	1 John
2 Jn	2 John
3 Jn	3 John
Jude	Jude
Rev	Revelation

THE COVENANT
HYMNAL

INDEXES

SCRIPTURE READINGS (chronological)
SCRIPTURE READINGS (topical)
AUTHORS, COMPOSERS, AND SOURCES
TUNES (alphabetical)
TUNES (metrical)
SCRIPTURE REFERENCES IN HYMNS
TOPICAL
FIRST LINES

scripture readings (chronological)

INDEXES
tunes (alphabetical)

INDEXES
tunes (metrical)

6.5.6.5.D., Amphibrachic
332 Longstaff
333

6.5.6.5.D., Trochaic
223 King's Weston
338 Penitence
357 Whitworth

6.5.6.5.D. with Refrain
369 St. Gertrude
411 Wye Valley

6.5.6.5.6.6.6.5.
365 St. Dunstan's

6.5.10.D. with Refrain
550 Rescue

6.6.4.6.6.6.4.
581 America
582
583
275 Italian Hymn
522
557
306 Olivet

6.6.5.6.6.5.7.8.6.
410 Jesu, meine Freude

6.6.6.6.4.4.4.4.
166 St. John

6.6.6.6.6.6.
37 Laudes Domini

6.6.6.6.D.
288 Invitation
299 Jewett
599 Leoni
243 Spanish Hymn

6.6.6.6.8.8.
228 Darwall's 148th
249
256
192 Marlee
647 Wales

6.6.6.6.8.8.8.
576 Rhosymedre

6.6.7.6.
520 Gemenskap

6.6.7.7.7.7.
115 Auf meinen lieben Gott

6.6.8.4.D.
28 Leoni

6.6.8.6.6.8.3.3.6.6.
7 Arnsberg

6.6.9.D.
307 Elfåker

6.6.9.D. with Refrain
450 Trust and Obey

6.7.6.7. with Refrain
219 Vruechten

6.7.6.7.6.6.6.6.
101 Darmstadt
334
18 Nun danket
540 St. Joan

6.7.7.7.D.
526 Fealty

7.3.7.3.7.7.7.3.
553 Jesus Saves

7.4.7.4.D.
466 So nimm denn meine Hände

7.6.7.6.
146 Christmas Dawn
48 Nocturn

7.6.7.6. with Refrain
73 Loven Gud
429 Near the Cross

7.6.7.6.D.
497 Andrew
254 Angel's Story
482 Aurelia
624
625
630
79 Blomstertid
303 Crucifix
366 Day of Rest
389 Dedekam
183 Ellacombe
606 Ewing
97 Far-Off Lands
605 Glädje
614
574 Greenland
45 Holy Wings
218 Lancashire
481
532
543 Llangloffan
589
196 Meirionydd
407
575
279 Munich
117 Passion Chorale
182
197
107 Rockport
308 St. Hilda
178 St. Theodulph
595
627
55 Sanctuary
120 Vigil
374 Webb
533
84 Wedlock
619 Wie lieblich ist der Maien

7.6.7.6.D., Trochaic
210 St. Kevin
134 Tempus adest floridum

7.6.7.6.D. with Refrain
285 Evangel
530 Hankey
620 Wir pflügen

7.6.7.6.6.7.6.
141 Es ist ein Ros'

7.6.7.6.7.7.
457 Varndean

7.6.7.6.7.7.6.
114 Enchiridion

7.6.7.6.7.7.6.6.
119 Messiah

7.6.7.6.7.7.7.6.
24 Amsterdam
356

7.6.7.7.6.7.6.
292 Röslein

7.6.8.6.D.
373 Alford

7.6.8.6.8.6.8.6.
187 St. Christopher

7.7.6.7.7.8.
515 Innsbruck

7.7.7.3.
90 Guds Godhet

7.7.7.6.
478 Song 13

7.7.7.6. with Refrain
517 Sons of God